Solid State Electronic Devices

Multilevel copper metallization of a complementary metal oxide semiconductor (CMOS) chip. This scanning electron micrograph (scale: 1 cm = 3.5 microns) of a CMOS integrated circuit shows six levels of copper metallization that are used to carry electrical signals on the chip. The inter-metal dielectric insulators have been chemically etched away here to reveal the copper interconnects. (Photograph courtesy of IBM.)

SEVENTH EDITION

Solid State
Electronic Devices

BEN G. STREETMAN AND SANJAY KUMAR BANERJEE

Microelectronics Research Center
Department of Electrical and Computer Engineering
The University of Texas at Austin

PEARSON

Delhi • Chennai

Authorized adaptation from the United Kingdom edition, entitled *Solid State Electronic Devices*, 7th Edition, ISBN 978-1-292-06055-2 by Streetman, Ben G. and Banerjee, Sanjay Kumar, published by Pearson Education, Copyright © Pearson Education Limited 2016.

Indian Subcontinent Adaptation
Copyright © 2016 Pearson India Education Services Pvt. Ltd

ISBN 978-93-325-5508-2

First Impression, 2015
Second Impression, 2016

This edition is manufactured in India and is authorized for sale only in India, Bangladesh, Bhutan, Pakistan, Nepal, Sri Lanka and the Maldives. Circulation of this edition outside of these territories is UNAUTHORIZED.

Published by Pearson India Education Services Pvt. Ltd, CIN: U72200TN2005PTC057128, formerly known as TutorVista Global Pvt. Ltd, licensee of Pearson Education in South Asia.

Head Office: A-8 (A), 7th Floor, Knowledge Boulevard, Sector 62, Noida 201 309, Uttar Pradesh, India.
Registered Office: Module G4, Ground Floor, Elnet Software City, TS-140, Blocks 2 & 9,
Rajiv Gandhi Salai, Taramani, Chennai 600 113, Tamil Nadu, India.
Fax: 080-30461003, Phone: 080-30461060
www.pearson.co.in, Email: companysecretary.india@pearson.com

Printed in India by Saurabh Printers Pvt. Ltd.

CONTENTS

5 JUNCTIONS 181

PREFACE

This book is an introduction to semiconductor devices for undergraduate electrical engineers, other interested students, and practicing engineers and scientists whose understanding of modern electronics needs updating. The book is organized to bring students with a background in sophomore physics to a level of understanding that will allow them to read much of the current literature on new devices and applications.

An undergraduate course in electronic devices has two basic purposes: (1) to provide students with a sound understanding of existing devices, so that their studies of electronic circuits and systems will be meaningful and (2) to develop the basic tools with which they can later learn about newly developed devices and applications. Perhaps the second of these objectives is the more important in the long run; it is clear that engineers and scientists who deal with electronics will continually be called upon to learn about new devices and processes in the future. For this reason, we have tried to incorporate the basics of semiconductor materials and conduction processes in solids, which arise repeatedly in the literature when new devices are explained. Some of these concepts are often omitted in introductory courses, with the view that they are unnecessary for understanding the fundamentals of junctions and transistors. We believe this view neglects the important goal of equipping students for the task of understanding a new device by reading the current literature. Therefore, in this text most of the commonly used semiconductor terms and concepts are introduced and related to a broad range of devices.

GOALS

- updated discussion of MOS devices, both in the underlying theory of ballistic FETs as well as discussion of advanced MOSFETs such as FinFETs, strained Si devices, metal gate/ high-k devices, III-V high channel mobility devices
- updated treatment of optoelectronic devices, including high bandgap nitride semiconductors and quantum cascade lasers
- brand new section on nanoelectronics to introduce students to exciting concepts such as 2D materials including graphene and topological insulators, 1D nanowires and nanotubes, and 0D quantum dots;
- discussion of spintronics, and novel resistive and phase change memories
- about 100 new problems, and current references which extend concepts in the text.

WHAT IS NEW IN THIS EDITION

READING LISTS   As a further aid in developing techniques for independent study, the reading list at the end of each chapter includes a few articles which students can read comfortably as they study this book. We do not expect that students will read all articles recommended in the reading lists; nevertheless, some exposure to periodicals is useful in laying the foundation for a career of constant updating and self-education. We have also added a summary of the key concepts at the end of each chapter.

PROBLEMS   One of the keys to success in understanding this material is to work problems that exercise the concepts. The problems at the end of each chapter are designed to facilitate learning the material. Very few are simple "plug-in" problems. Instead, they are chosen to reinforce or extend the material presented in the chapter. In addition, we have added "self quiz" problems that test the conceptual understanding on the part of the students.

UNITS   In keeping with the goals described above, examples and problems are stated in terms of units commonly used in the semiconductor literature. The basic system of units is rationalized MKS, although cm is often used as a convenient unit of length. Similarly, electron volts (eV) are often used rather than joules (J) to measure the energy of electrons. Units for various quantities are given in Appendices I and II.

PRESENTATION   In presenting this material at the undergraduate level, one must anticipate a few instances which call for a phrase such as "It can be shown . . ." This is always disappointing; on the other hand, the alternative is to delay study of solid state devices until the graduate level, where statistical mechanics, quantum theory, and other advanced background can be freely invoked. Such a delay would result in a more elegant treatment of certain subjects, but it would prevent undergraduate students from enjoying the study of some very exciting devices.

The discussion includes both silicon and compound semiconductors, to reflect the continuing growth in importance for compounds in optoelectronic and high-speed device applications. Topics such as heterojunctions, lattice-matching using ternary and quaternary alloys, variation of band gap with alloy composition, and properties of quantum wells add to the breadth of the discussion. Not to be outdone by the compounds, silicon-based devices have continued their dramatic record of advancement. The discussion of FET structures and Si integrated circuits reflects these advancements. Our objective is not to cover all the latest devices, which can only be done in the journal and conference literature. Instead, we have chosen devices to discuss which are broadly illustrative of important principles.

The first four chapters of the book provide background on the nature of semiconductors and conduction processes in solids (Chapters 3, 4). Included is a brief introduction to quantum concepts (Chapter 2) for those students who do not already have this background from other courses. Chapter 5 describes the p-n junction and some of its applications. Chapters 6 and 7 deal with the principles of transistor operation. Chapter 8 covers optoelectronics, and Chapter 9 discusses integrated circuits. Chapter 10 applies the theory of junctions and conduction processes to microwave and power devices. A completely new section on nanoelectronics has been added. All of the devices covered are important in today's electronics; furthermore, learning about these devices should be an enjoyable and rewarding experience. We hope this book provides that kind of experience for its readers.

ACKNOWLEDGMENTS

The seventh edition benefits greatly from comments and suggestions provided by students and teachers of the first six editions. The book's readers have generously provided comments which have been invaluable in developing the present version. We remain indebted to those persons mentioned in the Preface of the first six editions, who contributed so much to the development of the book. In particular, Nick Holonyak has been a source of continuing information and inspiration for all seven editions. Additional thanks go to our colleagues at UT–Austin who have provided special assistance, particularly Leonard Frank Register, Emanuel Tutuc, Ray Chen, Ananth Dodabalapur, Seth Bank, Misha Belkin, Zheng Wang, Neal Hall, Deji Akinwande, Jack Lee, and Dean Neikirk. Hema Movva provided useful assistance with the typing of the homework solutions. We thank the many companies and organizations cited in the figure captions for generously providing photographs and illustrations of devices and fabrication processes. Bob Doering at TI, Mark Bohr at Intel, Chandra Mouli at Micron, Babu Chalamala at MEMC and Kevin Lally at TEL deserve special mention for the new pictures in this edition. Finally, we recall with gratitude many years of association with Joe Campbell, Karl Hess, and the late Al Tasch, valued colleagues and friends.

Ben G. Streetman
Sanjay Kumar Banerjee

The publishers would like to thank Dr K. Subba Rao, Professor and Head, Department of Electronics and Communication Engineering, DVR College of Engineering and Technology, affiliated to JNTU Hyderabad, for his valuable inputs for enhancing the content of this book to suit the requirements of Indian universities.

ABOUT THE AUTHORS

Ben G. Streetman is Dean Emeritus of the Cockrell School of Engineering at The University of Texas at Austin. He is an Emeritus Professor of Electrical and Computer Engineering, where he held the Dula D. Cockrell Centennial Chair. He was the founding Director of the Microelectronics Research Center (1984–1996) and served as Dean of Engineering from 1996 to 2008. His teaching and research interests involve semiconductor materials and devices. After receiving a Ph.D. from The University of Texas at Austin (1966) he was on the faculty (1966–1982) of the University of Illinois at Urbana-Champaign. He returned to The University of Texas at Austin in 1982. His honors include the Education Medal of the Institute of Electrical and Electronics Engineers (IEEE), the Frederick Emmons Terman Medal of the American Society for Engineering Education (ASEE), and the Heinrich Welker Medal from the International Conference on Compound Semiconductors. He is a member of the National Academy of Engineering and the American Academy of Arts and Sciences. He is a Fellow of the IEEE and the Electrochemical Society. He has been honored as a Distinguished Alumnus of The University of Texas at Austin and as a Distinguished Graduate of the UT College of Engineering. He has received the General Dynamics Award for Excellence in Engineering Teaching, and was honored by the Parents' Association as a Teaching Fellow for outstanding teaching of undergraduates. He has served on numerous panels and committees in industry and government, and several corporate boards. He has published more than 290 articles in the technical literature. Thirty-four students of Electrical Engineering, Materials Science, and Physics have received their Ph.D.s under his direction.

Sanjay Kumar Banerjee is the Cockrell Chair Professor of Electrical and Computer Engineering, and Director of the Microelectronics Research Center at The University of Texas at Austin. He received his B.Tech. from the Indian Institute of Technology, Kharagpur, and his M.S. and Ph.D. from the University of Illinois at Urbana-Champaign in 1979, 1981, and 1983, respectively, in electrical engineering. He worked at TI from 1983–1987 on the world's first 4Megabit DRAM, for which he was a co-recipient of an ISSCC Best Paper Award. He has more than 900 archival refereed publications and conference papers, 30 U.S. patents, and has supervised over 50 Ph.D. students. His honors include the NSF Presidential Young Investigator Award (1988), the Texas Atomic Energy Centennial Fellowship (1990–1997), Cullen Professorship (1997–2001), and the Hocott Research Award from the University of Texas. He has received the ECS Callinan Award (2003), Industrial R&D 100 Award (2004), Distinguished Alumnus Award, IIT (2005), IEEE Millennium Medal (2000) and IEEE Andrew S. Grove Award (2014). He is a Fellow of IEEE, APS and AAAS. He is interested in beyond-CMOS nanoelectronic transistors based on 2D materials and spintronics, fabrication and modeling of advanced MOSFETs, and solar cells.

Solid State Electronic Devices

Chapter 1

Crystal Properties and Growth of Semiconductors

OBJECTIVES

1. Describe what a semiconductor is
2. Perform simple calculations about crystals
3. Understand what is involved in bulk Czochralski and thin-film epitaxial crystal growth
4. Learn about crystal defects

In studying solid state electronic devices we are interested primarily in the electrical behavior of solids. However, we shall see in later chapters that the transport of charge through a metal or a semiconductor depends not only on the properties of the electron but also on the arrangement of atoms in the solid. In this chapter we shall discuss some of the physical properties of semiconductors compared with other solids, the atomic arrangements of various materials, and some methods of growing semiconductor crystals. Topics such as crystal structure and crystal growth technology are often the subjects of books rather than introductory chapters; thus we shall consider only a few of the more important and fundamental ideas that form the basis for understanding electronic properties of semiconductors and device fabrication.

Semiconductors are a group of materials having electrical conductivities intermediate between metals and insulators. It is significant that the conductivity of these materials can be varied over orders of magnitude by changes in temperature, optical excitation, and impurity content. This variability of electrical properties makes the semiconductor materials natural choices for electronic device investigations.

1.1 SEMICONDUCTOR MATERIALS

Semiconductor materials are found in column IV and neighboring columns of the periodic table (Table 1–1). The column IV semiconductors, silicon and germanium, are called *elemental* semiconductors because they are composed of single species of atoms. In addition to the elemental materials, compounds of column III and column V atoms, as well as certain combinations from II and VI, and from IV, make up the *compound* semiconductors.

As Table 1–1 indicates, there are numerous semiconductor materials. As we shall see, the wide variety of electronic and optical properties of these semiconductors provides the device engineer with great flexibility in the design of electronic and optoelectronic functions. The elemental semiconductor Ge was widely used in the early days of semiconductor development for transistors and diodes. Silicon is now used for the majority of rectifiers, transistors, and integrated circuits (ICs). However, the compounds are widely used in high-speed devices and devices requiring the emission or absorption of light. The two-element (*binary*) III–V compounds such as GaN, GaP, and GaAs are common in light-emitting diodes (LEDs). As discussed in Section 1.2.4, three-element (*ternary*) compounds such as GaAsP and four-element (*quaternary*) compounds such as InGaAsP can be grown to provide added flexibility in choosing materials properties.

Fluorescent materials such as those used in television screens usually are II–VI compound semiconductors such as ZnS. Light detectors are commonly made with InSb, CdSe, or other compounds such as PbTe and HgCdTe. Si and Ge are also widely used as infrared and nuclear radiation detectors. Light-emitting diodes are made using GaN and other III–V compounds. Semiconductor lasers are made using GaAs, AlGaAs, and other ternary and quaternary compounds.

One of the most important characteristics of a semiconductor, which distinguishes it from metals and insulators, is its *energy band gap*. This property, which we will discuss in detail in Chapter 3, determines among other things the wavelengths of light that can be absorbed or emitted by the semiconductor. For example, the band gap of GaAs is about 1.43 electron volts (eV), which

Table 1–1 Common semiconductor materials: (a) the portion of the periodic table where semiconductors occur; (b) elemental and compound semiconductors.

(a)	II	III	IV	V	VI
		B	C	N	
		Al	Si	P	S
	Zn	Ga	Ge	As	Se
	Cd	In		Sb	Te

(b)	Elemental	IV compounds	Binary III–V compounds	Binary II–VI compounds
	Si	SiC	AlP	ZnS
	Ge	SiGe	AlAs	ZnSe
			AlSb	ZnTe
			GaN	CdS
			GaP	CdSe
			GaAs	CdTe
			GaSb	
			InP	
			InAs	
			InSb	

corresponds to light wavelengths in the near infrared. In contrast, GaP has a band gap of about 2.3 eV, corresponding to wavelengths in the green portion of the spectrum.[1] The band gap E_g for various semiconductor materials is listed along with other properties in Appendix III. As a result of the wide variety of semiconductor band gaps, LEDs and lasers can be constructed with wavelengths over a broad range of the infrared and visible portions of the spectrum.

The electronic and optical properties of semiconductor materials are strongly affected by impurities, which may be added in precisely controlled amounts. Such impurities are used to vary the conductivities of semiconductors over wide ranges and even to alter the nature of the conduction processes from conduction by negative charge carriers to positive charge carriers. For example, an impurity concentration of one part per million can change a sample of Si from a poor conductor to a good conductor of electric current. This process of controlled addition of impurities, called *doping*, will be discussed in detail in subsequent chapters.

To investigate these useful properties of semiconductors, it is necessary to understand the atomic arrangements in the materials. Obviously, if slight alterations in purity of the original material can produce such dramatic changes in electrical properties, then the nature and specific arrangement of atoms in each semiconductor must be of critical importance. Therefore, we begin our study of semiconductors with a brief introduction to crystal structure.

In this section we discuss the arrangements of atoms in various solids. We shall distinguish between single crystals and other forms of materials and then investigate the periodicity of crystal lattices. Certain important crystallographic terms will be defined and illustrated in reference to crystals having a basic cubic structure. These definitions will allow us to refer to certain planes and directions within a lattice. Finally, we shall investigate the diamond lattice; this structure, with some variations, is typical of most of the semiconductor materials used in electronic devices.

1.2
CRYSTAL LATTICES

1.2.1   Periodic Structures

A crystalline solid is distinguished by the fact that the atoms making up the crystal are arranged in a periodic fashion. That is, there is some basic arrangement of atoms that is repeated throughout the entire solid. Thus the crystal appears exactly the same at one point as it does at a series of other equivalent points, once the basic periodicity is discovered. However, not all solids are crystals (Fig. 1–1); some have no periodic structure at all (*amorphous* solids), and others are composed of many small regions of single-crystal material (*polycrystalline* solids). The high-resolution micrograph shown in Fig. 6–33 illustrates the periodic array of atoms in the single-crystal silicon of a transistor channel compared with the amorphous SiO_2 (glass) of the oxide layer.

---

[1]The conversion between the energy E of a photon of light (eV) and its wavelength λ (μm) is $\lambda = 1.24/E$. For GaAs, $\lambda = 1.24/1.43 = 0.87$ μm.

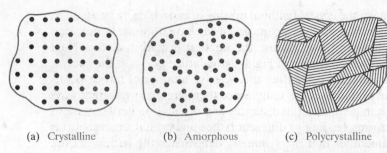

(a) Crystalline   (b) Amorphous   (c) Polycrystalline

Figure 1–1
Three types of solids, classified according to atomic arrangement: (a) crystalline and (b) amorphous materials are illustrated by microscopic views of the atoms, whereas (c) polycrystalline structure is illustrated by a more macroscopic view of adjacent single-crystalline regions, such as (a).

The periodicity in a crystal is defined in terms of a symmetric array of points in space called the *lattice*. We can add atoms at each lattice point in an arrangement called a *basis*, which can be one atom or a group of atoms having the same spatial arrangement, to get a *crystal*. In every case, the lattice contains a volume or *cell* that represents the entire lattice and is regularly repeated throughout the crystal. As an example of such a lattice, Fig. 1–2 shows a two-dimensional arrangement of atoms called a rhombic lattice, with a *primitive* cell ODEF, which is the smallest such cell. Notice that we can define vectors **a** and **b** such that if the primitive cell is translated by integral multiples of these vectors, a new primitive cell identical to the original is found (e.g., O'D'E'F'). These vectors, **a** and **b** (and **c** if the lattice is three dimensional), are called the *primitive vectors* for the lattice. Points within the lattice are indistinguishable if the vector between the points is

$$\mathbf{r} = p\mathbf{a} + q\mathbf{b} + s\mathbf{c} \qquad (1–1)$$

where p, q, and s are integers. The primitive cell shown has lattice points *only* at the corners of the cell. The primitive cell is not unique, but it must cover

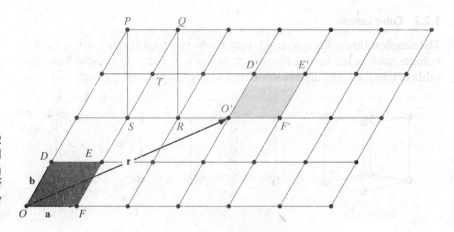

Figure 1–2
A two-dimensional lattice showing translation of a unit cell by $\mathbf{r} = 3\mathbf{a} + 2\mathbf{b}$.

the entire volume of the crystal (without missing or extra bits) by translations by integer numbers of primitive vectors, and it can have *only* one lattice point per cell. The convention is to choose the smallest primitive vectors. Note that, in the primitive cell shown in Fig. 1–2, the lattice points at the corners are shared with adjacent cells; thus, the *effective* number of lattice points belonging to the primitive cell is unity. Since there are many different ways of placing atoms in a volume, the distances and orientation between atoms can take many forms, leading to different lattice and crystal structures. It is important to remember that the *symmetry* determines the lattice, not the magnitudes of the distances between the lattice points.

In many lattices, however, the primitive cell is not the most convenient to work with. For example, in Fig. 1–2, we see that the rhombic arrangement of the lattice points is such that it can also be considered to be rectangular (PQRS) with a lattice point in the center at T (a so-called *centered rectangular* lattice). (Note that this is not true of all rhombic lattices!) Clearly, it is simpler to deal with a rectangle rather than a rhombus. So, in this case we can choose to work with a larger rectangular *unit* cell, PQRS, rather than the smallest primitive cell, ODEF. A unit cell allows lattice points not only at the corners but also at the face center (and body center in 3-D) if necessary. It is sometimes used instead of the primitive cell if it can represent the symmetry of the lattice better (in this example "centered rectangular" two-dimensional lattice). It replicates the lattice by integer translations of *basis* vectors.

The importance of the unit cell lies in the fact that we can analyze the crystal as a whole by investigating a representative volume. For example, from the unit cell we can find the distances between nearest atoms and next nearest atoms for calculation of the forces holding the lattice together; we can look at the fraction of the unit cell volume filled by atoms and relate the density of the solid to the atomic arrangement. But even more important for our interest in electronic devices, the properties of the periodic crystal lattice determine the allowed energies of electrons that participate in the conduction process. Thus the lattice determines not only the mechanical properties of the crystal but also its electrical properties.

1.2.2   Cubic Lattices

The simplest three-dimensional lattice is one in which the unit cell is a cubic volume, such as the three cells shown in Fig. 1–3. The *simple cubic* structure (abbreviated *sc*) has an atom located at each corner of the unit cell. The

a

Simple cubic

a

Body-centered cubic

a

Face-centered cubic

Figure 1–3
Unit cells for three types of cubic lattice structures.

Figure 1–4
Packing of hard spheres in an fcc lattice.

body-centered cubic (*bcc*) lattice has an additional atom at the center of the cube, and the *face-centered cubic* (*fcc*) unit cell has atoms at the eight corners and centered on the six faces. All three structures have different primitive cells, but the same cubic unit cell. We will generally work with unit cells.

As atoms are packed into the lattice in any of these arrangements, the distances between neighboring atoms will be determined by a balance between the forces that attract them together and other forces that hold them apart. We shall discuss the nature of these forces for particular solids in Section 3.1.1. For now, we can calculate the maximum fraction of the lattice volume that can be filled with atoms by approximating the atoms as hard spheres. For example, Fig. 1–4 illustrates the packing of spheres in a fcc cell of side a, such that the nearest neighbors touch. The dimension a for a cubic unit cell is called the *lattice constant*. For the fcc lattice the nearest neighbor distance is one-half the diagonal of a face, or $\frac{1}{2}(a\sqrt{2})$. Therefore, for the atom centered on the face to just touch the atoms at each corner of the face, the radius of the sphere must be one-half the nearest neighbor distance, or $\frac{1}{4}(a\sqrt{2})$.

EXAMPLE 1–1   Find the fraction of the fcc unit cell volume filled with hard spheres.

SOLUTION

$$\text{Nearest atom separation} = \frac{5\sqrt{2}}{2}\,\text{Å} = 3.54\,\text{Å}$$

$$\text{Tetrahedral radius} = 1.77\,\text{Å}$$

$$\text{Volume of each atom} = 23.14\,\text{Å}^3$$

$$\text{Number of atoms per cube } 6 \cdot \frac{1}{2} + 8 \cdot \frac{1}{8} = 4 \text{ atoms}$$

$$\text{Packing fraction } \frac{23.1\,\text{Å}^3 \cdot 4}{(5\,\text{Å})^3} = 0.74 = 74\%$$

1.2.3 Planes and Directions

In discussing crystals it is very helpful to be able to refer to planes and directions within the lattice. The notation system generally adopted uses a set of three integers to describe the position of a plane or the direction of a vector within the lattice. We first set up an *xyz* coordinate system with the origin at any lattice point (it does not matter which one because they are all equivalent!), and the axes are lined up with the edges of the cubic unit cell. The three integers describing a particular plane are found in the following way:

1. Find the intercepts of the plane with the crystal axes and express these intercepts as integral multiples of the basis vectors (the plane can be moved in and out from the origin, retaining its orientation, until such an integral intercept is discovered on each axis).

2. Take the reciprocals of the three integers found in step 1 and reduce these to the smallest set of integers *h, k,* and *l,* which have the same relationship to each other as the three reciprocals.

3. Label the plane (*hkl*).

EXAMPLE 1–2

The plane illustrated in Fig. 1–5 has intercepts at 2**a**, 4**b**, and 1**c** along the three crystal axes. Taking the reciprocals of these intercepts, we get $\frac{1}{2}$, $\frac{1}{4}$, and 1. These three fractions have the same relationship to each other as the integers 2, 1, and 4 (obtained by multiplying each fraction by 4). Thus the plane can be referred to as a (214) plane. The only exception is if the intercept is a fraction of the lattice constant *a*. In that case, we do not reduce it to the lowest set of integers. For example, in Fig. 1–3, planes parallel to the cube faces, but going through the body center atoms in the bcc lattice, would be (200) and not (100).

Figure 1–5
A (214) crystal plane.

The three integers *h, k,* and *l* are called the *Miller indices*; these three numbers define a set of parallel planes in the lattice. One advantage of taking the reciprocals of the intercepts is avoidance of infinities in the notation. One intercept is infinity for a plane parallel to an axis; however, the reciprocal of such an intercept is taken as zero. If a plane contains one of the axes, it is parallel to that axis and has a zero reciprocal intercept. If a plane passes through the origin, it can be translated to a parallel position for calculation of the Miller indices. If an intercept occurs on the negative branch of an axis, the minus sign is placed above the Miller index for convenience, such as ($h\bar{k}l$).

From a crystallographic point of view, many planes in a lattice are equivalent; that is, a plane with given Miller indices can be shifted about in the lattice simply by choice of the position and orientation of the unit cell. The indices of such equivalent planes are enclosed in braces { } instead of parentheses. For example, in the cubic lattice of Fig. 1–6, all the cube faces are crystallographically equivalent in that the unit cell can be rotated in various directions and still appear the same. The six equivalent faces are collectively designated as {100}.

A direction in a lattice is expressed as a set of three integers with the same relationship as the components of a vector in that direction. The three vector components are expressed in multiples of the basis vectors, and the three integers are reduced to their smallest values while retaining the relationship among them. For example, the body diagonal in the cubic lattice (Fig. 1–7a) is composed of the components 1**a,** 1**b,** and 1**c;** therefore, this diagonal is the [111] direction. (Brackets are used for direction indices.) As in the case of planes, many directions in a lattice are equivalent, depending only on the arbitrary choice of orientation for the axes. Such equivalent direction indices are placed in angular brackets ⟨ ⟩. For example, the crystal axes in the cubic lattice [100], [010], and [001] are all equivalent and are called ⟨100⟩ directions (Fig. 1–7b).

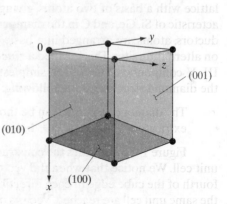

Figure 1–6
Equivalence of the cube faces ({100} planes) by rotation of the unit cell within the cubic lattice.

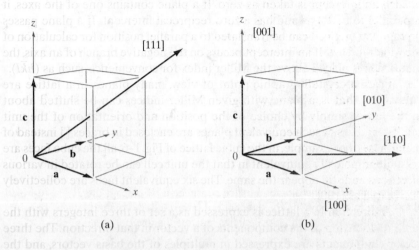

Figure 1–7
Crystal directions
in the cubic
lattice.

(a)   (b)

Two useful relationships in terms of Miller indices describe the distance between planes and angles between directions. The distance d between two adjacent planes labeled (hkl) is given in terms of the lattice constant, a, as

$$d = a/(h^2 + k^2 + l^2)^{1/2} \qquad (1\text{–}2a)$$

The angle θ between two different Miller index directions is given by

$$\cos \theta = \{h_1h_2 + k_1k_2 + l_1l_2\}\{(h_1^2 + k_1^2 + l_1^2)^{1/2}(h_2^2 + k_2^2 + l_2^2)^{1/2}\} \quad (1\text{–}2b)$$

Comparing Figs. 1–6 and 1–7, we notice that in cubic lattices a direction $[hkl]$ is perpendicular to the plane (hkl). This is convenient in analyzing lattices with cubic unit cells, but it should be remembered that it is not necessarily true in noncubic systems.

1.2.4 The Diamond Lattice

The basic crystal structure for many important semiconductors is the fcc lattice with a basis of two atoms, giving rise to the *diamond* structure, characteristic of Si, Ge, and C in the diamond form. In many compound semiconductors, atoms are arranged in a basic diamond structure, but are different on alternating sites. This is called a *zinc blende* structure and is typical of the III–V compounds. One of the simplest ways of stating the construction of the diamond structure is the following:

The diamond structure can be thought of as an fcc lattice with an extra atom placed at $a/4 + b/4 + c/4$ from each of the fcc atoms.

Figure 1–8a illustrates the construction of a diamond lattice from an fcc unit cell. We notice that when the vectors are drawn with components one-fourth of the cube edge in each direction, only four additional points within the same unit cell are reached. Vectors drawn from any of the other fcc atoms simply determine corresponding points in adjacent unit cells. This method of

Figure 1–8
Diamond lattice structure: (a) a unit cell of the diamond lattice constructed by placing atoms $\frac{1}{4}, \frac{1}{4}, \frac{1}{4}$ from each atom in an fcc; (b) top view (along any $\langle 100 \rangle$ direction) of an extended diamond lattice. The colored circles indicate one fcc sublattice and the black circles indicate the interpenetrating fcc.

constructing the diamond lattice implies that the original fcc has associated with it a second interpenetrating fcc displaced by $\frac{1}{4}, \frac{1}{4}, \frac{1}{4}$. The two interpenetrating fcc *sublattices* can be visualized by looking down on the unit cell of Fig. 1–8a from the top (or along any $\langle 100 \rangle$ direction). In the top view of Fig. 1–8b, atoms belonging to the original fcc are represented by open circles, and the interpenetrating sublattice is shaded. If the atoms are all similar, we call this structure a diamond lattice; if the atoms differ on alternating sites, it is a zinc blende structure. For example, if one fcc sublattice is composed of Ga atoms and the interpenetrating sublattice is As, the zinc blende structure of GaAs results. Most of the compound semiconductors have this type of lattice, although some of the II–VI compounds are arranged in a slightly different structure called the *wurtzite* lattice. We shall restrict our discussion here to the diamond and zinc blende structures, since they are typical of most of the commonly used semiconductors.

EXAMPLE 1–3

Calculate the volume density of Si atoms (number of atoms/cm³), given that the lattice constant of Si is 5.43 Å. Calculate the areal density of atoms (number/cm²) on the (100) plane.

SOLUTION

On the (100) plane, we have four atoms on corners and one on the face center.

$$(100) \text{ plane: } \frac{4 \times \dfrac{1}{4} + 1}{(5.43 \times 10^{-8})(5.43 \times 10^{-8})} = 6.8 \times 10^{14} \, \text{cm}^{-2}$$

For Si, we have eight corner lattice points, six face centered points, and two atoms

$$\text{Number of atoms per cube} = (8 \times \frac{1}{8} + \frac{1}{2} \times 6) \times 2 = 8$$

$$\text{Volume density} = \frac{8}{(5.43 \times 10^{-8})^3} = 5.00 \times 10^{22} \text{ cm}^{-3}$$

A particularly interesting and useful feature of the III–V compounds is the ability to vary the mixture of elements on each of the two interpenetrating fcc sublattices of the zinc blende crystal. For example, in the ternary compound AlGaAs, it is possible to vary the composition of the ternary alloy by choosing the fraction of Al or Ga atoms on the column III sublattice. It is common to represent the composition by assigning subscripts to the various elements. For example, $Al_xGa_{1-x}As$ refers to a ternary alloy in which the column III sublattice in the zinc blende structure contains a fraction x of Al atoms and $1-x$ of Ga atoms. The composition $Al_{0.3}Ga_{0.7}As$ has 30 percent Al and 70 percent Ga on the column III sites, with the interpenetrating column V sublattice occupied entirely by As atoms. It is extremely useful to be able to grow ternary alloy crystals such as this with a given composition. For the $Al_xGa_{1-x}As$ example we can grow crystals over the entire composition range from $x = 0$ to $x = 1$, thus varying the electronic and optical properties of the material from that of GaAs ($x = 0$) to that of AlAs ($x = 1$). To vary the properties even further, it is possible to grow four-element (quaternary) compounds such as $In_xGa_{1-x}As_yP_{1-y}$ having a very wide range of properties.

It is important from an electronic point of view to notice that each atom in the diamond and zinc blende structures is surrounded by four nearest neighbors (Fig. 1–9). The importance of this relationship of each atom to its neighbors will become evident in Section 3.1.1 when we discuss the bonding forces which hold the lattice together.

The fact that atoms in a crystal are arranged in certain planes is important to many of the mechanical, metallurgical, and chemical properties of the material. For example, crystals often can be cleaved along certain atomic planes, resulting in exceptionally planar surfaces. This is a familiar result in cleaved diamonds for jewelry; the facets of a diamond reveal clearly the triangular, hexagonal, and rectangular symmetries of intersecting planes in various crystallographic directions. Semiconductors with diamond and zinc blende lattices have similar cleavage planes. Chemical reactions, such as etching of the crystal, often take place preferentially along certain directions. These properties serve as interesting illustrations of crystal symmetry, but in addition, each plays an important role in fabrication processes for many semiconductor devices.

**1.3
BULK CRYSTAL
GROWTH**

The progress of solid state device technology since the invention of the transistor in 1948 has depended not only on the development of device concepts but also on the improvement of materials. For example, the fact that ICs can be made today is the result of a considerable breakthrough in the growth of pure, single-crystal Si in the early and mid-1950s. The requirements on the growing of device-grade semiconductor crystals are more stringent than those for any other materials. Not only must semiconductors be available in large single crystals, but also the purity must be controlled within extremely close limits. For example, Si crystals now being used in devices are grown with concentrations of most impurities of less than one part in ten billion. Such purities require careful handling and treatment of the material at each step of the manufacturing process.

1.3.1 Starting Materials

The raw feedstock for Si crystal is silicon dioxide (SiO_2). We react SiO_2 with C in the form of coke in an arc furnace at very high temperatures (~1800°C) to reduce SiO_2 according to the following reaction:

$$SiO_2 + 2C \rightarrow Si + 2CO \qquad (1-3)$$

This forms metallurgical grade Si (MGS) which has impurities such as Fe, Al, and heavy metals at levels of several hundred to several thousand parts per million (ppm). Refer back to Example 1–3 to see that 1 ppm of Si corresponds to an impurity level of $5 \times 10^{16} \, cm^{-3}$. While MGS is clean enough for metallurgical applications such as using Si to make stainless steel, it is not pure enough for electronic applications; it is also not single crystal.

The MGS is refined further to yield semiconductor-grade or electronic-grade Si (EGS), in which the levels of impurities are reduced to parts per billion or ppb ($1 \text{ ppb} = 5 \times 10^{13} \text{ cm}^{-3}$). This involves reacting the MGS with dry HCl according to the following reaction to form trichlorosilane, $SiHCl_3$, which is a liquid with a boiling point of 32°C:

$$Si + 3HCl \rightarrow SiHCl_3 + H_2 \tag{1-4}$$

Along with $SiHCl_3$, chlorides of impurities such as $FeCl_3$ are formed which fortunately have boiling points that are different from that of $SiHCl_3$. This allows a technique called fractional distillation to be used, in which we heat up the mixture of $SiHCl_3$ and the impurity chlorides, and condense the vapors in different distillation towers held at appropriate temperatures. We can thereby separate pure $SiHCl_3$ from the impurities. $SiHCl_3$ is then converted to highly pure EGS by reaction with H_2,

$$2SiHCl_3 + 2H_2 \rightarrow 2Si + 6HCl \tag{1-5}$$

1.3.2 Growth of Single-Crystal Ingots

Next, we have to convert the high purity but still polycrystalline EGS to single-crystal Si ingots or boules. This is generally done today by a process commonly called the *Czochralski* method. In order to grow single-crystal material, it is necessary to have a seed crystal which can provide a template for growth. We melt the EGS in a quartz-lined graphite crucible by resistively heating it to the melting point of Si (1412°C).

A seed crystal is lowered into the molten material and then is raised slowly, allowing the crystal to grow onto the seed (Fig. 1–10a). Generally, the

(a) (b)

Figure 1–10
Pulling of a Si crystal from the melt (Czochralski method): (a) schematic diagram of the crystal growth process; (b) an 8-in. diameter, ⟨100⟩ oriented Si crystal being pulled from the melt. (Photograph courtesy of MEMC Electronics Intl.)

(a)

(b)

Figure 1-11
(a) Silicon crystal grown by the Czochralski method. This large single-crystal ingot provides 300 mm (12-in.) diameter wafers when sliced using a saw. The ingot is about 1.0 m long (including the tapered regions), and weighs about 140 kg. (b) technician holding a 300 mm wafer. (Photograph courtesy of MEMC Electronics Intl.)

crystal is rotated slowly as it grows to provide a slight stirring of the melt and to average out any temperature variations that would cause inhomogeneous solidification. This technique is widely used in growing Si, Ge, and some of the compound semiconductors.

In pulling compounds such as GaAs from the melt, it is necessary to prevent volatile elements (e.g., As) from vaporizing. In one method a layer of B_2O_3, which is dense and viscous when molten, floats on the surface of the molten GaAs to prevent As evaporation. This growth method is called *liquid-encapsulated Czochralski (LEC)* growth.

In Czochralski crystal growth, the shape of the ingot is determined by a combination of the tendency of the cross section to assume a polygonal shape due to the crystal structure and the influence of surface tension, which encourages a circular cross section. The crystal facets are noticeable in the initial growth near the seed crystal in Fig. 1–10b. However, the cross section of the large ingot in Fig. 1–11 is almost circular.

In the fabrication of Si ICs (Chapter 9) it is economical to use very large Si wafers, so that many IC chips can be made simultaneously. As a result, considerable research and development have gone into methods for growing very large Si crystals. For example, Fig. 1–11 illustrates a ~12-inch or 300-mm diameter Si ingot, 1.0 m long and weighing 140 kg, and a 300 mm wafer.

1.3.3 Wafers

After the single-crystal ingot is grown, it is then mechanically processed to manufacture wafers. The first step involves mechanically grinding the more-or-less cylindrical ingot into a perfect cylinder with a precisely controlled diameter. This is important because in a modern IC fabrication facility, many processing tools and wafer handling robots require tight tolerances on the size of the wafers. Using X-ray crystallography, crystal planes in the ingot are identified. For reasons discussed in Section 6.4.3, most Si ingots are grown along the ⟨100⟩ direction (Fig. 1–10). For such ingots, a small notch is ground on one side of the cylinder to delineate a {110} face of the crystal. This is useful because for ⟨100⟩ Si wafers, the {110} cleavage planes are orthogonal to each other. This notch then allows the individual IC chips to be made oriented along {110} planes so that when the chips are sawed apart, there is less chance of spurious cleavage of the crystal, which could cause good chips to be lost.

Next, the Si cylinder is sawed into individual wafers about 775 μm thick, by using a diamond-tipped inner-hole blade saw, or a wire saw (Fig. 1–12). State-of-the-art wafers today are 300 mm in diameter; the next size will be 450 mm. The resulting wafers are mechanically lapped and ground on both sides to achieve a flat surface, and to remove the mechanical damage due to sawing. Such damage would have a detrimental effect on devices. The flatness of the wafer is critical from the point of view of "depth of focus" or how sharp an image can be focussed on the wafer surface during photolithography, as discussed in Chapter 5. The Si wafers are then rounded or "chamfered" along the edges to minimize the likelihood of chipping the wafers during processing. Finally, the wafers undergo chemical–mechanical

Figure 1–12
Steps involved in manufacturing Si wafers. (Photograph courtesy of MEMC Electronics Intl.)

polishing using a slurry of very fine SiO_2 particles in a basic NaOH solution to give the front surface of the wafer a mirror-like finish. The wafers are now ready for IC fabrication (Fig. 1–12). The economic value added in this process is impressive. From sand (SiO_2) costing pennies, we can obtain Si wafers costing a few hundred dollars, on which we can make hundreds of microprocessors, for example, each costing several hundred dollars.

1.3.4 Doping

As previously mentioned, there are some impurities in the molten EGS. We may also add intentional impurities or dopants to the Si melt to change its electronic properties. At the solidifying interface between the melt and the solid, there will be a certain distribution of impurities between the two phases. An important quantity that identifies this property is the *distribution coefficient* k_d, which is the ratio of the concentration of the impurity in the solid C_S to the concentration in the liquid C_L at equilibrium:

$$k_d = \frac{C_S}{C_L} \tag{1–6}$$

The distribution coefficient is a function of the material, the impurity, the temperature of the solid–liquid interface, and the growth rate. For an impurity with a distribution coefficient of one-half, the relative concentration of the impurity in the molten liquid to that in the refreezing solid is two to one. Thus the concentration of impurities in that portion of material that solidifies first is one-half the original concentration C_0. The distribution coefficient is thus important during growth from a melt. This can be illustrated by an example involving Czochralski growth:

Find the weight of As ($k_d = 0.3$) added to 1 kg Si in Czochralski growth for 10^{15} cm^{-3} doping.   **EXAMPLE 1–4**

$$\text{atomic weight of As} = 74.9\tfrac{g}{mol}$$

SOLUTION

$$C_s = k_d \cdot C_L = 10^{15}\frac{1}{cm^3} \rightarrow C_L \frac{10^{15}\frac{1}{cm^3}}{0.3} = 3.33 \cdot 10^{15}\frac{1}{cm^3}$$

Assume As may be neglected for overall melt weight and volume

$$\frac{1000g\ Si}{2.33\frac{g}{cm^3}} = 429.2\ cm^3\ Si$$

$$3.33 \cdot 10^{15}\tfrac{1}{cm^3} \cdot 429.2\ cm^3 = 1.43 \cdot 10^{18}\ As\ atoms$$

$$\frac{1.43 \cdot 10^{18}\ atoms \cdot 74.9\frac{g}{mol}}{6.02 \cdot 10^{23}\frac{atoms}{mol}} = 1.8 \cdot 10^{-4}g\ As = 1.8 \cdot 10^{-7}kg\ As$$

One of the most important and versatile methods of crystal growth for device applications is the growth of a thin crystal layer on a wafer of a compatible crystal. The substrate crystal may be a wafer of the same material as the grown layer or a different material with a similar lattice structure. In this process the substrate serves as the seed crystal onto which the new crystalline material grows. The growing crystal layer maintains the crystal structure and orientation of the substrate. The technique of growing an oriented single-crystal layer on a substrate wafer is called *epitaxial growth*, or *epitaxy*. As we shall see in this section, epitaxial growth can be performed at temperatures considerably below the melting point of the substrate crystal. A variety of methods are used to provide the appropriate atoms to the surface of the growing layer. These methods include *chemical vapor deposition (CVD)*,[2]   **1.4 EPITAXIAL GROWTH**

---

[2]The generic term *chemical vapor deposition* includes the deposition of layers that may be polycrystalline or amorphous. When a CVD process results in a single-crystal epitaxial layer, a more specific term is *vapor-phase epitaxy* (VPE).

growth from a melt (*liquid-phase epitaxy, LPE*), and evaporation of the elements in a vacuum (*molecular beam epitaxy, MBE*). With this wide range of epitaxial growth techniques, it is possible to grow a variety of crystals for device applications, having properties specifically designed for the electronic or optoelectronic device being made.

1.4.1 Lattice-Matching in Epitaxial Growth

When Si epitaxial layers are grown on Si substrates, there is a natural matching of the crystal lattice, and high-quality single-crystal layers result. On the other hand, it is often desirable to obtain epitaxial layers that differ somewhat from the substrate, which is known as *heteroepitaxy*. This can be accomplished easily if the lattice structure and lattice constant a match for the two materials. For example, GaAs and AlAs both have the zinc blende structure, with a lattice constant of about 5.65 Å. As a result, epitaxial layers of the ternary alloy AlGaAs can be grown on GaAs substrates with little lattice mismatch. Similarly, GaAs can be grown on Ge substrates (see Appendix III).

Since AlAs and GaAs have similar lattice constants, it is also true that the ternary alloy AlGaAs has essentially the same lattice constant over the entire range of compositions from AlAs to GaAs. As a result, one can choose the composition x of the ternary compound $Al_xGa_{1-x}As$ to fit the particular device requirement, and grow this composition on a GaAs wafer. The resulting epitaxial layer will be lattice-matched to the GaAs substrate.

Figure 1–13 illustrates the energy band gap E_g as a function of lattice constant a for several III–V ternary compounds as they are varied over their composition ranges. For example, as the ternary compound InGaAs is varied by choice of composition on the column III sublattice from InAs to GaAs, the band gap changes from 0.36 to 1.43 eV while the lattice constant of the crystal varies from 6.06 Å for InAs to 5.65 Å for GaAs. Clearly, we cannot grow this ternary compound over the entire composition range on a particular binary substrate, which has a fixed lattice constant. As Fig. 1–13 illustrates, however, it is possible to grow a specific composition of InGaAs on an InP substrate. The vertical (invariant lattice constant) line from InP to the InGaAs curve shows that a midrange ternary composition (actually, $In_{0.53}Ga_{0.47}As$) can be grown lattice-matched to an InP substrate. Similarly, a ternary InGaP alloy with about 50 percent Ga and 50 percent In on the column III sublattice can be grown lattice-matched to a GaAs substrate. To achieve a broader range of alloy compositions, grown lattice-matched on particular substrates, it is helpful to use quaternary alloys such as InGaAsP. The variation of compositions on both the column III and column V sublattices provides additional flexibility in choosing a particular band gap while providing lattice-matching to convenient binary substrates such as GaAs or InP.

In the case of GaAsP, the lattice constant is intermediate between that of GaAs and GaP, depending upon the composition. For example, GaAsP crystals used in red LEDs have 40 percent phosphorus and 60 percent arsenic on the column V sublattice. Since such a crystal cannot be grown directly on

Figure 1-13
Relationship between band gap and lattice constant for alloys in the InGaAsP and AlGaAsSb systems. The dashed vertical lines show the lattice constants for the commercially available binary substrates GaAs and InP. For the marked example of $In_xGa_{1-x}As$, the ternary composition $x = 0.53$ can be grown lattice-matched on InP, since the lattice constants are the same. For quaternary alloys, the compositions on both the III and V sublattices can be varied to grow lattice-matched epitaxial layers along the dashed vertical lines between curves. For example, $In_xGa_{1-x}As_yP_{1-y}$ can be grown on InP substrates, with resulting band gaps ranging from 0.75 eV to 1.35 eV. In using this figure, assume the lattice constant a of a ternary alloy varies linearly with the composition x.

either a GaAs or a GaP substrate, it is necessary to gradually change the lattice constant as the crystal is grown. Using a GaAs or Ge wafer as a substrate, the growth is begun at a composition near GaAs. A region ~25 μm thick is grown while gradually introducing phosphorus until the desired As/P ratio is achieved. The desired epitaxial layer (e.g., 100 μm thick) is then grown on this graded layer. By this method epitaxial growth always occurs on a crystal of similar lattice constant. Although some crystal dislocations occur due to lattice strain in the graded region, such crystals are of high quality and can be used in LEDs.

In addition to the widespread use of lattice-matched epitaxial layers, the advanced epitaxial growth techniques described in the following sections allow the growth of very thin (~100 Å) layers of lattice-mismatched crystals. If the mismatch is only a few percent and the layer is thin, the epitaxial layer grows with a lattice constant in compliance with that of the seed crystal (Fig. 1–14). The resulting layer is in compression or tension along the surface plane as its lattice constant adapts to the seed crystal (Fig. 1–14). Such a layer is called *pseudomorphic* because it is not lattice-matched to the substrate without strain. However, if the epitaxial layer exceeds a critical layer thickness, t_c, which depends on the lattice mismatch, the strain energy leads to formation of defects called *misfit dislocations*. Using thin alternating layers of slightly mismatched crystal layers, it is possible to grow a *strained-layer superlattice (SLS)* in which alternate layers are in tension and compression. The overall SLS lattice constant is an average of that of the two bulk materials.

1.4.2 Vapor-Phase Epitaxy

The advantages of low temperature and high-purity epitaxial growth can be achieved by crystallization from the vapor phase. Crystalline layers can be grown onto a seed or substrate from a chemical vapor of the semiconductor material

$t < t_c$ (a)   SiGe   Si $t > t_c$ (b)

Figure 1–14
Heteroepitaxy and misfit dislocations. For example, in heteroepitaxy of a SiGe layer on Si, the lattice mismatch between SiGe and Si leads to compressive strain in the SiGe layer. The amount of strain depends on the mole fraction of Ge. (a) For layer thicknesses less than the critical layer thickness, t_c, pseudomorphic growth occurs. (b) However, above t_c, misfit dislocations form at the interface which may reduce the usefulness of the layers in device applications.

or from mixtures of chemical vapors containing the semiconductor. *Vapor-phase epitaxy (VPE)* is a particularly important source of semiconductor material for use in devices. Some compounds such as GaAs can be grown with better purity and crystal perfection by vapor epitaxy than by other methods. Furthermore, these techniques offer great flexibility in the actual fabrication of devices. When an epitaxial layer is grown on a substrate, it is relatively simple to obtain a sharp demarcation between the type of impurity doping in the substrate and in the grown layer. The advantages of this freedom to vary the impurity will be discussed in subsequent chapters. We point out here, however, that Si IC devices (Chapter 9) are usually built in layers grown by VPE on Si wafers.

Epitaxial layers are generally grown on Si substrates by the controlled deposition of Si atoms onto the surface from a chemical vapor containing Si. In one method, a gas of silicon tetrachloride reacts with hydrogen gas to give Si and anhydrous HCl:

$$SiCl_4 + 2H_2 \rightleftharpoons Si + 4HCl \qquad (1\text{--}7)$$

If this reaction occurs at the surface of a heated crystal, the Si atoms released in the reaction can be deposited as an epitaxial layer. The HCl remains gaseous at the reaction temperature and does not disturb the growing crystal. As indicated, this reaction is reversible. This is very important because it implies that by adjusting the process parameters, the reaction in Eq. (1–7) can be driven to the left (providing etching of the Si rather than deposition). This etching can be used for preparing an atomically clean surface on which epitaxy can occur.

This vapor epitaxy technique requires a chamber into which the gases can be introduced and a method for heating the Si wafers. Since the chemical reactions take place in this chamber, it is called a *reaction chamber* or, more simply, a *reactor*. Hydrogen gas is passed through a heated vessel in which SiCl₄ is evaporated; then the two gases are introduced into the reactor over the substrate crystal, along with other gases containing the desired doping impurities. The Si slice is placed on a graphite susceptor or some other material that can be heated to the reaction temperature with an rf heating coil or tungsten halogen lamps. This method can be adapted to grow epitaxial layers of closely controlled impurity concentration on many Si slices simultaneously (Fig. 1–15).

Figure 1–15
A barrel-type reactor for Si vapor-phase epitaxy. These are atmospheric pressure systems. The Si wafers are held in slots cut on the sides of a SiC-coated graphite susceptor that flares out near the base to promote gas flow patterns conducive to uniform epitaxy.

Gas inlet
Gas baffle
Wafers
Quartz chamber
Radio frequency source
Susceptor
Pedestal
Vent

The reaction temperature for the hydrogen reduction of $SiCl_4$ is approximately 1150–1250°C. Other reactions may be employed at somewhat lower temperatures, including the use of dichlorosilane (SiH_2Cl_2) at 1000–1100°C, or the pyrolysis of silane (SiH_4) at 500–1000°C. Pyrolysis involves the breaking up of the silane at the reaction temperature:

$$SiH_4 \rightarrow Si + 2H_2 \tag{1–8}$$

There are several advantages of the lower reaction temperature processes, including the fact that they reduce migration of impurities from the substrate to the growing epitaxial layer.

In some applications it is useful to grow thin Si layers on insulating substrates. For example, vapor-phase epitaxial techniques can be used to grow ~1 μm Si films on sapphire and other insulators.

Vapor-phase epitaxial growth is also important in the III–V compounds, such as GaAs, GaP, and the ternary alloy GaAsP, which is widely used in the fabrication of LEDs. Substrates are held at about 800°C on a rotating wafer holder while phosphine, arsine, and gallium chloride gases are mixed and passed over the samples. The GaCl is obtained by reacting anhydrous HCl with molten Ga within the reactor. Variation of the crystal composition for GaAsP can be controlled by altering the mixture of arsine and phosphine gases.

Another useful method for epitaxial growth of compound semiconductors is called *metal-organic vapor-phase epitaxy* (*MOVPE*), or *organometallic vapor-phase epitaxy* (*OMVPE*). For example, the organometallic compound trimethylgallium can be reacted with arsine to form GaAs and methane:

$$(CH_3)_3Ga + AsH_3 \rightarrow GaAs + 3CH_4 \tag{1–9}$$

This reaction takes place at about 700°C, and epitaxial growth of high-quality GaAs layers can be obtained. Other compound semiconductors can also be grown by this method. For example, trimethylaluminum can be added to the gas mixture to grow AlGaAs. This growth method is widely used in the fabrication of a variety of devices, including solar cells and lasers. The convenient variability of the gas mixture allows the growth of multiple thin layers similar to those discussed below for molecular beam epitaxy.

1.4.3 Molecular Beam Epitaxy

One of the most versatile techniques for growing epitaxial layers is called *molecular beam epitaxy* (*MBE*). In this method the substrate is held in a high vacuum while molecular or atomic beams of the constituents impinge upon its surface (Fig. 1–16a). For example, in the growth of AlGaAs layers on GaAs substrates, the Al, Ga, and As components, along with dopants, are heated in separate cylindrical cells. Collimated beams of these constituents escape into the vacuum and are directed onto the surface of the substrate.

Figure 1–16

Crystal growth by molecular beam epitaxy (MBE): (a) evaporation cells inside a high-vacuum chamber directing beams of Al, Ga, As, and dopants onto a GaAs substrate; (b) scanning electron micrograph of the cross section of an MBE-grown crystal having alternating layers of GaAs (dark lines) and AlGaAs (light lines). Each layer is four monolayers ($4 \times a/2 = 11.3$ Å;) thick.

Figure 1-17
Molecular
beam epitaxy
facility in the
Microelectronics
Research Center
at the University
of Texas at Austin.

The rates at which these atomic beams strike the surface can be closely controlled, and growth of very high-quality crystals results. The sample is held at a relatively low temperature (about 600°C for GaAs) in this growth procedure. Abrupt changes in doping or in crystal composition (e.g., changing from GaAs to AlGaAs) can be obtained by controlling shutters in front of the individual beams. Using slow growth rates (≤1 μm/h), it is possible to control the shutters to make composition changes on the scale of the lattice constant. For example, Fig. 1–16b illustrates a portion of a crystal grown with alternating layers of GaAs and AlGaAs only four monolayers thick. Because of the high vacuum and close controls involved, MBE requires a rather sophisticated setup (Fig. 1–17). However, the versatility of this growth method makes it very attractive for many applications.

As MBE has developed in recent years, it has become common to replace some of the solid sources shown in Fig. 1–16 with gaseous chemical sources. This approach, called *chemical beam epitaxy*, or *gas-source MBE*, combines many of the advantages of MBE and VPE.

1.5
WAVE
PROPAGATION
IN DISCRETE,
PERIODIC
STRUCTURES

In the next two chapters, we will discuss the propagation of various types of waves in finite size crystals. It is instructive to look at some of the general attributes of such waves in a medium made of discrete, periodic atoms. Recall that a wave is characterized by various parameters such as wavelength, λ, angular frequency, $\omega = 2\pi v$, phase, φ, and intensity, $I = A^2$, where A is the amplitude of the wave [Fig. 1–18a]. The speed of the wave, $v_p = \lambda v$. Instead of wavelength, one can also describe a wave in terms of the wavevector, $k = 2\pi/\lambda$. The velocity v_p, which is called the *phase velocity* of the wave, then can also be written as ω/k. In general, one may deal with not a single wave train, but a wave packet, made up of a superposition of various waves [Fig. 1–18b]. The wave packet can be shown to travel with a *group velocity*, $v_g = d\omega/dk$. A plane wave, ψ, propagating in the $\pm x$ direction can be written as $\psi = A \exp\{j(kx \pm \omega t)\}$, where j is the imaginary number. Equivalently, one can take linear combinations of these plane waves and describe them as standing waves $\sin(kx \pm \omega t)$ and/or $\cos(kx \pm \omega t)$.

There are a few quirks when one looks at plane waves propagating in a finite crystal with lattice constant a and of length $L = Na$, where N is the number of atoms [Fig. 1–18a]. Plane traveling waves cannot propagate in a finite crystal—reflections at the boundaries will give rise to standing wave patterns. It turns out that the mathematics is simpler in terms of plane waves propagating in an infinite crystal. As long as we are interested in the bulk, rather than the surface, properties of the crystal, one can artificially create an infinite crystal by repeating the finite crystal of length L over all space, and requiring that the value of the wave is equal on the two faces of the finite crystal, $\psi(0) = \psi(L)$. This is known as the *periodic boundary condition* [Fig. 1–18b].

The second quirk about these waves is that in a *discrete* medium such as a crystal, where atoms are located at a spacing a, the wavelengths are physically distinguishable only up to a point. This is clear from Fig. 1–18a, where one sees that two waves representing the displacement of the atoms are physically indistinguishable. This means that the wavelengths below $2a$, or wave vectors, k, greater than $2\pi/2a = \pi/a$ are meaningless. The maximum range of k is known as the Brillouin zone. Notice that this would not be true in a *continuous* medium, that is, where the lattice constant a approaches zero.

(a)

(b)

Figure 1–18
(a) The displacement pattern of the atoms shown in black in a one-dimensional crystal can be described equivalently by a longer or shorter wavelength. The shortest possible wavelength (i.e., largest k vector) determines the Brillouin zone. In a finite crystal, we have a standing wave pattern. (b) A more complicated wave involving a mixing of two wavelengths (or Fourier components in k-space) giving rise to a beat pattern. By using a periodic boundary condition for the finite crystal in (a), one ends up with propagating waves rather than standing waves, making the math simpler.

Problems of wave propagation in periodic structures can be described in so-called *real space, x,* or alternatively in reciprocal *k-space.* An analogy would be describing a periodic signal $f(t) = f(t + T)$, either in the time domain or by taking the Fourier transform, in the frequency domain, $F(\omega)$. Here, the time period T is equivalent to the length of the crystal, L. One can extend this analogy further by considering not continuous signals $f(t)$, but sampled time-domain signals as in digital signal processing. If the sampling rate is Δt, one must use a Discrete Fourier Transform, where the highest relevant frequency is the Nyquist frequency. The sampling rate Δt corresponds to the lattice constant, *a,* and the Nyquist frequency corresponds to the edge of the Brillouin zone.

Incidentally, in Chapter 3 we will see that such waves describing physical displacement of atoms correspond to sound waves propagating in the crystal, and are called phonons. In Chapters 2 and 3, we will see that electrons propagating in crystals can also be described by a wave using the language of quantum mechanics, in term of a complex "wavefunction." However, such electron wavefunctions are described by the plane waves mentioned above multiplied by another function $U(k_x, x) = U(k_x, x+a)$ having the same periodicity as the lattice. Such wavefunctions are known as Bloch functions.

SUMMARY

1.1 Semiconductor devices are at the heart of information technology. Elemental semiconductors such as Si appear in column IV of the periodic table, while compound semiconductors such as GaAs consist of elements symmetrically around column IV. More complicated alloy semiconductors are used to optimize optoelectronic properties.

1.2 These devices are generally made in single-crystal material for best performance. Single crystals have long-range order, while polycrystalline and amorphous materials have short-range and no order, respectively.

1.3 Lattices are determined by symmetry. In 3-D, these are called Bravais lattices. When we put a basis of atom(s) on the lattice sites, we get a crystal. Common semiconductors have an fcc symmetry with a basis of two identical or different atoms, resulting in diamond or zinc blende crystals, respectively.

1.4 The fundamental building block of a lattice is a *primitive* cell with lattice points at its corners. Sometimes it is easier to describe the crystal in terms of a larger "unit" cell with lattice points not only at the corners but also at body or face centers.

1.5 Translating unit cells by integer numbers of basis vectors can replicate the lattice. Planes and directions in a lattice can be defined in terms of Miller indices.

1.6 Real crystals can have defects in 0-, 1-, 2-, and 3-D, some of which are benign, but many of which are harmful for device operation.

1.7 Semiconductor bulk crystals are grown from a melt by the Czochralski method, starting from a seed. Single-crystal epitaxial layers can be grown on top of semiconductor wafers in various ways, such as VPE, metal-organic chemical vapor deposition (MOCVD), or MBE. One can thereby optimize doping and band-structure properties for device fabrication.

1.1 Using Appendix III, which of the listed semiconductors in Table 1–1 has the largest band gap? The smallest? What are the corresponding wavelengths if light is emitted at the energy E_g? Is there a noticeable pattern in the band gap energy of III–V compounds related to the column III element?

1.2 For a bcc lattice structure with a lattice constant of 3 Å, calculate the separating distance between the nearest atoms, the radius, and the volume of each atoms. Also find the maximum packing fraction.

1.3 Label the planes illustrated in Fig. P1–3.

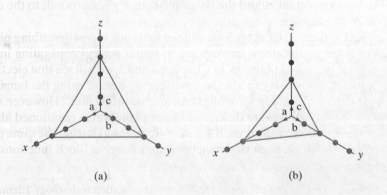

Figure P1-3

(a)   (b)

1.4 Sketch a bcc unit cell with a monoatomic basis. If the atomic density is $1.6 \times 10^{22}\,\text{cm}^{-3}$, calculate the lattice constant. What is the atomic density per unit area on the (110) plane? What is the radius of each atom? What are interstitials and vacancies?

1.5 Calculate the densities of Si and GaAs from the lattice constants (Appendix III), atomic weights, and Avogadro's number. Compare the results with densities given in Appendix III. The atomic weights of Si, Ga, and As are 28.1, 69.7, and 74.9, respectively.

1.6 The atomic radius of Ga and As are 136 pm and 114 pm, respectively. Using hard sphere approximation, find the lattice constant of GaAs and the volume of the primitive cell. [1 Å = 100 pm].

1.7 Sketch an fcc lattice unit cell (lattice constant = 5 Å) with a monoatomic basis, and calculate the atomic density per unit area on (110) planes. What is the atomic density per unit volume? Indicate an interstitial defect in this cell.

1.8 Sketch a view down a $\langle 110 \rangle$ direction of a diamond lattice, using Fig. 1–9 as a guide. Include lines connecting nearest neighbors.

1.9 Show by a sketch that the bcc lattice can be represented by two interpenetrating sc lattices. To simplify the sketch, show a $\langle 100 \rangle$ view of the lattice.

1.10 (a) Find the number of atoms/cm^2 on the (100) surface of a Si wafer.

(b) What is the distance (in Å) between nearest In neighbors in InP.

1.11 The ionic radii of Na^+ (atomic weight 23) and Cl^- (atomic weight 35.5) are 1.0 Å and 1.8 Å, respectively. Treating the ions as hard spheres, calculate the density of NaCl. Compare this with the measured density of 2.17 g/cm^3.

1.12 Sketch an sc unit cell with lattice constant **a** = 4 Å, whose diatomic basis of atom A is located at the lattice sites, and with atom B displaced by (**a**/2,0,0). Assume that both atoms have the same size and we have a close-packed structure (i.e., nearest neighbor atoms touch each other). Calculate

(i) the packing fraction (i.e., fraction of the total volume occupied by atoms),

(ii) the number of B atoms per unit *volume,*

(iii) the number of A atoms per unit *area* on (100) planes.

1.13 How many atoms are found inside a unit cell of an sc, a bcc, and an fcc crystal? How far apart in terms of lattice constant *a* are the nearest neighbor atoms in each case, measured from center to center?

1.14 Draw a cube such as Fig. 1–7, and show four {111} planes with different orientations. Repeat for {110} planes.

1.15 Find the maximum fractions of the unit cell volume that can be filled by hard spheres in the sc, fcc, and diamond lattices.

1.16 Calculate the densities of Ge and InP from the lattice constants (Appendix III), atomic weights, and Avogadro's number. Compare the results with the densities given in Appendix III.

1.17 Beginning with a sketch of an fcc lattice, add atoms at $\left(\frac{1}{4},\frac{1}{4},\frac{1}{4}\right)$ from each fcc atom to obtain the diamond lattice. Show that only the four added atoms in Fig. 1–8a appear in the diamond unit cell.

1.18 Assuming that the lattice constant varies linearly with composition x for a ternary alloy (e.g., see the variation for InGaAs in Fig. 1–13), what composition of $AlSb_xAs_{1-x}$ is lattice-matched to InP? What composition of $In_xGa_{1-x}P$ is lattice-matched to GaAs? What is the band gap energy in each case?

[*Note*: Such linear variations of crystal properties (e.g., lattice constant and band gap) with mole fraction in alloys is known as *Vegard's law*. A second-order polynomial or quadratic fit to the data is called the *bowing* parameter.]

1.19 (a) Find the composition of $In_{1-x}Ga_xAs$ grown lattice-matched on InP substrate. The lattice constants are: $a(InAs) = 6.0584$ Å, $a(GaAs) = 5.6533$ Å, and $a(InP) = 5.8688$ Å.

(b) An alloy of $In_{0.2}Ga_{0.8}As$ is grown pseudomorphically on a GaAs substrate. Determine the maximum thickness of the grown layer.

READING LIST   **Ashcroft, N. W., and N. D. Mermin.** *Solid State Physics.* Philadelphia: W.B. Saunders, 1976.

Kittel, C. *Introduction to Solid State Physics,* 7th ed. New York: Wiley, 1996.

Plummer, J. D., M. D. Deal, and P. B. Griffin. *Silicon VLSI Technology.* Upper Saddle River, NJ: Prentice Hall, 2000.

Stringfellow, G. B. *Organometallic Vapor-Phase Epitaxy.* New York: Academic Press, 1989.

Swaminathan, V., and A. T. Macrander. *Material Aspects of GaAs and InP Based Structures.* Englewood Cliffs, NJ: Prentice Hall, 1991.

Question 1

(a) Label the following planes using the correct notation for a cubic lattice of unit cell edge length *a* (shown within the unit cell).

(b) Write out all of the equivalent ⟨100⟩ directions using the correct notation.

(c) On the two following sets of axes, (1) sketch the [011] direction and (2) a (111) plane (for a cubic system with primitive vectors *a, b,* and *c*).

Question 2

(a) Which of the following three unit cells are *primitive cells* for the two-dimensional lattice? Circle the correct combination **in bold** below.

1 / 2 / 3 / 1 and 2 / 1 and 3 / 2 and 3 / 1, 2, and 3

answer:

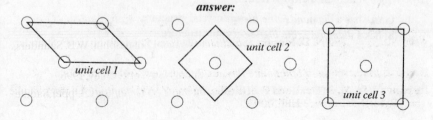

(b) The following planes (shown within the first quadrant for $0 < x, y, z < a$ only, with the dotted lines for reference only) are all from what one set of *equivalent* planes? Use correct notation:

(c) Which of the following three planes (shown within the first quadrant only) is a (121) plane? Circle the correct diagram.

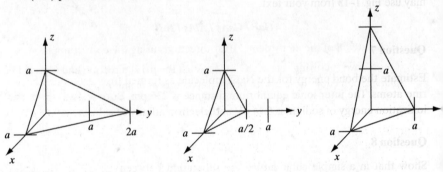

Question 3

(a) Diamond and zinc blende crystal structures are both composed of a Bravais lattice with a two-atom basis. Circle the correct unit cell for this Bravais lattice.

(b) Which statement below is true?

1. GaAs has a *diamond / zinc blende* crystal structure.
2. Si has a *diamond / zinc blende* crystal structure.

Question 4

Give some examples of zero-dimensional, one-dimensional, two-dimensional, and three-dimensional defects in a semiconductor.

Question 5

(a) What is the difference between a primitive cell and a unit cell? What is the utility of both concepts?

(b) What is the difference between a lattice and a crystal? How many different one-dimensional lattices can you have?

Question 6

Consider growing InAs on the following crystal substrates: InP, AlAs, GaAs, and GaP. For which case would the *critical thickness* of the InAs layer be greatest? You may use Fig. 1–13 from your text.

GaP / GaAs / AlAs / InP

Question 7

Estimate the bond energy for the NaCl molecule as formed from sodium and chlorine atoms. The inter ionic equilibrium distance is 236 pm. Born constant is 8. The ionization energy of sodium is 5.14 eV and electron affinity of chlorine is 3.65 eV.

Question 8

Show that in a simple cubic lattice the separation between the successive lattice planes (100) and (111) are ion the ratio of 1:0.71:0.58. Calculate the ratio d100:d111 for a simple cubic structure.

Question 9

NaCl crystal has FCC structure. The density of NaCl is 2.18 gm/cm^2. Calculate the distance between the two adjacent atoms. (Molecular weight of NaCl is 58.5)

Question 10

Chromium has BCC structure. Its atomic radius is 0.1249 nm. Calculate the free volume/Unit cell.

Question 11

The Madeluing constant of KCl is 1.75. Its neighbor separation is 0.314 nm. Find the cohesive energy per atom. (Given that the repulsive exponent value is 5.77, ionization energy potassium is 4.1 eV, electron affinity of chlorine is 3.6 eV)

Question 12

Calculate the potential energy of the system of Na$^+$ and Cl$^-$ ions when they are 0.25 nm apart.

Chapter 2

Atoms and Electrons

OBJECTIVES

1. Understand the wave–particle duality of nature in quantum mechanics
2. Study the Bohr model of atoms
3. Apply the Schrödinger equation to simple problems
4. Understand the electronic structure of atoms and the periodic table
5. Understand how semiconductor properties are determined

Since this book is primarily an introduction to solid state devices, it would be preferable not to delay this discussion with subjects such as atomic theory, quantum mechanics, and electron models. However, the behavior of solid state devices is directly related to these subjects. For example, it would be difficult to understand how an electron is transported through a semiconductor device without some knowledge of the electron and its interaction with the crystal lattice. Therefore, in this chapter we shall investigate some of the important properties of electrons, with special emphasis on two points: (1) the electronic structure of atoms, and (2) the interaction of atoms and electrons with excitation, such as the absorption and emission of light. By studying electron energies in an atom, we lay the foundation for understanding the influence of the lattice on electrons participating in current flow through a solid. Our discussions concerning the interaction of light with electrons form the basis for later descriptions of changes in the conductivity of a semiconductor with optical excitation, properties of light-sensitive devices, and lasers.

First, we shall investigate some of the experimental observations which led to the modern concept of the atom, and then we shall give a brief introduction to the theory of quantum mechanics. Several important concepts will emerge from this introduction: the electrons in atoms are restricted to certain energy levels by quantum rules; the electronic structure of atoms is determined from these quantum conditions; and this "quantization" defines certain allowable transitions involving absorption and emission of energy by the electrons.

The main effort of science is to describe what happens in nature, in as complete and concise a form as possible. In physics this effort involves observing natural phenomena, relating these observations to previously established theory, and finally establishing a physical model for the observations. For example, we can explain the behavior of a spring-supported weight moving up and down periodically after an initial displacement, because the differential equations describing such a simple harmonic motion have been established by Newtonian classical mechanics.

**2.1
INTRODUCTION
TO PHYSICAL
MODELS**

When a new physical phenomenon is observed, it is necessary to find out how it fits into the established models and "laws" of physics. In the vast majority of cases this involves a direct extension of the mathematics of well-established models to the particular conditions of the new problem. In fact, it is not uncommon for a scientist or engineer to predict that a new phenomenon should occur before it is actually observed, simply by a careful study and extension of existing models and laws. The beauty of science is that natural phenomena are not isolated events but are related to other events by a few analytically describable laws. However, it does happen occasionally that a set of observations cannot be described in terms of existing theories. In such cases it is necessary to develop models which are based as far as possible on existing laws, but which contain new aspects arising from the new phenomena. Postulating new physical principles is a serious business, and it is done only when there is no possibility of explaining the observations with established theory. When new assumptions and models are made, their justification lies in the following question: "Does the model describe precisely the observations, and can reliable predictions be made based on the model?" The model is good or poor depending on the answer to this question.

In the 1920s it became necessary to develop a new theory to describe phenomena on the atomic scale. A long series of careful observations had been made that clearly indicated that many events involving electrons and atoms did not obey the classical laws of mechanics. It was necessary, therefore, to develop a new kind of mechanics to describe the behavior of particles on this small scale. This new approach, called *quantum mechanics*, describes atomic phenomena very well and also properly predicts the way in which electrons behave in solids—our primary interest here. Through the years, quantum mechanics has been so successful that now it stands beside the classical laws as a valid description of nature.

A special problem arises when students first encounter the theory of quantum mechanics. The problem is that quantum concepts are largely mathematical in nature and do not involve the "common sense" quality associated with classical mechanics. At first, many students find quantum concepts difficult, not so much because of the mathematics involved, but because they feel the concepts are somehow divorced from "reality." This is a reasonable reaction, since ideas which we consider to be real or intuitively satisfying are usually based on our own observation. Thus the classical laws of motion are easy to understand because we observe bodies in motion every day. On the other hand, we observe the effects of atoms and electrons only indirectly, and naturally we have very little feeling for what is happening on the atomic scale. It is necessary, therefore, to depend on the facility of the theory to predict experimental results rather than to attempt to force classical analogs onto the nonclassical phenomena of atoms and electrons.

Our approach in this chapter will be to investigate the important experimental observations that led to the quantum theory, and then to indicate how the theory accounts for these observations. Discussions of quantum theory must necessarily be largely qualitative in such a brief presentation, and those topics that are most important to solid state theory will be emphasized here. Several good references for further individual study are given at the end of this chapter.

2.2 EXPERIMENTAL OBSERVATIONS

The experiments that led to the development of quantum theory were concerned with the interaction of light and matter. On the one hand, there were phenomena such as interference or diffraction which clearly indicated that light has a wave character as proposed by Huygens, in contrast to the particle or *corpuscular* view of light proposed by Newton. But on the other hand, many experiments at the turn of the 20th century clearly showed that a new theory of light was needed.

2.2.1 The Photoelectric Effect

An important observation by Planck indicated that radiation from a heated sample, known as blackbody radiation, is emitted in discrete units of energy called *quanta*; the energy units were described by $h\nu$, where ν is the frequency of the radiation, and h is a quantity now called Planck's constant ($h = 6.63 \times 10^{-34}$ J-s). Soon after Planck developed this hypothesis, Einstein interpreted an important experiment that clearly demonstrated the discrete nature (*quantization*) of light. This experiment involved absorption of optical energy by the electrons in a metal and the relationship between the amount of energy absorbed and the frequency of the light (Fig. 2–1). Let us suppose that monochromatic light is incident on the surface of a metal plate in a vacuum. The electrons in the metal absorb energy from the light, and some of the electrons receive enough energy to be ejected from the metal surface into

Figure 2–1
The photoelectric effect: (a) electrons are ejected from the surface of a metal when exposed to light of frequency ν in a vacuum; (b) plot of the maximum kinetic energy of ejected electrons vs. frequency of the incoming light.

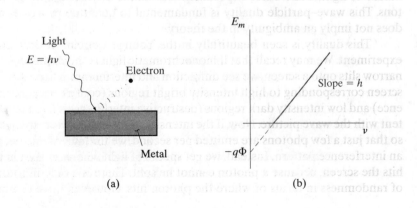

(a)   (b)

the vacuum. This phenomenon is called the *photoelectric effect*. If the energy of the escaping electrons is measured, a plot can be made of the maximum energy as a function of the frequency ν of the incident light (Fig. 2–1b).

One simple way of finding the maximum energy of the ejected electrons is to place another plate above the one shown in Fig. 2–1a and then create an electric field between the two plates. The potential necessary to retard all electron flow between the plates gives the energy E_m. For a particular frequency of light incident on the sample, a maximum energy E_m is observed for the emitted electrons. The resulting plot of E_m vs. ν is linear, with a slope equal to Planck's constant. The equation of the line shown in Fig. 2–1b is

$$E_m = h\nu - q\Phi \qquad\qquad (2\text{–}1)$$

where q is the magnitude of the electronic charge. The quantity Φ (volts) is a characteristic of the particular metal used. When Φ is multiplied by the electronic charge, an energy (joules) is obtained which represents the minimum energy required for an electron to escape from the metal into a vacuum. The energy $q\Phi$ is called the *work function* of the metal. These results indicate that the electrons receive an energy $h\nu$ from the light and lose an amount of energy $q\Phi$ in escaping from the surface of the metal.

This experiment demonstrates clearly that Planck's hypothesis was correct—light energy is contained in discrete units rather than in a continuous distribution of energies. Other experiments also indicate that, in addition to the wave nature of light, the quantized units of light energy can be considered as localized packets of energy, called *photons*. (Interestingly, this is reminiscent of the Newtonian picture.) We get the Planck relationship

$$E = h\nu = (h/2\pi)(2\pi\nu) = \hbar\omega \qquad\qquad (2\text{–}2a)$$

The photoelectron energy was found *not* to increase with increasing light intensity; instead the *number* of photoelectrons increases. This is in sharp contrast to what classical physics would have predicted. A higher amplitude or intensity wave packs more energy, and should have increased the photoelectron energy. Instead, we find in quantum physics that a higher intensity light corresponds to a larger *number* of these photons, and hence a larger *number* of photoelectrons. Some experiments emphasize the wave nature of light, while other experiments reveal the discrete nature of photons. This wave–particle duality is fundamental to quantum processes and does not imply an ambiguity in the theory.

This duality is seen beautifully in the Young's double slit diffraction experiment. We may recall that if monochromatic light is shone through two narrow slits onto a screen, we see diffraction and interference patterns on the screen corresponding to high intensity bright regions (constructive interference) and low intensity dark regions (destructive interference). This is consistent with the wave picture. Now, if the intensity of the light source is reduced, so that just a few photons are emitted per second, we find that we do not get an interference pattern. Instead, we get specks of light wherever the photon hits the screen, because a photon cannot be split. There is a certain amount of randomness in terms of where the photon hits. However, if we continue with the experiment, these random hits of the photons gradually build up the interference pattern, corresponding to the wave picture. Statistically, there are more photon hits in the bright regions of the screen, and fewer hits in the dark spots. Similar results were subsequently observed with electrons and other subatomic particles. This wave–particle duality is fundamental to the development of quantum mechanics.

Hence, based on the wave–particle duality of light, Louis de Broglie proposed that particles of matter (such as electrons) similarly could manifest a wave character in certain experiments. This observation was confirmed by the diffraction of electrons by the periodic array of atoms in a crystal observed by Davisson and Germer. De Broglie proposed that a particle of momentum $p = mv$ has a wavelength given by

$$\lambda = h/p = h/mv$$
$$\Rightarrow p = h/\lambda = (h/2\pi)(2\pi/\lambda) = \hbar k \tag{2–2b}$$

The Planck and de Broglie relationships are fundamental in quantum physics and are valid for *all* situations and objects, including photons and electrons. They connect the wave description of phenomena (frequency and wavelength) to a particle description (energy and momentum).

The relation between frequency and wavelength (or equivalently, energy and momentum), known as the *dispersion relationship,* however, is *not* the same for different objects. For example, for photons, the wavelength (λ) is related to frequency by $\nu = c/\lambda \Rightarrow E = \hbar\omega = \hbar(2\pi\nu) = \hbar 2\pi(c/\lambda) = \hbar ck = cp$, where c is the speed of light. For electrons, it is an approximately parabolic dispersion relationship, $E(k)$, also known as the band structure, as discussed in Chapter 3.

2.2.2 Atomic Spectra

One of the most valuable experiments of modern physics is the analysis of absorption and emission of light by atoms. The de Broglie wave property of electrons is key to understanding these experiments. For example, an electric discharge can be created in a gas, so that the atoms begin to emit light with wavelengths characteristic of the gas. We see this effect in a neon sign, which is typically a glass tube filled with neon or a gas mixture, with electrodes for creating a discharge. If the intensity of the emitted light is measured as a function of wavelength, one finds a series of sharp lines rather than a continuous distribution of wavelengths. By the early 1900s the characteristic spectra for several atoms were well known. A portion of the measured emission spectrum for hydrogen is shown in Fig. 2–2, in which the vertical lines represent the positions of observed emission peaks on the wavelength scale. Photon energy $h\nu$ is then related to wavelength by the dispersion relation $\lambda = c/\nu$.

The lines in Fig. 2–2 appear in several groups labeled the *Lyman,* *Balmer,* and *Paschen* series after their early investigators. Once the hydrogen spectrum was established, scientists noticed several interesting relationships among the lines. The various series in the spectrum were observed to follow certain empirical forms:

Lyman   Balmer   Paschen

0   2   4   6   8   10   12   14   16   18   20
λ (thousands of angstroms)

Figure 2–2
Some important
lines in the
emission spectrum
of hydrogen.

Figure 2–3
Relationships
among photon
energies in
the hydrogen
spectrum.

Lyman: $\nu = cR\left(\dfrac{1}{1^2} - \dfrac{1}{n^2}\right)$, $n = 2, 3, 4, \ldots$ (2–3a)

Balmer: $\nu = cR\left(\dfrac{1}{2^2} - \dfrac{1}{n^2}\right)$, $n = 3, 4, 5, \ldots$ (2–3b)

Paschen: $\nu = cR\left(\dfrac{1}{3^2} - \dfrac{1}{n^2}\right)$, $n = 4, 5, 6, \ldots$ (2–3c)

where R is a constant called the Rydberg constant ($R = 109{,}678 \text{ cm}^{-1}$). If the photon energies $h\nu$ are plotted for successive values of the integer $\mathbf{n}$, we notice that each energy can be obtained by taking sums and differences of other photon energies in the spectrum (Fig. 2–3). For example, E_{42} in the Balmer series is the difference between E_{41} and E_{21} in the Lyman series. This relationship among the various series is called the *Ritz combination principle*. Naturally, these empirical observations stirred a great deal of interest in constructing a comprehensive theory for the origin of the photons given off by atoms.

The results of emission spectra experiments led Niels Bohr to construct a model for the hydrogen atom, based on the mathematics of planetary systems. If the electron in the hydrogen atom has a series of planetary-type orbits available to it, it can be excited to an outer orbit and then can fall to any one of the inner orbits, giving off energy corresponding to one of the lines of Fig. 2–3. To develop the model, Bohr made several postulates:

**2.3
THE BOHR MODEL**

1. Electrons exist in certain stable, circular orbits about the nucleus. This assumption implies that the orbiting electron does not give off radiation as classical electromagnetic theory would normally require of a charge experiencing angular acceleration; otherwise, the electron would not be stable in the orbit but would spiral into the nucleus as it lost energy by radiation.

2. The electron may shift to an orbit of higher or lower energy, thereby gaining or losing energy equal to the difference in the energy levels (by absorption or emission of a photon of energy $h\nu$).

$$h\nu = E_2 - E_1$$

(2–4)

3. The angular momentum p_θ of the electron in an orbit is always an integral multiple of Planck's constant divided by 2π ($h/2\pi$ is often abbreviated $\hbar$ for convenience). This assumption,

$$p_\theta = n\hbar, \quad n = 1, 2, 3, 4, \ldots$$

(2–5)

is necessary to obtain the observed results of Fig. 2–3. Although Bohr proposed this *ad hoc* relationship simply to explain the data, one can see that this is equivalent to having an integer number of de Broglie wavelengths fit within the circumference of the electron orbit. These were called *pilot* waves, guiding the motion of the electrons around the nucleus. The de Broglie wave concept provided the inspiration for the Schrödinger wave equation in quantum mechanics discussed in Section 2.4.

If we visualize the electron in a stable orbit of radius r about the proton of the hydrogen atom, we can equate the electrostatic force between the charges to the centripetal force:

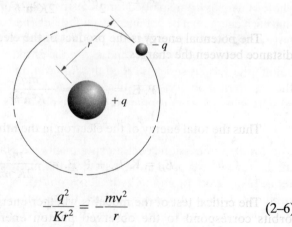

$$-\frac{q^2}{Kr^2} = -\frac{mv^2}{r}$$

(2–6)

where $K = 4\pi\epsilon_0$ in MKS units, m is the mass of the electron, and v is its velocity. From assumption 3 we have

$$p_\theta = mvr = n\hbar \qquad (2\text{-}7)$$

Since n takes on integral values, r should be denoted by r_n to indicate the nth orbit. Then Eq. (2-7) can be written

$$m^2v^2 = \frac{n^2\hbar^2}{r_n^2} \qquad (2\text{-}8)$$

Substituting Eq. (2-8) in Eq. (2-6) we find that

$$\frac{q^2}{Kr_n^2} = \frac{1}{mr_n} \cdot \frac{n^2\hbar^2}{r_n^2} \qquad (2\text{-}9)$$

$$r_n = \frac{Kn^2\hbar^2}{mq^2} \qquad (2\text{-}10)$$

for the radius of the nth orbit of the electron. Now we must find the expression for the total energy of the electron in this orbit, so that we can calculate the energies involved in transitions between orbits.

From Eqs. (2-7) and (2-10) we have

$$v = \frac{n\hbar}{mr_n} \qquad (2\text{-}11)$$

$$v = \frac{n\hbar q^2}{Kn^2\hbar^2} = \frac{q^2}{Kn\hbar} \qquad (2\text{-}12)$$

Therefore, the kinetic energy of the electron is

$$\text{K. E.} = \frac{1}{2}mv^2 = \frac{mq^4}{2K^2n^2\hbar^2} \qquad (2\text{-}13)$$

The potential energy is the product of the electrostatic force and the distance between the charges:

$$\text{P. E.} = -\frac{q^2}{Kr_n} = -\frac{mq^4}{K^2n^2\hbar^2} \qquad (2\text{-}14)$$

Thus the total energy of the electron in the nth orbit is

$$E_n = \text{K. E.} + \text{P. E.} = -\frac{mq^4}{2K^2n^2\hbar^2} \qquad (2\text{-}15)$$

The critical test of the model is whether energy differences between orbits correspond to the observed photon energies of the hydrogen

Figure 2–4
Electron orbits
and transitions in
the Bohr model
of the hydrogen
atom. Orbit
spacing is not
drawn to scale.

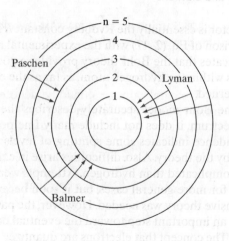

spectrum. The transitions between orbits corresponding to the Lyman, Balmer, and Paschen series are illustrated in Fig. 2–4. The energy difference between orbits n_1 and n_2 is given by

$$E_{n2} - E_{n1} = \frac{mq^4}{2K^2\hbar^2}\left(\frac{1}{n_1^2} - \frac{1}{n_2^2}\right) \qquad (2\text{–}16)$$

The frequency of light given off by a transition between these orbits is

$$\nu_{21} = \left[\frac{mq^4}{2K^2\hbar^2 h}\right]\left(\frac{1}{n_1^2} - \frac{1}{n_2^2}\right) \qquad (2\text{–}17)$$

EXAMPLE 2–1

Show Eq. (2–17) corresponds to Eq. (2–3). That is, show: $c \cdot R = \dfrac{m \cdot q^4}{2 \cdot K^2 \cdot \hbar^2 \cdot h}$.

SOLUTION

From Eq. (2–17) and the solution to Eq. (2–3),

$$\nu_{21} = \frac{c}{\lambda} = \frac{2.998 \cdot 10^8 \frac{m}{s}}{9.11 \cdot 10^{-8}\ m \cdot \dfrac{n_1^2\, n_2^2}{n_2^2 - n_1^2}} = 3.29 \cdot 10^{15}\ Hz \cdot \left(\frac{1}{n_1^2} - \frac{1}{n_2^2}\right)$$

From Eq. (2–3),

$$\nu_{21} = c \cdot R \cdot \left(\frac{1}{n_1^2} - \frac{1}{n_2^2}\right) = 2.998 \cdot 10^8 \frac{m}{s} \cdot 1.097 \cdot 10^7 \frac{1}{m} \cdot \left(\frac{1}{n_1^2} - \frac{1}{n_2^2}\right)$$

$$= 3.29 \cdot 10^{15}\ Hz \cdot \left(\frac{1}{n_1^2} - \frac{1}{n_2^2}\right)$$

The pre-factor is essentially the Rydberg constant R times the speed of light c. A comparison of Eq. (2–17) with the experimental results summed up by Eq. (2–3) indicates that the Bohr theory provides a good model for electronic transitions within the hydrogen atom, as far as the early experimental evidence is concerned.

Whereas the Bohr model accurately describes the gross features of the hydrogen spectrum, it does not include many fine points. For example, experimental evidence indicates some splitting of levels in addition to the levels predicted by the theory. Also, difficulties arise in extending the model to atoms more complicated than hydrogen. Attempts were made to modify the Bohr model for more general cases, but it soon became obvious that a more comprehensive theory was needed. However, the partial success of the Bohr model was an important step toward the eventual development of the quantum theory. The concept that electrons are quantized in certain allowed energy levels, and the relationship of photon energy and transitions between levels, had been established firmly by the Bohr theory.

The principles of quantum mechanics were developed from two different points of view at about the same time (the late 1920s). One approach, developed by Heisenberg, utilizes the mathematics of matrices and is called *matrix mechanics.* Independently, Schrödinger developed an approach utilizing a wave equation, now called *wave mechanics.* These two mathematical formulations appear to be quite different. However, closer examination reveals that beyond the formalism, the basic principles of the two approaches are the same. It is possible to show, for example, that the results of matrix mechanics reduce to those of wave mechanics after mathematical manipulation. We shall concentrate here on the wave mechanics approach, since solutions to a few simple problems can be obtained with it, involving less mathematical discussion.

**2.4
QUANTUM
MECHANICS**

2.4.1 Probability and the Uncertainty Principle

It is impossible to describe with absolute precision events involving individual particles on the atomic scale. Instead, we must speak of the average values (*expectation values*) of position, momentum, and energy of a particle such as an electron. It is important to note, however, that the uncertainties revealed in quantum calculations are not based on some shortcoming of the theory. In fact, a major strength of the theory is that it describes the probabilistic nature of events involving atoms and electrons. The fact is that such quantities as the position and momentum of an electron *do not exist* apart from a particular uncertainty. The magnitude of this inherent uncertainty is described by the *Heisenberg uncertainty principle*:[1]

---

[1]This is often called the *principle of indeterminacy.* This is a better term, since the parameters cannot be determined with better accuracy than specified in these equations.

In any measurement of the position and momentum of a particle, the uncertainties in the two measured quantities will be related by

$$\boxed{(\Delta x)(\Delta p_x) \geq \hbar/2} \qquad (2\text{--}18)$$

Similarly, the uncertainties in an energy measurement will be related to the uncertainty in the time at which the measurement was made by

$$\boxed{(\Delta E)(\Delta t) \geq \hbar/2} \qquad (2\text{--}19)$$

These limitations indicate that simultaneous measurement of position and momentum or of energy and time is inherently inaccurate to some degree. Of course, Planck's constant h is a rather small number (6.63×10^{-34} J-s), and we are not concerned with this inaccuracy in the measurement of x and p_x for a truck, for example. On the other hand, measurements of the position of an electron and its speed are seriously limited by the uncertainty principle.

One implication of the uncertainty principle is that we cannot properly speak of *the* position of an electron, for example, but must look for the "probability" of finding an electron at a certain position. Thus one of the important results of quantum mechanics is that a *probability density function* can be obtained for a particle in a certain environment, and this function can be used to find the expectation value of important quantities such as position, momentum, and energy. We are familiar with the methods for calculating discrete (single-valued) probabilities from common experience. For example, it is clear that the probability of drawing a particular card out of a random deck is $\frac{1}{52}$, and the probability that a tossed coin will come up heads is $\frac{1}{2}$. The techniques for making predictions when the probability varies are less familiar, however. In such cases it is common to define a probability of finding a particle within a certain volume. Given a probability density function $P(x)$ for a one-dimensional problem, the probability of finding the particle in a range from x to $x + dx$ is $P(x)dx$. Since the particle will be *somewhere*, this definition implies that

$$\int_{-\infty}^{\infty} P(x)dx = 1 \qquad (2\text{--}20)$$

if the function $P(x)$ is properly chosen. Equation (2–20) is implied by stating that the function $P(x)$ is *normalized* (i.e., the integral equals unity).

To find the average value of a function of x, we need only multiply the value of that function in each increment dx by the probability of finding the particle in that dx and sum over all x. Thus the average value of $f(x)$ is

$$\langle f(x) \rangle = \int_{-\infty}^{\infty} f(x)P(x)dx \qquad (2\text{--}21a)$$

If the probability density function is not normalized, this equation should be written

$$\langle f(x) \rangle = \frac{\displaystyle\int_{-\infty}^{\infty} f(x)P(x)dx}{\displaystyle\int_{-\infty}^{\infty} P(x)dx} \tag{2-21b}$$

2.4.2 The Schrödinger Wave Equation

There are several ways to develop the wave equation by applying quantum concepts to various classical equations of mechanics. One of the simplest approaches is to consider a few basic postulates, develop the wave equation from them, and rely on the accuracy of the results to serve as a justification of the postulates. In more advanced texts these assumptions are dealt with in more convincing detail.

Basic Postulates

1. Each particle in a physical system is described by a wavefunction $\Psi(x, y, z, t)$. This function and its space derivative ($\partial\Psi/\partial x + \partial\Psi/\partial y + \partial\Psi/\partial z$) are continuous, finite, and single valued.

2. In dealing with classical quantities such as energy E and momentum p, we must relate these quantities with abstract quantum mechanical operators defined in the following way:

Classical variable	Quantum operator
x	x
$f(x)$	$f(x)$
$p(x)$	$\dfrac{\hbar}{j}\dfrac{\partial}{\partial x}$
E	$-\dfrac{\hbar}{j}\dfrac{\partial}{\partial t}$

and similarly for the other two directions.

3. The probability of finding a particle with wavefunction Ψ in the volume $dx\, dy\, dz$ is $\Psi^*\Psi\, dx\, dy\, dz$.[2] The product $\Psi^*\Psi$ is normalized according to Eq. (2–20) so that

$$\int_{-\infty}^{\infty} \Psi^*\Psi\, dx\, dy\, dz = 1$$

and the average value $\langle Q \rangle$ of any variable Q is calculated from the wavefunction by using the operator form Q_{op} defined in postulate 2:

$$\langle Q \rangle = \int_{-\infty}^{\infty} \Psi^* Q_{op}\, \Psi\, dx\, dy\, dz$$

[2] Ψ^* is the *complex conjugate* of Ψ, obtained by reversing the sign on each j. Thus, $(e^{jx})^* = e^{-jx}$.

Once we find the wavefunction Ψ for a particle, we can calculate its average position, energy, and momentum, within the limits of the uncertainty principle. Thus, a major part of the effort in quantum calculations involves solving for Ψ within the conditions imposed by a particular physical system. We notice from assumption 3 that the probability density function is $\Psi^*\Psi$, or $|\Psi|^2$.

The classical equation for the energy of a particle can be written:

$$\text{Kinetic energy} \;+\; \text{potential energy} \;=\; \text{total energy} \tag{2-22}$$

$$\frac{1}{2m}p^2 \;+\; V \;=\; E$$

In quantum mechanics we use the operator form for these variables (postulate 2); the operators are allowed to operate on the wavefunction Ψ. For a one-dimensional problem Eq. (2-22) becomes[3]

$$-\frac{\hbar^2}{2m}\frac{\partial^2 \Psi(x,t)}{\partial x^2} + V(x)\Psi(x,t) = -\frac{\hbar}{j}\frac{\partial \Psi(x,t)}{\partial t} \tag{2-23}$$

which is the Schrödinger wave equation. In three dimensions the equation is

$$\boxed{-\frac{\hbar^2}{2m}\nabla^2\Psi + V\Psi = -\frac{\hbar}{j}\frac{\partial \Psi}{\partial t}} \tag{2-24}$$

where $\nabla^2\Psi$ is

$$\frac{\partial^2 \Psi}{\partial x^2} + \frac{\partial^2 \Psi}{\partial y^2} + \frac{\partial^2 \Psi}{\partial z^2}$$

The wavefunction Ψ in Eqs. (2-23) and (2-24) includes both space and time dependencies. It is common to calculate these dependencies separately and combine them later. Furthermore, many problems are time independent, and only the space variables are necessary. Thus we try to solve the wave equation by breaking it into two equations by the technique of separation of variables. Let $\Psi(x,t)$ be represented by the product $\psi(x)\phi(t)$. Using this product in Eq. (2-23) we obtain

$$-\frac{\hbar^2}{2m}\frac{\partial^2 \psi(x)}{\partial x^2}\phi(t) + V(x)\psi(x)h(t) = -\frac{\hbar}{j}\psi(x)\frac{\partial h(t)}{\partial t} \tag{2-25}$$

Now the variables can be separated to obtain the time-dependent equation in one dimension,

$$\boxed{\frac{d\phi(t)}{dt} + \frac{jE}{\hbar}\phi(t) = 0} \tag{2-26a}$$

---

[3]The operational interpretation of $(\partial/\partial x)^2$ is the second-derivative form $\partial^2/\partial x^2$; the square of j is -1.

and the time-independent equation,

$$\left[-\frac{\hbar^2}{2m}\frac{d^2}{dx^2} + V(x) \right]\psi(x) = E\psi(x) \qquad (2\text{–}26b)$$

This type of equation, where an operator operating on a function equals a constant times the function, is known as an eigenvalue equation, from the German word *eigen* meaning "proper." We can show that the separation constant E corresponds to the total energy (kinetic plus potential) of the particle. We get different eigenfunctions ψ_n corresponding to different eigenenergies, E_n. Since the time-dependent Equation (2–26a) is a first-order differential equation, its solution is simply $\phi(t) = \exp(-jE/\hbar t) = \exp(-j\omega t)$ (using the Planck relation). This form is the *universal* time dependence of all eigenfunctions.

We can show in quantum mechanics that any arbitrary wavefunction can be written as a linear combination of these eigenfunctions, with pre-factors or weighting coefficients that depend on the initial conditions. As an analogy, remember that an arbitrary vector, **V**, can be expanded as a linear combination in terms of unit vectors or *basis* vectors along the x, y, and z axes:

$$\mathbf{V} = V_x\mathbf{x} + V_y\mathbf{y} + V_z\mathbf{z} \qquad (2\text{–}27a)$$

with coefficients V_x, V_y, and V_z.

A wavefunction can similarly be written as a linear combination of various eigenfunctions, with appropriate pre-factors, each evolving in time as shown above:

$$\psi(x, t) = \sum_n c_n\psi_n \exp(-jE_n/\hbar t) \qquad (2\text{–}27b)$$

Hence, eigenfunctions are sometimes also known as *basis* functions. But unlike real vectors expandable in terms of three basis vectors in real space, these eigenfunctions span an infinite number of dimensions in an abstract space known as *Hilbert space*. If we measure the energy of the particle, we will get one of these eigenenergies with a probability given by c_n^2. If we keep repeating these measurements, each time we get a *different* eigenenergy with corresponding probabilities, c_n^2. This leads to the famous uncertainties in quantum mechanics. The *average* of many quantum mechanical measurements will correspond to the classical physics result. These equations are the basis of wave mechanics. From them we can determine the wavefunctions for particles in various simple systems. The only thing that changes from one quantum mechanical problem to the other is the form of $V(x)$. For calculations involving electrons, the potential term $V(x)$ usually results from an electrostatic or magnetic field.

2.4.3 Potential Well Problem

It is quite difficult to find solutions to the Schrödinger equation for most realistic potential fields. One can solve the problem with some effort for the hydrogen atom, for example, but solutions for more complicated atoms are

Figure 2-5
The problem of
a particle in a
potential well:
(a) potential
energy diagram;
(b) wavefunctions
in the first three
quantum states;
(c) probability
density
distribution for the
second state.

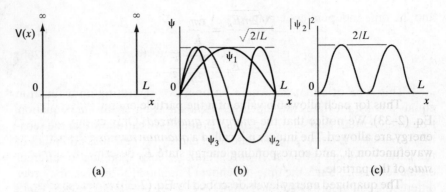

(a)   (b)   (c)

hard to obtain. There are several important problems, however, which illustrate the theory without complicated manipulation. The simplest problem is the potential energy well with infinite boundaries. Let us assume a particle is trapped in a potential well with $V(x)$ zero except at the boundaries $x = 0$ and L, where it is infinitely large (Fig. 2-5a):

$$V(x) = 0,\ 0 < x < L$$
$$V(x) = \infty,\ x = 0,\ L \tag{2-28}$$

Inside the well we set $V(x) = 0$ in Eq. (2-26b):

$$\frac{d^2\psi(x)}{dx^2} + \frac{2m}{\hbar^2}E\psi(x) = 0,\quad 0 < x < L \tag{2-29}$$

This is the wave equation for a free particle; it applies to the potential well problem in the region with no potential $V(x)$.

Possible solutions to Eq. (2-29) are sin kx and cos kx, where k is $\sqrt{2mE}/\hbar$. In choosing a solution, however, we must examine the boundary conditions. The only allowable value of ψ at the walls is zero. Otherwise, there would be a nonzero $|\psi|^2$ outside the potential well, which is impossible because a particle cannot penetrate an infinite barrier. Therefore, we must choose only the sine solution and define k such that sin kx goes to zero at $x = L$:

$$\psi = A\ \sin\ kx,\quad k = \frac{\sqrt{2mE}}{\hbar} \tag{2-30}$$

The constant A is the amplitude of the wavefunction and will be evaluated from the normalization condition (postulate 3). If ψ is to be zero at $x = L$, then k must be some integral multiple of π/L:

$$k = \frac{n\pi}{L},\quad n = 1, 2, 3, \ldots \tag{2-31}$$

From Eqs. (2-30) and (2-31) we can solve for the total energy E_n for each value of the integer **n**:

$$\frac{\sqrt{2mE_n}}{\hbar} = \frac{n\pi}{L} \tag{2-32}$$

$$E_n = \frac{n^2\pi^2\hbar^2}{2mL^2} \tag{2-33}$$

Thus for each allowable value of **n** the particle energy is described by Eq. (2–33). We notice that the *energy is quantized*. Only certain values of energy are allowed. The integer **n** is called a *quantum number*; the particular wavefunction ψ_n and corresponding energy state E_n describe the *quantum state* of the particle.

The quantized energy levels described by Eq. (2–33) appear in a variety of small-geometry structures encountered in semiconductor devices. We shall return to this potential well problem (often called the "particle-in-a-box" problem) in later discussions.

The constant A is found from postulate 3:

$$\int_{-\infty}^{\infty} \psi^*\psi \, dx = \int_{0}^{L} A^2\left(\sin\frac{n\pi}{L}x\right)^2 dx = A^2\frac{L}{2} \tag{2-34}$$

Setting Eq. (2–34) equal to unity we obtain

$$A = \sqrt{\frac{2}{L}}, \qquad \psi_n = \sqrt{\frac{2}{L}} \sin\frac{n\pi}{L}x \tag{2-35}$$

The first three wavefunctions ψ_1, ψ_2, and ψ_3 are sketched in Fig. 2–5b. The probability density function $\psi^*\psi$, or $|\psi|^2$, is sketched for ψ_2 in Fig. 2–5c.

Another useful form of the potential is $V(x) = kx^2$, a parabolic potential well, which corresponds to the simple harmonic oscillator (SHO). The shape of the wavefunctions and the eigenenergies are obviously going to be different from the rectangular potential well above. The eigenenergies in this case are found to be equally spaced, and given by $E_n = (n + 1/2)\hbar\omega$ for various positive integer values of **n**, corresponding to **n** quanta of these SHO. In Chapter 3, we will discuss elastic waves in a lattice due to simple harmonic oscillations of atoms in a parabolic inter-atomic potential, whose quantized units are known as phonons (in analogy with the photons we discussed above). The energy of these phonons is given by $\hbar\omega$.

Given a plane wave $\psi = A \exp(jk_x x)$, what is the expectation value for p_x, the x-component of momentum? **EXAMPLE 2–2**

SOLUTION

$$\langle p_x \rangle = \frac{\displaystyle\int_{-\infty}^{\infty} A^* e^{-jk_x x}\left(\frac{\hbar}{j}\frac{\partial}{\partial x}\right) A e^{jk_x x}\, dx}{\displaystyle\int_{-\infty}^{\infty} |A|^2 e^{-jk_x x} e^{jk_x x}\, dx} = (\hbar k_x) \text{ after normalization}$$

This is the de Broglie relationship. If we try to evaluate these integrals directly, we run into the problem that both numerator and denominator tend to infinity, because an *ideal* plane wave is strictly not a normalizable wavefunction. The trick to use is to choose the limits of integration from, say, $-L/2$ to $+L/2$ in a region of length L. The factor L cancels out in the numerator and denominator. *Then* we can consider L approaches infinity. For wavefunctions that are normalizable, such a mathematical "trick" does not have to be used.

If we include the time dependence also, we get $\Psi = A \exp(jk_xx - j\omega t)$. We can also calculate the expectation value of the energy operator,

$$\langle E \rangle = \frac{\displaystyle\int_{-\infty}^{\infty} A^* e^{-j(k_x x - \omega t)} \left(-\frac{\hbar}{j} \frac{\partial}{\partial t} \right) A e^{j(k_x x - \omega t)} \, dx}{\displaystyle\int_{-\infty}^{\infty} |A|^2 e^{-jk_x x} e^{jk_x x} \, dx}$$

$$= (\hbar\omega) \text{ after normalization}$$

which is the Planck relation.

2.4.4 Tunneling

The wavefunctions are relatively easy to obtain for the potential well with infinite walls, since the boundary conditions force ψ to zero at the walls. A slight modification of this problem illustrates a principle that is very important in some solid state devices—the quantum mechanical *tunneling* of an electron through a barrier of finite height and thickness. Let us consider the potential barrier of Fig. 2–6. If the barrier is not infinite, the boundary conditions do not force ψ to zero at the barrier. Instead, we must use the condition that ψ and its slope $d\psi/dx$ are continuous at each boundary of the barrier (postulate 1). Thus ψ must have a nonzero value within the barrier and also on the other side. Since ψ has a value to the right of the barrier, $\psi^*\psi$ exists there also, implying that there is some probability of finding the particle beyond the barrier. We notice that the particle does not go over the barrier; its total energy is assumed to be less than the barrier height V_0. The mechanism by which the particle "penetrates" the barrier is called tunneling. However, no classical analog, including classical descriptions of tunneling through barriers, is appropriate for this effect. Quantum mechanical tunneling is intimately bound to the uncertainty principle. If the barrier is sufficiently thin, we cannot say with certainty that the particle exists only on one side. However, the wavefunction amplitude for the particle is reduced by the barrier as Fig. 2–6 indicates, so that by making the thickness W greater,

Figure 2–6
Quantum
mechanical
tunneling: (a)
potential barrier
of height V_0 and
thickness W; (b)
probability density
for an electron
with energy
$E < V_0$, indicating
a nonzero
value of the
wavefunction
beyond the
barrier.

we can reduce ψ on the right-hand side to the point that negligible tunneling occurs. Tunneling is important only over very small dimensions, but it can be of great importance in the conduction of electrons in solids, as we shall see in Chapters 5, 6, and 10.

A novel electronic device called the resonant tunneling diode has been developed. This device operates by tunneling electrons through "particle in a potential well" energy levels of the type described in Section 2.4.3.

The Schrödinger equation describes accurately the interactions of particles with potential fields, such as electrons within atoms. Indeed, the modern understanding of atomic theory (the modern atomic *models*) comes from the wave equation and from Heisenberg's matrix mechanics. It should be pointed out, however, that the problem of solving the Schrödinger equation directly for complicated atoms is extremely difficult. In fact, only the hydrogen atom is generally solved directly; atoms of atomic number greater than one are usually handled by techniques involving approximations. Many atoms such as the alkali metals (Li, Na, etc.), which have a neutral core with a single electron in an outer orbit, can be treated by a rather simple extension of the hydrogen atom results. The hydrogen atom solution is also important in identifying the basic selection rules for describing allowed electron energy levels. These quantum mechanical results must coincide with the experimental spectra, and we expect the energy levels to include those predicted by the Bohr model. Without actually working through the mathematics for the hydrogen atom, in this section we shall investigate the energy level schemes dictated by the wave equation.

**2.5
ATOMIC
STRUCTURE AND
THE PERIODIC
TABLE**

2.5.1 The Hydrogen Atom

Finding the wavefunctions for the hydrogen atom requires a solution of the Schrödinger equation in three dimensions for a Coulombic potential field. Since the problem is spherically symmetric, the spherical coordinate system is used in the calculation (Fig. 2–7). The term $V(x, y, z)$ in Eq. (2–24) must be replaced by $V(r, \theta, \phi)$, representing the Coulomb potential which the electron experiences in the vicinity of the proton. The Coulomb potential varies only with r in spherical coordinates

$$V(r, \theta, \phi) = V(r) = -(4\pi\epsilon_0)^{-1}\frac{q^2}{r} \tag{2–36}$$

as in Eq. (2–14).

When the separation of variables is made, the time-independent equation can be written as

$$\psi(r, \theta, \phi) = R(r)\Theta(\theta)\Phi(\phi) \tag{2–37}$$

Thus the wavefunctions are found in three parts. Separate solutions must be obtained for the r-dependent equation, the θ-dependent equation, and the ϕ-dependent equation. After these three equations are solved, the total wavefunction ψ is obtained from the product.

As in the simple potential well problem, each of the three hydrogen atom equations gives a solution which is quantized. Thus we would expect a quantum number to be associated with *each* of the three parts of the wave equation. As an illustration, the ϕ-dependent equation obtained after separation of variables is

$$\frac{d^2\Phi}{d\phi^2} + m^2\Phi = 0 \tag{2–38}$$

Figure 2–7
The spherical coordinate system.

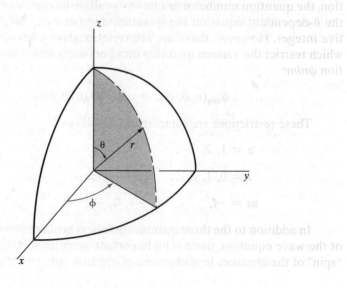

where **m** is a quantum number. The solution to this equation is

$$\Phi_m(\phi) = Ae^{jm\phi} \qquad (2\text{--}39)$$

where A can be evaluated by the normalization condition, as before:

$$\int_0^{2\pi} \Phi_m^*(\phi)\Phi_m(\phi)d\phi = 1 \qquad (2\text{--}40)$$

$$A^2 \int_0^{2\pi} e^{-jm\phi}e^{jm\phi}\, d\phi = A^2 \int_0^{2\pi} d\phi = 2\pi A^2 \qquad (2\text{--}41)$$

Thus the value of A is

$$A = \frac{1}{\sqrt{2\pi}} \qquad (2\text{--}42)$$

and the ϕ-dependent wavefunction is

$$\Phi_m(\phi) = \frac{1}{\sqrt{2\pi}}e^{jm\phi} \qquad (2\text{--}43)$$

Since values of ϕ repeat every 2π radians, Φ should repeat also. This occurs if **m** is an integer, including negative integers and zero. Thus the wavefunctions for the ϕ-dependent equation are quantized with the following selection rule for the quantum numbers:

$$\mathbf{m} = \ldots, -3, -2, -1, 0, +1, +2, +3, \ldots \qquad (2\text{--}44)$$

By similar treatments, the functions $R(r)$ and $\Theta(\theta)$ can be obtained, each being quantized by its own selection rule. For the r-dependent equation, the quantum number **n** can be any positive integer (not zero), and for the θ-dependent equation the quantum number l can be zero or a positive integer. However, there are interrelationships among the equations which restrict the various quantum numbers used with a single wavefunction ψnlm:

$$\psi_{nlm}(r, \theta, \phi) = R_n(r)\Theta_l(\theta)\Phi_m(\phi) \qquad (2\text{--}45)$$

These restrictions are summarized as follows:

$$\mathbf{n} = 1, 2, 3, \ldots \qquad (2\text{--}46a)$$

$$l = 0, 1, 2, \ldots, (\mathbf{n} - 1) \qquad (2\text{--}46b)$$

$$\mathbf{m} = -l, \ldots, -2, -1, 0, +1, +2, \ldots, +l \qquad (2\text{--}46c)$$

In addition to the three quantum numbers arising from the three parts of the wave equation, there is an important quantization condition on the "spin" of the electron. Investigations of electron spin employ the theory of relativity as well as quantum mechanics; therefore, we shall simply state that the intrinsic angular momentum **s** of an electron with ψ_{nlm} specified is

$$s = \pm \frac{\hbar}{2} \tag{2-47}$$

That is, in units of $\hbar$, the electron has a spin of $\frac{1}{2}$, and the angular momentum produced by this spin is positive or negative depending on whether the electron is "spin up" or "spin down." The important point for our discussion is that each allowed energy state of the electron in the hydrogen atom is uniquely described by four quantum numbers: **n**, l, **m** and **s**.[4]

Using these four quantum numbers, we can identify the various states which the electron can occupy in a hydrogen atom. The number **n**, called the *principal* quantum number, specifies the "orbit" of the electron in Bohr terminology. Of course, the concept of orbit is replaced by probability density functions in quantum mechanical calculations. It is common to refer to states with a given principal quantum number as belonging to a *shell* rather than an orbit.

There is considerable fine structure in the energy levels about the Bohr orbits, due to the dictates of the other three quantum conditions. For example, an electron with **n** = 1 (the first Bohr orbit) can have only l = 0 and **m** = 0 according to Eq. (2–46), but there are two spin states allowed from Eq. (2–47). For **n** = 2, l can be 0 or 1, and **m** can be −1, 0, or +1. The various allowed combinations of quantum numbers appear in the first four columns of Table 2–1. From these combinations it is apparent that the electron in a hydrogen atom can occupy any one of a large number of excited states in addition to the lowest (*ground*) state ψ_{100}. Energy differences between the various states properly account for the observed lines in the hydrogen spectrum.

2.5.2 The Periodic Table

The quantum numbers discussed in Section 2.5.1 arise from the solutions to the hydrogen atom problem. Thus the energies obtainable from the wavefunctions are unique to the hydrogen atom and cannot be extended to more complicated atoms without appropriate alterations. However, the quantum number selection rules are valid for more complicated structures, and we can use these rules to gain an understanding of the arrangement of atoms in the periodic table of chemical elements. Without these selection rules, it is difficult to understand why only two electrons fit into the first Bohr orbit of an atom, whereas eight electrons are allowed in the second orbit. After even the brief discussion of quantum numbers given above, we should be able to answer these questions with more insight.

Before discussing the periodic table, we must be aware of an important principle of quantum theory, the *Pauli exclusion principle*. This rule states

---

[4]In many texts, the numbers we have called **m** and **s** are referred to as m_l and m_s, respectively.

Table 2-1 Quantum numbers to $n = 3$ and allowable states for the electron in a hydrogen atom: The first four columns show the various combinations of quantum numbers allowed by the selection rules of Eq. (2–46); the last two columns indicate the number of allowed states (combinations of **n**, *l*, **m**, and **s**) for each *l* (subshell) and **n** (shell, or Bohr orbit).

n	*l*	m	s/ℏ	Allowable states in subshell	Allowable states in complete shell
1	0	0	$\pm\frac{1}{2}$	2	2
2	0	0	$\pm\frac{1}{2}$	2	8
	1	−1	$\pm\frac{1}{2}$		
		0	$\pm\frac{1}{2}$	6	
		1	$\pm\frac{1}{2}$		
3	0	0	$\pm\frac{1}{2}$	2	18
	1	−1	$\pm\frac{1}{2}$		
		0	$\pm\frac{1}{2}$	6	
		1	$\pm\frac{1}{2}$		
	2	−2	$\pm\frac{1}{2}$		
		−1	$\pm\frac{1}{2}$		
		0	$\pm\frac{1}{2}$	10	
		1	$\pm\frac{1}{2}$		
		2	$\pm\frac{1}{2}$		

that no two electrons in an interacting system[5] can have the same set of quantum numbers **n**, *l*, **m**, and **s**. In other words, only two electrons can have the same three quantum numbers **n**, *l*, and **m**, and those two must have opposite spin. The importance of this principle cannot be overemphasized; it is basic to the electronic structure of all atoms in the periodic table. One implication of this principle is that by listing the various combinations of quantum numbers, we can determine into which shell each electron of a complicated atom fits, and how many electrons are allowed per shell. The quantum states summarized in Table 2–1 can be used to indicate the electronic configurations for atoms in the lowest energy state.

In the first electronic shell ($n = 1$), *l* can be only zero since the maximum value of *l* is always $n - 1$. Similarly, **m** can be only zero since **m** runs from the negative value of *l* to the positive value of *l*. Two electrons with opposite spin can fit in this ψ_{100} state; therefore, the first shell can have at most two electrons. For the helium atom (atomic number $Z = 2$) in the

[5]An interacting system is a system in which electron wave functions overlap—in this case, an atom with two or more electrons.

Table 2–2 Electronic configurations for atoms in the ground state.

Atomic number (Z)	Element	n=1 l=0 1s	2s	2p	3s	3p	3d	4s	4p	Shorthand notation
										Number of electrons (spanning)
1	H	1								$1s^1$
2	He	2								$1s^2$
3	Li		1							$1s^2\,2s^1$
4	Be	helium core, 2 electrons	2							$1s^2\,2s^2$
5	B		2	1						$1s^2\,2s^2\,2p^1$
6	C		2	2						$1s^2\,2s^2\,2p^2$
7	N		2	3						$1s^2\,2s^2\,2p^3$
8	O		2	4						$1s^2\,2s^2\,2p^4$
9	F		2	5						$1s^2\,2s^2\,2p^5$
10	Ne		2	6						$1s^2\,2s^2\,2p^6$
11	Na				1					[Ne] $3s^1$
12	Mg				2					$3s^2$
13	Al				2	1				$3s^2\,3p^1$
14	Si	neon core, 10 electrons			2	2				$3s^2\,3p^2$
15	P				2	3				$3s^2\,3p^3$
16	S				2	4				$3s^2\,3p^4$
17	Cl				2	5				$3s^2\,3p^5$
18	Ar				2	6				$3s^2\,3p^6$
19	K							1		[Ar] $4s^1$
20	Ca							2		$4s^2$
21	Sc						1	2		$3d^1\,4s^2$
22	Ti						2	2		$3d^2\,4s^2$
23	V						3	2		$3d^3\,4s^2$
24	Cr						5	1		$3d^5\,4s^1$
25	Mn						5	2		$3d^5\,4s^2$
26	Fe						6	2		$3d^6\,4s^2$
27	Co	argon core, 18 electrons					7	2		$3d^7\,4s^2$
28	Ni						8	2		$3d^8\,4s^2$
29	Cu						10	1		$3d^{10}\,4s^1$
30	Zn						10	2		$3d^{10}\,4s^2$
31	Ga						10	2	1	$3d^{10}\,4s^2\,4p^1$
32	Ge						10	2	2	$3d^{10}\,4s^2\,4p^2$
33	As						10	2	3	$3d^{10}\,4s^2\,4p^3$
34	Se						10	2	4	$3d^{10}\,4s^2\,4p^4$
35	Br						10	2	5	$3d^{10}\,4s^2\,4p^5$
36	Kr						10	2	6	$3d^{10}\,4s^2\,4p^6$

ground state, both electrons will be in the first Bohr orbit ($n = 1$), both will have $l = 0$ and $m = 0$, and they will have opposite spin. Of course, one or both of the He atom electrons can be excited to one of the higher energy states of Table 2–1 and subsequently relax to the ground state, giving off a photon characteristic of the He spectrum.

As Table 2–1 indicates, there can be two electrons in the $l = 0$ subshell, six electrons when $l = 1$, and ten electrons for $l = 2$. The electronic configurations of various atoms in the periodic table can be deduced from this list of allowed states. The ground state electron structures for a number of atoms are listed in Table 2–2. There is a simple shorthand notation for electronic structures which is commonly used instead of such a table. The only new convention to remember in this notation is the naming of the l values:

$$l = 0, 1, 2, 3, 4, \ldots$$

$$s, p, d, f, g, \ldots$$

This convention was created by early spectroscopists who referred to the first four spectral groups as *s*harp, *p*rincipal, *d*iffuse, and *f*undamental. Alphabetical order is used beyond f. With this convention for l, we can write an electron state as follows:

$$(\mathbf{n} = 3) \quad 3p^6 \quad (l = 1)$$

6 electrons in the $3p$ subshell

For example, the total electronic configuration for Si ($Z = 14$) in the ground state is

$$1s^2 2s^2 2p^6 3s^2 3p^2$$

We notice that Si has a closed Ne configuration (see Table 2–2) plus four electrons in an outer $\mathbf{n} = 3$ orbit ($3s^2 3p^2$). These are the four valence electrons of Si; two valence electrons are in an s state and two are in a p state. The Si electronic configuration can be written [Ne] $3s^2 3p^2$ for convenience, since the Ne configuration $1s^2 2s^2 2p^6$ forms a closed shell (typical of the inert elements).

Figure 2–8a shows the orbital model of a Si atom, which has a nucleus consisting of 14 protons (with a charge of $+14$) and neutrons, 10 core electrons in shells $n = 1$ and 2, and 4 valence electrons in the $3s$ and $3p$ subshells. Figure 2–8b shows the energy levels of the various electrons in the Coulombic potential well of the nucleus. Since unlike charges attract each other, there is an attractive potential between the negatively charged electrons and the positively charged nucleus. As indicated in Eq. (2–36), a Coulomb potential varies as $1/r$ as a function of distance from the charge, in this case the Si nucleus. The potential energy gradually goes to zero when we approach infinity. We end up getting "particle-in-a-box" states for these electrons in this potential well, as discussed in Section 2.4.3 and Eq. (2–33). Of course, in this case the shape of the potential well is not rectangular, as shown in Fig. 2–5a, but Coulombic, as shown in Fig. 2–8b. Therefore, the energy levels have a form closer to those of the H atom as shown in Eq. (2–15), rather than in Eq. (2–33).

If we solve the Schrödinger equation for the Si atom as we did in Section 2.5.1 for the H atom, we can get the radial and angular dependence of

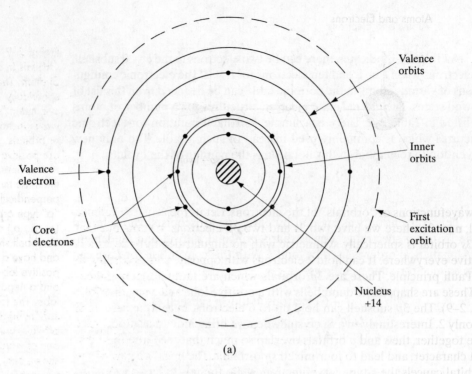

Valence
orbits

Inner
orbits

Valence
electron

Core
electrons

First
excitation
orbit

Nucleus
+14

(a)

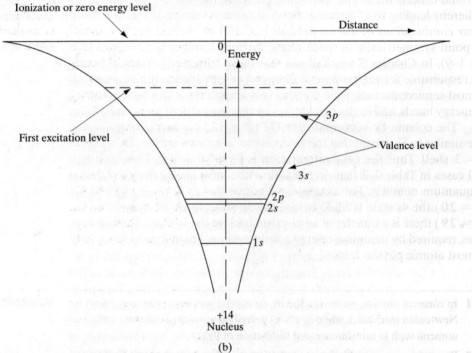

Ionization or zero energy level

Distance

0

Energy

First excitation level

3p

Valence level

3s

2p
2s

1s

+14
Nucleus

(b)

Figure 2–8

Electronic structure and energy levels in a Si atom: (a) the orbital model of a Si atom showing the 10 core electrons (**n** = 1 and 2), and the four valence electrons (**n** = 3); (b) energy levels in the Coulombic potential of the nucleus are also shown schematically.

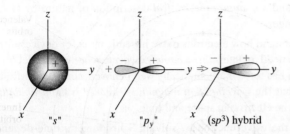

Figure 2–9
Orbitals in a
Si atom: The
spherically
symmetric "s" type
wavefunctions
or orbitals
are positive
everywhere, while
the three mutually
perpendicular
"p" type orbitals
(p_x, p_y, p_z) are
dumbbell shaped
and have a
positive lobe
and a negative
lobe. The four
sp^3 "hybridized"
orbitals, only
one of which is
shown here, point
symmetrically in
space and lead
to the diamond
lattice in Si.

the wavefunctions or "orbitals" of the electrons. Let us focus on the valence shell, **n** = 3, where we have two 3s and two 3p electrons. It turns out that the 3s orbital is spherically symmetric with no angular dependence, and is positive everywhere. It can hold 2 electrons with opposite spin according to the Pauli principle. There are 3p orbitals which are mutually perpendicular. These are shaped like dumbbells with a positive lobe and a negative lobe (Fig. 2–9). The 3p subshell can hold up to 6 electrons, but in the case of Si has only 2. Interestingly, in a Si crystal when we bring individual atoms very close together, the s and p orbitals overlap so much that they lose their distinct character, and lead to four mixed sp^3 orbitals. The negative part of the p orbital cancels the s-type wavefunction, while the positive part enhances it, thereby leading to a "directed" bond in space. As shown in Fig. 2–9, these *linear combinations of atomic orbitals* (*LCAO*) or "hybridized" sp^3 orbitals point symmetrically in space along the four tetragonal directions (see Fig. 1–9). In Chapter 3 we shall see that these "directed" chemical bonds are responsible for the tetragonal diamond or zinc blende lattice structure in most semiconductors. They are also very important in the understanding of energy bands, and in the conduction of charges in these semiconductors.

The column IV semiconductor Ge ($Z = 32$) has an electronic structure similar to Si, except that the four valence electrons are outside a closed **n** = 3 shell. Thus the Ge configuration is [Ar] $3d^{10}4s^24p^2$. There are several cases in Table 2–2 that do not follow the most straightforward choice of quantum numbers. For example, we notice that in K ($Z = 19$) and Ca ($Z = 20$) the 4s state is filled before the 3d state; in Cr ($Z = 24$) and Cu ($Z = 29$) there is a transfer of an electron back to the 3d state. These exceptions, required by minimum energy considerations, are discussed more fully in most atomic physics texts.

SUMMARY

2.1 In *classical* physics, *matter* (including electrons) was described as *particles* by Newtonian mechanics, while *light* was described as *waves,* consistent with phenomena such as interference and diffraction of light.

2.2 Phenomena such as blackbody radiation and the photoelectric effect forced Planck and Einstein to introduce a *particle* aspect to light (photons). Analysis of atomic spectra then led Bohr and de Broglie to analogously introduce a *wave aspect* to *subatomic particles* such as electrons. This led to a *wave–particle* duality and a *quantum mechanical* description of nature by Heisenberg and Schrödinger.

2.3 To understand how electrons move in semiconductor devices or interact with light, we need to determine a *complex wavefunction* of the electron. The wavefunction has to be mathematically well behaved, consistent with the interpretation that the *wavefunction magnitude squared is the probability density* of finding the electron in space and time.

2.4 We get the wavefunction by solving Schrödinger's time-dependent partial differential equation. The application of *boundary conditions* (the potential energy profile) allows certain (proper) *eigenfunctions* as valid solutions, with corresponding *eigenenergies,* determined by *allowed quantum numbers*. Results of physical measurements are *no longer deterministic* (as in classical mechanics), but *probabilistic,* with an *expectation* value given by an average using the wavefunction of appropriate quantum mechanical *operators* corresponding to physical quantities.

2.5 Application of these principles to the simplest atom (H) introduces four quantum numbers—**n, l, m,** and **s,** which are subject to appropriate quantum mechanical rules. Extrapolating these ideas to more complicated atoms such as Si leads to the idea of electronic structure and the *periodic table,* if we apply the *Pauli exclusion principle* that one can have a maximum of one electron for one set of these quantum numbers.

PROBLEMS

2.1 (a) Sketch a simple vacuum tube device and the associated circuitry for measuring E_m in the photoelectric effect experiment. The electrodes can be placed in a sealed glass envelope.

(b) Sketch the photocurrent I vs. retarding voltage V that you would expect to measure for a given electrode material and configuration. Make the sketch for several intensities of light at a given wavelength.

(c) The work function of platinum is 4.09 eV. What retarding potential will be required to reduce the photocurrent to zero in a photoelectric experiment with Pt electrodes if the wavelength of incident light is 2440 Å? Remember that an energy of $q\Phi$ is lost by each electron in escaping the surface.

2.2 In a photoelectric effect experiment, the threshold wavelength for the ejection of photoelectrons from zinc is 310 nm. Calculate the work function for Zinc. Also, calculate the velocity for the photoelectrons by light of wavelength 2000 Å other than threshold.

2.3 (a) Show that the various lines in the hydrogen spectrum can be expressed in angstroms as

$$\lambda(\text{Å}) = \frac{911\,n_1^2 n^2}{n^2 - n_1^2}$$

where $n_1 = 1$ for the Lyman series, 2 for the Balmer series, and 3 for the Paschen series. The integer n is larger than n_1.

(b) Calculate λ for the Lyman series to $\mathbf{n} = 5$, the Balmer series to $\mathbf{n} = 7$, and the Paschen series to $\mathbf{n} = 10$. Plot the results as in Fig. 2–2. What are the wavelength limits for each of the three series?

2.4 Using Heisenberg's uncertainty principle, estimate the momentum uncertainty of a bound electron within an atom of diameter 10 fm. Use this calculated momentum uncertainty to find the minimum binding energy.

2.5 From Balmer's series calculation, first line in the H spectrum exhibits wavelength of 656.1 nm. Bohr's theory supports almost similar kind of radiative transition by transition of electron of H atom from third to second energy level. From this, find the value of the Rydberg constant.

2.6 Consider an electron with a normalized wave function defined as $\varphi(x) = 2\alpha\sqrt{\alpha}xe^{-\alpha x}$ for $x > 0 = 0$ for $x < 0$.

(a) For what value of x does $P(x) = |\varphi(x)|^2$ is at peak?

(b) Calculate $<x>$ and $<x^2>$.

(c) What is the probability of finding the particle between $x = 0$ and $x = 1/\alpha$?

2.7 A particle is described in 1-D by a wavefunction:
$\psi = Be^{-2x}$ for $x \geq 0$ and Ce^{+4x} for $x < 0$, and B and C are real constants. Calculate B and C to make ψ a valid wavefunction. Where is the particle most likely to be?

2.8 The electron wavefunction is Ce^{ikx} between $x = 2$ and 22 cm, and zero everywhere else. What is the value of C? What is the probability of finding the electron between $x = 0$ and 4 cm?

2.9 We define a potential well having energies V as a function of position x, as follows:
$V = \infty$ for $x = -0.5$ nm to 0; $V = 0$ eV for $x = 0$ to 5 nm; $V = 10$ eV for $x = 5$ to 6 nm, and $V = 0$ for $x > 6$ nm and $x < -0.5$ nm. We put an electron with energy 7 eV in the region x, between 0 and 5 nm. What is the probability of finding the electron at $x < 0$ nm? Is the probability of finding the electron at $x > 6$ nm zero or nonzero? What is this probability for $x > 6$ nm if the electron was described by classical mechanics and not quantum mechanics?

2.10 Discuss the number of electrons, protons, and neutrons present in the carbon (C) atom by analyzing its electronic shell structure.

2.11 Calculate the first 5 energy levels for an electron trapped in an infinite quantum well (QW) of width 0.59 nm.

2.12 An electron within an atom is described by the following wave function:
$\varphi(x,t) = \dfrac{e^{-iE_1t}}{\hbar}\varphi_1(x) + \dfrac{e^{-iE_2t}}{\hbar}\varphi_2(x)$. Calculate the expectation value of the energy and the energy separation ΔE.

2.13 Schematically show the number of electrons in the various subshells of an atom with the electronic shell structure $1s^2 2s^2 2p^4$ and an atomic weight of 21. Indicate how many protons and neutrons there are in the nucleus. Is this atom chemically reactive, and why?

READING LIST

Cohen-Tannouoji, C., B. Diu, and F. Laloe. *Quantum Mechanics.* New York: Wiley, 1977.

Datta, S. *Modular Series on Solid State Devices: Vol. 8. Quantum Phenomena.* Reading, MA: Addison-Wesley, 1989.

Feynman, R. P. *The Feynman Lectures on Physics, Vol. 3. Quantum Mechanics.* Reading, MA: Addison-Wesley, 1965.

Kroemer, H. *Quantum Mechanics.* Englewood Cliffs, NJ: Prentice Hall, 1994.

SELF QUIZ

Question 1

Decide whether *each* of the following one-dimensional functions defined between the limits x approaches negative infinity and x approaches positive infinity is an allowed quantum mechanical wavefunction (circle one answer in each case):

1. $\Psi(x) = C$ for $-|a| < x < |a|$; $\Psi(x) = 0$ otherwise   **allowed / not allowed**
2. $\Psi(x) = C(e^{x/a} + e^{-x/a})$ **allowed / not allowed**
3. $\Psi(x) = C \exp(-x^2/|a|)$ **allowed / not allowed**

where both C and a are nonzero and finite constants.

Question 2

Consider the finite potential well sketched below.

1. Can the measured value of a particle's energy in the well be 0 eV?
2. If the particle has an energy of $E < 1$ eV, can the measured value of the particle's position be $|x| > a$?

Question 3

(a) For a particle in the following potential well of minimum potential energy equal to 0 eV, could the ground state eigenenergy E_1 of the particle be equal to zero? Circle one choice below.

yes / no / not enough information provided

(b) Given the 3rd and 4th most energetic eigenstates of energies as shown above, is it possible under any circumstances that the expectation value of the particle's energy could be exactly $0.5(E_3 + E_4)$? (Do not assume the particle is in an energy eigenstate.) Circle one choice below.

yes / no / not enough information provided

(c) Consider the following *continuous, smooth,* and *normalizable* wavefunction $\Psi(x)$. Is this wavefunction an allowed quantum mechanical wavefunction for a particle (currently) above the potential $V(x)$ of part (a)? (Circle one.)

yes / no / can't tell

Question 4

Consider quantum mechanical particles incident from the left having well-defined energy as indicated by the vertical positions of the arrows, in the two systems shown below. Will the probability of being reflected be greater for the incident particle in System 1 than for the incident particle in System 2? Circle one choice below.

yes / no / not enough information provided

System 1
(narrow high potential barrier)

System 2
(wide low potential barrier)

Question 5

Suppose five precise measurements were made on a particle in rapid succession, such that the time evolution of the particle wavefunction *between* measurements could be neglected, in the following order: (1) position, (2) momentum, (3) momentum, (4) position, and (5) momentum. If the results of the first two measurements were x_o and p_o, respectively, what would be the results of the next three measurements (circle one each)?

measurement (3): momentum p_o/ **unknown**

measurement (4): position x_o/ **unknown**

measurement (5): momentum p_o/ **unknown**

Question 6

If the photoelectric effect were governed by classical physics rather than quantum mechanics, what would be result of the following experiments:

(a) By changing the intensity of the incident radiation, what would happen to the energy and number of ejected electrons?

(b) How about changing the frequency of the light?

Question 7

If the average energy required to create a Frankel defect in an ionic crystal is 1.35 eV, calculate the ratio of Frankel defect at 25 C and 350 C.

Question 8

A crystal plate is mounted on a X-ray spectrometer. The glancing angles of incidence for three reflections are 5°58', 12°01' and 18°12'. Show that these are successive orders of reflections from the same crystal plane.

Question 9

A certain crystal reflects monochromatic X-rays strongly when Bragg's angle is 21° for second order diffraction. Calculate the glancing angle for third order spectrum.

Question 10

An electron is bound in a one-dimensional infinite well of width 1×10^{-10} m. Find the energy values in the ground state and first two excited states.

Question 11

Calculate the de Brogile wavelength of a dust particle of mass 0.002 mg and moving with velocity of 3.50×10^4 m/s.

Chapter 3

Energy Bands and Charge Carriers in Semiconductors

OBJECTIVES

1. Understand conduction and valence energy bands, and how band gaps are formed
2. Appreciate the idea of doping in semiconductors
3. Use the density of states and Fermi Dirac statistics to calculate carrier concentrations
4. Calculate drift currents in an electric field in terms of carrier mobility, and how mobility is affected by scattering
5. Discuss the idea of "effective" masses

In this chapter we begin to discuss the specific mechanisms by which current flows in a solid. In examining these mechanisms we shall learn why some materials are good conductors of electric current, whereas others are poor conductors. We shall see how the conductivity of a semiconductor can be varied by changing the temperature or the number of impurities. These fundamental concepts of charge transport form the basis for later discussions of solid state device behavior.

3.1
BONDING FORCES AND ENERGY BANDS IN SOLIDS

In Chapter 2 we found that electrons are restricted to sets of discrete energy levels within atoms. Large gaps exist in the energy scale in which no energy states are available. In a similar fashion, electrons in solids are restricted to certain energies and are not allowed at other energies. The basic difference between the case of an electron in a solid and that of an electron in an isolated atom is that in the solid the electron has a *range*, or *band*, of available energies. The discrete energy levels of the isolated atom spread into bands of energies in the solid because in the solid the wavefunctions of electrons in neighboring atoms overlap, and an electron is not necessarily localized at a particular atom. Thus, for example, an electron in the outer orbit of one atom feels the influence of neighboring atoms, and its overall wavefunction is altered. Naturally, this influence affects the potential energy term and the boundary conditions in the

Schrödinger equation, and we would expect to obtain different energies in the solution. Usually, the influence of neighboring atoms on the energy levels of a particular atom can be treated as a small perturbation, giving rise to shifting and splitting of energy states into energy bands.

3.1.1 Bonding Forces in Solids

The interaction of electrons in neighboring atoms of a solid serves the very important function of holding the crystal together. For example, alkali halides such as NaCl are typified by *ionic bonding*. In the NaCl

(a)

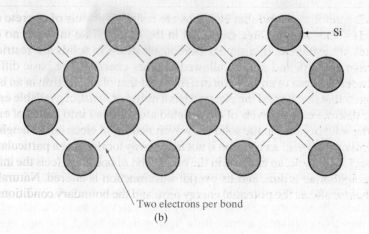

(b)

Figure 3–1
Different types of chemical bonding in solids: (a) an example of ionic bonding in NaCl; (b) covalent bonding in the Si crystal, viewed along a <100> direction (see also Figs. 1–8 and 1–9).

lattice, each Na atom is surrounded by six nearest neighbor Cl atoms, and vice versa. Four of the nearest neighbors are evident in the two-dimensional representation shown in Fig. 3–1a. The electronic structure of Na $(Z = 11)$ is [Ne] $3s^1$, and Cl $(Z = 17)$ has the structure [Ne] $3s^23p^5$. In the lattice each Na atom gives up its outer $3s$ electron to a Cl atom, so that the crystal is made up of ions with the electronic structures of the inert atoms Ne and Ar (Ar has the electronic structure [Ne] $3s^23p^6$). However, the ions have net electric charges after the electron exchange. The Na^+ ion has a net positive charge, having lost an electron, and the Cl^- ion has a net negative charge, having gained an electron.

Each Na^+ ion exerts an electrostatic attractive force upon its six Cl^- neighbors, and vice versa. These coulombic forces pull the lattice together until a balance is reached with repulsive forces. A reasonably accurate calculation of the atomic spacing can be made by considering the ions as hard spheres being attracted together (Example 1–1).

An important observation in the NaCl structure is that all electrons are tightly bound to atoms. Once the electron exchanges have been made between the Na and Cl atoms to form the Na^+ and Cl^- ions, the outer orbits of all atoms are completely filled. Since the ions have the closed-shell configurations of the inert atoms Ne and Ar, there are no loosely bound electrons to participate in current flow; as a result, NaCl is a good insulator.

In a metal atom the outer electronic shell is only partially filled, usually by no more than three electrons. We have already noted that the alkali metals (e.g., Na) have only one electron in the outer orbit. This electron is loosely bound and is given up easily in ion formation. This accounts for the great chemical activity in the alkali metals, as well as for their high electrical conductivity. In the metal the outer electron of each alkali atom is contributed to the crystal as a whole, so that the solid is made up of ions with closed shells immersed in a sea of free electrons. The forces holding the lattice together arise from an interaction between the positive ion cores and the surrounding free electrons. This is one type of *metallic bonding*. Obviously, there are complicated differences in the bonding forces for various metals, as evidenced by the wide range of melting temperatures (234 K for Hg, 3643 K for W). However, the metals have the sea of electrons in common, and these electrons are free to move about the crystal under the influence of an electric field.

A third type of bonding is exhibited by the diamond lattice semiconductors. We recall that each atom in the Ge, Si, or C diamond lattice is surrounded by four nearest neighbors, each with four electrons in the outer orbit. In these crystals each atom shares its valence electrons with its four neighbors (Fig. 3–1b). Bonding between nearest neighbor atoms is illustrated in the diamond lattice diagram of Fig. 1–9. The bonding forces arise from a quantum mechanical interaction between the shared electrons. This is known as *covalent bonding*; each electron pair constitutes a covalent bond. In the sharing process it is no longer relevant to ask which electron belongs to a particular atom—both belong to the bond. The two electrons are indistinguishable, except that they must have opposite spin to satisfy the Pauli exclusion principle. Covalent bonding is also found in certain molecules, such as H_2.

As in the case of the ionic crystals, no free electrons are available to the lattice in the covalent diamond structure of Fig. 3–1b. By this reasoning Ge and Si should also be insulators. However, we have pictured an idealized lattice at 0 K in this figure. As we shall see in subsequent sections, an electron can be thermally or optically excited out of a covalent bond and thereby become free to participate in conduction. This is an important feature of semiconductors.

Compound semiconductors such as GaAs have mixed bonding, in which both ionic and covalent bonding forces participate. Some ionic bonding is to be expected in a crystal such as GaAs because of the difference in placement of the Ga and As atoms in the periodic table. The ionic character of the bonding becomes more important as the atoms of the compound become further separated in the periodic table, as in the II–VI compounds. Such electronic structure, and specifically the idea that the outermost valence shell is *complete* if it has a stable set of eight electrons (Ne, Ar, Kr), is the basis of most of chemistry and many of the semiconducting properties.

3.1.2 Energy Bands

As isolated atoms are brought together to form a solid, various interactions occur between neighboring atoms, including those described in the preceding section. The forces of attraction and repulsion between atoms will find a balance at the proper interatomic spacing for the crystal. In the process, important changes occur in the electron energy level configurations, and these changes result in the varied electrical properties of solids.

In Fig. 2–8, we showed the orbital model of a Si atom, along with the energy levels of the various electrons in the coulombic potential well of the nucleus. Let us focus on the outermost shell or valence shell, **n** = 3, where two 3s and two 3p electrons interact to form the four "hybridized" sp^3 electrons when the atoms are brought close together. In Fig. 3–2, we schematically show the coulombic potential wells of two atoms close to each other, along with the wavefunctions of two electrons centered on the two nuclei. By solving the Schrödinger equation for such an interacting system, we find that the composite two-electron wavefunctions are *linear combinations* of the individual *atomic orbitals* (LCAO). The odd or antisymmetric combination is called the antibonding orbital, while the even or symmetric combination is the bonding orbital. It can be seen that the bonding orbital has a higher value of the wavefunction (and therefore the electron probability density) than the antibonding state in the region between the two nuclei. This corresponds to the covalent bond between the atoms.

Fundamental particles in nature have either integer spin and are called bosons (e.g., photons), or half-integer spin and are known as fermions (e.g., electrons). The quantum mechanical wavefunction of the electron has a

ψ_1 ψ_2

Atomic orbitals

Antibonding orbital

+

−

Bonding orbital

+ +

$V(r)$

Antibonding energy level

Bonding energy level

Figure 3–2
Linear combinations of atomic orbitals (LCAO): The LCAO when two atoms are brought together leads to two distinct "normal" modes—a higher energy antibonding orbital, and a lower energy bonding orbital. Note that the electron probability density is high in the region between the ion cores (covalent "bond"), leading to lowering of the bonding energy level and the cohesion of the crystal. If instead of two atoms, one brings together N atoms, there will be N distinct LCAO, and N closely spaced energy levels in a band.

spatial (or orbital) part and a spin-dependent part. It can be shown that fermion wavefunctions of a multi-electron system must be antisymmetric. When the spatial part is symmetric, the electron spins must be anti-parallel, and vice versa. Hence, the two electrons in the bonding orbital have opposite spins, while those in the anti-bonding state have parallel spins. This "explains" the Pauli exclusion principle. When we try to put two electrons into a quantum state, they must have opposite spins. Parallel spin electrons quantum mechanically *repel* each other, as seen for the antisymmetric orbital. (This should not be confused with Coulomb repulsion of the electrons.) Later on in Chapter 10, we will see that these concepts have important ramifications for nanoelectronics. To determine the energy levels of the bonding and the antibonding states, it is important to recognize that in the region between the two nuclei the Coulombic potential energy $V(r)$ is lowered (solid line in Fig. 3–2) compared to isolated atoms (dashed lines). It is easy to see why the potential energy would be lowered in this region, because an electron here would be attracted by two nuclei, rather than just one. For the bonding state the electron probability density is higher in this region of lowered potential energy than for the antibonding state. As a result, the original isolated atomic energy level would be split into two, a lower bonding energy level and a higher antibonding level. It is the lowering of the energy of the bonding state that gives rise to cohesion of the crystal. For even smaller interatomic spacings, the energy of the crystal goes up because of repulsion between the nuclei, and other electronic interactions. Since the probability density is given by the square of the wavefunction, if the entire wavefunction is multiplied by -1, it does not lead to a different LCAO. The important point to note in this discussion is that the number of distinct LCAO, and the number of distinct energy levels, depends on the number of atoms that are brought together. The lowest energy level corresponds to the totally symmetric LCAO, the highest corresponds to the totally antisymmetric case, and the other combinations lead to energy levels in between.

Qualitatively, we can see that as atoms are brought together, the application of the Pauli exclusion principle becomes important. When two atoms are completely isolated from each other so that there is no interaction of electron wavefunctions between them, they can have identical electronic structures. As the spacing between the two atoms becomes smaller, however, electron wavefunctions begin to overlap. The exclusion principle dictates that no two electrons in a given interacting system may have the same quantum state; thus there must be at most one electron per level after there is a splitting of the discrete energy levels of the isolated atoms into new levels belonging to the pair rather than to individual atoms.

In a solid, many atoms are brought together, so that the split energy levels form essentially continuous *bands* of energies. As an example, Fig. 3–3 illustrates the imaginary formation of a silicon crystal from isolated silicon atoms. Each isolated silicon atom has an electronic structure $1s^2 2s^2 2p^6 3s^2 3p^2$ in the ground state. Each atom has available two $1s$ states, two $2s$ states, six $2p$ states, two $3s$ states, six $3p$ states, and higher states (see Tables 2–1 and 2–2). If we consider N atoms, there will be $2N$, $2N$, $6N$, $2N$, and $6N$ states of type $1s$, $2s$, $2p$, $3s$, and $3p$, respectively. As the interatomic spacing decreases, these energy levels split into bands, beginning with the outer ($\mathbf{n} = 3$) shell. As the "$3s$" and "$3p$" bands grow, they merge into a single band composed of a mixture of energy levels. This band of "$3s$–$3p$" levels contains $8N$ available states. As the distance between atoms approaches the equilibrium interatomic spacing of silicon, this band splits into two bands separated by an *energy gap* E_g. The upper band (called the *conduction band*) contains $4N$ states, as does the lower (*valence*) band. Thus, apart from the low-lying and tightly bound "core" levels, the silicon crystal has two bands of available energy levels separated by an energy gap E_g wide, which contains no allowed energy levels for electrons to occupy. This gap is sometimes called a "forbidden band," since in a perfect crystal it contains no electron energy states.

We should pause at this point and count electrons. The lower "$1s$" band is filled with the $2N$ electrons which originally resided in the collective $1s$ states of the isolated atoms. Similarly, the $2s$ band and the $2p$ bands will have $2N$ and $6N$ electrons in them, respectively. However, there were $4N$ electrons in the original isolated $\mathbf{n} = 3$ shells ($2N$ in $3s$ states and $2N$ in $3p$ states).

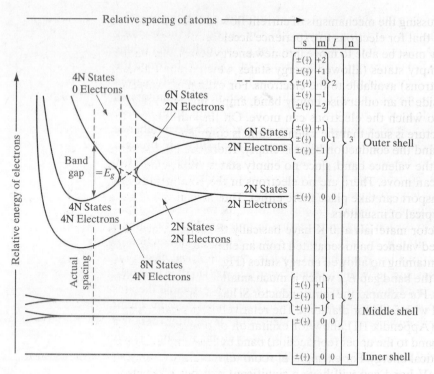

Figure 3–3
Energy levels in Si as a function of interatomic spacing. The core levels (**n** = 1, 2) in Si are completely filled with electrons. At the actual atomic spacing of the crystal, the 2N electrons in the 3s subshell and the 2N electrons in the 3p subshell undergo sp^3 hybridization, and all end up in the lower 4N states (valence band), while the higher-lying 4N states (conduction band) are empty, separated by a band gap.

These 4N electrons must occupy states in the valence band or the conduction band in the crystal. At 0 K the electrons will occupy the lowest energy states available to them. In the case of the Si crystal, there are exactly 4N states in the valence band available to the 4N electrons. Thus at 0 K, *every* state in the valence band will be filled, while the conduction band will be completely empty of electrons. As we shall see, this arrangement of completely filled and empty energy bands has an important effect on the electrical conductivity of the solid.

3.1.3 Metals, Semiconductors, and Insulators

Every solid has its own characteristic energy band structure. This variation in band structure is responsible for the wide range of electrical characteristics observed in various materials. The silicon band structure of Fig. 3–3, for example, can give a good picture of why silicon in the diamond lattice is a good insulator. To reach such a conclusion, we must consider the properties of completely filled and completely empty energy bands in the current conduction process.

Before discussing the mechanisms of current flow in solids further, we can observe here that for electrons to experience acceleration in an applied electric field, they must be able to move into new energy states. This implies there must be empty states (allowed energy states which are not already occupied by electrons) available to the electrons. For example, if relatively few electrons reside in an otherwise empty band, ample unoccupied states are available into which the electrons can move. On the other hand, the silicon band structure is such that the valence band is completely filled with electrons at 0 K and the conduction band is empty. There can be no charge transport within the valence band, since no empty states are available into which electrons can move. There are no electrons in the conduction band, so no charge transport can take place there either. Thus silicon at 0 K has a high resistivity typical of insulators.

Semiconductor materials at 0 K have basically the same structure as insulators—a filled valence band separated from an empty conduction band by a band gap containing no allowed energy states (Fig. 3–4). The difference lies in the size of the band gap E_g, which is much smaller in semiconductors than in insulators. For example, the semiconductor Si has a band gap of about 1.1 eV compared with 5 eV for diamond. The relatively small band gaps of semiconductors (Appendix III) allow for excitation of electrons from the lower (valence) band to the upper (conduction) band by reasonable amounts of thermal or optical energy. For example, at room temperature a semiconductor with a 1-eV band gap will have a significant number of electrons excited thermally across the energy gap into the conduction band, whereas an insulator with $E_g = 10$ eV will have a negligible number of such excitations. Thus an important difference between semiconductors and insulators is that the number of electrons available for conduction can be increased greatly in semiconductors by thermal or optical energy.

In metals the bands either overlap or are only partially filled. Thus electrons and empty energy states are intermixed within the bands so that electrons can move freely under the influence of an electric field. As expected from the metallic band structures of Fig. 3–4, metals have a high electrical conductivity.

3.1.4 Direct and Indirect Semiconductors

The "thought experiment" of Section 3.1.2, in which isolated atoms were brought together to form a solid, is useful in pointing out the existence of energy bands and some of their properties. Other techniques are generally used, however, when quantitative calculations are made of band structures. In a typical calculation, a single electron is assumed to travel through a perfectly periodic lattice. The wavefunction of the electron is assumed to be in the form of a plane wave[1] moving, for example, in the x-direction with

---

[1] Discussions of plane waves are available in most sophomore physics texts or in introductory electromagnetics texts.

Figure 3–4
Typical band
structures at 0 K.

propagation constant **k**, also called a *wavevector*. The space-dependent wave-function for the electron is

$$\psi_k(x) = U(\mathbf{k}_x, x)e^{j\mathbf{k}_x x} \qquad (3\text{–}1)$$

where the function $U(\mathbf{k}_x, x)$ modulates the wavefunction according to the periodicity of the lattice. Such wavefunctions are called Bloch functions after the physicist Felix Bloch.

In such a calculation, allowed values of energy can be plotted vs. the propagation constant **k**. Since the periodicity of most lattices is different in various directions, the $(E, \mathbf{k})$ diagram must be plotted for the various crystal directions, and the full relationship between E and **k** is a complex surface which should be visualized in three dimensions.

The band structure of GaAs has a minimum in the conduction band and a maximum in the valence band for the same **k** value ($\mathbf{k} = 0$). On the other hand, Si has its valence band maximum at a different value of **k** than its conduction band minimum. Thus an electron making a smallest-energy transition from the conduction band to the valence band in GaAs can do so without a change in **k** value; on the other hand, a transition from the minimum point in the Si conduction band to the maximum point of the valence band requires some change in **k**. Thus there are two classes of semiconductor energy bands: *direct* and *indirect* (Fig. 3–5). We can show that an indirect transition, involving a change in **k**, requires a change of momentum for the electron.

The direct and indirect semiconductors are identified in Appendix III. In a direct semiconductor such as GaAs, an electron in the conduction band can fall to an empty state in the valence band, giving off the energy difference E_g as a photon of light. On the other hand, an electron in the conduction band minimum of an indirect semiconductor such as Si cannot fall directly to the valence band maximum but must undergo a momentum change as well

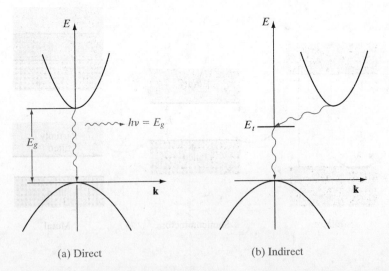

Figure 3-5
Direct and indirect electron transitions in semiconductors: (a) direct transition with accompanying photon emission; (b) indirect transition via a defect level.

(a) Direct   (b) Indirect

as changing its energy. For example, it may go through some defect state (E_t) within the band gap. We shall discuss such defect states in Sections 4.2.1 and 4.3.2. In an indirect transition which involves a change in **k**, part of the energy is generally given up as heat to the lattice rather than as an emitted photon. This difference between direct and indirect band structures is very important for deciding which semiconductors can be used in devices requiring light output. For example, semiconductor light emitters and lasers (Chapter 8) generally must be made of materials capable of direct band-to-band transitions or of indirect materials with vertical transitions between defect states.

Band diagrams such as those shown in Fig. 3–5 are cumbersome to draw in analyzing devices, and do not provide a view of the variation of electron energy with distance in the sample. Therefore, in most discussions we shall use simple band pictures such as those shown in Fig. 3–4, remembering that electron transitions across the band gap may be direct or indirect.

3.1.5 Variation of Energy Bands with Alloy Composition

As III–V ternary and quaternary alloys are varied over their composition ranges (see Sections 1.2.4 and 1.4.1), their band structures change. For example, Fig. 3–6 illustrates the band structure of GaAs and AlAs, and the way in which the bands change with composition x in the ternary compound $Al_xGa_{1-x}As$. The binary compound GaAs is a direct material, with a band gap of 1.43 eV at room temperature. For reference, we call the direct ($\mathbf{k} = 0$) conduction band minimum Γ. There are also two higher-lying indirect minima in the GaAs conduction band, but these are sufficiently far above Γ that few electrons reside there (we discuss an important exception in Chapter 10 in which high-field excitation of electrons into the indirect minima leads to the Gunn effect). We call the lowest-lying GaAs indirect minimum L and the other X. In AlAs the direct Γ minimum is much higher than the indirect X minimum, and this material is therefore indirect with a band gap of 2.16 eV at room temperature.

Figure 3–6

Variation of direct and indirect conduction bands in AlGaAs as a function of composition: (a) the $(E, \mathbf{k})$ diagram for GaAs, showing three minima in the conduction band; (b) AlAs band diagram; (c) positions of the three conduction band minima in $Al_xGa_{1-x}As$ as x varies over the range of compositions from GaAs ($x = 0$) to AlAs ($x = 1$). The smallest band gap, E_g (shown in color), follows the direct Γ band to $x = 0.38$, and then follows the indirect X band.

In the ternary alloy $Al_xGa_{1-x}As$ all of these conduction band minima move up relative to the valence band as the composition x varies from 0 (GaAs) to 1 (AlAs). However, the indirect minimum X moves up less than the others, and for compositions above about 38 percent Al this indirect minimum becomes the lowest-lying conduction band. Therefore, the ternary alloy AlGaAs is a direct semiconductor for Al compositions on the column III sublattice up to about 38 percent, and is an indirect semiconductor for higher Al mole fractions. The band gap energy E_g is shown in color on Fig. 3–6c.

The variation of energy bands for the ternary alloy $GaAs_{1-x}P_x$ is generally similar to that of AlGaAs shown in Fig. 3–6. GaAsP is a direct semiconductor from GaAs to about $GaAs_{.55}P_{.45}$ and is indirect from this composition to GaP (see Fig. 8–11). This material is often used in visible LEDs.

Since light emission is most efficient for direct materials, in which electrons can drop from the conduction band to the valence band without changing **k** (and therefore momentum), LEDs in GaAsP are generally made in materials grown with a composition less than $x = 0.45$. For example, most red LEDs in this material are made at about $x = 0.4$, where the Γ minimum is still the lowest-lying conduction band edge, and where the photon resulting from a direct transition from this band to the valence band is in the red portion of the spectrum (about 1.9 eV). The use of impurities to enhance radiative recombination in indirect material will be discussed in Section 8.2.

The mechanism of current conduction is relatively easy to visualize in the case of a metal; the metal atoms are imbedded in a "sea" of relatively free electrons, and these electrons can move as a group under the influence of an electric field. This free electron view is oversimplified, but many important conduction properties of metals can be derived from just such a model. However, we cannot account for all of the electrical properties of semiconductors in this way. Since the semiconductor has a filled valence band and an empty conduction band at 0 K, we must consider the increase in conduction band electrons by thermal excitations across the band gap as the temperature is raised. In addition, after electrons are excited to the conduction band, the empty states left in the valence band can contribute to the conduction process. The introduction of impurities has an important effect on the energy band structure and on the availability of charge carriers. Thus there is considerable flexibility in controlling the electrical properties of semiconductors.

3.2 CHARGE CARRIERS IN SEMICONDUCTORS

3.2.1 Electrons and Holes

As the temperature of a semiconductor is raised from 0 K, some electrons in the valence band receive enough thermal energy to be excited across the band gap to the conduction band. The result is a material with some electrons in an otherwise empty conduction band and some unoccupied states in

Figure 3–7
Electron–hole
pairs in a
semiconductor.

an otherwise filled valence band (Fig. 3–7).[2] For convenience, an empty state in the valence band is referred to as a *hole*. If the conduction band electron and the hole are created by the excitation of a valence band electron to the conduction band, they are called an *electron–hole pair* (abbreviated EHP).

After excitation to the conduction band, an electron is surrounded by a large number of unoccupied energy states. For example, the equilibrium number of EHPs in pure Si at room temperature is only about 10^{10} EHP/cm^3, compared to the Si atom density of 5×10^{22} atoms/cm^3. Thus the few electrons in the conduction band are free to move about via the many available empty states.

The corresponding problem of charge transport in the valence band is somewhat more complicated. However, it is possible to show that the effects of current in a valence band containing holes can be accounted for by simply keeping track of the holes themselves.

In a filled band, all available energy states are occupied. For every electron moving with a given velocity, there is an equal and opposite electron motion elsewhere in the band. If we apply an electric field, the net current is zero because for every electron j moving with velocity v_j there is a corresponding electron j' with velocity $-v_j$. Figure 3–8 illustrates this effect in

Figure 3–8
A valence band
with all states
filled, including
states j and
j', marked for
discussion. The
jth electron with
wavevector k_j
is matched by
an electron at j'
with the opposite
wavevector $-k_j$.
There is no net
current in the
band unless
an electron is
removed. For
example, if the
jth electron is
removed, the
motion of the
electron at j'
is no longer
compensated.

[2]In Fig. 3–7 and in subsequent discussions, we refer to the bottom of the conduction band as E_c and the top of the valence band as E_v.

terms of the electron energy vs. wavevector plot for the valence band. Since **k** is proportional to electron momentum, it is clear the two electrons have oppositely directed velocities. With N electrons/cm^3 in the band we express the current density using a sum over all of the electron velocities, and including the charge $-q$ on each electron. In a unit volume,

$$J = (-q) \sum_i^N \mathrm{v}_i = 0 \qquad (filled\ band) \qquad (3\text{--}2a)$$

Now if we create a hole by removing the jth electron, the net current density in the valence band involves the sum over all velocities, minus the contribution of the electron we have removed:

$$J = (-q) \sum_i^N \mathrm{v}_i - (-q)\mathrm{v}_j \qquad (jth\ electron\ missing) \qquad (3\text{--}2b)$$

But the first term is zero, from Eq. (3–2a). Thus the net current is $+q\mathrm{v}_j$. In other words, the current contribution of the hole is equivalent to that of a positively charged particle with velocity v_j, that of the missing electron. Of course, the charge transport is actually due to the motion of the new uncompensated electron (j'). Its current contribution $(-q)(-\mathrm{v}_j)$ is equivalent to that of a positively charged particle with velocity $+\mathrm{v}_j$. For simplicity, it is customary to treat empty states in the valence band as charge carriers with positive charge and positive mass.

A simple analogy may help in understanding the behavior of holes. If we have two bottles, one completely filled with water and one completely empty, we can ask ourselves "Will there be any net transport of water when we tilt the bottles?" The answer is "no." In the case of the empty bottle, the answer is obvious. In the case of the completely full bottle also, there cannot be any net motion of water because there is no empty space for water to move into. Similarly, an empty conduction band completely devoid of electrons or a valence band completely full of electrons cannot give rise to a net motion of electrons, and thus to current conduction.

Next, we imagine transferring some water droplets from the full bottle into the empty bottle, leaving behind some air bubbles, and ask ourselves the same question. Now when we tilt the bottles there will be net transport of water: the water droplets will roll downhill in one bottle and the air bubbles will move uphill in the other. Similarly, a few electrons in an otherwise empty conduction band move opposite to an electric field, while holes in an otherwise filled valence band move in the direction of the field. The bubble analogy is imperfect, but it may provide a physical feel for why the charge and mass of a hole have opposite signs from those of an electron.

In all the following discussions we shall concentrate on the electrons in the conduction band and on the holes in the valence band. We can account for the current flow in a semiconductor by the motion of these two types of charge carriers. We draw valence and conduction bands on an electron energy scale E, as in Fig. 3–8. However, we should remember that in the valence band, hole energy increases oppositely to electron energy, because the two carriers have opposite charge. Thus hole energy increases downward in Fig. 3–8 and holes, seeking the lowest energy state available, are generally found at the *top* of the valence band. In contrast, conduction band electrons are found at the bottom of the conduction band.

It would be instructive to compare the $(E, \mathbf{k})$ band diagrams with the "simplified" band diagrams that are used for routine device analysis (Fig. 3–9). As discussed in Examples 3–1 and 3–2, an $(E, \mathbf{k})$ diagram is a plot of the total electron energy (potential plus kinetic) as a function of the crystal-direction–dependent electron wavevector (which is proportional to the momentum and therefore the velocity) at some point in space. Hence, the bottom of the conduction band corresponds to zero electron velocity or kinetic energy, and simply gives us the potential energy at that point in space. For holes, the top of the valence band corresponds to zero kinetic energy. For simplified band diagrams, we plot the edges of the conduction and valence bands (i.e., the potential energy) as a function of position in the device. Energies higher in the band correspond to additional kinetic energy of the electron. Also, the fact that the band edge corresponds to the electron potential energy tells us that the variation of the band edge in space is related to the electric field at different points in the semiconductor. We will show this relationship explicitly in Section 4.4.2.

Figure 3–9
Superimposition of the $(E, \mathbf{k})$ band structure on the E-versus-position simplified band diagram for a semiconductor in an electric field. Electron energies increase going up, while hole energies increase going down. Similarly, electron and hole wavevectors point in opposite directions and these charge carriers move opposite to each other, as shown.

In Fig. 3–9, an electron at location A sees an electric field given by the slope of the band edge (potential energy), and gains kinetic energy (at the expense of potential energy) by moving to point B. Correspondingly, in the $(E, \mathbf{k})$ diagram, the electron starts at $k = 0$, but moves to a nonzero wavevector $\mathbf{k}_B$. The electron then loses kinetic energy to heat by scattering mechanisms (discussed in Section 3.4.3) and returns to the bottom of the band at B. The slopes of the (E, x) band edges at different points in space reflect the local electric fields at those points. Hence, if the electric field between A and B were not constant, as shown in Fig. 3–9, the slope of the band edge would also not be constant but vary at each point reflecting the magnitude and direction of the local electric field. In practice, the electron may lose its kinetic energy in stages by a series of scattering events, as shown by the colored dashed lines.

In a long semiconductor bar ($E_G = 2$ eV), conduction band electrons come in from the left in the positive x-direction with a kinetic energy of 3 eV. They move from location A to B to C to D. Between A and B, the electric field is zero; between locations B and C, there is a linearly varying voltage increase of 4 V; between C and D, the field is again zero. Assuming no scattering, sketch a *simplified* band diagram describing the motion of these electrons. Assuming that these electrons can be described as plane waves, with a free-electron mass, write down the wavefunction of the electrons at D. Leave your result in terms of an arbitrary normalization constant. *Draw a band diagram and give the wavefunction at D in terms of the normalization constant.*

EXAMPLE 3–1

SOLUTION

General wavefunction: $\Psi(x, t) = \alpha \times e^{i(kx - \omega t)}$

Energy at D $= \hbar \cdot \omega = \dfrac{\hbar^2 \cdot k^2}{2 \cdot m_o} = 3\text{eV} + 4\text{eV} = 7\text{eV}$

$$= 7\text{eV} \cdot 1.6 \cdot 10^{-19} \tfrac{\text{J}}{\text{eV}} = 1.12 \cdot 10^{-18}\,\text{J}$$

$$\omega = \frac{1.12 \cdot 10^{-18}\,\text{J}}{\hbar} = \frac{1.12 \cdot 10^{-18}\,\text{J}}{1.06 \cdot 10^{-34}\,\text{J} \cdot \text{s}} = 1.06 \cdot 10^{16}\,\text{Hz}$$

$$k = \sqrt{\frac{1.12 \cdot 10^{-18} J \cdot 2 \cdot m_o}{\hbar^2}} = \sqrt{\frac{1.12 \cdot 10^{-18} J \cdot 2 \cdot 9.11 \cdot 10^{-31} kg}{(1.06 \cdot 10^{-34} J \cdot s)^2}}$$

$$= 1.35 \cdot 10^{10} \tfrac{1}{m}$$

Wavefunction at D:

$$\Psi(x,t) = \alpha \cdot e^{i(1.35 \cdot 10^{10} \frac{1}{m} \cdot x - 1.06 \cdot 10^{16} Hz \cdot t)} \text{ where } \alpha \text{ is the normalization constant}$$

3.2.2 Effective Mass

The electrons in a crystal are not completely free, but instead interact with the periodic potential of the lattice. As a result, their "wave–particle" motion cannot be expected to be the same as for electrons in free space. Thus, in applying the usual equations of electrodynamics to charge carriers in a solid, we must use altered values of particle mass. In doing so, we account for most of the influences of the lattice, so that the electrons and holes can be treated as "almost free" carriers in most computations. The calculation of effective mass must take into account the shape of the energy bands in three-dimensional **k**-space, taking appropriate averages over the various energy bands.

EXAMPLE 3–2   Find the $(E, \mathbf{k})$ relationship for a free electron and relate it to the electron mass.

SOLUTION   From Example 2–2, the electron momentum is $p = mv = \hbar \mathbf{k}$. Then

$$E = \frac{1}{2}mv^2 = \frac{1}{2}\frac{p^2}{m} = \frac{\hbar^2}{2m}k^2$$

Thus the electron energy is parabolic with wavevector **k**. The electron mass is inversely related to the curvature (second derivative) of the $(E, \mathbf{k})$ relationship, since

$$\frac{d^2 E}{d\mathbf{k}^2} = \frac{\hbar^2}{m}$$

Although electrons in solids are not free, most energy bands are close to parabolic at their minima (for conduction bands) or maxima (for valence bands). We can also approximate effective mass near those band extrema from the curvature of the band.

The effective mass of an electron in a band with a given $(E, \mathbf{k})$ relationship is found in Example 3–2 to be

$$m^* = \frac{\hbar^2}{d^2E/d\mathbf{k}^2} \tag{3-3}$$

Thus the curvature of the band determines the electron effective mass. For example, in Fig. 3–6a it is clear that the electron effective mass in GaAs is much smaller in the direct Γ conduction band (strong curvature) than in the L or X minima (weaker curvature, smaller value in the denominator of the m^* expression).

A particularly interesting feature of Figs. 3–5 and 3–6 is that the curvature of $d^2E/d\mathbf{k}^2$ is positive at the conduction band minima, but is negative at the valence band maxima. Thus, the electrons near the top of the valence band have *negative effective mass*, according to Eq. (3–3). Valence band electrons with negative charge and negative mass move in an electric field in the same direction as holes with positive charge and positive mass. As discussed in Section 3.2.1, we can fully account for charge transport in the valence band by considering hole motion.

For a band centered at $\mathbf{k} = 0$ (such as the Γ band in GaAs), the $(E, \mathbf{k})$ relationship near the minimum is usually parabolic:

$$E = \frac{\hbar^2}{2m^*}\mathbf{k}^2 + E_c \tag{3-4}$$

Comparing this relation to Eq. (3–3) indicates that the effective mass m^* is constant in a parabolic band. On the other hand, many conduction bands have complex $(E, \mathbf{k})$ relationships that depend on the direction of electron transport with respect to the principal crystal directions. In this case, the effective mass is a tensor quantity. However, we can use appropriate averages over such bands in most calculations.

Figure 3–10a shows the band structures for Si and GaAs viewed along two major directions. While the shape is parabolic near the band edges (as indicated in Figure 3–5 and Example 3–2), there are significant non-parabolicities at higher energies. The energies are plotted along the high symmetry [111] and [100] directions in the crystal. The $\mathbf{k} = 0$ point is denoted as Γ. When we go along the [100] direction, we reach a valley near X, while we reach the L valley along the [111] direction. (Since the energies are plotted along different directions, the curves do not look symmetric.) The valence band maximum in most semiconductors is at the Γ point. It has three branches: the *heavy hole* band with the smallest curvature, a *light hole band* with a larger curvature, and a *split-off band* at a different energy. We notice that for GaAs the conduction band minimum and the valence band maximum are both at $\mathbf{k} = 0$; therefore it is direct band gap. Silicon, on the other hand, has six equivalent conduction minima at X along the six equivalent $\langle 100 \rangle$ directions; therefore, it is indirect.

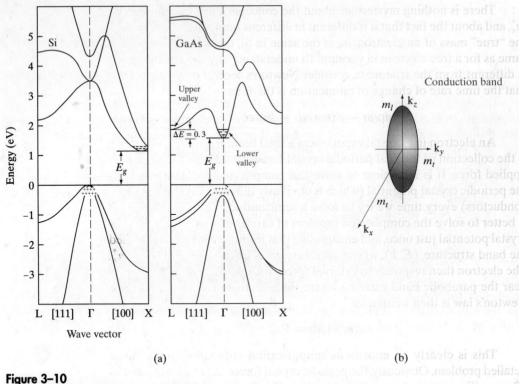

Figure 3–10
Realistic band structures in semiconductors: (a) conduction and valence bands in Si and GaAs along [111] and [100]; (b) ellipsoidal constant energy surface for Si, near the six conduction band minima along the X-directions. (From Chelikowsky and Cohen, Phys. Rev. B14, 556, 1976.)

Figure 3–10b shows the constant energy surface for electrons in one of the six conduction bands for Si. The way to relate these surfaces to the band structures shown in Fig. 3–10a is to consider a certain value of energy, and determine all the **k** vectors in three dimensions for which we get this energy. We find that for Si we have six cigar-shaped ellipsoidal equi-energy surfaces near the conduction band minima along the six equivalent X-directions, with a longitudinal effective mass, m_l, along the major axis, and two transverse effective masses, m_t, along the minor axes. For GaAs, the conduction band is more or less spherical for low energies. On the other hand, we have warped spherical surfaces in the valence band. The importance of these surfaces will be clear in Sections 3.3.2 and 3.4.1 when we consider different types of effective masses in semiconductors.

In any calculation involving the mass of the charge carriers, we must use effective mass values for the particular material involved. In all subsequent discussions, the electron effective mass is denoted by m_n^* and the hole effective mass by m_p^*. The n subscript indicates the electron as a negative charge carrier, and the p subscript indicates the hole as a positive charge carrier.

There is nothing mysterious about the concept of an "effective" mass, m_n^*, and about the fact that it is different in different semiconductors. Indeed, the "true" mass of an electron, m, is the same in Si, Ge, or GaAs—it is the same as for a free electron in vacuum. To understand why the effective mass is different from the true mass, consider Newton's second law, which states that the time rate of change of momentum is the force.

$$dp/dt = d(mv)/dt = \text{Force} \tag{3–5a}$$

An electron in a crystal experiences a total force $F_{int} + F_{ext}$, where F_{int} is the collection of internal periodic crystal forces, and F_{ext} is the externally applied force. It is inefficient to solve this complicated problem involving the periodic crystal potential (which is obviously different in different semiconductors) every time we try to solve a semiconductor device problem. It is better to solve the complicated problem of carrier motion in the periodic crystal potential just once, and encapsulate that information in what is called the band structure, (E, k), whose curvature gives us the effective mass, m_n^*. The electron then responds to external forces with this new m_n^*. For carriers near the parabolic band extrema where the effective mass is as described, Newton's law is then written as:

$$d(m_n^* v)/dt = F_{ext} \tag{3–5b}$$

This is clearly an enormous simplification compared to the more detailed problem. Obviously, the periodic crystal forces depend on the details of a specific semiconductor; therefore, the effective mass is different in different materials.

The velocity of the electron, v, is the *group velocity* of a quantum mechanical electron wavepacket that we introduced in Section 1.5.

$$v = d\omega/dk = (1/\hbar)\,dE/dk \tag{3–5c}$$

If $E(k)$ is given by a simple parabolic relation as in Eq. (3–4), we see that $v = \hbar k/m_n^* = p/m_n^*$. But in general, the carrier velocity is proportional to the slope of the band structure. So, for instance, if an electron is at the Si conduction band minimum (Fig. 3–10a), its velocity is zero, even though $\hbar k$ is nonzero here. For simple parabolic $E(k)$ as in Eq. (3–4),

$$\text{Eq. (3–5b) can then also be written as } F_{ext} = d(\hbar k)/dt \tag{3–5d}$$

Since, F_{ext} is not the *total* force imposed on the electron, clearly $\hbar k$ cannot be the *true* momentum. It is called the crystal momentum or quasi-momentum. Equations (3–5c) and (3–5d) are the fundamental equations governing carrier motion in semiconductors, and are known as semi-classical dynamics.

Once we determine the band curvature effective mass components from the orientation-dependent (E, k), we have to combine them appropriately for different types of calculations. We shall see in Section 3.3.2 that when we are interested in determining the numbers of carriers in the bands, we have to use a "density-of-states" effective mass by taking the geometric mean of the band curvature effective masses, and the number of equivalent band extrema. On the other hand, we will find in Section 3.4.1 that in problems involving the motion of carriers, one must take the harmonic mean of the band curvature effective masses to get the "conductivity" effective mass.

3.2.3 Intrinsic Material

A perfect semiconductor crystal with no impurities or lattice defects is called an *intrinsic* semiconductor. In such material there are no charge carriers at 0 K, since the valence band is filled with electrons and the conduction band is empty. At higher temperatures EHPs are generated as valence band electrons are excited thermally across the band gap to the conduction band. These EHPs are the only charge carriers in intrinsic material.

The generation of EHPs can be visualized in a qualitative way by considering the breaking of covalent bonds in the crystal lattice (Fig. 3–11). If one of the Si valence electrons is broken away from its position in the bonding structure such that it becomes free to move about in the lattice, a conduction electron is created and a broken bond (hole) is left behind. The energy required to break the bond is the band gap energy E_g. This model helps in visualizing the physical mechanism of EHP creation, but the energy band model is more productive for purposes of quantitative calculation. One important difficulty in the "broken bond" model is that the free electron and the hole seem deceptively localized in the lattice. Actually, the positions of the free electron and the hole are spread out over several lattice spacings and should be considered quantum mechanically by probability distributions (see Section 2.4).

Since the electrons and holes are created in pairs, the conduction band electron concentration n (electrons per cm^3) is equal to the concentration of holes in the valence band p (holes per cm^3). Each of these intrinsic carrier concentrations is commonly referred to as n_i. Thus *for intrinsic material*

$$n = p = n_i \qquad (3\text{–}6)$$

At a given temperature there is a certain concentration of EHPs n_i. Obviously, if a steady state carrier concentration is maintained, there must

$n = p = n_i$

Si

e^- : Electron
h^+ : Hole

Figure 3–11
Electron–hole pairs in the covalent bonding model of the Si crystal.

be *recombination* of EHPs at the same rate at which they are generated. Recombination occurs when an electron in the conduction band makes a transition (direct or indirect) to an empty state (hole) in the valence band, thus annihilating the pair. If we denote the generation rate of EHPs as g_i (EHP/cm^3-s) and the recombination rate as r_i, equilibrium requires that

$$r_i = g_i \qquad (3\text{--}7a)$$

Each of these rates is temperature dependent. For example, $g_i(T)$ increases when the temperature is raised, and a new carrier concentration n_i is established such that the higher recombination rate $r_i(T)$ just balances generation. At any temperature, we can predict that the rate of recombination of electrons and holes r_i is proportional to the equilibrium concentration of electrons n_0 and the concentration of holes p_0:

$$r_i = \alpha_r n_0\, p_0 = \alpha_r n_i^2 = g_i \qquad (3\text{--}7b)$$

The factor α_r is a constant of proportionality which depends on the particular mechanism by which recombination takes place. We shall discuss the calculation of n_i as a function of temperature in Section 3.3.3; recombination processes will be discussed in Chapter 4.

3.2.4 Extrinsic Material

In addition to the intrinsic carriers generated thermally, it is possible to create carriers in semiconductors by purposely introducing impurities into the crystal. This process, called *doping*, is the most common technique for varying the conductivity of semiconductors. By doping, a crystal can be altered so that it has a predominance of either electrons or holes. Thus there are two types of doped semiconductors, n-type (mostly electrons) and p-type (mostly holes). When a crystal is doped such that the equilibrium carrier concentrations n_0 and p_0 are different from the intrinsic carrier concentration n_i, the material is said to be *extrinsic*.

When impurities or lattice defects are introduced into an otherwise perfect crystal, additional levels are created in the energy band structure, usually within the band gap. For example, an impurity from column V of the periodic table (P, As, and Sb) introduces an energy level very near the conduction band in Ge or Si. This level is filled with electrons at 0 K, and very little thermal energy is required to excite these electrons to the conduction band (Fig. 3–12a). Thus at about 50–100 K virtually all of the electrons in the impurity level are "donated" to the conduction band. Such an impurity level is called a *donor* level, and the column V impurities in Ge or Si are called donor impurities. From Fig. 3–12a we note that the material doped with donor impurities can have a considerable concentration of electrons in the conduction band, even when the temperature is too low for the intrinsic EHP concentration to be appreciable. Thus semiconductors doped with a significant number of donor atoms will have $n_0 \gg (n_i, p_0)$ at room temperature. This is n-type material.

Figure 3–12
Energy band
model and
chemical bond
model of dopants
in semiconductors:
(a) donation of
electrons from
donor level to
conduction band;
(b) acceptance
of valence band
electrons by an
acceptor level,
and the resulting
creation of holes;
(c) donor and
acceptor atoms
in the covalent
bonding model of
a Si crystal.

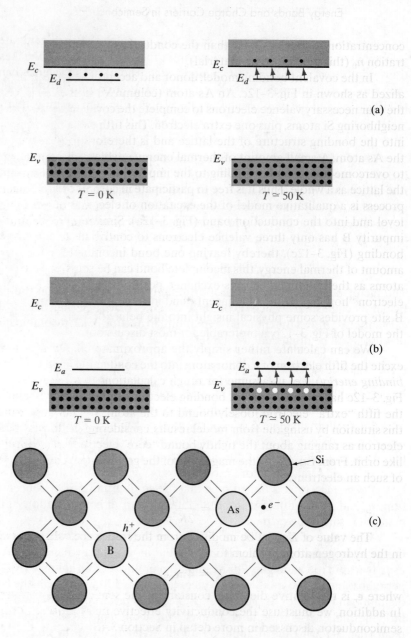

Atoms from column III (B, Al, Ga, and In) introduce impurity levels
in Ge or Si near the valence band. These levels are empty of electrons at
0 K (Fig. 3–12b). At low temperatures, enough thermal energy is available
to excite electrons from the valence band into the impurity level, leaving
behind holes in the valence band. Since this type of impurity level "accepts"
electrons from the valence band, it is called an *acceptor* level, and the column
III impurities are acceptor impurities in Ge and Si. As Fig. 3–12b indicates,
doping with acceptor impurities can create a semiconductor with a hole

concentration p_0 much greater than the conduction band electron concentration n_0 (this type is p-type material).

In the covalent bonding model, donor and acceptor atoms can be visualized as shown in Fig. 3–12c. An As atom (column V) in the Si lattice has the four necessary valence electrons to complete the covalent bonds with the neighboring Si atoms, plus one extra electron. This fifth electron does not fit into the bonding structure of the lattice and is therefore loosely bound to the As atom. A small amount of thermal energy enables this extra electron to overcome its coulombic binding to the impurity atom and be donated to the lattice as a whole. Thus it is free to participate in current conduction. This process is a qualitative model of the excitation of electrons out of a donor level and into the conduction band (Fig. 3–12a). Similarly, the column III impurity B has only three valence electrons to contribute to the covalent bonding (Fig. 3–12c), thereby leaving one bond incomplete. With a small amount of thermal energy, this incomplete bond can be transferred to other atoms as the bonding electrons exchange positions. Again, the idea of an electron "hopping" from an adjacent bond into the incomplete bond at the B site provides some physical insight into the behavior of an acceptor, but the model of Fig. 3–12b is preferable for most discussions.

We can calculate rather simply the approximate energy required to excite the fifth electron of a donor atom into the conduction band (the donor *binding energy*). Let us assume for rough calculations that the As atom of Fig. 3–12c has its four covalent bonding electrons rather tightly bound and the fifth "extra" electron loosely bound to the atom. We can approximate this situation by using the Bohr model results, considering the loosely bound electron as ranging about the tightly bound "core" electrons in a hydrogen-like orbit. From Eq. (2–15) the magnitude of the ground-state energy (**n = 1**) of such an electron is

$$E = \frac{mq^4}{2K^2\hbar^2} \tag{3–8}$$

The value of K must be modified from the free-space value $4\pi\epsilon_0$ used in the hydrogen atom problem to

$$K = 4\pi\epsilon_0\epsilon_r \tag{3–9}$$

where ϵ_r is the relative dielectric constant of the semiconductor material. In addition, we must use the conductivity effective mass m_n^* typical of the semiconductor, discussed in more detail in Section 3.4.1.

It was mentioned in Section 3.2 that the covalent bonding model gives a false impression of the localization of carriers. As an illustration, calculate the radius of the electron orbit around the donor in Fig. 3–12c, assuming a ground state hydrogen-like orbit in Si. Compare with the Si lattice constant. Use $m_n^* = 0.26\, m_0$ for Si.

EXAMPLE 3–3

From Eq. (2–10) with $n = 1$ and using $\epsilon_r = 11.8$ for Si,

SOLUTION

$$r = \frac{4\pi\epsilon_r\epsilon_0\hbar^2}{m_n^* q^2} = \frac{11.8(8.85 \times 10^{-12})(6.63 \times 10^{-34})^2}{\pi(0.26)(9.11 \times 10^{-31})(1.6 \times 10^{-19})^2}$$

$$r = 2.41 \times 10^{-9}\, m = 24.1\, \text{Å}.$$

Note that this is more than four lattice spacings $a = 5.43$ Å.

Generally, the column V donor levels lie approximately 0.01 eV below the conduction band in Ge, and the column III acceptor levels lie about 0.01 eV above the valence band. In Si the usual donor and acceptor levels lie about 0.03–0.06 eV from a band edge.

In III–V compounds, column VI impurities occupying column V sites serve as donors. For example, S, Se, and Te are donors in GaAs, since they substitute for As and provide an extra electron compared with the As atom. Similarly, impurities from column II (Be, Zn, Cd) substitute for column III atoms to form acceptors in the III–V compounds. A more ambiguous case arises when a III–V material is doped with Si or Ge, from column IV. These impurities are called *amphoteric,* meaning that Si or Ge can serve as donors or acceptors depending on whether they reside on the column III or column V sublattice of the crystal. In GaAs it is common for Si impurities to occupy Ga sites. Since the Si has an extra electron compared with the Ga it replaces, it serves as a donor. However, an excess of As vacancies arising during growth or processing of the GaAs can cause Si impurities to occupy As sites, where they serve as acceptors.

The importance of doping will become obvious when we discuss electronic devices made from junctions between p-type and n-type semiconductor material. The extent to which doping controls the electronic properties of semiconductors can be illustrated here by considering changes in the sample resistance which occur with doping. In Si, for example, the intrinsic carrier concentration n_i is about $10^{10}\, \text{cm}^{-3}$ at room temperature. If we dope Si with 10^{15} As atoms/cm^3, the conduction electron concentration changes by five orders of magnitude. The resistivity of Si changes from about $2 \times 10^5\, \Omega$-cm to 5 Ω-cm with this doping.

When a semiconductor is doped n-type or p-type, one type of carrier dominates. In the example given above, the conduction band electrons outnumber the holes in the valence band by many orders of magnitude. We refer to the small number of holes in n-type material as *minority carriers* and the relatively large number of conduction band electrons as *majority carriers.* Similarly, electrons are the minority carriers in p-type material, and holes are the majority carriers.

3.2.5   Electrons and Holes in Quantum Wells

We have discussed single-valued (*discrete*) energy levels in the band gap arising from doping, and a *continuum* of allowed states in the valence and conduction bands. A third possibility is the formation of discrete levels for electrons and holes as a result of quantum-mechanical confinement.

One of the most useful applications of molecular beam epitaxy (MBE) or organometallic vapor-phase epitaxy (OMVPE) growth of multilayer compound semiconductors, as described in Section 1.4, is the fact that a continuous single crystal can be grown in which adjacent layers have different band gaps. For example, Fig. 3–13 shows the spatial variation in conduction and valence bands for a multilayer structure in which a very thin layer of GaAs is sandwiched between two layers of AlGaAs, which has a wider band gap than the GaAs. We will discuss the details of such *heterojunctions* (junctions between dissimilar materials) in Section 5.8. It is interesting to point out here, however, that a consequence of confining electrons and holes in a very thin layer is that these particles behave according to the *particle in a potential well* problem in the confinement direction, with quantum states calculated in Section 2.4.3. (The particles are actually free to move in the other two directions, but we will ignore that for now. In Section 8.4.6, we discuss that we form two-dimensional electron and hole gases in such quantum wells, leading to formation of "subbands," rather than discrete quantum states as discussed here.) Therefore, instead of having the continuum of states normally available in the conduction band, the conduction band electrons in the narrow-gap material are confined to discrete quantum states as described by Eq. (2–33), modified for effective mass and finite barrier height. Similarly, the states in the valence band available for holes are restricted to discrete levels in the quantum well. This is one of the clearest demonstrations of the

Figure 3–13
Energy band discontinuities for a thin layer of GaAs sandwiched between layers of wider band gap AlGaAs. In this case, the GaAs region is so thin that quantum states are formed in the valence and conduction bands. Electrons in the GaAs conduction band reside on "particle in a potential well" states such as E_1 shown here, rather than in the usual conduction band states. Holes in the quantum well occupy similar discrete states, such as E_h.

quantum mechanical results discussed in Chapter 2. From a practical device point of view, the formation of discrete quantum states in the GaAs layer of Fig. 3–13 changes the energy at which photons can be emitted. An electron on one of the discrete conduction band states (E_1 in Fig. 3–13) can make a transition to an empty discrete valence band state in the GaAs quantum well (such as E_h), giving off a photon of energy $E_g + E_1 + E_h$, greater than the GaAs band gap. Semiconductor lasers have been made in which such a quantum well is used to raise the energy of the transition from the infrared, typical of GaAs, to the red portion of the spectrum. We will see other examples of quantum wells in semiconductor devices in later chapters.

3.3 CARRIER CONCENTRATIONS

In calculating semiconductor electrical properties and analyzing device behavior, it is often necessary to know the number of charge carriers per cm³ in the material. The majority carrier concentration is usually obvious in heavily doped material, since one majority carrier is obtained for each impurity atom (for the standard doping impurities). The concentration of minority carriers is not obvious, however, nor is the temperature dependence of the carrier concentrations.

To obtain equations for the carrier concentrations we must investigate the distribution of carriers over the available energy states. This type of distribution is not difficult to calculate, but the derivation requires some background in statistical methods. Since we are primarily concerned here with the application of these results to semiconductor materials and devices, we shall accept the distribution function as given.

3.3.1 The Fermi Level

Electrons in solids obey *Fermi–Dirac* statistics.[3] In the development of this type of statistics, one must consider the indistinguishability of the electrons, their wave nature, and the Pauli exclusion principle. The rather simple result of these statistical arguments is that the distribution of electrons over a range of allowed energy levels at thermal equilibrium is

$$f(E) = \frac{1}{1 + e^{(E-E_F)/kT}} \tag{3–10}$$

where k is Boltzmann's constant ($k = 8.62 \times 10^{-5}$ eV/K $= 1.38 \times 10^{-23}$ J/K). The function $f(E)$, the *Fermi–Dirac distribution function*, gives the probability

---

[3]Examples of other types of statistics are *Maxwell–Boltzmann* for classical particles (e.g., gas) and *Bose–Einstein* for photons. For two discrete energy levels, E_2 and E_1 (with $E_2 > E_1$), classical gas atoms follow a Boltzmann distribution; the number of atoms n_2 in state E_2 is related to the number n_1 in E_1 at thermal equilibrium by

$$\frac{n_2}{n_1} = \frac{N_2 e^{-E_2/kT}}{N_1 e^{-E_1/kT}} = \frac{N_2}{N_1} e^{-(E_2 - E_1)/kT}$$

assuming the two levels have N_2 and N_1 number of states, respectively. The exponential term exp($-\Delta E/kT$) is commonly called the *Boltzmann factor*. It appears also in the denominator of the Fermi–Dirac distribution function. We shall return to the Boltzmann distribution in Chapter 8 in discussions of the properties of lasers.

that an available energy state at E will be occupied by an electron at absolute temperature T. The quantity E_F is called the *Fermi level,* and it represents an important quantity in the analysis of semiconductor behavior. We notice that, for an energy E equal to the Fermi level energy E_F, the occupation probability is

$$f(E_F) = [1 + e^{(E_F-E_F)/kT}]^{-1} = \frac{1}{1+1} = \frac{1}{2} \qquad (3\text{--}11)$$

Thus an energy state at the Fermi level has a probability of $\frac{1}{2}$ of being occupied by an electron.

A closer examination of $f(E)$ indicates that at 0 K the distribution takes the simple rectangular form shown in Fig. 3–14. With $T = 0$ in the denominator of the exponent, $f(E)$ is $1/(1 + 0) = 1$ when the exponent is negative $(E < E_F)$, and is $1/(1 + \infty) = 0$ when the exponent is positive $(E > E_F)$. This rectangular distribution implies that at 0 K every available energy state up to E_F is filled with electrons, and all states above E_F are empty.

At temperatures higher than 0 K, some probability exists for states above the Fermi level to be filled. For example, at $T = T_1$ in Fig. 3–14 there is some probability $f(E)$ that states above E_F are filled, and there is a corresponding probability $[1-f(E)]$ that states below E_F are empty. The Fermi function is symmetrical about E_F for all temperatures; that is, the probability $f(E_F + \Delta E)$ that a state ΔE above E_F is filled is the same as the probability $[1 - f(E_F - \Delta E)]$ that a state ΔE below E_F is empty. The symmetry of the distribution of empty and filled states about E_F makes the Fermi level a natural reference point in calculations of electron and hole concentrations in semiconductors.

In applying the Fermi–Dirac distribution to semiconductors, we must recall that $f(E)$ is the probability of occupancy of an *available* state at E. Thus if there is no available state at E (e.g., in the band gap of a semiconductor), there is no possibility of finding an electron there. We can best visualize the relation between $f(E)$ and the band structure by turning the $f(E)$ vs. E diagram on its side so that the E scale corresponds to the energies of the

Figure 3–14
The Fermi–Dirac distribution function. (Derivation in Appendix V)

Figure 3–15
The Fermi
distribution
function applied
to semiconductors:
(a) intrinsic
material; (b)
n-type material;
(c) p-type
material.

(a) Intrinsic

(b) n-type

(c) p-type

band diagram (Fig. 3–15). For intrinsic material we know that the concentration of holes in the valence band is equal to the concentration of electrons in the conduction band. Therefore, the Fermi level E_F must lie at the middle of the band gap in intrinsic material.[4] Since $f(E)$ is symmetrical about E_F, the electron probability "tail" of $f(E)$ extending into the conduction band of Fig. 3–15a is symmetrical with the hole probability tail $[1 - f(E)]$ in the valence band. The distribution function has values within the band gap between E_v and E_c, but there are no energy states available, and no electron occupancy results from $f(E)$ in this range.

The tails in $f(E)$ are exaggerated in Fig. 3–15 for illustrative purposes. Actually, the probability values at E_v and E_c are quite small for intrinsic material at reasonable temperatures. For example, in Si at 300 K, $n_i = p_i \approx 10^{10}\ \text{cm}^{-3}$, whereas the densities of available states at E_v and E_c are on the order of $10^{19}\ \text{cm}^{-3}$. Thus the probability of occupancy $f(E)$ for an individual state in the conduction band and the hole probability $[1 - f(E)]$ for a state in the valence band are quite small. Because of the relatively large density of states in each band, small changes in $f(E)$ can result in significant changes in carrier concentration.

In n-type material there is a high concentration of electrons in the conduction band compared with the hole concentration in the valence band

---

[4]Actually the intrinsic E_F is displaced slightly from the middle of the gap, since the densities of available states in the valence and conduction bands are not equal (Section 3.3.2).

(recall Fig. 3–12a). Thus in n-type material the distribution function $f(E)$ must lie above its intrinsic position on the energy scale (Fig. 3–15b). Since $f(E)$ retains its shape for a particular temperature, the larger concentration of electrons at E_c in n-type material implies a correspondingly smaller hole concentration at E_v. We notice that the value of $f(E)$ for each energy level in the conduction band (and therefore the total electron concentration n_0) increases as E_F moves closer to E_c. Thus the energy difference $(E_c - E_F)$ gives a measure of n; we shall express this relation mathematically in the following section.

For p-type material the Fermi level lies near the valence band (Fig. 3–15c) such that the $[1 - f(E)]$ tail below E_v is larger than the $f(E)$ tail above E_c. The value of $(E_F - E_v)$ indicates how strongly p-type the material is.

It is usually inconvenient to draw $f(E)$ vs. E on every energy band diagram to indicate the electron and hole distributions. Therefore, it is common practice merely to indicate the position of E_F in band diagrams. This is sufficient information, since for a particular temperature the position of E_F implies the distributions in Fig. 3–15.

3.3.2 Electron and Hole Concentrations at Equilibrium

The Fermi distribution function can be used to calculate the concentrations of electrons and holes in a semiconductor, if the densities of available states in the valence and conduction bands are known. For example, the concentration of electrons in the conduction band is

$$n_0 = \int_{E_c}^{\infty} f(E)N(E)dE \qquad (3\text{-}12)$$

where $N(E)dE$ is the density of states (cm^{-3}) in the energy range dE. The subscript 0 used with the electron and hole concentration symbols (n_0, p_0) indicates equilibrium conditions. The number of electrons per unit volume in the energy range dE is the product of the density of states and the probability of occupancy $f(E)$. Thus the total electron concentration is the integral over the entire conduction band, as in Eq. (3–12).[5] The function $N(E)$ can be calculated by using quantum mechanics and the Pauli exclusion principle (Appendix IV).

It is shown in Appendix IV that $N(E)$ is proportional to $E^{1/2}$, so the density of states in the conduction band increases with electron energy. On the other hand, the Fermi function becomes extremely small for large energies. The result is that the product $f(E)N(E)$ decreases rapidly above E_c, and very few electrons occupy energy states far above the conduction band edge. Similarly, the probability of finding an empty state (hole) in the valence band

[5]The upper limit is actually improper in Eq. (3–12), since the conduction band does not extend to infinite energy. This is unimportant in the calculation of n_0, however, since $f(E)$ becomes negligibly small for large values of E. Most electrons occupy states near the bottom of the conduction band at equilibrium.

[1 − f(E)] decreases rapidly below E_v, and most holes occupy states near the top of the valence band. This effect is demonstrated in Fig. 3–16, which shows the density of available states, the Fermi function, and the resulting number of electrons and holes occupying available energy states in the conduction and valence bands at thermal equilibrium (i.e., with no excitations except thermal energy). For holes, increasing energy points down in Fig. 3–16, since the E scale refers to electron energy.

The result of the integration of Eq. (3–12) is the same as that obtained if we represent all of the distributed electron states in the conduction band by an *effective density of states* N_c located at the conduction band edge E_c.

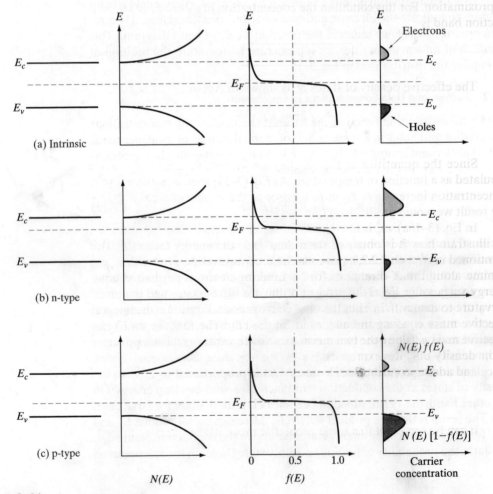

Figure 3–16
Schematic band diagram, density of states, Fermi–Dirac distribution, and the carrier concentrations for (a) intrinsic, (b) n-type, and (c) p-type semiconductors at thermal equilibrium.

Therefore, the conduction band electron concentration is simply the effective density of states at E_c times the probability of occupancy at E_c[6]

$$n_0 = N_c f(E_c) \qquad (3\text{--}13)$$

In this expression we assume the Fermi level E_F lies at least several kT below the conduction band. Then the exponential term is large compared with unity, and the Fermi function $f(E_c)$ can be simplified as

$$f(E_c) = \frac{1}{1 + e^{(E_c - E_F)/kT}} \simeq e^{-(E_c - E_F)/kT} \qquad (3\text{--}14)$$

Since kT at room temperature is only 0.026 eV, this is generally a good approximation. For this condition the concentration of electrons in the conduction band is

$$\boxed{n_0 = N_c e^{-(E_c - E_F)/kT}} \qquad (3\text{--}15)$$

The effective density of states N_c is shown in Appendix IV to be

$$N_c = 2\left(\frac{2\pi m_n^* kT}{h^2}\right)^{3/2} \qquad (3\text{--}16a)$$

Since the quantities in Eq. (3–16a) are known, values of N_c can be tabulated as a function of temperature. As Eq. (3–15) indicates, the electron concentration increases as E_F moves closer to the conduction band. This is the result we would predict from Fig. 3–15b.

In Eq. (3–16a), m_n^* is the density-of-states effective mass for electrons. To illustrate how it is obtained from the band curvature effective masses mentioned in Section 3.2.2, let us consider the 6 equivalent conduction band minima along the X-directions for Si. Looking at the cigar-shaped equi-energy surfaces in Fig. 3–10b, we find that we have more than one band curvature to deal with in calculating effective masses. There is a longitudinal effective mass m_l along the major axis of the ellipsoid, and the transverse effective mass m_t along the two minor axes. Since we have $(m_n^*)^{3/2}$ appearing in the density-of-states expression Eq. (3–16a), by using dimensional equivalence and adding contributions from all 6 valleys, we get

$$(m_n^*)^{3/2} = 6(m_l m_t^2)^{1/2} \qquad (3\text{--}16b)$$

It can be seen that this is the geometric mean of the effective masses.

---

[6]The simple expression for n_0 obtained in Eq. (3–13) is the direct result of integrating Eq. (3–12), as in Appendix IV. Equations (3–15) and (3–19) properly include the effects of the conduction and valence bands through the density-of-states terms.

EXAMPLE 3-4   Calculate the density-of-states effective mass of electrons in Si.

SOLUTION   For Si, $m_l = 0.98\,m_0$; $m_t = 0.19\,m_0$ from Appendix III.
There are six equivalent X valleys in the conduction band.

$$m_n^* = 6^{2/3}[0.98(0.19)^2]^{1/3}\,m_0 = 1.1\,m_0$$

Note: For GaAs, the conduction band equi-energy surfaces are spherical. So there is only one band curvature effective mass, and it is equal to the density-of-states effective mass ($= 0.067\,m_0$).

By similar arguments, the concentration of holes in the valence band is

$$p_0 = N_v[1 - f(E_v)] \tag{3-17}$$

where N_v is the effective density of states in the valence band. The probability of finding an empty state at E_v is

$$1 - f(E_v) = 1 - \frac{1}{1 + e^{(E_v - E_F)/kT}} \simeq e^{-(E_F - E_v)/kT} \tag{3-18}$$

for E_F larger than E_v by several kT. From these equations, the concentration of holes in the valence band is

$$\boxed{p_0 = N_v e^{-(E_F - E_v)/kT}} \tag{3-19}$$

The effective density of states in the valence band reduced to the band edge is

$$N_v = 2\left(\frac{2\pi m_p^* kT}{h^2}\right)^{3/2} \tag{3-20}$$

As expected from Fig. 3–15c, Eq. (3–19) predicts that the hole concentration increases as E_F moves closer to the valence band.

The electron and hole concentrations predicted by Eqs. (3–15) and (3–19) are valid whether the material is intrinsic or doped, provided thermal equilibrium is maintained. Thus *for intrinsic material, E_F lies at some intrinsic level E_i near the middle of the band gap* (Fig. 3–15a), and the intrinsic electron and hole concentrations are

$$n_i = N_c e^{-(E_c - E_i)/kT}, \quad p_i = N_v e^{-(E_i - E_v)/kT} \tag{3-21}$$

The product of n_0 and p_0 at equilibrium is a constant for a particular material and temperature, even if the doping is varied:

$$n_0 p_0 = (N_c e^{-(E_c - E_F)/kT})(N_v e^{-(E_F - E_v)/kT}) = N_c N_v e^{-(E_c - E_v)/kT} \tag{3-22a}$$

$$= N_c N_v e^{-E_g/kT}$$

$$n_i p_i = (N_c e^{-(E_c - E_i)/kT})(N_v e^{-(E_i - E_v)/kT}) = N_c N_v e^{-E_g/kT} \tag{3-22b}$$

The intrinsic electron and hole concentrations are equal (since the carriers are created in pairs), $n_i = p_i$; thus the intrinsic concentration is

$$n_i = \sqrt{N_c N_v}\, e^{-E_g/2kT} \tag{3-23}$$

The constant product of electron and hole concentrations in Eq. (3–22) can be written conveniently as

$$\boxed{n_0 p_0 = n_i^2} \tag{3-24}$$

This is an important relation, and we shall use it extensively in later calculations. The intrinsic concentration for Si at room temperature is approximately $n_i = 1.5 \times 10^{10}$ cm^{-3}.

Comparing Eqs. (3–21) and (3–23), we note that the intrinsic level E_i is the middle of the band gap $(E_c - E_i = E_g/2)$, if the effective densities of states N_c and N_v are equal. There is usually some difference in effective mass for electrons and holes, however, and N_c and N_v are slightly different as Eqs. (3–16) and (3–20) indicate. The intrinsic level E_i is displaced from the middle of the band gap, more for GaAs than for Ge or Si.

Another convenient way of writing Eqs. (3–15) and (3–19) is

$$\boxed{n_0 = n_i e^{(E_F - E_i)/kT}} \tag{3-25a}$$

$$p_0 = n_i e^{(E_i - E_F)/kT} \tag{3-25b}$$

obtained by the application of Eq. (3–21). This form of the equations indicates directly that the electron concentrations is n_i when E_F is at the intrinsic level E_i, and that n_0 increases exponentially as the Fermi level moves away from E_i toward the conduction band. Similarly, the hole concentration p_0 varies from n_i to larger values as E_F moves from E_i toward the valence band. Since these equations reveal the qualitative features of carrier concentration so directly, they are particularly convenient to remember.

A Si sample is doped with 10^{17} As atoms/cm^3. What is the equilibrium hole concentration p_0 at 300 K? Where is E_F relative to E_i?

EXAMPLE 3–5

Since $N_d \gg n_i$, we can approximate $n_0 = N_d$ and

SOLUTION

$$p_0 = \frac{n_i^2}{n_0} = \frac{2.25 \times 10^{20}}{10^{17}} = 2.25 \times 10^3 \text{ cm}^{-3}$$

From Eq. (3–25a), we have

$$E_F - E_i = kT \ln \frac{n_0}{n_i} = 0.0259 \ln \frac{10^{17}}{1.5 \times 10^{10}} = 0.407 \text{ eV}$$

The resulting band diagram is:

3.3.3 Temperature Dependence of Carrier Concentrations

The variation of carrier concentration with temperature is indicated by Eq. (3–25). Initially, the variation of n_0 and p_0 with T seems relatively straightforward in these relations. The problem is complicated, however, by the fact that n_i has a strong temperature dependence [Eq. (3–23)] and that E_F can also vary with temperature. Let us begin by examining the intrinsic carrier concentration. By combining Eqs. (3–23), (3–16a), and (3–20) we obtain

$$n_i(T) = 2\left(\frac{2\pi k T}{h^2}\right)^{3/2}(m_n^* m_p^*)^{3/4}\, e^{-E_g/2kT} \tag{3–26}$$

The exponential temperature dependence dominates $n_i(T)$, and a plot of $\ln n_i$ vs. $10^3/T$ appears linear (Fig. 3–17).[7] In this figure we neglect variations due to the $T^{3/2}$ dependence of the density-of-states function and the fact that E_g varies somewhat with temperature.[8] The value of n_i at any temperature is a definite number for a given semiconductor, and is known for most materials. Thus we can take n_i as given in calculating n_0 or p_0 from Eq. (3–25).[9]

With n_i and T given, the unknowns in Eq. (3–25) are the carrier concentrations and the Fermi level position relative to E_i. One of these two quantities must be given if the other is to be found. If the carrier concentration is held at a certain value, as in heavily doped extrinsic material, E_F can be obtained from Eq. (3–25). The temperature dependence of electron concentration in a doped semiconductor can be visualized as shown in Fig. 3–18. In this example, Si is doped n-type with a donor concentration N_d of 10^{15} cm^{-3}. At very low temperatures (large $1/T$), negligible intrinsic EHPs exist, and

---

[7] When plotting quantities such as carrier concentration, which involve a Boltzmann factor, it is common to use an inverse temperature scale. This allows terms which are exponential in $1/T$ to appear linear in the semi-logarithmic plot. When reading such graphs, remember that temperature increases from right to left.

[8] For Si the band gap E_g varies from about 1.11 eV at 300 K to about 1.16 eV at 0 K.

[9] Care must be taken to use consistent units in these calculations. For example, if an energy such as E_g is expressed in electron volts (eV), it should be multiplied by q (1.6×10^{-19} C) to convert to joules if k is in J/K; alternatively, E_g can be kept in eV and the value of k in eV/K can be used. At 300 K we can use $kT = 0.0259$ eV and E_g in eV.

Figure 3–17
Intrinsic carrier
concentration
for Ge, Si, and
GaAs as a
function of inverse
temperature. The
room temperature
values are marked
for reference.

the donor electrons are bound to the donor atoms. As the temperature is raised, these electrons are donated to the conduction band, and at about 100 K ($1000/T = 10$) all the donor atoms are ionized. This temperature range is called the *ionization* region. Once the donors are ionized, the conduction band electron concentration is $n_0 \simeq N_d = 10^{15}\,\text{cm}^{-3}$, since one electron is obtained for each donor atom. When every available extrinsic electron has been transferred to the conduction band, n_0 is virtually constant with temperature until the concentration of intrinsic carriers n_i becomes comparable to the extrinsic concentration N_d. Finally, at higher temperatures n_i is much greater than N_d, and the intrinsic carriers dominate. In most devices it is desirable to control the carrier concentration by doping rather than by thermal EHP generation. Thus one usually dopes the material such that the extrinsic range extends beyond the highest temperature at which the device is to be used.

Figure 3–18
Carrier
concentration
vs. inverse
temperature for
Si doped with
10^{15} donors/cm^3.

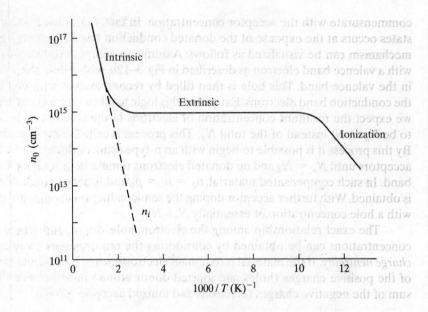

commensurate with the acceptor concentration. In fact, a filling of those states occurs at the expense of the donated conduction electrons. This mechanism can be visualized as follows: Assume an acceptor atom is filled with a valence band electron as described in Fig. 3–12a, leaving a hole in the valence band. This hole is then filled by recombination with one of the conduction band electrons. Extending this logic to all the acceptor atoms, we expect the resultant concentration of electrons in the conduction band to be $n_0 \simeq N_d - N_a$ instead of the total N_d. This process is called *compensation*. By this process it is possible to begin with an n-type semiconductor and add acceptors until $N_a = N_d$ and no donated electrons remain in the conduction band. In such compensated material, $n_0 = n_i = p_0$ and intrinsic conduction is obtained. With further acceptor doping the semiconductor becomes p-type with a hole concentration of essentially $N_a - N_d$.

The exact relationship among the electron, hole, donor, and acceptor concentrations can be obtained by considering the requirements for space charge neutrality. If the material is to remain electrostatically neutral, the sum of the positive charges (holes and ionized donor atoms) must balance the sum of the negative charges (electrons and ionized acceptor atoms):

$$p_0 + N_d^+ = n_0 + N_a^-$$

Thus in Fig. 3–19 the net electron concentration in the conduction band is

3.3.4 Compensation and Space Charge Neutrality

When the concept of doping was introduced, we assumed the material contained either N_d donors or N_a acceptors, so that the extrinsic majority carrier concentrations were $n_0 \simeq N_d$ or $p_0 \simeq N_a$, respectively, for the n-type or p-type material. It often happens, however, that a semiconductor contains both donors and acceptors. For example, Fig. 3–19 illustrates a semiconductor for which both donors and acceptors are present, but $N_d > N_a$. The predominance of donors makes the material n-type, and the Fermi level is therefore in the upper part of the band gap. Since E_F is well above the acceptor level E_a, this level is essentially filled with electrons. However, with E_F above E_i, we cannot expect a hole concentration in the valence band

Figure 3–19
Compensation
in an n-type
semiconductor
$(N_d > N_a)$.

commensurate with the acceptor concentration. In fact, the filling of the E_a states occurs at the expense of the donated conduction band electrons. The mechanism can be visualized as follows: Assume an acceptor state is filled with a valence band electron as described in Fig. 3–12b, with a hole resulting in the valence band. This hole is then filled by recombination with one of the conduction band electrons. Extending this logic to all the acceptor atoms, we expect the resultant concentration of electrons in the conduction band to be $N_d - N_a$ instead of the total N_d. This process is called *compensation*. By this process it is possible to begin with an n-type semiconductor and add acceptors until $N_a = N_d$ and no donated electrons remain in the conduction band. In such compensated material, $n_0 = n_i = p_0$ and intrinsic conduction is obtained. With further acceptor doping the semiconductor becomes p-type with a hole concentration of essentially $N_a - N_d$.

The exact relationship among the electron, hole, donor, and acceptor concentrations can be obtained by considering the requirements for *space charge neutrality*. If the material is to remain electrostatically neutral, the sum of the positive charges (holes and ionized donor atoms) must balance the sum of the negative charges (electrons and ionized acceptor atoms):

$$p_0 + N_d^+ = n_0 + N_a^- \qquad (3\text{–}27)$$

Thus in Fig. 3–19 the net electron concentration in the conduction band is

$$n_0 = p_0 + (N_d^+ - N_a^-) \qquad (3\text{–}28)$$

If the material is doped n-type ($n_0 \gg p_0$) and all the impurities are ionized, we can approximate Eq. (3–28) by $n_0 \simeq N_d - N_a$.

Since the intrinsic semiconductor itself is electrostatically neutral and the doping atoms we add are also neutral, the requirement of Eq. (3–27) must be maintained at equilibrium. The electron and hole concentrations and the Fermi level adjust such that Eqs. (3–27) and (3–25) are satisfied.

3.4 DRIFT OF CARRIERS IN ELECTRIC AND MAGNETIC FIELDS

Knowledge of carrier concentrations in a solid is necessary for calculating current flow in the presence of electric or magnetic fields. In addition to the values of n and p, we must be able to take into account the collisions of the charge carriers with the lattice and with the impurities. These processes will affect the ease with which electrons and holes can flow through the crystal, that is, their *mobility* within the solid. As should be expected, these collision and scattering processes depend on temperature, which affects the thermal motion of the lattice atoms and the velocity of the carriers.

3.4.1 Conductivity and Mobility

The charge carriers in a solid are in constant motion, even at thermal equilibrium. At room temperature, for example, the thermal motion of an individual electron may be visualized as random scattering from lattice vibrations, impurities, other electrons, and defects (Fig. 3–20a). Since the scattering is random,

Figure 3–20
(a) Random
thermal motion
of an electron
in a solid; (b)
well-directed drift
velocity with an
applied electric
field.

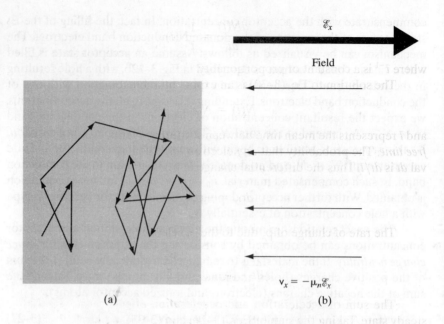

(a)   (b)

there is no net motion of the group of n electrons/cm^3 over any period of time. This is not true of an individual electron, of course. The probability of the electron in Fig. 3–20a returning to its starting point after some time t is negligibly small. However, if a large number of electrons is considered (e.g., 10^{16} cm^{-3} in an n-type semiconductor), there will be no preferred direction of motion for the group of electrons and no net current flow.

If an electric field $\mathscr{E}_x$ is applied in the x-direction, each electron experiences a net force $-q\mathscr{E}_x$ from the field. This force may be insufficient to alter appreciably the random path of an individual electron; the effect when averaged over all the electrons, however, is a net motion of the group in the $-x$-direction (Fig. 3–20b). If p_x is the x-component of the total momentum of the group, the force of the field on the n electrons/cm^3 is

$$- nq\mathscr{E}_x = \left.\frac{dp_x}{dt}\right|_{\text{field}} \tag{3–29}$$

Initially, Eq. (3–29) seems to indicate a continuous acceleration of the electrons in the $-x$-direction. This is not the case, however, because the net acceleration of Eq. (3–29) is just balanced in steady state by the decelerations of the collision processes. Thus while the steady field $\mathscr{E}_x$ does produce a net momentum p_{-x}, the net rate of change of momentum when collisions are included must be zero in the case of steady state current flow.

To find the total rate of momentum change from collisions, we must investigate the collision probabilities more closely. If the collisions are truly random, there will be a constant probability of collision at any time for each electron. Let us consider a group of N_0 electrons at time $t = 0$ and define $N(t)$ as the number of electrons that *have not* undergone a collision by time t. The rate of decrease in $N(t)$ at any time t is proportional to the number left unscattered at t,

$$-\frac{dN(t)}{dt} = \frac{1}{\bar{t}}N(t) \tag{3-30}$$

where $\bar{t}^{-1}$ is a constant of proportionality.

The solution to Eq. (3–30) is an exponential function

$$N(t) = N_0 e^{-t/t} \tag{3-31}$$

and $\bar{t}$ represents the mean time between scattering events,[10] called the *mean free time*. The probability that any electron has a collision in the time interval dt is $dt/\bar{t}$. Thus the differential change in p_x due to collisions in time dt is

$$dp_x = -p_x\frac{dt}{\bar{t}} \tag{3-32}$$

The rate of change of p_x due to the decelerating effect of collisions is

$$\left.\frac{dp_x}{dt}\right|_{collisions} = -\frac{p_x}{\bar{t}} \tag{3-33}$$

The sum of acceleration and deceleration effects must be zero for steady state. Taking the sum of Eqs. (3–29) and (3–33), we have

$$-\frac{p_x}{\bar{t}} - nq\mathcal{E}_x = 0 \tag{3-34}$$

The average momentum per electron is

$$\langle p_x \rangle = \frac{p_x}{n} = -q\bar{t}\mathcal{E}_x \tag{3-35}$$

where the angular brackets indicate an average over the entire group of electrons. As expected for steady state, Eq. (3–35) indicates that the electrons have *on the average* a constant net velocity in the negative x-direction:

$$\langle v_x \rangle = \frac{\langle p_x \rangle}{m_n^*} = -\frac{q\bar{t}}{m_n^*}\mathcal{E}_x \tag{3-36}$$

Actually, the individual electrons move in many directions by thermal motion during a given time period, but Eq. (3–36) tells us the *net drift* of an average electron in response to the electric field. The drift speed described by Eq. (3–36) is usually much smaller than the random speed due to the thermal motion v_{th}.

The current density resulting from this net drift is just the number of electrons crossing a unit area per unit time ($n\langle v_x \rangle$) multiplied by the charge on the electron ($-q$):

---

[10]Equations (3–30) and (3–31) are typical of events dominated by random processes, and the forms of these equations occur often in many branches of physics and engineering. For example, in the radioactive decay of unstable nuclear isotopes, N_0 nuclides decay exponentially with a mean lifetime $\bar{t}$. Other examples will be found in this text, including the absorption of light in a semiconductor and the recombination of excess EHPs.

$$J_x = -qn\langle v_x \rangle$$

$$\frac{\text{ampere}}{\text{cm}^2} = \frac{\text{coulomb}}{\text{electron}} \cdot \frac{\text{electrons}}{\text{cm}^3} \cdot \frac{\text{cm}}{\text{s}}$$

(3–37)

Using Eq. (3–36) for the average velocity, we obtain

$$J_x = \frac{nq^2 \bar{t}}{m_n^*} \mathscr{E}_x$$

(3–38)

Thus the current density is proportional to the electric field, as we expect from Ohm's law:

$$J_x = \sigma \mathscr{E}_x, \quad \text{where } \sigma \equiv \frac{nq^2 \bar{t}}{m_n^*}$$

(3–39)

The conductivity $\sigma (\Omega\text{-cm})^{-1}$ can be written

$$\sigma = qn\mu_n, \quad \text{where } \mu_n \equiv \frac{q\bar{t}}{m_n^*}$$

(3–40a)

The quantity μ_n, called the *electron mobility,* describes the ease with which electrons drift in the material. Mobility is a very important quantity in characterizing semiconductor materials and in device development.

Here m_n^* is the conductivity effective mass for electrons, different from the density-of-states effective mass mentioned in Eq. (3–16b). While we use the density-of-states effective mass to count the number of carriers in bands, we must use the conductivity effective mass for charge transport problems. To illustrate how it is obtained from the band curvature effective masses mentioned in Section 3.2.2, once again let us consider the six equivalent conduction band minima along the X-directions for Si, with the band curvature longitudinal effective mass, m_l, along the major axis of the ellipsoid, and the transverse effective mass, m_t, along the two minor axes (Fig. 3–10b). Since we have $1/m_n^*$ in the mobility expression Eq. (3–40a), by using dimensional equivalence, we can write the conductivity effective mass as the harmonic mean of the band curvature effective masses.

$$\frac{1}{m_n^*} = \frac{1}{3}\left(\frac{1}{m_l} + \frac{2}{m_t} \right)$$

(3–40b)

EXAMPLE 3–6   Calculate the conductivity effective mass of electrons in Si.

SOLUTION   For Si, $m_l = 0.98\, m_0$; $m_t = 0.19\, m_0$ (Appendix III).
There are six equivalent X valleys in the conduction band.

$$1/m_n^* = 1/3(1/m_x + 1/m_y + 1/m_z) = 1/3(1/m_l + 2/m_t)$$

$$1/m_n^* = \frac{1}{3}\left(\frac{1}{0.98\,m_0} + \frac{2}{0.19\,m_0}\right)$$

$$m_n^* = 0.26\,m_0$$

Note: For GaAs, the conduction band equi-energy surfaces are spherical. So there is only one band curvature effective mass. (The density of states effective mass and the conductivity effective mass are both $0.067\,m_0$.)

The mobility defined in Eq. (3–40a) can be expressed as the average particle drift velocity per unit electric field. Comparing Eqs. (3–36) and (3–40a), we have

$$\mu_n = -\frac{\langle v_x \rangle}{\mathscr{E}_x} \tag{3–41}$$

The unit of mobility is $(cm/s)/(V/cm) = cm^2/V\text{-}s$, as Eq. (3–41) suggests. The minus sign in the definition results in a positive value of mobility, since electrons drift opposite to the field.

The current density can be written in terms of mobility as

$$J_x = qn\mu_n\mathscr{E}_x \tag{3–42}$$

This derivation has been based on the assumption that the current is carried primarily by electrons. For hole conduction we change n to p, $-q$ to $+q$, and μ_n to μ_p, where $\mu_p = +\langle v_x \rangle/\mathscr{E}_x$ is the mobility for holes. If both electrons and holes participate, we must modify Eq. (3–42) to

$$\boxed{J_x = q(n\mu_n + p\mu_p)\mathscr{E}_x = \sigma\mathscr{E}_x} \tag{3–43}$$

Values of μ_n and μ_p are given for many of the common semiconductor materials in Appendix III. According to Eq. (3–40), the parameters determining mobility are m^* and mean free time $\bar{t}$. Effective mass is a property of the material's band structure, as described by Eq. (3–3). Thus we expect m_n^* to be small in the strongly curved Γ minimum of the GaAs conduction band (Fig. 3–6), with the result that μ_n is very high. In a more gradually curved band, a larger m^* in the denominator of Eq. (3–40) leads to a smaller value of mobility. It is reasonable to expect that lighter particles are more mobile than heavier particles (which is satisfying, since the common-sense value of effective mass is not always apparent). The other parameter determining mobility is the mean time between scattering events, $\bar{t}$. In Section 3.4.3 we shall see that this is determined primarily by temperature and impurity concentration in the semiconductor.

3.4.2 Drift and Resistance

Let us look more closely at the drift of electrons and holes. If the semiconductor bar of Fig. 3–21 contains both types of carrier, Eq. (3–43) gives the conductivity of the material. The resistance of the bar is then

$$R = \frac{\rho L}{wt} = \frac{L}{wt}\frac{1}{\sigma} \tag{3–44}$$

where ρ is the resistivity (Ω-cm). The physical mechanism of carrier drift requires that the holes in the bar move as a group in the direction of the electric field and that the electrons move as a group in the opposite direction. Both the electron and the hole components of current are in the direction of the field, since conventional current is positive in the direction of hole flow and opposite to the direction of electron flow. The drift current described by Eq. (3–43) is constant throughout the bar. A valid question arises, therefore, concerning the nature of the electron and hole flow at the contacts and in the external circuit. We should specify that the contacts to the bar of Fig. 3–21 are *ohmic*, meaning that they are perfect sources and sinks of both carrier types and have no special tendency to inject or collect either electrons or holes.

   If we consider that current is carried around the external circuit by electrons, there is no problem in visualizing electrons flowing into the bar at one end and out at the other (always opposite to I). Thus for every electron leaving the left end ($x = 0$) of the bar in Fig. 3–21, there is a corresponding electron entering at $x = L$, so that the electron concentration in the bar remains constant at n. But what happens to the holes at the contacts? As a hole reaches the ohmic contact at $x = L$, it recombines with an electron, which must be supplied through the external circuit. As this hole disappears, a corresponding hole must appear at $x = 0$ to maintain space charge

Electric field current

Hole motion

Electron motion

w

t

$x = L$

x

0

Electron motion

I

E

Figure 3–21
Drift of electrons and holes in a semiconductor bar.

neutrality. It is reasonable to consider the source of this hole as the generation of an EHP at $x = 0$, with the hole flowing into the bar and the electron flowing into the external circuit.

3.4.3 Effects of Temperature and Doping on Mobility

The two basic types of scattering mechanisms that influence electron and hole mobility are *lattice scattering* and *impurity scattering*. In lattice scattering a carrier moving through the crystal is scattered by a vibration of the lattice, resulting from the temperature.[11] The frequency of such scattering events increases as the temperature increases, since the thermal agitation of the lattice becomes greater. Therefore, we should expect the mobility to decrease as the sample is heated (Fig. 3–22). On the other hand, scattering from crystal defects such as ionized impurities becomes the dominant mechanism at low temperatures. Since the atoms of the cooler lattice are less agitated, lattice scattering is less important; however, the thermal motion of the carriers is also slower. Since a slowly moving carrier is likely to be scattered more strongly by an interaction with a charged ion than is a carrier with greater momentum, impurity scattering events cause a decrease in mobility with decreasing temperature. As Fig. 3–22 indicates, the approximate temperature dependencies are $T^{-3/2}$ for lattice scattering and $T^{3/2}$ for impurity scattering. Since the scattering probability of Eq. (3–32) is inversely proportional to the mean free time and therefore to mobility, the mobilities due to two or more scattering mechanisms add inversely:

$$\frac{1}{\mu} = \frac{1}{\mu_1} + \frac{1}{\mu_2} + \dots \tag{3–45}$$

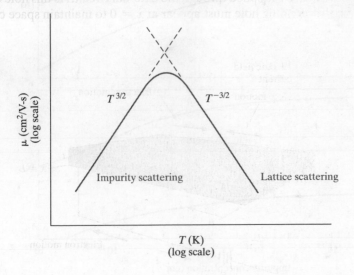

Figure 3–22
Approximate temperature dependence of mobility with both lattice and impurity scattering.

[11]Collective vibrations of atoms in the crystal are called *phonons*. Thus lattice scattering is also known as *phonon scattering*.

As a result, the mechanism causing the lowest mobility value dominates, as shown in Fig. 3–22.

As the concentration of impurities increases, the effects of impurity scattering are felt at higher temperatures. For example, the electron mobility μ_n of intrinsic silicon at 300 K is 1350 cm^2/(V-s). With a donor doping concentration of 10^{17} cm^{-3}, however, μ_n is 700 cm^2/(V-s). Thus, the presence of the 10^{17} ionized donors/cm^3 introduces a significant amount of impurity scattering. This effect is illustrated in Fig. 3–23, which shows the variation of mobility with doping concentration at room temperature.

Figure 3–23
Variation of mobility with total doping impurity concentration $(N_a + N_d)$ for Ge, Si, and GaAs at 300 K.

(a) A Si bar 1 μm long and 100 μm² in cross-sectional area is doped with 10^{17} cm^{-3} phosphorus. Find the current at 300 K with 10 V applied.

(b) How long does it take an average electron to drift 1 μm in pure Si at an electric field of 100 V/cm? Repeat for 10^5 V/cm.

EXAMPLE 3–7

SOLUTION

(a) *Find the current at 300 K with 10 V applied for a Si bar 1 μm long, 100 μm² in cross sectional area, and doped with 10^{17}cm^{-3} phosphorous.*

With $\mathcal{E} = \dfrac{10\ V}{10^{-4}\ cm} = 10^5 \frac{V}{cm}$ the sample is in the velocity saturation regime.

From Fig. 3–24, $v_s = 10^7\ \frac{cm}{s}$.

$$I = q \cdot A \cdot n \cdot v_s = 1.6 \cdot 10^{-19}\ C \cdot 10^{-6}\ cm^2 \cdot 10^{17} \tfrac{1}{cm^3} \cdot 10^7\ \tfrac{cm}{s} = 0.16\ A$$

(b) *In pure Si, find time for an electron to drift 1 μm in an electric field of 100 $\frac{v}{cm}$? For 10^5 $\frac{v}{cm}$?*

From Appendix III, $\mu_n = 1350\ \frac{cm^2}{V\text{-}s}$

low field: $v_d = \mu_n \cdot \mathcal{E} = 1350\ \frac{cm^2}{V\text{-}s} \cdot 100\ \frac{V}{cm} = 1.35 \cdot 10^5\ \frac{cm}{s}$

$$t = \frac{L}{v_d} = \frac{10^{-4}\ cm}{1.35 \cdot 10^5\ \frac{cm}{s}} = 7.4 \cdot 10^{-10}\ s = 0.74\ ns$$

high field: scattering limited velocity $v_s = 10^7\ \frac{cm}{s}$ from Figure 3–24

$$t = \frac{L}{v_s} = \frac{10^{-4}\ cm}{10^7\ \frac{cm}{s}} = 10^{-11} s = 10\ ps$$

Figure 3–24
Saturation of electron drift velocity at high electric fields for Si.

3.4.4 High-Field Effects

One assumption implied in the derivation of Eq. (3–39) was that Ohm's law is valid in the carrier drift processes. That is, it was assumed that the drift current is proportional to the electric field and that the proportionality constant (σ) is not a function of field $\mathscr{E}$. This assumption is valid over a wide range of $\mathscr{E}$. However, large electric fields ($> 10^3$ V/cm) can cause the drift velocity and therefore the current $J = -qnv_d$ to exhibit a sublinear dependence on the electric field. This dependence of σ upon is an example of a *hot carrier* effect, which implies that the carrier drift velocity v_d is comparable to the thermal velocity v_{th}.

In many cases an upper limit is reached for the carrier drift velocity in a high field (Fig. 3–24). This limit occurs near the mean thermal velocity ($\approx 10^7$ cm/s) and represents the point at which added energy imparted by the field is transferred to the lattice rather than increasing the carrier velocity. The result of this *scattering limited velocity* is a fairly constant current at high field. This behavior is typical of Si, Ge, and some other semiconductors. However, there are other important effects in some materials; for example, in Chapter 10 we shall discuss a *decrease* in electron velocity at high fields for GaAs and certain other materials, which results in negative conductivity and current instabilities in the sample. Another important high-field effect is avalanche multiplication, which we shall discuss in Section 5.4.2.

3.4.5 The Hall Effect

If a magnetic field is applied perpendicular to the direction in which holes drift in a p-type bar, the path of the holes tends to be deflected (Fig. 3–25). Using vector notation, the total force on a single hole due to the electric and magnetic fields is

$$\mathbf{F} = q(\mathscr{E} + \mathbf{v} \times \mathscr{B}) \tag{3–46}$$

Figure 3–25
The Hall effect.

In the y-direction the force is

$$F_y = q(\mathscr{E}_y - v_x\mathscr{B}_z) \tag{3-47}$$

The important result of Eq. (3–47) is that unless an electric field $\mathscr{E}_y$ is established along the width of the bar, each hole will experience a net force (and therefore an acceleration) in the $-y$-direction due to the $qv_x\mathscr{B}_z$ product. Therefore, to maintain a steady state flow of holes down the length of the bar, the electric field $\mathscr{E}_y$ must just balance the product $v_x\mathscr{B}_z$:

$$\mathscr{E}_y = v_x\mathscr{B}_z \tag{3-48}$$

so that the net force F_y is zero. Physically, this electric field is set up when the magnetic field shifts the hole distribution slightly in the $-y$-direction. Once the electric field $\mathscr{E}_y$ becomes as large as $v_x\mathscr{B}_z$, no net lateral force is experienced by the holes as they drift along the bar. The establishment of the electric field $\mathscr{E}_y$ is known as the *Hall effect*, and the resulting voltage $V_{AB} = \mathscr{E}_y w$ is called the *Hall voltage*. If we use the expression derived in Eq. (3–37) for the drift velocity (using $+q$ and p_0 for holes), the field $\mathscr{E}_y$ becomes

$$\mathscr{E}_y = \frac{J_x}{qp_0}\mathscr{B}_z = R_H J_x \mathscr{B}_z, \quad R_H \equiv \frac{1}{qp_0} \tag{3-49}$$

Thus the Hall field is proportional to the product of the current density and the magnetic flux density. The proportionality constant $R_H = (qp_0)^{-1}$ is called the *Hall coefficient*. A measurement of the Hall voltage for a known current and magnetic field yields a value for the hole concentration p_0

$$p_0 = \frac{1}{qR_H} = \frac{J_x\mathscr{B}_z}{q\mathscr{E}_y} = \frac{(I_x/wt)\mathscr{B}_z}{q(V_{AB}/w)} = \frac{I_x\mathscr{B}_z}{qtV_{AB}} \tag{3-50}$$

Since all of the quantities in the right-hand side of Eq. (3–50) can be measured, the Hall effect can be used to give quite accurate values for carrier concentration.

If a measurement of resistance R is made, the sample resistivity ρ can be calculated:

$$\rho(\Omega - cm) = \frac{Rwt}{L} = \frac{V_{CD}/I_x}{L/wt} \tag{3-51}$$

Since the conductivity $\sigma = 1/\rho$ is given by $q\mu_p p_0$, the mobility is simply the ratio of the Hall coefficient and the resistivity:

$$\mu_p = \frac{\sigma}{qp_0} = \frac{1/\rho}{q(1/qR_H)} = \frac{R_H}{\rho} \tag{3-52}$$

Measurements of the Hall coefficient and the resistivity over a range of temperatures yield plots of majority carrier concentration and mobility vs. temperature. Such measurements are extremely useful in the analysis of semiconductor materials. Although the discussion here has been related to p-type material, similar results are obtained for n-type material. A negative value of q is used for electrons, and the Hall voltage V_{AB} and Hall coefficient R_H are negative. In fact, measurement of the sign of the Hall voltage is a common technique for determining if an unknown sample is p-type or n-type.

EXAMPLE 3–8   Referring to Fig. 3–25, consider a semiconductor bar with $w = 0.1$ mm, $t = 10$ μm, and $L = 5$ mm. For $\mathscr{B} = 10$ kG in the direction shown (1 kG $= 10^{-5}$ Wb/cm^2) and a current of 1 mA, we have $V_{AB} = -2$ mV and $V_{CD} = 100$ mV. Find the type, concentration, and mobility of the majority carrier.

SOLUTION

$$\mathscr{B}_z = 10^{-4} \text{ Wb/cm}^2$$

From the sign of V_{AB}, we can see that the majority carriers are electrons:

$$n_0 = \frac{I_x \mathscr{B}_z}{qt(-V_{AB})} = \frac{(10^{-3})(10^{-4})}{1.6 \times 10^{-19}(10^{-3})(2 \times 10^{-3})} = 3.125 \times 10^{17} \text{ cm}^{-3}$$

$$\rho = \frac{R}{L/wt} = \frac{V_{CD}/I_x}{L/wt} = \frac{0.1/10^{-3}}{0.5/0.01 \times 10^{-3}} = 0.002 \ \Omega \cdot \text{cm}$$

$$\mu_n = \frac{1}{\rho q n_0} = \frac{1}{(0.002)(1.6 \times 10^{-19})(3.125 \times 10^{17})} = 10,000 \text{ cm}^2(\text{V} \cdot \text{s})^{-1}$$

**3.5
INVARIANCE OF
THE FERMI LEVEL
AT EQUILIBRIUM**

In this chapter we have discussed homogeneous semiconductors, without variations in doping and without junctions between dissimilar materials. In the following chapters we will be considering cases in which nonuniform doping occurs in a given semiconductor, or junctions occur between different semiconductors or a semiconductor and a metal. These cases are crucial to the various types of electronic and optoelectronic devices made in semiconductors. In anticipation of those discussions, an important concept should be established here regarding the demands of equilibrium. That concept can be summarized by noting that *no discontinuity or gradient can arise in the equilibrium Fermi level E_F.*

To demonstrate this assertion, let us consider two materials in intimate contact such that electrons can move between the two (Fig. 3–26). These may be, for example, dissimilar semiconductors, n- and p-type regions, a metal and a semiconductor, or simply two adjacent regions of a nonuniformly doped semiconductor. Each material is described by a Fermi–Dirac distribution function and some distribution of available energy states that electrons can occupy.

Figure 3–26
Two materials in intimate contact at equilibrium. Since the net motion of electrons is zero, the equilibrium Fermi level must be constant throughout.

There is no current, and therefore no net charge transport, at thermal equilibrium. There is also no net transfer of energy. Therefore, for each energy E in Fig. 3–26 any transfer of electrons from material 1 to material 2 must be exactly balanced by the opposite transfer of electrons from 2 to 1. We will let the density of states at energy E in material 1 be called $N_1(E)$ and in material 2 we will call it $N_2(E)$. At energy E the rate of transfer of electrons from 1 to 2 is proportional to the number of filled states at E in material 1 times the number of empty states at E in material 2:

$$\text{rate from 1 to 2} \propto N_1(E)f_1(E) \cdot N_2(E)[1 - f_2(E)] \qquad (3\text{–}53)$$

where $f(E)$ is the probability of a state being filled at E in each material, that is, the Fermi–Dirac distribution function given by Eq. (3–10). Similarly,

$$\text{rate from 2 to 1} \propto N_2(E)f_2(E) \cdot N_1(E)[1 - f_1(E)] \qquad (3\text{–}54)$$

At equilibrium these must be equal:

$$N_1(E)f_1(E) \cdot N_2(E)[1 - f_2(E)] = N_2(E)f_2(E) \cdot N_1(E)[1 - f_1(E)] \qquad (3\text{–}55)$$

Rearranging terms, we have, at energy E,

$$N_1f_1N_2 - N_1f_1N_2f_2 = N_2f_2N_1 - N_2f_2N_1f_1 \qquad (3\text{–}56)$$

which results in

$$f_1(E) = f_2(E), \quad \text{that is,} \quad [1 + e^{(E-E_{F1})/kT}]^{-1} = [1 + e^{(E-E_{F2})/kT}]^{-1} \qquad (3\text{–}57)$$

Therefore, we conclude that $E_{F1} = E_{F2}$. That is, there is no discontinuity in the equilibrium Fermi level. More generally, we can state that the Fermi level at equilibrium must be constant throughout materials in intimate contact. One way of stating this is that no gradient exists in the Fermi level at equilibrium:

$$\boxed{\frac{dE_F}{dx} = 0} \qquad (3\text{–}58)$$

We will make considerable use of this result in the chapters to follow.

SUMMARY

3.1 In a diamond lattice, each Si atom (with four valence electrons) is surrounded by four Si atoms that form four *covalent* bonds consisting of shared electron pairs, thereby forming an *octet* of electrons in the valence shell. In zinc blende structures such as GaAs, electrons are partly shared (covalent bonding) and partly transferred from Ga to As (*ionic* bonding).

3.2 In crystals, electronic *wavefunctions overlap* to give various linear combinations of atomic orbitals (LCAO). Bonding or symmetric combinations of the wavefunctions of valence-shell electrons form (*almost*) *continuous allowed bands* of energies in the (*almost*) *filled valence* band, separated by an energy gap from higher energy states in an (*almost*) *empty conduction* band that correspond to the antibonding or antisymmetric LCAOs. Empty electronic states in the valence band can be considered to be positively charged carriers (*holes*), while filled states in the conduction band are negatively charged (*conduction*) *electrons*.

3.3 If the band gaps are large, we get insulators; if they are small (~1 eV), we get semiconductors; and if they are zero, we get conductors (metals).

3.4 *Simplified* band diagrams plot *electron energy* in the conduction band (*increasing upward*) as a function of position. The *band edge* corresponds to *potential* energy, and the distance from the band edge gives the *kinetic* energy. *Hole energies increase downward* in the valence band.

3.5 Carrier energies can also be plotted as a function of wavevector **k** (proportional to velocity or momentum) to give $(E, \mathbf{k})$ *band structures*, which can be direct (conduction band minimum directly above valence band maximum) or indirect. The *curvature* of the $(E, \mathbf{k})$ is inversely proportional to the *effective mass* m^* of the carriers. The m^* accounts for the interactions of the carriers with the periodic crystal potential.

3.6 In a pure semiconductor, we have an *intrinsic* concentration of electrons (or holes), n_i, that result from *thermal* generation–recombination between the valence and conduction band (or bond breaking). If we replace some Si atoms (with four valence electrons) with *donor* impurities with five valence electrons, they donate conduction electrons, n $(=N_d^+)$; similarly, *acceptors* create holes p.

3.7 The number of electrons, n, is the integral with respect to energy from the bottom to the top of the conduction band of the product of the available *density of states* (DOS) and the *Fermi–Dirac* (FD) distribution function. For parabolic band structures, we get a parabolic DOS. The FD function is the average occupancy of an electronic state. The electron concentration n can also be expressed as the product of an *effective* DOS at the band edge and the FD occupancy at E_c, and similarly for holes p. The np product in equilibrium is constant (n_i^2).

3.8 Electrons in a solid execute *random Brownian* motion with an average kinetic energy related to the thermal energy kT. In an electric field, electrons *drift* (on top of the random motion) with a velocity equal to *mobility* times field in the *ohmic* regime and *saturation velocity* at *high fields*. The drift current is proportional to carrier concentration times drift velocity. Negatively charged electrons drift opposite to the electric field, and the current is opposite to the motion. Positively charged holes drift in the direction of the electric field, and the current goes in the same direction as the hole flow.

3.9 Carrier mobility is determined by *scattering,* caused by *deviations* from a periodic lattice potential, such as lattice vibrations (phonons) or ionized impurities. Carrier mobility and concentration can be obtained by the Hall effect and resistivity measurements.

PROBLEMS

3.1 Find the approximate binding energy for gallium nitride (GaN) having the following specifications: $\epsilon_r = 9.7$, $m_n^* = 0.13\, m_0$.

3.2 Calculate values for the Fermi function $f(E)$ at 300 K and plot vs. energy in eV as in Fig. 3–14. Choose $E_F = 1$ eV and make the calculated points closer together near the Fermi level to obtain a smooth curve. Notice that $f(E)$ varies quite rapidly within a few kT of E_F. Show that the probability that a state ΔE above E_F is occupied is the same as the probability that the state ΔE below E_F is empty.

3.3 (a) A Si substrate at room temperature is doped with $2.70 \times 10^{16}/cm^3$ donor atoms. Determine the electron and hole concentrations of the sample and the type of the substrate. [Given: $n_i = 1.5 \times 10^{10}/cm^3$, $Nc = 6.0953 \times 10^{19}/cm^3$, $Eg = 1.1$ eV]

   (b) If the above sample is overdoped with $5 \times 10^{16}/cm^3$ acceptor atoms, what will be the new electron and hole concentrations for the substrate? What will be the type of the substrate after acceptor doping?

3.4 Derive an expression for the total number of states in a semiconductor material between E_c and $E_c + kT$, where E_c is the conduction band edge, K is the Boltzmann's constant, and T is the temperature. Determine the DOS for Si at room temperature.

3.5 At room temperature, an intrinsic AlAs has 4X minima along <100> directions, and the following data are available: Electronics mass for Γ valley and X valley are 0.15 m_0 and 0.76 m_0. The hole mass is 0.76 m_0. At what temperature the number of electrons in the Γ minima and X minima will be equal if the energy separation between them is 0.40 eV? The band gap for AlAs is 2.23 eV.

3.6 Since the effective mass of electrons in a conduction band decreases with increasing curvature of the band according to Eq. (3–3), comment on the electron effective mass in the Γ valley of GaAs compared with the indirect X or L valleys. (See Fig. 3–10.) How is this effective mass difference reflected in the electron mobility for GaAs and GaP shown in Appendix III? From Fig. 3–10, what would you expect to happen to the conductivity of GaAs if Γ-valley electrons drifting in an electric field were suddenly promoted to the L valley?

3.7 Calculate the band gap of Si from Eq. (3–23) and plot n_i vs. $1000/T$ (Fig. 3–17). [*Hint:* The slope cannot be measured directly from a semilogarithmic plot; read the values from two points on the plot and take the natural logarithm as needed for the solution.]

3.8 Consider a Ge crystal at room temperature doped with $5 \times 10^{15}/cm^3$ As atoms. Find the equilibrium electron, the hole concentrations, and the position of the Fermi level w.r.t intrinsic energy level (E_i) and conduction energy band (E_c). Draw the energy band diagram also.

3.9 Ideally in a semiconductor, intrinsic energy level should be in the middle of the band gap. Estimate the position of the intrinsic energy level (Ei) for intrinsic Ge at 300 K, assuming the effective mass values for electrons and holes are $m_e = 0.041\, m_0$ and $m_p = 0.28\, m_0$, respectively.

3.10 A Ge sample is doped with $10^{14}/cm^3$ As atoms/cm^3. What will be the equilibrium hole concentration? What is the relative position of Fermi level w.r.t intrinsic energy level?

[Given: $n_i = 2.5 \times 10^{13}/cm^3$]

3.11 A new semiconductor has $N_c = 10^{19}\, cm^{-3}$, $N_v = 5 \times 10^{18}\, cm^{-3}$, and $E_g = 2$ eV. If it is doped with 10^{17} donors (fully ionized), calculate the electron, hole, and intrinsic carrier concentrations at 627°C. Sketch the simplified band diagram, showing the position of E_F.

3.12 (a) Show that the minimum conductivity of a semiconductor sample occurs when $n_0 = n_i \sqrt{\mu_p/\mu_n}$. [Hint: Begin with Eq. (3–43) and apply Eq. (3–24).]

(b) What is the expression for the minimum conductivity σ_{min}?

(c) Calculate σ_{min} for Si at 300 K and compare with the intrinsic conductivity.

3.13 A 2 cm long piece of Si with cross-sectional area of 0.1 cm^2 is doped with donors at $10^{15}\, cm^{-3}$, and has a resistance of 90 ohms. The saturation velocity of electrons in Si is 10^7 cm/s for fields above 10^5 V/cm. Calculate the electron drift velocity, if we apply a voltage of 100 V across the piece. What is the current through the piece if we apply a voltage of 10^6 V across it?

3.14 In an n-type semiconductor rectangular bar, if the length of the bar becomes four times of the original length and doping is decreased by half of its original doping, then how it will affect the conductivity and current density through the bar if the applied voltage remains the same?

3.15 Predict the effect on mobility and resistivity of Si crystal at room temperature if every millionth of Si atom is replaced by an atom of indium (In). Given, the concentration of Si atoms is $5 \times 10^{28}/m^3$, the intrinsic carrier concentration is $1.5 \times 10^{10}/cm^3$, the intrinsic conductivity of Si is 0.00044 S/m, the intrinsic resistivity of Si is $R = 2300$ Ω.m, and the mobility of electrons and holes are 0.135 m^2/V-sec and 0.048 m^2/V-sec, respectively.

3.16 For a Si bar having a length of 4 μm, doped n-type at $10^{17}/cm^3$, calculate the current for an applied voltage of 2 V having a cross sectional area of 0.01 cm^2. If the voltage is now raised at 100 V, what will be the change in current? Electron and hole mobilities are 1350 cm^2/V-sec and 400 cm^2/V-sec for low electric field. For higher field saturation, the velocity for electron is Vs = 10^7 cm/sec.

3.17 A semiconductor has a band gap of 1 eV, effective density of states, $N_c = 10^{19}\,cm^{-3}$, $N_v = 4 \times 10^{19}\,cm^{-3}$, electron and hole mobilities of 4000 and 2500 cm^2/V-s, respectively. It is subjected to the following potentials at the various locations as follows (assume linear variation of potentials between locations):

Point A at $x = 0$ microns, V = 0 V

Point B at $x = 2$ microns, V = -2V

Point C at 4 microns, V = $+4$ V

Point D is at 8 microns; electric field is zero between C and D.

Sketch the simplified band diagram, properly labeling the positions, energies, and directions of electric fields.

If the electron concentration at location B is $10^{18}\,cm^{-3}$, and assuming things are close to equilibrium, what is the hole concentration there? If an electron at the conduction band edge at B goes toward C, how long does it take to get there? If there is negligible scattering at low electric fields, how long does it take to go from C to D?

3.18 Sketch, with proper labeling of energies and distances, the simplified band diagram of a semiconductor with a band gap of 2 eV which is subjected to the following electrostatic potential profile: 0 V for $x = 0$ to 1 μm; linearly increasing from 0 to 1.5 V between 1 μm and 4 μm; constant potential after that from $x = 4$ to 5 μm. We launch an electron to the right, at $x = 0$ with a kinetic energy of 0.5 eV. Assuming there is no scattering, what is its kinetic energy at $x = 2$ μm? If the effective mass of this electron is 0.5 m_0, how long does it take the electron to travel from $x = 4$ to 5 μm? If the donor density in this semiconductor is $10^{17}\,cm^{-3}$, what is the electron drift current density at $x = 4.5$ μm?

3.19 (a) Sketch and label the simplified band diagram of a semiconductor with a band gap of 1.5 eV subjected to the following: From $x = 0$ to 2 μm, the voltage is constant. From $x = 2$ μm to 4 μm, there is an electric field of 2 V/μm pointing to the right. Then from $x = 4$ μm to 8 μm, the voltage increases by 3 V.

(b) A semiconductor has a electron band structure $E(k) = (4k^2 + 5)$ eV, where k has units of Å^{-1} $(1\ \text{Å} = 10^{-10}\,m)$. Calculate the effective mass of the electrons. Why is the effective mass different from the actual electron mass of 9.1×10^{-31} kg?

3.20 A doped Si sample A of thickness 3 mm shows a Hall voltage of $V_y = 3$ mV for current density $J = 300$ A/m^2, under a magnetic field of $B_z = 1$ Weber/m^2. Find the type of the semiconductor and doping concentration.

3.21 A semiconductor bar of length 8 μm and cross-sectional area 2 μm^2 is *uniformly doped* with donors with a much higher concentration than the intrinsic concentration $(10^{11}\,cm^{-3})$ such that ionized impurity scattering causes its majority carrier mobility to be a function of doping $N_d(cm^{-3})$

$$\mu = 800/\sqrt{[N_d/(10^{20}\,cm^{-3})]}\,cm^2/V\text{-}s$$

If the *electron drift* current for an applied voltage of 160 V is 10 mA, calculate the doping concentration in the bar. If the minority carrier mobility is 500 cm^2/V-s, and its saturation velocity is 10^6 cm/s for fields above 100 kV/cm calculate the hole drift current. What are the *electron and hole diffusion* currents in the middle of the bar?

3.22 Use Eq. (3–45) to calculate and plot the mobility vs. temperature $\mu(T)$ from 10 K to 500 K for Si doped with $N_d = 10^{14}$, 10^{16}, and 10^{18} donors cm^{-3}. Consider the mobility to be determined by impurity and phonon (lattice) scattering. Impurity scattering limited mobility can be described by

$$\mu_I = 3.29 \times 10^{15}\, \frac{\epsilon_r^z T^{3/2}}{N_d^+(m_n^*/m_0)^{1/2}\left[\ln(1 + z) - \dfrac{z}{1 + z}\right]}$$

where

$$z = 1.3 \times 10^{13}\epsilon_r T^2 (m_n^*/m_0)(N_d^+)^{-1}$$

Assume that the ionized impurity concentration N_d^+ is equal to N_d at all temperatures. The conductivity effective mass m_n^* for Si is 0.26 m_0. Acoustic phonon (lattice) scattering limited mobility can be described by

$$\mu_{AC} = 1.18 \times 10^{-5}\, c_1(m_n^*/m_0)^{-5/2} T^{-3/2}(E_{AC})^{-2}$$

where the stiffness (c_1) is given by

$$c_1 = 1.9 \times 10^{12}\ dyne\ cm^{-2}\ for\ Si$$

and the conduction band acoustic deformation potential (E_{AC}) is

$$E_{AC} = 9.5\ eV\ for\ Si$$

3.23 Rework Prob. 3.22 considering carrier freeze-out onto donors at low T. That is, consider

$$N_d^+ = \frac{N_d}{1 + \exp(E_d/kT)}$$

as the ionized impurity concentration. Consider the donor ionization energy (E_d) to be 45 meV for Si.

3.24 Consider a Si sample kept at room temperature having a band gap $E_g = 1.12$ eV.

(a) If the Fermi level E_F is located exactly at the middle of the band gap for this sample, then what will be the probability of finding an electron at $E = E_C + 2kT$?

(b) If the Fermi level E_F is located such that $E_F = E_V$, then what will be the probability of finding an electron at $E = E_V + kT$?

3.25 In soldering wires to a sample such as that shown in Fig. 3–25, it is difficult to align the Hall probes A and B precisely. If B is displaced slightly down the length of the bar from A, an erroneous Hall voltage results. Show that the true Hall voltage V_H can be obtained from two measurements of V_{AB}, with the magnetic field first in the $+z$-direction and then in the $-z$-direction.

3.26 Consider a Si bar with width of 0.02 cm, thickness of 8 μm, and length of 0.6 cm. Due to Hall measurement, magnetic field generated at z-direction is 10-5 Wb/cm^2 and a current of 0.8 mA. If the voltage at the two end is +1 mV and $V_{CD} = 50$ mV, then find the type, concentration, and mobility of the majority carriers.

READING LIST

Blakemore, J. S. *Semiconductor Statistics.* New York: Dover Publications, 1987.

Hess, K. *Advanced Theory of Semiconductor Devices,* 2d ed. New York: IEEE Press, 2000.

Kittel, C. *Introduction to Solid State Physics,* 7th ed. New York: Wiley, 1996.

Neamen, D. A. *Semiconductor Physics and Devices: Basic Principles.* Homewood, IL: Irwin, 2003.

Pierret, R. F. *Semiconductor Device Fundamentals.* Reading, MA: Addison-Wesley, 1996.

Schubert, E. F. *Doping in III–V Semiconductors.* Cambridge: Cambridge University Press, 1993.

Singh, J. *Semiconductor Devices.* New York: McGraw-Hill, 1994.

Wang, S. *Fundamentals of Semiconductor Theory and Device Physics.* Englewood Cliffs, NJ: Prentice Hall, 1989.

Wolfe, C. M., G. E. Stillman, and N. Holonyak, Jr. *Physical Properties of Semiconductors.* Englewood Cliffs, NJ: Prentice Hall, 1989.

Question 1

(a) The following three diagrams show three different energy bands of some hypothetical crystalline materials (energy varies vertically). The only difference between the three materials is the assumed Fermi level energy E_F. Characterize each material as a *metal*, an *insulator*, or a *semiconductor*.

(b) Assuming you can see through one and only one of the materials of part (a) above, which one would it most likely be? *Material 1 / Material 2 / Material 3*

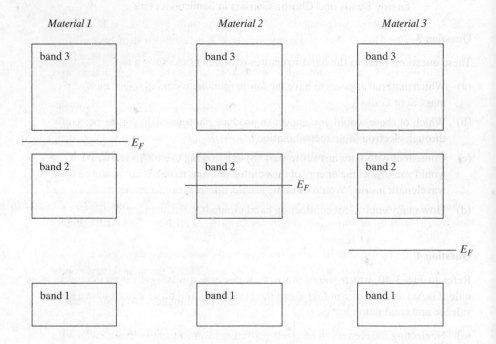

Material 1   *Material 2*   *Material 3*

band 3

band 3

band 3

E_F

band 2

band 2

band 2

E_F

E_F

band 1

band 1

band 1

Question 2

Consider the following conduction band energy E vs. wavevector $\mathbf{k}_x$ dispersion relation.

(a) Which energy valley has the greater effective mass in the x-direction m_x (circle one)? **Γ-valley / X-valley**

(b) Consider two electrons, one each located at the positions of the heavy crosses. Which has the greater velocity magnitude (circle one)? **The one in the Γ-valley / The one in the X-valley**

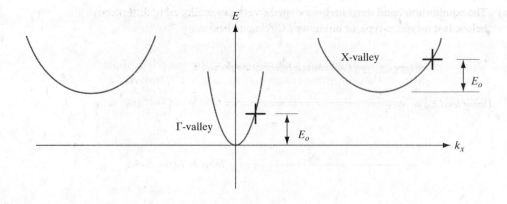

Question 3

These questions refer to the band structures of Si and GaAs shown in Fig. 3–10.

(a) Which material appears to have the *lowest* (conduction band) electron effective mass, Si or GaAs?

(b) Which of these would you expect to produce photons (light) more efficiently through electron–hole recombination?

(c) Consistent with your answer to part (b) and making use of Appendix III, what would you expect the energy of the emitted photons to be? What would be their wavelength in μm? Would these be visible, infrared, or ultraviolet?

(d) How many equivalent conduction band minima do we have for Si? GaAs?

Question 4

Refer to Fig. 3–10, which shows the E vs. k dispersion relations for gallium arsenide (GaAs) and for silicon (Si) along the [111] and [100] directions, showing both valence and conduction bands.

(a) Neglecting differences in electron scattering rates in the two materials, would you expect Si or GaAs to have the greatest electron mobility μ_n?

(b) If a constant force were applied in the [100] direction for a short period of time on an electron initially located at the conduction band minimum of each semiconductor and if scattering were neglected, would the magnitude of change in k in Si be greater, equal to, or smaller than the magnitude of the change in k in GaAs for the same force F?

greater / equal / smaller

Question 5

(a) The equilibrium band diagram for a doped direct gap semiconductor is shown below. Is it n-type, p-type, or unknown? Circle one below.

n-type / p-type / not enough information provided

Donor level E_d — $= = = = = = = = = = = = = =$ Conduction band edge E_c

$\cdots\cdots\cdots\cdots\cdots\cdots\cdots\cdots\cdots\cdots\cdots\cdots$ Intrinsic Fermi level E_i

Acceptor level E_a $\cdots\cdots\cdots\cdots\cdots\cdots\cdots\cdots$ Fermi level E_F
$- - - - - - - - - - - -$
Valence band edge E_v

(b) Based on the band diagram above (E_i is in the middle of the gap), would you expect that the conduction band density-of-states effective mass is greater than, equal to, or smaller than the valence band effective mass? Circle one:

Greater than / equal / smaller than

(c) What, if any, of the following conditions by themselves could lead to the above band diagram? Circle each correct answer.

(a) very high temperature
(b) very high acceptor doping
(c) very low acceptor doping

Question 6

A hypothetical semiconductor has an intrinsic carrier concentration of $1.0 \times 10^{10}/cm^3$ at 300 K, it has conduction and valence band effective densities of states N_c and N_v, both equal to $10^{19}/cm^3$.

(a) What is the band gap E_g?

(b) If the semiconductor is doped with $N_d = 1 \times 10^{16}$ donors/cm³, what are the equilibrium electron and hole concentrations at 300 K?

(c) If the same piece of semiconductor, already having $N_d = 1 \times 10^{16}$ donors/cm³, is also doped with $N_a = 2 \times 10^{16}$ acceptors/cm³, what are the new equilibrium electron and hole concentrations at 300 K?

(d) Consistent with your answer to part (c), what is the Fermi level position with respect to the intrinsic Fermi level, $E_F - E_i$?

Question 7

What is the difference between density of states and *effective* density of states, and why is the latter such a useful concept?

Question 8

(a) Does mobility have any meaning at very high field? Why?

(b) How do you measure mobility and carrier concentration?

Question 9

Find the relaxation time of conduction electronics in a metal resistivity $1.54 \times 10^{\wedge}(-8)$ ohm-m. If the metal has $5.86 \times 10^{\wedge}(28)$ conduction electrons per m³.

Question 10

Find the resistance of an intrinsic germanium rod 1.0 cm long, 1.0 mm wide and 1.0 mm thick at 300 K. The intrinsic carrier density is $2.5 \times 10^{\wedge}(19)$ per m³ at 300 K, and the mobility of electrons and holes are 0.39 and 0.19 m(2)V(−1)s(−1) respectively.

Question 11

Find the diffusion coefficient of electrons in silicon at 300 K if ue is 0.19 m²/V-s.

Question 12

The respectively of an intrinsic semiconductor is 4.5 ohm-m at 20 C and 2.0 ohm-m at 32 C. What is the energy band gap.

Question 13

A Ge diode has a saturation current of 1 nA at 20 C. Find its current when it is forward biased by 0.4 V. Find the current in the same diode when the temperature rises 110 C.

Question 14

If the effective mass of holes in a semiconductor is 5 times that of electron, at what temperature would the Fermi level shifted by 15% from the middle of the forbidden energy band? (Given that the energy gap for the semiconductor is 1.20 eV)

Chapter 4

Excess Carriers in Semiconductors

OBJECTIVES

1. Understand how photons interact with direct and indirect band gap semiconductors
2. Understand generation–recombination of excess carriers, possibly through trap sites
3. Introduce quasi-Fermi levels in nonequilibrium
4. Calculate diffusion currents from carrier concentration gradients and diffusivity
5. Use the continuity equation to study time dependence of carrier concentrations

Most semiconductor devices operate by the creation of charge carriers in excess of the thermal equilibrium values. These excess carriers can be created by optical[1] excitation or electron bombardment, or as we shall see in Chapter 5, they can be injected across a forward-biased p-n junction. However the excess carriers arise, they can dominate the conduction processes in the semiconductor material. In this chapter we shall investigate the creation of excess carriers by optical absorption and the resulting properties of photoluminescence and photoconductivity. We shall study more closely the mechanism of electron–hole pair recombination and the effects of carrier trapping. Finally, we shall discuss the diffusion of excess carriers due to a carrier gradient, which serves as a basic mechanism of current conduction along with the mechanism of drift in an electric field.

4.1
OPTICAL ABSORPTION[1]

An important technique for measuring the band gap energy of a semiconductor is the absorption of incident photons by the material. In this experiment photons of selected wavelengths are directed at the sample, and relative transmission of the various photons is observed. Since photons with energies greater than the band gap energy are absorbed while photons with energies

---

[1]In this context the word "optical" does not necessarily imply that the photons absorbed are in the visible part of the spectrum. Many semiconductors absorb photons in the infrared region, but this is included in the term "optical absorption."

Figure 4–1
Optical absorption
of a photon with
$hv > E_g$: (a) An
EHP is created
during photon
absorption; (b) the
excited electron
gives up energy
to the lattice by
scattering events;
(c) the electron
recombines with
a hole in the
valence band.

less than the band gap are transmitted, this experiment gives an accurate measure of the band gap energy.

It is apparent that a photon with energy $hv \geq E_g$ can be absorbed in a semiconductor (Fig. 4–1). Since the valence band contains many electrons and the conduction band has many empty states into which the electrons may be excited, the probability of photon absorption is high. As Fig. 4–1 indicates, an electron excited to the conduction band by optical absorption may initially have more energy than is common for conduction band electrons (almost all electrons are near E_c unless the sample is very heavily doped). Thus the excited electron loses energy to the lattice in scattering events until its velocity reaches the thermal equilibrium velocity of other conduction band electrons. The electron and hole created by this absorption process are *excess carriers*; since they are out of balance with their environment, they must eventually recombine. While the excess carriers exist in their respective bands, however, they are free to contribute to the conductivity of the material.

A photon with energy less than E_g is unable to excite an electron from the valence band to the conduction band. Thus in a pure semiconductor, there is negligible absorption of photons with $hv < E_g$. This explains why some materials are transparent in certain wavelength ranges. We are able to "see through" certain insulators, such as a good NaCl crystal, because a large energy gap containing no electron states exists in the material. If the band gap is about 2 eV wide, only long wavelengths (infrared) and the red part of the visible spectrum are transmitted; on the other hand, a band gap of about 3 eV allows infrared and the entire visible spectrum to be transmitted.

If a beam of photons with $hv > E_g$ falls on a semiconductor, there will be some predictable amount of absorption, determined by the properties of the material. We would expect the ratio of transmitted to incident light intensity to depend on the photon wavelength and the thickness of the sample. To calculate this dependence, let us assume that a photon beam of intensity I_0 (photons/cm^2-s) is directed at a sample of thickness l (Fig. 4–2). The beam contains only photons of wavelength λ, selected by a monochromator. As the beam passes through the sample, its intensity at a distance x from the surface can be calculated by considering the probability of absorption within any

Figure 4–2
Optical absorption
experiment.

Figure 4–2
Optical absorption
experiment.

increment dx. Since a photon which has survived to x without absorption has no memory of how far it has traveled, its probability of absorption in any dx is constant. Thus the degradation of the intensity, $d\mathbf{I}(x)/dx$, is proportional to the intensity remaining at x:

$$-\frac{d\mathbf{I}(x)}{dx} = \alpha\mathbf{I}(x) \tag{4–1}$$

The solution to this equation is

$$\mathbf{I}(x) = \mathbf{I}_0 e^{-\alpha x} \tag{4–2}$$

and the intensity of light transmitted through the sample thickness l is

$$\mathbf{I}_t = \mathbf{I}_0 e^{-\alpha l} \tag{4–3}$$

The coefficient α is called the *absorption coefficient* and has units of cm^{-1}. This coefficient will of course vary with the photon wavelength and with the material. In a typical plot of α vs. wavelength (Fig. 4–3), there is negligible absorption at long wavelengths ($h\nu$ small) and considerable absorption of photons with energies larger than E_g. According to Eq. (2–2), the relation between photon energy and wavelength is $E = hc/\lambda$. If E is given in electron volts and λ in micrometers, this becomes $E = 1.24/\lambda$.

Figure 4–4 indicates the band gap energies of some of the common semiconductors, relative to the visible, infrared, and ultraviolet portions of the spectrum. We observe that GaAs, Si, Ge, and InSb lie outside the visible region, in the infrared. Other semiconductors, such as GaP and CdS, have band gaps wide enough to pass photons in the visible range. It is important to note here that a semiconductor absorbs photons with energies equal to the band gap, *or larger*. Thus Si absorbs not only band gap light ($\sim$1 μm) but also shorter wavelengths, including those in the visible part of the spectrum.

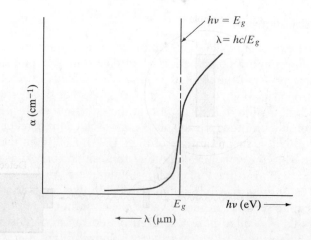

Figure 4–3
Dependence of optical absorption coefficient α for a semiconductor on the wavelength of incident light.

Figure 4–4
Band gaps of some common semiconductors relative to the optical spectrum.

When electron–hole pairs are generated in a semiconductor, or when carriers are excited into higher impurity levels from which they fall to their equilibrium states, light can be given off by the material. Many of the semiconductors are well suited for light emission, particularly the compound semiconductors with direct band gaps. The general property of light emission is called *luminescence*.[2] This overall category can be subdivided according to the excitation mechanism: If carriers are excited by photon absorption, the radiation resulting from the recombination of the excited carriers is called *photoluminescence*; if the excited carriers are created by high-energy electron bombardment of the material, the mechanism is called *cathodoluminescence*; if the excitation occurs by the introduction of current into the sample, the resulting luminescence is called *electroluminescence*. Other types of excitation are possible, but these three are the most important for device applications.

4.2 LUMINESCENCE

[2]The emission processes considered here should not be confused with radiation due to incandescence which occurs in heated materials. The various luminescent mechanisms can be considered "cold" processes as compared to the "hot" process of incandescence, which increases with temperature. In fact, most luminescent processes become more efficient as the temperature is lowered.

4.2.1 Photoluminescence

The simplest example of light emission from a semiconductor occurs for direct excitation and recombination of an electron–hole pair (EHP), as depicted in Fig. 3–5a. If the recombination occurs directly rather than via a defect level, band gap light is given off in the process. For steady state excitation, the recombination of EHPs occurs at the same rate as the generation, and one photon is emitted for each photon absorbed. Direct recombination is a fast process; the mean lifetime of the EHP is usually on the order of 10^{-8} s or less. Thus the emission of photons stops within approximately 10^{-8} s after the excitation is turned off. Such fast luminescent processes are often referred to as *fluorescence*. In some materials, however, emission continues for periods up to seconds or minutes after the excitation is removed. These slow processes are called *phosphorescence,* and the materials are called *phosphors*. An example of a slow process is shown in Fig. 4–5. This material contains a defect level (perhaps due to an impurity) in the band gap which has a strong tendency to temporarily capture (*trap*) electrons from the conduction band. The events depicted in the figure are as follows: (a) An incoming photon with $h\nu_1 > E_g$ is absorbed, creating an EHP; (b) the excited electron gives up energy to the lattice by scattering until it nears the bottom of the conduction band; (c) the electron is *trapped* by the impurity level E_t and remains trapped until it can be thermally reexcited to the conduction band (d); (e) finally direct recombination occurs as the electron falls to an empty state in the valence band, giving off a photon ($h\nu_2$) of approximately the band gap energy. The delay time between excitation and recombination can be relatively long if the probability of thermal reexcitation from the trap (d) is small. Even longer delay times result if the electron is retrapped several times before recombination. If the trapping probability is greater than the probability of recombination, an electron may make several trips between the trap and the conduction band before recombination finally occurs. In such material the emission of phosphorescent light persists for a relatively long time after the excitation is removed.

Figure 4–5
Excitation and recombination mechanisms in photoluminescence with a trapping level for electrons.

The color of light emitted by a phosphor such as ZnS depends primarily on the impurities present, since many radiative transitions involve impurity levels within the band gap. This selection of colors is particularly useful in the fabrication of a color television screen.

One of the most common examples of photoluminescence is the fluorescent lamp. Typically such a lamp is composed of a glass tube filled with gas (e.g., a mixture of argon and mercury), with a fluorescent coating on the inside of the tube. When an electric discharge is induced between electrodes in the tube, the excited atoms of the gas emit photons, largely in the visible and ultraviolet regions of the spectrum. This light is absorbed by the luminescent coating, and the visible photons are emitted. The efficiency of such a lamp is considerably better than that of an incandescent bulb, and the wavelength mixture in light given off can be adjusted by proper selection of the fluorescent material.

A 0.46-μm-thick sample of GaAs is illuminated with monochromatic light of $hv = 2\,\text{eV}$. The absorption coefficient α is $5 \times 10^4\,\text{cm}^{-1}$. The power incident on the sample is 10 mW.

EXAMPLE 4–1

(a) Find the total energy absorbed by the sample per second (J/s).

(b) Find the rate of excess thermal energy given up by the electrons to the lattice before recombination (J/s).

(c) Find the number of photons per second given off from recombination events, assuming perfect quantum efficiency.

(a) From Eq. (4–3),

SOLUTION

$$I_t = I_0 e^{-\alpha l} = 10^{-2}\,\exp(-5 \times 10^4 \times 0.46 \times 10^{-4})$$

$$= 10^{-2} e^{-2.3} = 10^{-3}\,\text{W}$$

2 eV

E_c

$hv \simeq 1.43\,\text{eV}$

E_v

Figure 4–6
Excitation and band-to-band recombination leading to photoluminescence.

Thus the absorbed power is

$$10 - 1 = 9\,\text{mW} = 9 \times 10^{-3}\,\text{J/s}$$

(b) The fraction of each photon energy unit which is converted to heat is

$$\frac{2 - 1.43}{2} = 0.285$$

Thus the amount of energy converted to heat per second is

$$0.285 \times 9 \times 10^{-3} = 2.57 \times 10^{-3}\,\text{J/s}$$

(c) Assuming one emitted photon for each photon absorbed (perfect quantum efficiency), we have

$$\frac{9 \times 10^{-3}\,\text{J/s}}{1.6 \times 10^{-19}\,\text{J/eV} \times 2\,\text{eV/photon}} = 2.81 \times 10^{16}\,\text{photons/s}$$

Alternative solution: Recombination radiation accounts for $9 - 2.57 = 6.43$ mW at 1.43 eV/photon.

$$\frac{6.43 \times 10^{-3}}{1.6 \times 10^{-19} \times 1.43} = 2.81 \times 10^{16}\,\text{photons/s}$$

4.2.2 Electroluminescence

There are many ways by which electrical energy can be used to generate photon emission in a solid. In LEDs an electric current causes the injection of minority carriers into regions of the crystal where they can recombine with majority carriers, resulting in the emission of recombination radiation. This important effect (*injection electroluminescence*) will be discussed in Chapter 8 in terms of p-n junction theory.

The first electroluminescent effect to be observed was the emission of photons by certain phosphors in an alternating electric field (the Destriau effect). In this device, a phosphor powder such as ZnS is held in a binder material (often a plastic) of a high dielectric constant. When an a-c electric field is applied, light is given off by the phosphor. Such cells can be useful as lighting panels, although their efficiency has thus far been too low for most applications and their reliability is poor.

4.3
CARRIER LIFETIME
AND PHOTO-
CONDUCTIVITY

When excess electrons and holes are created in a semiconductor, there is a corresponding increase in the conductivity of the sample as indicated by Eq. (3–43). If the excess carriers arise from optical luminescence, the resulting increase in conductivity is called *photoconductivity*. This is an important effect, with useful applications in the analysis of semiconductor materials and in the operation of several types of devices. In this section we shall examine the mechanisms by which excess electrons and holes recombine and apply the recombination kinetics to the analysis of photoconductive devices. However, the importance of recombination is not limited to cases in which the excess carriers are created optically. In fact, virtually every semiconductor device depends in some way on the recombination of excess electrons and holes. Therefore, the concepts developed in this section will be used extensively in the analyses of diodes, transistors, lasers, and other devices in later chapters.

4.3.1 Direct Recombination of Electrons and Holes

It was pointed out in Section 3.1.4 that electrons in the conduction band of a semiconductor may make transitions to the valence band (i.e., recombine with holes in the valence band) either directly or indirectly. In direct recombination, an excess population of electrons and holes decays by electrons falling from the conduction band to empty states (holes) in the valence band. Energy lost by an electron in making the transition is given up as a photon. Direct recombination occurs *spontaneously*; that is, the probability that an electron and a hole will recombine is constant in time. As in the case of carrier scattering, this constant probability leads us to expect an exponential solution for the decay of the excess carriers. In this case the rate of decay of electrons at any time t is proportional to the number of electrons remaining at t and the number of holes, with some constant of proportionality for recombination, α_r. The *net* rate of change in the conduction band electron concentration is the thermal generation rate $\alpha_r n_i^2$ from Eq. (3–7) minus the recombination rate

$$\frac{dn(t)}{dt} = \alpha_r n_i^2 - \alpha_r n(t) p(t) \tag{4-4}$$

Let us assume the excess electron–hole population is created at $t = 0$, for example by a short flash of light, and the initial excess electron and hole concentrations Δn and Δp are equal.[3] Then as the electrons and holes recombine in pairs, the instantaneous concentrations of excess carriers $\Delta n(t)$ and $\Delta p(t)$ are also equal. Thus we can write the total concentrations of Eq. (4–4) in terms of the equilibrium values n_0 and p_0 and the excess carrier concentrations $\delta n(t) = \delta p(t)$. Using Eq. (3–24) we have

$$\frac{d\delta n(t)}{dt} = \alpha_r n_i^2 - \alpha_r [n_0 + \delta n(t)][p_0 + \delta p(t)]$$

$$= -\alpha_r [(n_0 + p_0)\delta n(t) + \delta n^2(t)] \tag{4-5}$$

---

[3]We will use $\delta n(t)$ and $\delta p(t)$ to mean instantaneous excess carrier concentrations, and Δn, Δp for their values at $t = 0$. Later we will use similar symbolism for spatial distributions, such as $\delta n(x)$ and $\Delta n(x = 0)$.

This nonlinear equation would be difficult to solve in its present form. Fortunately, it can be simplified for the case of low-level injection. If the excess carrier concentrations are small, we can neglect the Δn^2 term. Furthermore, if the material is extrinsic, we can usually neglect the term representing the equilibrium minority carriers. For example, if the material is p-type ($p_0 \gg n_0$), Eq. (4–5) becomes

$$\frac{d\delta n(t)}{dt} = -\alpha_r p_0 \delta n(t) \tag{4–6}$$

The solution to this equation is an exponential decay from the original excess carrier concentration Δn:

$$\delta n(t) = \Delta n e^{-\alpha_r p_0 t} = \Delta n e^{-t/\tau_n} \tag{4–7}$$

Excess electrons in a p-type semiconductor recombine with a decay constant $\tau_n = (\alpha_r p_0)^{-1}$, called the *recombination lifetime*. Since the calculation is made in terms of the minority carriers, τ_n is often called the *minority carrier lifetime*. The decay of excess holes in n-type material occurs with $\tau_p = (\alpha_r n_0)^{-1}$. In the case of direct recombination, the excess majority carriers decay at exactly the same rate as the minority carriers.

There is a large percentage change in the minority carrier electron concentration in Example 4–2 and a small percentage change in the majority hole concentration. Basically, the approximations of extrinsic material and low-level injection allow us to represent $n(t)$ in Eq. (4–4) by the excess concentration $\delta n(t)$ and $p(t)$ by the equilibrium value p_0. Figure 4-7 indicates that this is a good approximation for the example. A more general expression for the carrier lifetime is

$$\tau_n = \frac{1}{\alpha_r(n_0 + p_0)} \tag{4–8}$$

This expression is valid for n- or p-type material if the injection level is low.

EXAMPLE 4–2   A numerical example may be helpful in visualizing the approximations made in the analysis of direct recombination. Let us assume a sample of GaAs is doped with 10^{15} acceptors/cm^3. The intrinsic carrier concentration of GaAs is approximately 10^6 cm^{-3}; thus the minority electron concentration is $n_0 = n_i^2/p_0 = 10^{-3}$ cm^{-3}. Certainly the approximation of $p_0 \gg n_0$ is valid in this case. Now if 10^{14} EHP/cm^3 are created at $t = 0$, we can calculate the decay of these carriers in time. The approximation of $\delta n \ll p_0$ is reasonable, as Fig. 4–7 indicates. This figure shows the decay in time of the excess populations for a carrier recombination lifetime of $\tau_n = \tau_p = 10^{-8}$ s.

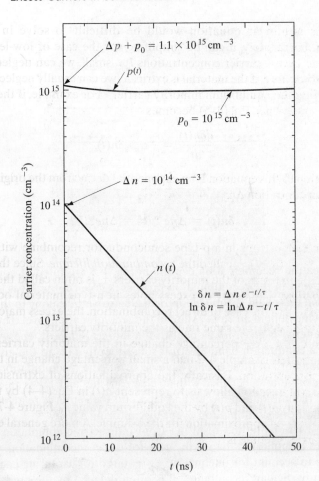

$\Delta p + p_0 = 1.1 \times 10^{15} \text{ cm}^{-3}$

$p(t)$

10^{15}

$p_0 = 10^{15} \text{ cm}^{-3}$

$\Delta n = 10^{14} \text{ cm}^{-3}$

10^{14}

Carrier concentration (cm^{-3})

$n(t)$

$\delta n = \Delta n \, e^{-t/\tau}$
$\ln \delta n = \ln \Delta n - t/\tau$

10^{13}

10^{12}

0   10   20   30   40   50

t (ns)

Figure 4–7

Decay of excess electrons and holes by recombination, for $\Delta n = \Delta p = 0.1 p_0$, with n_0 negligible, and $\tau = 10$ ns (Example 4–2). The exponential decay of $\delta n(t)$ is linear on this semilogarithmic graph.

4.3.2 Indirect Recombination; Trapping

In column IV semiconductors and in certain compounds, the probability of direct electron–hole recombination is very small (Appendix III). There is some band gap light given off by materials such as Si and Ge during recombination, but this radiation is very weak and may be detected only by sensitive equipment. The vast majority of the recombination events in indirect materials occur via *recombination levels* within the band gap, and the resulting energy loss by recombining electrons is usually given up to the lattice as heat rather than by the emission of photons. Any impurity or lattice defect can serve as a recombination center if it is capable of receiving a carrier of one type and subsequently capturing the opposite type of carrier, thereby annihilating the pair. For example, Fig. 4–8 illustrates a recombination level E_r which is below E_F at equilibrium and therefore is substantially filled with electrons. When excess electrons and holes are created in this material, each EHP recombines at E_r in two steps: (a) hole capture and (b) electron capture.

Figure 4–8
Capture processes
at a recombination
level: (a) hole
capture at a filled
recombination
center; (b) electron
capture at an
empty center.

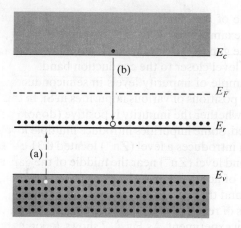

Since the recombination centers in Fig. 4–8 are filled at equilibrium, the first event in the recombination process is hole capture. It is important to note that this event is equivalent to an electron at E_r falling to the valence band, leaving behind an empty state in the recombination level. Thus in hole capture, energy is *given up* as heat to the lattice. Similarly, energy is given up when a conduction band electron subsequently falls to the empty state in E_r. When both of these events have occurred, the recombination center is back to its original state (filled with an electron), but an EHP is missing. Thus one EHP recombination has taken place, and the center is ready to participate in another recombination event by capturing a hole.

The carrier lifetime resulting from indirect recombination is somewhat more complicated than is the case for direct recombination, since it is necessary to account for unequal times required for capturing each type of carrier. In particular, recombination is often delayed by the tendency for a captured carrier to be thermally reexcited to its original band before capture of the opposite type of carrier can occur (Section 4.2.1). For example, if electron capture (b) does not follow immediately after hole capture (a) in Fig. 4–8, the hole may be thermally reexcited to the valence band. Energy is required for this process, which is equivalent to a valence band electron being raised to the empty state in the recombination level. This process delays the recombination, since the hole must be captured again before recombination can be completed.

When a carrier is trapped temporarily at a center and then is reexcited without recombination taking place, the process is often called *temporary trapping*. Although the nomenclature varies somewhat, it is common to refer to an impurity or defect center as a *trapping center* (or simply *trap*) if, after capture of one type of carrier, the most probable next event is reexcitation. If the most probable next event is capture of the opposite type of carrier, the center is predominately a recombination center. The recombination can be slow or fast, depending on the average time the first carrier is held before the second carrier is captured. In general, trapping levels located deep in the band gap are slower in releasing trapped carriers than are the levels located near one of the bands. This results from the fact that more energy is required, for example, to reexcite a trapped electron from a center near the middle of the gap to the conduction band than is required to reexcite an electron from a level closer to the conduction band.

As an example of impurity levels in semiconductors, Fig. 4–9[4] shows the energy level positions of various impurities in Si. In this diagram a superscript indicates whether the impurity is positive (donor) or negative (acceptor) when ionized. Some impurities introduce multiple levels in the band gap; for example, Zn introduces a level (Zn^-) located 0.31 eV above the valence band and a second level ($Zn^=$) near the middle of the gap. Each Zn impurity atom is capable of accepting two electrons from the semiconductor, one in the lower level and then one in the upper level.

The effects of recombination and trapping can be measured by a *photoconductive decay* experiment. As Fig. 4–7 shows, a population of excess electrons and holes disappears with a decay constant characteristic of the particular recombination process. The conductivity of the sample during the decay is

$$\sigma(t) = q[n(t)\mu_n + p(t)\mu_p] \tag{4-9}$$

Therefore, the time dependence of the carrier concentrations can be monitored by recording the sample resistance as a function of time. A typical

Figure 4–9
Energy levels of impurities in Si. The energies are measured from the nearest band edge (E_v or E_c); donor levels are designated by a plus sign and acceptors by a minus sign.

[4]References: S. M. Sze and J. C. Irvin, "Resistivity, Mobility, and Impurity Levels in GaAs, Ge and Si at 300 K," *Solid State Electronics*, vol. 11, pp. 599–602 (June 1968); E. Schibli and A. G. Milnes, "Deep Impurities in Silicon," *Materials Science and Engineering*, vol. 2, pp. 173–180 (1967).

Figure 4–10
Experimental
arrangement for
photoconductive
decay measure-
ments, and a typi-
cal oscilloscope
trace.

experimental arrangement is shown schematically in Fig. 4–10. A source of
short pulses of light is required, along with an oscilloscope for displaying
the sample voltage as the resistance varies. Microsecond light pulses can be
obtained by periodically discharging a capacitor through a flash tube containing a gas such as xenon. For shorter pulses, special techniques such as the
use of a pulsed laser must be used.

4.3.3 Steady State Carrier Generation; Quasi-Fermi Levels

In the previous discussion we emphasized the transient decay of an excess
EHP population. However, the various recombination mechanisms are also
important in a sample at thermal equilibrium or with a steady state EHP
generation–recombination (G–R) balance.[5] For example, a semiconductor
at equilibrium experiences thermal generation of EHPs at a rate $g(T) = g_i$
described by Eq. (3–7). This generation is balanced by the recombination rate
so that the equilibrium concentrations of carriers n_0 and p_0 are maintained:

$$g(T) = \alpha_r n_i^2 = \alpha_r n_0 p_0 \qquad (4\text{–}10)$$

This equilibrium rate balance can include generation from defect centers as
well as band-to-band generation.

If a steady light is shone on the sample, an optical generation rate g_{op}
will be added to the thermal generation, and the carrier concentrations n and
p will increase to new steady state values. We can write the balance between
generation and recombination in terms of the equilibrium carrier concentrations and the departures from equilibrium δn and δp:

$$g(T) + g_{op} = \alpha_r np = \alpha_r(n_0 + \delta n)(p_0 + \delta p) \qquad (4\text{–}11)$$

For steady state recombination and no trapping, $\Delta n = \Delta p$; thus
Eq. (4–11) becomes

$$g(T) + g_{op} = \alpha_r n_0 p_0 + \alpha_r[(n_0 + p_0)\delta n + \delta n^2] \qquad (4\text{–}12)$$

---

[5]The term *equilibrium* refers to a condition of no external excitation except for temperature, and no net
motion of charge (e.g., a sample at a constant temperature, in the dark, with no fields applied). *Steady
state* refers to a non-equilibrium condition in which all processes are constant and are balanced by
opposing processes (e.g., a sample with a constant current or a constant optical generation of EHPs just
balanced by recombination).

The term $\alpha_r n_0 p_0$ is just equal to the thermal generation rate $g(T)$. Thus, neglecting the δn^2 term for low-level excitation, we can rewrite Eq. (4-12) as

$$g_{op} = \alpha_r(n_0 + p_0)\delta n = \frac{\delta n}{\tau_n} \qquad (4\text{-}13)$$

The excess carrier concentration can be written as

$$\delta n = \delta p = g_{op}\tau_n \qquad (4\text{-}14)$$

More general expressions are given in Eq. (4-16), which allow for the case $\tau_p \neq \tau_n$, when trapping is present.

EXAMPLE 4-3

As a numerical example, let us assume that 10^{13} EHP/cm^3 are created optically every microsecond in a Si sample with $n_0 = 10^{14}$ cm^{-3} and $\tau_n = \tau_p = 2$ μs. The steady state excess electron (or hole) concentration is then 2×10^{13} cm^{-3} from Eq. (4-14). While the percentage change in the majority electron concentration is small, the minority carrier concentration changes from

$$p_0 = n_i^2/n_0 = (2.25 \times 10^{20})/10^{14} = 2.25 \times 10^6 \text{ cm}^{-3} \quad (equilibrium)$$

to

$$p = 2 \times 10^{13} \text{ cm}^{-3} \qquad (steady\ state)$$

Note that the equilibrium equation $n_0 p_0 = n_i^2$ cannot be used with the subscripts removed; that is, $np \neq n_i^2$ when excess carriers are present.

The steady state electron concentration is

$$n = n_0 + \delta n = 1.2 \times 10^{14} = (1.5 \times 10^{10})e^{(F_n - E_i)/0.0259}$$

where $kT \simeq 0.0259$ eV at room temperature. Thus the electron quasi-Fermi level position $F_n - E_i$ is found from

$$F_n - E_i = 0.0259 \ln(8 \times 10^3) = 0.233 \text{ eV}$$

and F_n lies 0.233 eV above the intrinsic level. By a similar calculation, the hole quasi-Fermi level lies 0.186 eV below E_i (Fig. 4-11). In this example, the equilibrium Fermi level is $0.0259 \ln(6.67 \times 10^3) = 0.228$ eV above the intrinsic level.

Figure 4-11
Quasi-Fermi levels F_n and F_p for a Si sample with $n_0 = 10^{14}$ cm^{-3}, $\tau_p = 2$ μs, and $g_{op} = 10^{19}$ EHP/cm^3-s (Example 4-4).

It is often desirable to refer to the steady state electron and hole concentrations in terms of Fermi levels, which can be included in band diagrams for various devices. The Fermi level E_F used in Eq. (3–25) is meaningful only when no excess carriers are present. However, we can write expressions for the steady state concentrations in the same *form* as the equilibrium expressions by defining separate *quasi-Fermi levels* F_n and F_p for electrons and holes. The resulting carrier concentration equations

$$\begin{aligned} n &= n_i e^{(F_n - E_i)/kT} \\ p &= n_i e^{(E_i - F_p)/kT} \end{aligned} \qquad (4\text{--}15)$$

can be considered as defining relations for the quasi-Fermi levels.[6]

The quasi-Fermi levels of Fig. 4–11 illustrate dramatically the deviation from equilibrium caused by the optical excitation; the steady state F_n is only slightly above the equilibrium E_F, whereas F_p is greatly displaced below E_F. From the figure it is obvious that the excitation causes a large percentage change in minority carrier hole concentration and a relatively small change in the electron concentration.

In summary, the quasi-Fermi levels F_n and F_p are the steady state analogues of the equilibrium Fermi level E_F. When excess carriers are present, the deviations of F_n and F_p from E_F indicate how far the electron and hole populations are from the equilibrium values n_0 and p_0. A given concentration of excess EHPs causes a large shift in the minority carrier quasi-Fermi level compared with that for the majority carriers. The separation of the quasi-Fermi levels $F_n - F_p$ is a direct measure of the deviation from equilibrium (at equilibrium $F_n = F_p = E_F$). The concept of quasi-Fermi levels is very useful in visualizing minority and majority carrier concentrations in devices where these quantities vary with position.

4.3.4 Photoconductive Devices

There are a number of applications for devices which change their resistance when exposed to light. For example, such light detectors can be used in the home to control automatic night lights which turn on at dusk and turn off at dawn. They can also be used to measure illumination levels, as in exposure meters for cameras. Many systems include a light beam aimed at the photoconductor, which signals the presence of an object between the source and detector. Such systems are useful in moving-object counters, burglar alarms, and many other applications. Detectors are used in optical signaling systems in which information is transmitted by a light beam and is received at a photoconductive cell.

Considerations in choosing a photoconductor for a given application include the sensitive wavelength range, time response, and optical sensitivity of the material. In general, semiconductors are most sensitive to photons

---

[6]In some texts the quasi-Fermi level is called *IMREF*, which is Fermi spelled backward.

with energies equal to the band gap or slightly more energetic than band gap. Less energetic photons are not absorbed, and photons with $h\nu \gg E_g$ are absorbed at the surface and contribute little to the bulk conductivity. Therefore, the table of band gaps (Appendix III) indicates the photon energies to which most semiconductor photodetectors respond. For example, CdS ($E_g = 2.42$ eV) is commonly used as a photoconductor in the visible range, and narrow-gap materials such as Ge (0.67 eV) and InSb (0.18 eV) are useful in the infrared portion of the spectrum. Some photoconductors respond to excitations of carriers from impurity levels within the band gap and therefore are sensitive to photons of less than band gap energy.

The optical sensitivity of a photoconductor can be evaluated by examining the steady state excess carrier concentrations generated by an optical generation rate g_{op}. If the mean time each carrier spends in its respective band before capture is τ_n and τ_p, we have

$$\delta n = \tau_n g_{op} \quad \text{and} \quad \delta p = \tau_p g_{op} \qquad (4-16)$$

and the photoconductivity change is

$$\Delta\sigma = q g_{op}(\tau_n \mu_n + \tau_p \mu_p) \qquad (4-17)$$

For simple recombination, τ_n and τ_p will be equal. If trapping is present, however, one of the carriers may spend little time in its band before being trapped. From Eq. (4–17) it is obvious that for maximum photoconductive response, we want high mobilities and long lifetimes. Some semiconductors are especially good candidates for photoconductive devices because of their high mobility; for example, InSb has an electron mobility of about 10^5 cm^2/V-s and therefore is used as a sensitive infrared detector in many applications.

The time response of a photoconductive cell is limited by the recombination times, the degree of carrier trapping, and the time required for carriers to drift through the device in an electric field. Often these properties can be adjusted by proper choice of material and device geometry, but in some cases improvements in response time are made at the expense of sensitivity. For example, the drift time can be reduced by making the device short, but this substantially reduces the responsive area of the device. In addition, it is often desirable that the device have a large dark resistance, and for this reason, shortening the length may not be practical. There is usually a compromise between sensitivity, response time, dark resistance, and other requirements in choosing a device for a particular application.

When excess carriers are created nonuniformly in a semiconductor, the electron and hole concentrations vary with position in the sample. Any such spatial variation (*gradient*) in n and p calls for a net motion of the carriers from regions of high carrier concentration to regions of low carrier concentration. This type of motion is called *diffusion* and represents an important charge transport process in semiconductors. The two basic processes

**4.4
DIFFUSION OF
CARRIERS**

of current conduction are diffusion due to a carrier gradient and drift in an electric field.

4.4.1 Diffusion Processes

When a bottle of perfume is opened in one corner of a closed room, the scent is soon detected throughout the room. If there is no convection or other net motion of air, the scent spreads by diffusion. The diffusion is the natural result of the *random motion* of the individual molecules. Consider, for example, a volume of arbitrary shape with scented air molecules inside and unscented molecules outside the volume. All the molecules undergo random thermal motion and collisions with other molecules. Thus each molecule moves in an arbitrary direction until it collides with another air molecule, after which it moves in a new direction. If the motion is truly random, a molecule at the edge of the volume has equal probabilities of moving into or out of the volume on its next step (assuming the curvature of the surface is negligible on the molecular scale). Therefore, after a mean free time $\bar{t}$, half the molecules at the edge will have moved into the volume and half will have moved out of the volume. The net effect is that the volume containing scented molecules has increased. This process will continue until the molecules are uniformly distributed in the room. Only then will a given volume gain as many molecules as it loses in a given time. In other words, net diffusion will continue as long as gradients exist in the distribution of scented molecules.

Carriers in a semiconductor diffuse in a carrier gradient by random thermal motion and scattering from the lattice and impurities. For example, a pulse of excess electrons injected at $x = 0$ at time $t = 0$ will spread out in time as shown in Fig. 4–12. Initially, the excess electrons are concentrated at

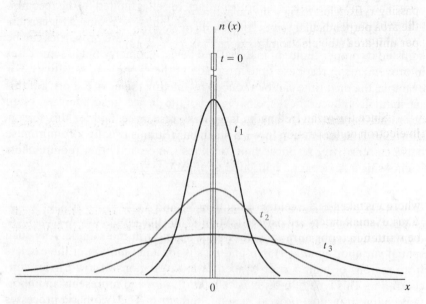

Figure 4–12
Spreading of a pulse of electrons by diffusion.

Figure 4–13
An arbitrary
electron
concentration
gradient in one
dimension: (a)
division of $n(x)$
into segments of
length equal to a
mean free path
for the electrons;
(b) expanded
view of two of the
segments centered
at x_0.

$x = 0$; as time passes, however, electrons diffuse to regions of low electron concentration until finally $n(x)$ is constant.

We can calculate the rate at which the electrons diffuse in a one-dimensional problem by considering an arbitrary distribution $n(x)$ such as Fig. 4–13a. Since the mean free path $\bar{l}$ between collisions is a small incremental distance, we can divide x into segments $\bar{l}$ wide, with $n(x)$ evaluated at the center of each segment (Fig. 4–13b).

The electrons in segment (1) to the left of x_0 in Fig. 4–13b have equal chances of moving left or right, and in a mean free time $\bar{t}$ one-half of them will move into segment (2). The same is true of electrons within one mean free path of x_0 to the right; one-half of these electrons will move through x_0 from right to left in a mean free time. Therefore, the *net* number of electrons passing x_0 from left to right in one mean free time is $\frac{1}{2}(n_1\bar{l}A) - \frac{1}{2}(n_2\bar{l}A)$, where the area perpendicular to x is A. The rate of electron flow in the $+x$-direction per unit area (the electron flux density ϕ_n) is given by

$$\phi_n(x_0) = \frac{\bar{l}}{2\bar{t}}(n_1 - n_2) \qquad (4\text{–}18)$$

Since the mean free path $\bar{l}$ is a small differential length, the difference in electron concentration $(n_1 - n_2)$ can be written as

$$n_1 - n_2 = \frac{n(x) - n(x + \Delta x)}{\Delta x}\bar{l} \qquad (4\text{–}19)$$

where x is taken at the center of segment (1) and $\Delta x = \bar{l}$. In the limit of small Δx (i.e., small mean free path $\bar{l}$ between scattering collisions), Eq. (4–18) can be written in terms of the carrier gradient $dn(x)/dx$:

$$\phi_n(x) = \frac{\bar{l}^2}{2\bar{t}} \lim_{\Delta x \to 0} \frac{n(x) - n(x + \Delta x)}{\Delta x} = \frac{-\bar{l}^2}{2\bar{t}} \frac{dn(x)}{dx} \qquad (4\text{–}20)$$

The quantity $\bar{l}^2/2\bar{t}$ is called the *electron diffusion coefficient*[7] D_n, with units cm^2/s. The minus sign in Eq. (4–20) arises from the definition of the derivative; it simply indicates that the net motion of electrons due to diffusion is in the direction of *decreasing* electron concentration. This is the result we expect, since net diffusion occurs from regions of high particle concentration to regions of low particle concentration. By identical arguments, we can show that holes in a hole concentration gradient move with a diffusion coefficient D_p. Thus

$$\phi_n(x) = -D_n\frac{dn(x)}{dx} \tag{4–21a}$$

$$\phi_p(x) = -D_p\frac{dp(x)}{dx} \tag{4–21b}$$

The diffusion current crossing a unit area (the current density) is the particle flux density multiplied by the charge of the carrier:

$$J_n(\text{diff.}) = -(-q)D_n\frac{dn(x)}{dx} = +qD_n\frac{dn(x)}{dx} \tag{4–22a}$$

$$J_p(\text{diff.}) = -(+q)D_p\frac{dp(x)}{dx} = -qD_p\frac{dp(x)}{dx} \tag{4–22b}$$

It is important to note that electrons and holes move together in a carrier gradient [Eqs. (4–21)], but the resulting currents are in opposite directions [Eqs. (4–22)] because of the opposite charge of electrons and holes.

4.4.2 Diffusion and Drift of Carriers; Built-in Fields

If an electric field is present in addition to the carrier gradient, the current densities will each have a drift component and a diffusion component

$$J_n(x) = q\mu_n n(x)\mathscr{E}(x) + qD_n\frac{dn(x)}{dx} \tag{4–23a}$$

$$\underset{\text{drift}}{\qquad\qquad} \underset{\text{diffusion}}{\qquad\qquad}$$

$$J_p(x) = q\mu_p p(x)\mathscr{E}(x) - qD_p\frac{dp(x)}{dx} \tag{4–23b}$$

and the total current density is the sum of the contributions due to electrons and holes:

$$J(x) = J_n(x) + J_p(x) \tag{4–24}$$

---

[7]If motion in three dimensions were included, the diffusion would be smaller in the x-direction. Actually, the diffusion coefficient should be calculated from the true energy distributions and scattering mechanisms. Diffusion coefficients are usually determined experimentally for a particular material, as described in Section 4.4.5.

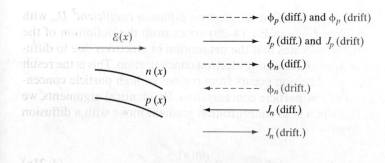

$\mathcal{E}(x)$

$n(x)$

$p(x)$

------→ ϕ_p (diff.) and ϕ_p (drift)

———→ J_p (diff.) and J_p (drift)

------→ ϕ_n (diff.)

←------ ϕ_n (drift.)

←——— J_n (diff.)

———→ J_n (drift.)

Figure 4–14
Drift and diffusion directions for electrons and holes in a carrier gradient and an electric field. Particle flow directions are indicated by dashed arrows, and the resulting currents are indicated by solid arrows.

We can best visualize the relation between the particle flow and the current of Eqs. (4–23) by considering a diagram such as shown in Fig. 4–14. In this figure an electric field is assumed to be in the x-direction, along with carrier distributions $n(x)$ and $p(x)$ which decrease with increasing x. Thus the derivatives in Eqs. (4–21) are negative, and diffusion takes place in the $+x$-direction. The resulting electron and hole diffusion currents [J_n (diff.) and J_p (diff.)] are in opposite directions, according to Eqs. (4–22). Holes drift in the direction of the electric field [ϕ_p (drift)], whereas electrons drift in the opposite direction because of their negative charge. The resulting drift current is in the $+x$-direction in each case. Note that the drift and diffusion components of the current are additive for holes when the field is in the direction of decreasing hole concentration, whereas the two components are subtractive for electrons under similar conditions. The total current may be due primarily to the flow of electrons or holes, depending on the relative concentrations and the relative magnitudes and directions of electric field and carrier gradients.

An important result of Eqs. (4–23) is that minority carriers can contribute significantly to the current through diffusion. Since the drift terms are proportional to carrier concentration, minority carriers seldom provide much drift current. On the other hand, diffusion current is proportional to the *gradient* of concentration. For example, in n-type material the minority hole concentration p may be many orders of magnitude smaller than the electron concentration n, but the gradient dp/dx may be significant. As a result, minority carrier currents through diffusion can sometimes be as large as majority carrier currents.

In discussing the motion of carriers in an electric field, we should indicate the influence of the field on the energies of electrons in the band diagrams. Assuming an electric field $\mathcal{E}(x)$ in the x-direction, we can draw the energy bands as in Fig. 4–15, to include the change in potential energy of electrons in the field. Since electrons drift in a direction opposite to the field, we expect the potential energy for electrons to increase in the direction of the field, as in Fig. 4–15. The electrostatic potential $\mathcal{V}(x)$ varies in the opposite direction, since it is defined in terms of positive charges and is therefore related to the electron potential energy $E(x)$ displayed in the figure by $\mathcal{V}(x) = E(x)/(-q)$.

Figure 4–15
Energy band
diagram of a
semiconductor
in an electric
field $\mathscr{E}(x)$.

From the definition of electric field,

$$\mathscr{E}(x) = -\frac{dV(x)}{dx} \tag{4–25}$$

we can relate $\mathscr{E}(x)$ to the electron potential energy in the band diagram by choosing some reference in the band for the electrostatic potential. We are interested only in the spatial variation $V(x)$ for Eq. (4–25). Choosing E_i as a convenient reference, we can relate the electric field to this reference by

$$\mathscr{E}(x) = -\frac{dV(x)}{dx} = -\frac{d}{dx}\left[\frac{E_i}{(-q)}\right] = \frac{1}{q}\frac{dE_i}{dx} \tag{4–26}$$

Therefore, the variation of band energies with $\mathscr{E}(x)$ as drawn in Fig. 4–15 is correct. The direction of the slope in the bands relative to $\mathscr{E}$ is simple to remember: Since the diagram indicates electron energies, we know the slope in the bands must be such that electrons drift "downhill" in the field. Therefore, $\mathscr{E}$ points "uphill" in the band diagram.

At equilibrium, no net current flows in a semiconductor. Thus any fluctuation which would begin a diffusion current also sets up an electric field which redistributes carriers by drift. An examination of the requirements for equilibrium indicates that the diffusion coefficient and mobility must be related. Setting Eq. (4–23b) equal to zero for equilibrium, we have

$$\mathscr{E}(x) = \frac{D_p}{\mu_p}\frac{1}{p(x)}\frac{dp(x)}{dx} \tag{4–27}$$

Using Eq. (3–25b) for $p(x)$,

$$\mathscr{E}(x) = \frac{D_p}{\mu_p}\frac{1}{kT}\left(\frac{dE_i}{dx} - \frac{dE_F}{dx}\right) \tag{4–28}$$

Table 4–1 Diffusion coefficient and mobility of electrons and holes for intrinsic semiconductors at 300 K. *Note:* Use Fig. 3–23 for doped semiconductors.

	D_n (cm^2/s)	D_p (cm^2/s)	μ_n (cm^2/V-s)	μ_p (cm^2/V-s)
Ge	100	50	3900	1900
Si	35	12.5	1350	480
GaAs	220	10	8500	400

The equilibrium Fermi level does not vary with x, and the derivative of E_i is given by Eq. (4–26). Thus Eq. (4–28) reduces to

$$\frac{D}{\mu} = \frac{kT}{q} \tag{4–29}$$

This result is obtained for either carrier type. This important equation is called the *Einstein relation*. It allows us to calculate either D or μ from a measurement of the other. Table 4-1 lists typical values of D and μ for several semiconductors at room temperature. It is clear from these values that $D/\mu \simeq 0.026$ V.

An important result of the balance of drift and diffusion at equilibrium is that *built-in* fields accompany gradients in E_i [see Eq. (4–26)]. Such gradients in the bands at equilibrium (E_F constant) can arise when the band gap varies due to changes in alloy composition. More commonly, built-in fields result from doping gradients. For example, a donor distribution $N_d(x)$ causes a gradient in $n_0(x)$, which must be balanced by a built-in electric field $\mathcal{E}(x)$.

4.4.3 Diffusion and Recombination; The Continuity Equation

In the discussion of diffusion of excess carriers, we have thus far neglected the important effects of recombination. These effects must be included in a description of conduction processes, however, since recombination can cause a variation in the carrier distribution. For example, consider a differential length $\Delta(x)$ of a semiconductor sample with area A in the yz-plane (Fig. 4–16). The hole current density leaving the volume, $J_p(x + \Delta x)$, can be larger or smaller than the current density entering, $J_p(x)$, depending on the generation and recombination of carriers taking place within the volume. The net increase in hole concentration per unit time, $\partial p/\partial t$, is the difference between the hole flux per unit volume entering and leaving, minus the recombination rate. We can convert hole current density to hole particle flux density by dividing J_p by q. The current densities are already expressed per unit area; thus dividing $J_p(x)/q$ by $\Delta(x)$ gives the number of carriers per unit volume entering ΔxA per unit time, and $(1/q)J_p(x + \Delta x)/\Delta x$ is the number leaving per unit volume and time:

$$\left.\frac{\partial p}{\partial t}\right|_{x\to x+\Delta x} = \frac{1}{q}\frac{J_p(x) - J_p(x + \Delta x)}{\Delta x} - \frac{\delta p}{\tau_p} \tag{4–30}$$

$$\underset{\text{hole buildup}}{\text{Rate of}} = \underset{\text{tion in } \delta xA \text{ per unit time}}{\text{increase of hole concentra-}} - \underset{\text{rate}}{\text{recombination}}$$

Figure 4–16
Current entering
and leaving a
volume ΔxA.

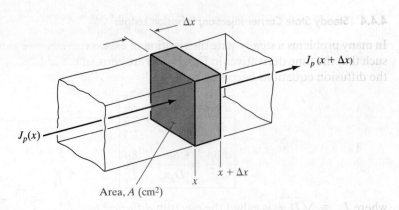

Figure 4–16
Current entering
and leaving a
volume ΔxA.

As Δx approaches zero, we can write the current change in derivative form:

$$\frac{\partial p(x,t)}{\partial t} = \frac{\partial \delta p}{\partial t} = -\frac{1}{q}\frac{\partial J_p}{\partial x} - \frac{\delta p}{\tau_p} \qquad (4\text{–}31a)$$

The expression (4–31a) is called the *continuity equation* for holes. For electrons we can write

$$\frac{\partial \delta n}{\partial t} = \frac{1}{q}\frac{\partial J_n}{\partial x} - \frac{\delta n}{\tau_n} \qquad (4\text{–}31b)$$

since the electronic charge is negative.

When the current is carried strictly by diffusion (negligible drift), we can replace the currents in Eqs. (4–31) by the expressions for diffusion current; for example, for electron diffusion we have

$$J_n(\text{diff.}) = qD_n\frac{\partial \delta n}{\partial x} \qquad (4\text{–}32)$$

Substituting this into Eq. (4–31b) we obtain the *diffusion equation* for electrons,

$$\frac{\partial \delta n}{\partial t} = D_n\frac{\partial^2 \delta n}{\partial x^2} - \frac{\delta n}{\tau_n} \qquad (4\text{–}33a)$$

and similarly for holes,

$$\frac{\partial \delta p}{\partial t} = D_p\frac{\partial^2 \delta p}{\partial x^2} - \frac{\delta p}{\tau_n} \qquad (4\text{–}33b)$$

These equations are useful in solving transient problems of diffusion with recombination. For example, a pulse of electrons in a semiconductor (Fig. 4–12) spreads out by diffusion and disappears by recombination. To solve for the electron distribution in time, $n(x, t)$, we would begin with the diffusion equation, Eq. (4–33a).

4.4.4 Steady State Carrier Injection; Diffusion Length

In many problems a steady state distribution of excess carriers is maintained, such that the time derivatives in Eqs. (4–33) are zero. In the steady state case the diffusion equations become

$$\frac{d^2\delta n}{dx^2} = \frac{\delta n}{D_n \tau_n} \equiv \frac{\delta n}{L_n^2} \tag{4–34a}$$

$$\frac{d^2\delta p}{dx^2} = \frac{\delta p}{D_p \tau_p} \equiv \frac{\delta p}{L_p^2} \tag{4–34b}$$

(steady state)

where $L_n \equiv \sqrt{D_n \tau_n}$ is called the electron *diffusion length* and L_p is the diffusion length for holes. We no longer need partial derivatives, since the time variation is zero for steady state.

The physical significance of the diffusion length can be understood best by an example. Let us assume that excess holes are somehow injected into a semi-infinite semiconductor bar at $x = 0$, and the steady state hole injection maintains a constant excess hole concentration at the injection point $\delta p(x = 0) = \Delta p$. The injected holes diffuse along the bar, recombining with a characteristic lifetime τ_p. In steady state we expect the distribution of excess holes to decay to zero for large values of x, because of the recombination (Fig. 4–17). For this problem we use the steady state diffusion equation for holes, Eq. (4–34b). The solution to this equation has the form

$$\delta p(x) = C_1 e^{x/L_p} + C_2 e^{-x/L_p} \tag{4–35}$$

We can evaluate C_1 and C_2 from the boundary conditions. Since recombination must reduce $\delta p(x)$ to zero for large values of x, $\delta p = 0$ at $x = \infty$ and therefore $C_1 = 0$. Similarly, the condition $\delta p = \Delta p$ at $x = 0$ gives $C_2 = \Delta p$, and the solution is

$$\delta p(x) = \Delta p e^{-x/L_p} \tag{4–36}$$

$$p(x) = p_0 + \Delta p e^{-x/L_p}$$

$$J_p(x) = -q D_p \frac{dp(x)}{dx}$$

$$= q \frac{D_p}{L_p} \delta p(x)$$

Figure 4–17
Injection of holes at $x = 0$, giving a steady state hole distribution $p(x)$ and a resulting diffusion current density $J_p(x)$.

The injected excess hole concentration dies out exponentially in x due to recombination, and the diffusion length L_p represents the distance at which the excess hole distribution is reduced to $1/e$ of its value at the point of injection. We can show that L_p is *the average distance a hole diffuses before recombining.* To calculate an average diffusion length, we must obtain an expression for the probability that an injected hole recombines in a particular interval dx. The probability that a hole injected at $x = 0$ *survives* to x without recombination is $\delta p(x)/\Delta p = \exp(-x/L_p)$, the ratio of the steady state concentrations at x and 0. On the other hand, the probability that a hole at x will *recombine* in the subsequent interval dx is

$$\frac{\delta p(x) - \delta p(x + dx)}{\delta p(x)} = \frac{-(d\delta p(x)/dx)dx}{\delta p(x)} = \frac{1}{L_p}dx \qquad (4\text{--}37)$$

Thus the total probability that a hole injected at $x = 0$ will recombine in a given dx is the product of the two probabilities:

$$\left(e^{-x/L_p}\right)\left(\frac{1}{L_p}dx\right) = \frac{1}{L_p}e^{-x/L_p}dx \qquad (4\text{--}38)$$

Then, using the usual averaging techniques described by Eq. (2–21), the average distance a hole diffuses before recombining is

$$\langle x \rangle = \int_0^\infty x\,\frac{e^{-x/L_p}}{L_p}\,dx = L_p \qquad (4\text{--}39)$$

The steady state distribution of excess holes causes diffusion, and therefore a hole current, in the direction of decreasing concentration. From Eqs. (4–22b) and (4–36) we have

$$J_p(x) = -qD_p\frac{dp}{dx} = -qD_p\frac{d\delta p}{dx} = q\,\frac{D_p}{L_p}\Delta p e^{-x/L_p} = q\,\frac{D_p}{L_p}\delta p(x) \quad (4\text{--}40)$$

Since $p(x) = p_0 + \delta p(x)$, the space derivative involves only the excess concentration. We notice that since $\delta p(x)$ is proportional to its derivative for an exponential distribution, the diffusion current at any x is just proportional to the excess concentration δp at that position.

Although this example seems rather restricted, its usefulness will become apparent in Chapter 5 in the discussion of p-n junctions. The injection of minority carriers across a junction often leads to exponential distributions as in Eq. (4–36), with the resulting diffusion current of Eq. (4–40).

EXAMPLE 4–4   In a very long p-type Si bar with cross-sectional area = 0.5 cm^2 and $N_a = 10^{17}$ cm^{-3}, we inject holes such that the steady state *excess* hole concentration is 5×10^{16} cm^{-3} at $x = 0$. What is the steady state separation between F_p and E_c at $x = 1000$ Å? What is the hole current there? How much is the excess stored hole charge? Assume that $\mu_p = 500 \text{ cm}^2/\text{V-s}$ and $\tau_p = 10^{-10}$ s.

$$D_p = \frac{kT}{q}\mu_p = 0.0259 \times 500 = 12.95 \text{ cm/s}$$

$$L_p = \sqrt{D_p\tau_p} = \sqrt{12.95 \times 10^{-10}} = 3.6 \times 10^{-5} \text{ cm}$$

$$p = p_0 + \Delta p e^{-\frac{x}{L_p}} = 10^{17} + 5 \times 10^{16} e^{-\frac{10^{-5}}{3.6 \times 10^{-5}}}$$

$$= 1.379 \times 10^{17} = n_i e^{(E_i - F_p)/kT} = (1.5 \times 10^{10} \text{ cm}^{-3})e^{(E_i - F_p)/kT}$$

$$E_i - F_p = \left(\ln \frac{1.379 \times 10^{17}}{1.5 \times 10^{10}}\right) \cdot 0.0259 = 0.415 \text{ eV}$$

$$E_c - F_p = 1.1/2 \text{ eV} + 0.415 \text{ eV} = \mathbf{0.965 \text{ eV}}$$

We can calculate the hole current from Eq. (4–40)

$$I_p = -qAD_p\frac{dp}{dx} = qA\frac{D_p}{L_p}(\Delta p)e^{-\frac{x}{L_p}}$$

$$= 1.6 \times 10^{-19} \times 0.5 \times \frac{12.95}{3.6 \times 10^{-5}} \times 5 \times 10^{16} e^{-\frac{10^{-5}}{3.6 \times 10^{-5}}}$$

$$= \mathbf{1.09 \times 10^3 \text{ A}}$$

$$Q_p = qA(\Delta p)L_p$$

$$= 1.6 \times 10^{-19}(0.5)(5 \times 10^{16})(3.6 \times 10^{-5})$$

$$= \mathbf{1.44 \times 10^{-7} \text{ C}}$$

4.4.5 The Haynes–Shockley Experiment

One of the classic semiconductor experiments is the demonstration of drift and diffusion of minority carriers, first performed by J. R. Haynes and W. Shockley in 1951 at the Bell Telephone Laboratories. The experiment allows independent measurement of the minority carrier mobility μ and diffusion coefficient D. The basic principles of the Haynes–Shockley experiment are as follows: A pulse of holes is created in an n-type bar (for example) that contains an electric field (Fig. 4–18); as the pulse drifts in the field and spreads out by diffusion, the excess hole concentration is monitored at some point down the bar; the time required for the holes to drift a given distance

Figure 4–18
Drift and diffusion
of a hole pulse in
an n-type bar: (a)
sample geometry;
(b) position and
shape of the pulse
for several times
during its drift
down the bar.

in the field gives a measure of the mobility; the spreading of the pulse during a given time is used to calculate the diffusion coefficient.

In Fig. 4–18 a pulse of excess carriers is created by a light flash at some point $x = 0$ in an n-type semiconductor ($n_0 \gg p_0$). We assume that the excess carriers have a negligible effect on the electron concentration but change the hole concentration significantly. The excess holes drift in the direction of the electric field and eventually reach the point $x = L$, where they are monitored. By measuring the drift time t_d, we can calculate the drift velocity v_d and, therefore, the hole mobility:

$$v_d = \frac{L}{t_d} \tag{4–41}$$

$$\mu_p = \frac{v_d}{\mathscr{E}} \tag{4–42}$$

Thus the hole mobility can be calculated directly from a measurement of the drift time for the pulse as it moves down the bar. In contrast with the Hall effect (Section 3.4.5), which can be used with resistivity to obtain the *major-ity* carrier mobility, the Haynes–Shockley experiment is used to measure the *minority* carrier mobility.

As the pulse drifts in the $\mathscr{E}$ field it also spreads out by diffusion. By measuring the spread in the pulse, we can calculate D_p. To predict the distribution of holes in the pulse as a function of time, let us first reexamine the case of diffusion of a pulse *without drift, neglecting recombination* (Fig. 4–12). The equation which the hole distribution must satisfy is the time-dependent diffusion equation, Eq. (4–33b). For the case of negligible recombination (τ_p long compared with the times involved in the diffusion), we can write the diffusion equation as

$$\frac{\partial \delta p(x, t)}{\partial t} = D_p \frac{\partial^2 \delta p(x, t)}{\partial x^2} \tag{4–43}$$

The function which satisfies this equation is called a *gaussian distribution*,

$$\delta p(x, t) = \left[\frac{\Delta P}{2\sqrt{\pi D_p t}}\right] e^{-x^2/4D_p t} \tag{4-44}$$

where ΔP is the number of holes per unit area created over a negligibly small distance at $t = 0$. The factor in brackets indicates that the peak value of the pulse (at $x = 0$) decreases with time, and the exponential factor predicts the spread of the pulse in the positive and negative x-directions (Fig. 4–19). If we designate the peak value of the pulse as $\widehat{\delta p}$ at any time (say t_d), we can use Eq. (4–44) to calculate D_p from the value of δp at some point x. The most convenient choice is the point $\Delta x/2$, at which δp is down by $1/e$ of its peak value $\widehat{\delta p}$. At this point we can write

$$e^{-1}\widehat{\delta p} = \widehat{\delta p}e^{-(\Delta x/2)^2/4D_p t_d} \tag{4-45}$$

$$D_p = \frac{(\Delta x)^2}{16t_d} \tag{4-46}$$

Since Δx cannot be measured directly, we use an experimental setup such as Fig. 4–20, which allows us to display the pulse on an oscilloscope as the carriers pass under a detector. As we shall see in Chapter 5, a forward-biased p-n junction serves as an excellent injector of minority carriers, and a reverse-biased junction serves as a detector. The measured quantity in Fig. 4–20 is the pulse width Δt displayed on the oscilloscope in time. It is related to Δx by the drift velocity, as the pulse drifts past the detector point (2)

$$\Delta x = \Delta t v_d = \Delta t \frac{L}{t_d} \tag{4-47}$$

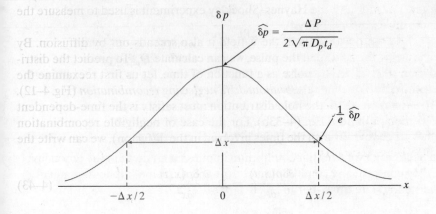

$$\widehat{\delta p} = \frac{\Delta P}{2\sqrt{\pi D_p t_d}}$$

$\frac{1}{e}\widehat{\delta p}$

$-\Delta x/2 \qquad 0 \qquad \Delta x/2$

Figure 4–19
Calculation of D_p from the shape of the δp distribution after time t_d. No drift or recombination is included.

Figure 4–20
The Haynes–Shockley experiment: (a) circuit schematic; (b) typical trace on the oscilloscope screen.

(a)

(b)

A/e = 0.368 A

EXAMPLE 4–5

An n-type Ge sample is used in the Haynes–Shockley experiment shown in Fig. 4–20. The length of the sample is 1 cm, and the probes (1) and (2) are separated by 0.95 cm. The battery voltage E_0 is 2 V. A pulse arrives at point (2) 0.25 ms after injection at (1); the width of the pulse Δt is 117 μs. Calculate the hole mobility and diffusion coefficient, and check the results against the Einstein relation.

SOLUTION

$$\mu_p = \frac{v_d}{\mathscr{E}} = \frac{0.95/(0.25 \times 10^{-3})}{2/1} = 1900 \text{ cm}^2/(\text{V-s})$$

$$D_p = \frac{(\Delta x)^2}{16 t_d} = \frac{(\Delta t L)^2}{16 t_d^3}$$

$$= \frac{(117 \times 0.95)^2 \times 10^{-12}}{16(0.25)^3 \times 10^{-9}} = 49.4 \text{ cm}^2\text{s}$$

$$\frac{D_p}{\mu_p} = \frac{49.4}{1900} = 0.026 = \frac{kT}{q}$$

4.4.6 Gradients in the Quasi-Fermi Levels

In Section 3.5 we saw that equilibrium implies no gradient in the Fermi level E_F. In contrast, any combination of drift and diffusion implies a gradient in the steady state quasi-Fermi level.

We can use the results of Eqs. (4–23), (4–26), and (4–29) to demonstrate the power of the concept of quasi-Fermi levels in semiconductors [see Eq. (4–15)]. If we take the general case of nonequilibrium electron concentration with drift and diffusion, we must write the total electron current as

$$J_n(x) = q\mu_n n(x)\mathscr{E}(x) + qD_n\frac{dn(x)}{dx} \tag{4-48}$$

where the gradient in electron concentration is

$$\frac{dn(x)}{dx} = \frac{d}{dx}[n_i e^{(F_n - E_i)/kT}] = \frac{n(x)}{kT}\left(\frac{dF_n}{dx} - \frac{dE_i}{dx}\right) \tag{4-49}$$

Using the Einstein relation, the total electron current becomes

$$J_n(x) = q\mu_n n(x)\mathscr{E}(x) + \mu_n n(x)\left[\frac{dF_n}{dx} - \frac{dE_i}{dx}\right] \tag{4-50}$$

But Eq. (4–26) indicates that the subtractive term in the brackets is just $q\mathscr{E}(x)$, giving a direct cancellation of $q\mu_n n(x)\mathscr{E}(x)$ and leaving

$$J_n(x) = \mu_n n(x)\frac{dF_n}{dx} \tag{4-51}$$

Thus, the processes of electron drift and diffusion are summed up by the spatial variation of the quasi-Fermi level. The same derivation can be made for holes, and we can write the current due to drift and diffusion in the form of a *modified Ohm's law*

$$J_n(x) = q\mu_n n(x)\frac{d(F_n/q)}{dx} = \sigma_n(x)\frac{d(F_n/q)}{dx} \tag{4-52a}$$

$$J_p(x) = q\mu_p p(x)\frac{d(F_p/q)}{dx} = \sigma_p(x)\frac{d(F_p/q)}{dx} \tag{4-52b}$$

Therefore, any drift, diffusion, or combination of the two in a semiconductor results in currents proportional to the gradients of the two quasi-Fermi levels. Conversely, a lack of current implies constant quasi-Fermi levels. One can use a hydrostatic analogy for quasi-Fermi levels and identify it as water pressure in a system. Just as water flows from a high-pressure region to a low-pressure region, until in equilibrium the water pressure is the same everywhere, similarly electrons flow from a high- to low-electron quasi-Fermi level region, until we get a flat Fermi level in equilibrium. Quasi-Fermi levels are sometimes also known as electrochemical potentials because, as we just saw, the driving force for carriers is governed partly by gradients of electrical potential (or electric field), which determines drift, and partly by gradients of carrier concentration (which is related to a thermodynamic concept called *chemical potential*), giving rise to diffusion.

4.1 *Excess* carriers, above the equilibrium values contributed by doping, may be created *optically* (or by electrical *biasing* in devices). *Generation–recombination* (G–R) of electron–hole pairs (*EHPs*) can occur by absorption of the photons with energy greater than the band gap, balanced by direct or indirect recombination.

4.2 Generation–recombination processes can be mediated by *traps*, especially deep traps near midgap. Band-to-band or trap-assisted G–R processes lead to an average *lifetime* for the excess carriers. Carrier lifetime multiplied by the optical generation rate establishes a steady state excess population of carriers. The square root of carrier lifetime multiplied by the diffusion coefficient determines the diffusion length.

4.3 In *equilibrium,* we have a *constant Fermi level*. In nonequilibrium with excess carriers, Fermi levels are generalized to separate *quasi-Fermi levels* for electrons and holes. The quasi-Fermi level splitting is a measure of the departure from equilibrium. Minority carrier quasi-Fermi levels change more than majority carrier quasi-Fermi levels because the relative change of minority carriers is larger. Gradients in the quasi-Fermi level determine the net drift–diffusion current.

4.4 *Diffusion flux* measures the flow of carriers from *high- to low-concentration* regions and is given by the *diffusivity* times the concentration *gradient*. The direction of diffusion current is opposite to the flux for the negative electrons, but in the same direction for the positive holes. Carrier diffusivity is related to mobility by the thermal voltage kT/q (*Einstein relation*).

4.5 When carriers move in a semiconductor due to drift or diffusion, the time-dependent carrier concentrations at different points is given by the *carrier continuity* equation, which says that if more carriers flow into a point than flow out, the concentration will increase as a function of time and vice versa. G–R processes also affect carrier concentrations.

4.1 With E_F located 0.4 eV above the valence band in a Si sample, what charge state would you expect for most Ga atoms in the sample? What would be the predominant charge state of Zn? Au? *Note:* By charge state we mean neutral, singly positive, doubly negative, etc.

4.2 On a Si sample, incident light is at $t = 0$ uniformly, which generates excess carriers for $t > 0$. The generation rate for carriers is $6 \times 10^{22}/cm^3$. Sample is doped with $2 \times 10^{17}/cm^3$ As atoms. Determine the conductivity of the sample at $t = 5$ ms. Find the separation of quasi Fermi levels at 300 K.

4.3 Construct a semilogarithmic plot such as Fig. 4–7 for Si doped with 2×10^{15} donors/cm^3 and having 4×10^{14} EHP/cm^3 created uniformly at $t = 0$. Assume that $\tau_n = \tau_p = 5\ \mu s$.

4.4 Calculate the recombination coefficient α_r for the low-level excitation described in Prob. 4.3. Assume that this value of α_r applies when the GaAs sample is uniformly exposed to a steady state optical generation rate $g_{op} = 10^{19}$ EHP/cm³-s. Find the steady state excess carrier concentration $\Delta n = \Delta p$.

4.5 An intrinsic Si sample is doped with donors from one side such that $N_d = N_0 \exp(-ax)$. (a) Find an expression for the built-in electric field at equilibrium over the range for which $N_d \gg n_i$. (b) Evaluate the field when $a = 1 \; (\mu m)^{-1}$. (c) Sketch a band diagram such as in Fig. 4–15 and indicate the direction of the field.

4.6 A Si sample with 10^{15}/cm³ donors is uniformly optically excited at room temperature such that 10^{19}/cm³ EHPs are generated per second. Find the separation of the quasi-Fermi levels and the change of conductivity upon shining the light. Electron and hole lifetimes are both 10 μs. $D_p = 12$ cm²/s.

4.7 An n-type Si sample is doped at 10^{15} cm⁻³. We shine light on it to create EHPs at 10^{19} cm⁻³/s. What is the steady state concentration of minority carriers, if the lifetime is 100 ns? How long does it take for the hole concentration to drop 10%, after the light is switched off? How long for the hole concentration to reach a value that is 10% higher than the thermal equilibrium value?

4.8 An n-type Si sample with $N_d = 10^{15}$ cm⁻³ is steadily illuminated such that $g_{op} = 10^{21}$ EHP/cm³-s. If $\tau_n = \tau_p = 1 \; \mu$s for this excitation, calculate the separation in the quasi-Fermi levels, $(F_n - F_p)$. Draw a band diagram such as Fig. 4–11.

4.9 For a 2-cm-long doped Si bar $(N_d = 10^{16} \text{cm}^{-3})$ with a cross-sectional area $= 0.05$ cm², what is the current if we apply 10 V across it? If we generate 10^{20} EHPs per second per cm³ uniformly in the bar and the lifetime $\tau_n = \tau_p = 10^{-4}$s, what is the new current? Assume the low-level α_r doesn't change for high-level injection. If the voltage is then increased to 100,000 V, what is the new current? Assume $\mu_p = 500$ cm²/V-s, but you must choose the appropriate value for electrons.

4.10 Design and sketch a photoconductor using a 5-μm-thick film of CdS, assuming that $\tau_n = \tau_p = 10^{-6}$s and $N_d = 10^{14} \text{cm}^{-3}$. The dark resistance (with $g_{op} = 0$) should be 10 MΩ, and the device must fit in a square 0.5 cm on a side; therefore, some sort of folded or zigzag pattern is in order. With an excitation of $g_{op} = 10^{21}$ EHP/cm³-s, what is the resistance change?

4.11 A 80 mW laser beam with wavelength $\lambda = 600$ nm is focused on a Si sample of 80 μm thickness. The absorption coefficient of the sample is $\alpha = 8 \times 10^3$/cm. Find the number of photons emitted per second, assuming perfect quantum efficiency. What power should be delivered to the sample as heat?

4.12 A material is doped such that electron concentration varies linearly across the sample, which is 0.5 μm thick. Donor concentration varies from 0 (at $x = 0$) to 10^{16}/cm³ (at $x = 0.5 \; \mu$m). Write equations for total electron and hole concentrations as a function of distance x. Determine electron and hole diffusion current densities if the diffusion coefficients are $D_n = 30$ cm²/V-sec and $D_p = 12$ cm²/V-sec. Find the expression for Fermi level (E_F) as a function of x.

4.13 For the steady state minority hole distribution shown in Fig. 4–17, find the expression for the hole quasi-Fermi level position $E_i - F_p(x)$ while $p(x) \gg p_0$ (i.e., while F_p is below E_F). On a band diagram, draw the variation of $F_p(x)$. Be careful—when the minority carriers are few (e.g., when Δp is n_i), F_p still has a long way to go to reach E_F.

4.14 We inject electrons into a p-type semiconductor 5 microns long such that the concentration varies linearly from 10^{20} cm^{-3} to 0 from left to right. If the mobility of the electrons is 500 cm^2/V-s, what is the current density if the electric fields are negligible?

4.15 We shine 10^{17} photons/cm^2-s which are all absorbed near the surface $x = 0$ of a p-type semiconductor, raising the temperature of the sample to 500 K. If the minority carrier lifetime is 200 ns in this material, electron mobility is 2000 cm^2/V-s, and hole mobility is 500 cm^2/V-s, calculate the electron diffusion current density 20 microns from the surface.

4.16 A long Si sample, n-doped at 10^{17} cm^{-3}, with a cross-sectional area of 0.5 cm^2 is optically excited by a laser such that 10^{20}/cm^3 EHPs are generated per second at $x = 0$ μm. They diffuse to the right. What is the total diffusion current at $x = 50$ μm? Electron and hole lifetimes are both 10 μs. $\mu_p = 500$ cm^2/V-s; $D_n = 36$ cm^2/s.

4.17 In an n-type semiconductor bar, there is an increase in electron concentration from left to right and an electric field pointing to the left. With a suitable sketch, indicate the directions of the electron drift and diffusion current flow and explain why. If we double the electron concentration everywhere, what happens to the diffusion current and the drift current? If we add a constant concentration of electrons everywhere, what happens to the drift and diffusion currents? Explain your answers with appropriate equations.

4.18 The current required to feed the hole injection at $x = 0$ in Fig. 4–17 is obtained by evaluating Eq. (4–40) at $x = 0$. The result is $I_p(x = 0) = qAD_p\Delta p/L_p$. Show that this current can be calculated by integrating the charge stored in the steady state hole distribution $\Delta p(x)$ and then dividing by the average hole lifetime τ_p. Explain why this approach gives $I_p(x = 0)$.

4.19 The direction of the built-in electric field can be deduced without math by sketching the result of a doping gradient on the band diagram. Starting with a flat Fermi level at equilibrium, place E_i near or far from E_F as the doping is varied for the two cases of a gradient in donor or acceptor doping as in Prob. 4.5. Show the electric field direction in each case, based on Eq. (4–26). If a *minority* carrier is injected into the impurity gradient region, in what direction is it accelerated in the two cases? This is an interesting effect that we will use later in discussing bipolar transistors.

4.20 In Prob. 4.5, the direction of the built-in electric field due to a gradient in doping was determined from Eqs. (4–23) and (4–26). In this problem, you are asked to explain qualitatively why the field must arise and find its direction. (a) Sketch a donor doping distribution as in Prob. 4.5, and explain the field required to keep the mobile electrons from diffusing down the gradient. Repeat for acceptors and holes. (b) Sketch a microscopic region of the doping distribution, showing ionized donors and the resulting mobile electrons. Explain the origin and direction of the field as the electrons attempt to diffuse toward lower concentrations. Repeat for acceptors and holes.

4.21 A p-type Si sample is used in the Haynes-Shockley experiment. The length of the sample is 2 cm, and two probes are separated by 1.8 cm. Voltage applied at the two ends is 5 V. A pulse arrives at the collection point at 0.608 ms, and the separation of the pulse is 180 sec. Calculate mobility and diffusion coefficient for minority carriers. Verify it from the Einstein relation.

4.22 A semiconductor bar of length 2 μm with intrinsic carrier concentration of 10^{13} cm^{-3} is *uniformly doped* with donors at a concentration of 2×10^{13} cm^{-3} and acceptors at a concentration of 10^{13} cm^{-3}. If $D_n = 26$ cm^2/s and $D_p = 52$ cm^2/s, calculate the *electron and hole drift* current densities for an applied voltage of 5 V. In this semiconductor, electrons are in the ohmic regime for fields less than 10^5 V/cm, but travel with a saturation velocity of 10^8 cm/s for fields above that. For holes, they are ohmic below 10^4 V/cm, and travel with a saturation velocity of 10^5 cm/s above that field. What are the *electron and hole diffusion* current densities in the middle of the bar? (Assume T = 300 K.)

4.23 A recently discovered semiconductor has $N_c = 10^{19}$ cm^{-3}, $N_v = 5 \times 10^{18}$ cm^{-3}, and $E_g = 2$ eV. If it is doped with 10^{17} donors (fully ionized), calculate the electron, hole, and intrinsic carrier concentrations at 627°C. Sketch the simplified band diagram, and specify the value of E_F and E_i with respect to the band edges. If we apply 5 V across a piece of this semiconductor 8 μm long, what is the current? The piece is 2 μm wide and 1.5 μm thick. The diffusion coefficient of holes and electrons is 25 cm^2/s and 75 cm^2/s, respectively.

4.24 A novel semiconductor sample has $L = 2$ μm, $W = 0.5$ μm, and thickness of 0.2 μm. It has an intrinsic carrier concentration of 10^{12} cm^{-3}. If it has an ionized donor concentration of 2×10^{12} cm^{-3}, calculate the electron and hole currents for an applied bias of 10 V across the length of the bar, assuming ohmic behavior for electrons, but holes are traveling at saturation velocity. The electron and hole diffusion coefficients are 20 cm^2/V-s and 5 cm^2/V-s, respectively. The electron and hole saturation velocities are 10^8 cm/s and 10^7 cm/s, respectively, in this semiconductor.

4.25 Sketch the simplified band diagram (with proper labeling of positions and energies) for a semiconductor bar with a band gap of 2 eV and $N_c = 10^{19}$ cm^{-3}, n$^+$ doped very heavily between 0 cm and 0.2 cm, n-type doped region (10^{17} cm^{-3}) from 0.2 cm to 0.7 cm, and then very heavily n$^+$ doped from 0.7 cm to 1 cm, to which we hook up a 0.5 V battery (positive terminal connected to left side of bar). There is negligible voltage drop across the highly conducting, heavily doped n$^+$ regions. (Draw a schematic of the bar, and align the band diagram under that schematic).

What is the current density if the electron diffusion coefficient is 100 cm^2/V-s. If the electrons were injected with negligible kinetic energy from the right side of the bar, and they traveled without scattering, what is the kinetic energy of the electrons at $x = 0.1$ cm, 0.6 cm, and 0.9 cm?

READING LIST

Ashcroft, N. W., and N. D. Mermin. *Solid State Physics.* Philadelphia: W.B. Saunders, 1976.

Bhattacharya, P. *Semiconductor Optoelectronic Devices.* Englewood Cliffs, NJ: Prentice Hall, 1994.

Blakemore, J. S. *Semiconductor Statistics.* New York: Dover Publications, 1987.

Neamen, D. A. *Semiconductor Physics and Devices: Basic Principles.* Homewood, IL: Irwin, 2003.

Pankove, J. I. *Optical Processes in Semiconductors.* Englewood Cliffs, NJ: Prentice Hall, 1971.

Pierret, R. F. *Semiconductor Device Fundamentals.* Reading, MA: Addison-Wesley, 1996.

Singh, J. *Semiconductor Devices.* New York: McGraw-Hill, 1994.

Wolfe, C. M., G. E. Stillman, and N. Holonyak, Jr. *Physical Properties of Semiconductors.* Englewood Cliffs, NJ: Prentice Hall, 1989.

SELF QUIZ   **Question 1**

Consider a p-type semiconductor that has a band gap of 1.0 eV and a minority electron lifetime of 0.1 μs, and is uniformly illuminated by light having photon energy of 2.0 eV.

(a) What rate of uniform excess carrier generation is required to generate a uniform electron concentration of $10^{10}/cm^3$?

(b) How much optical power per cm^3 must be absorbed in order to create the excess carrier population of part (a)? (You may leave your answer in units of eV/s-cm^3.)

(c) If the carriers recombine via photon emission, approximately how much optical power per cm^3 will be generated? (You may leave your answer in units of eV/s-cm^3.)

Question 2

(a) What do we mean by "deep" versus "shallow" traps? Which are more harmful for semiconductor devices and why? What is an example of a deep trap in Si?

(b) Are absorption lengths of slightly above band gap photons longer in Si or GaAs? Why?

(c) Do absorption coefficients of photons increase or decrease with photon energy? Why?

Question 3

Consider the following equilibrium band diagram for a portion of a semiconductor sample with a built-in electric field $\mathscr{E}$:

(a) Sketch the Fermi level as a function of position *through* the indicated point, E_F, across the width of the band diagram above.

(b) On the band diagram, sketch the direction of the electric field. Is the field constant or position dependent?

(c) On the following graph, sketch and label both the electron and hole concentrations as a function of position across the full width of the sample. Note that the carrier concentration scale is logarithmic such that exponential variations in the carrier concentration with position appear as straight lines. Note also that the horizontal axis corresponds to the intrinsic carrier concentration of n_i.

Question 4

(a) Indicate the directions of the hole and electron flux densities ϕ due to diffusion and drift under these *equilibrium* conditions corresponding to the previous Question 3.

(b) Indicate the directions of the hole and electron current densities j due to diffusion and drift under these *equilibrium* conditions.

Question 5

(a) What are the relevant equations that must be solved in general for a semiconductor device problem?

(b) In general how many components of conduction current can you have in a semiconductor device? What are they?

Question 6

(a) Consider a region in a semiconductor with an electric field directed toward the right ($\rightarrow$) and carrier concentrations increasing toward the left ($\leftarrow$). Indicate the directions of particle fluxes ϕ (circle one for each) and charge currents j due to drift and diffusion within that region.

(b) Based on your answers to part (a), indicate the directions of the charge currents j due to drift and diffusion within that region.

Question 7

Find the concentration of electrons and holes in a p-type silicon at 300 K assuming resistivity as 0.02 ohm-cm. Assume $u = 475$ m^2/V sec, $ni = 1.45 \times 10^{10}$ per cm^3.

Chapter 5
Junctions

OBJECTIVES

1. Determine the band diagram of a p-n junction in equilibrium and use the Poisson's equation to calculate electric fields and potentials
2. Determine current flow components in an "ideal" diode, and why reverse leakage in an ideal diode is independent of bias; study applications in rectifiers
3. Understand depletion capacitance due to dopant charges, and diffusion capacitance due to mobile carriers
4. Study second-order effects—high-level injection, generation–recombination in depletion region, series resistance, and graded junctions
5. Study metal–semiconductor junctions (Schottky and ohmic) and heterojunctions, in terms of vacuum level, electron affinity, and work function

Most semiconductor devices contain at least one junction between p-type and n-type material. These p-n junctions are fundamental to the performance of functions such as rectification, amplification, switching, and other operations in electronic circuits. In this chapter we shall discuss the equilibrium state of the junction and the flow of electrons and holes across a junction under steady state and transient conditions. This is followed by a discussion of metal–semiconductor junctions and heterojunctions between semiconductors having different band gaps. With the background provided in this chapter on junction properties, we can then discuss specific devices in later chapters.

5.1 FABRICATION OF p-n JUNCTIONS

Although this book deals primarily with how devices work rather than how they are made, it is instructive to have an overview of the fabrication process in order to appreciate device physics. We have already discussed in Chapter 1 how single-crystal substrates and epitaxial layers needed for high-quality devices are grown, and how the doping can be varied as a function of depth. However, we have not discussed how doping can be varied laterally across the surface, which is key to making integrated circuits on a wafer. Hence, it is necessary to be able to form patterned masks on the wafer corresponding to the circuitry, and introduce the dopants selectively through windows in the mask. We will first briefly describe the major process steps that form the underpinnings of modern integrated circuit manufacturing. Relatively few unit process steps can be used in different permutations and combinations to make everything from simple diodes to the most complex microprocessors.

5.1.1 Thermal Oxidation

Many fabrication steps involve heating up the wafer in order to enhance a chemical process. An important example of this is thermal oxidation of Si to form SiO_2. This involves placing a batch of wafers in a clean silica (quartz) tube which can be heated to very high temperatures ($\sim800-1000°C$) using heating coils in a furnace with ceramic brick insulating liners. An oxygen-containing gas such as dry O_2 or H_2O is flowed into the tube at atmospheric pressure, and flowed out at the other end. Traditionally, horizontal furnaces were used (Fig. 5–1a). More recently, it has become common to employ vertical furnaces (Fig. 5–1b). A batch of Si wafers is placed in the silica wafer holders, each facing down to minimize particulate contamination. The wafers are then moved into the furnace. The gases flow in from the top and flow out at the bottom, providing more uniform flow than in conventional horizontal furnaces. The overall reactions that occur during oxidation are:

$$Si + O_2 \rightarrow SiO_2 \,(\text{dry oxidation})$$

$$Si + 2H_2O \rightarrow SiO_2 + 2H_2 \,(\text{wet oxidation})$$

In both cases, Si is consumed from the surface of the substrate. For every micron of SiO_2 grown, 0.44 μm of Si is consumed, leading to a 2.2× volume expansion of the consumed layer upon oxidation. The oxidation proceeds by having the oxidant (O_2 or H_2O) molecules diffuse through the

Figure 5–1a
Silicon wafers being loaded into a furnace. For 8-inch and larger wafers, this type of horizontal loading is often replaced by a vertical furnace.

Pyrometer

Water outlet — Gas inlet →   ← Water inlet   ← Gas inlet

Electric furnace

Heater

Cassette

Water

Furnace tube

Clean bench

Cassette loader

Vacuum pump

Figure 5–1b
Vertical furnace for large Si wafers. The silica wafer holder is loaded with Si wafers and moved into the furnace above for oxidation, diffusion, or deposition operations.

already grown oxide to the Si–SiO$_2$ interface, where the above reactions take place. One of the very important reasons why Si integrated circuits exist (and by extension why modern computers exist) is that a stable thermal oxide can be grown on Si with excellent interface electrical properties. Other semiconductor materials do not have such a useful native oxide. We can argue that modern electronics and computer technology owe their existence to this simple oxidation process. Plots of oxide thickness as a function of time, at different temperatures, are shown for dry and wet oxidation of (100) Si in Appendix VI.

5.1.2 Diffusion

Another thermal process that was used extensively in IC fabrication in the past is thermal in-diffusion of dopants in furnaces such as those shown in Fig. 5–1a. The wafers are first oxidized and windows are opened in the oxide using the photolithography and etching steps described in Sections 5.1.6 and 5.1.7, respectively. Dopants such as B, P, or As are introduced into these patterned wafers in a high temperature (~800–1100°C) diffusion furnace, generally using a gas or vapor source. The dopants are gradually transported from the high concentration region near the surface into the substrate through diffusion, similar to that described for carriers in Section 4.4. The maximum number of impurities that can be dissolved (the solid solubility) in Si is shown for various impurities as a function of temperature in Appendix VII. The diffusivity of dopants in solids, D, has a strong Arrhenius dependence on temperature, T. It is given by $D = D_0 \exp-(E_A/kT)$, where D_0 is a constant depending on the material and the dopant, and E_A is the activation energy. The average distance the dopants diffuse is related to the diffusion length as in Section 4.4.4. In this case, the diffusion length is $\sqrt{Dt}$, where t is the processing time. The product Dt is sometimes called the *thermal budget*. The Arrhenius dependence of diffusivity on temperature explains why high temperatures are required for diffusion; otherwise, the diffusivities are far too low. Since D varies exponentially with T, it is critical to have very precise control over the furnace temperatures, within several degrees, in order to have control over the diffusion profiles (Fig. 5–2). The dopants are effectively blocked or masked by the oxide because their diffusivity in oxide is very low. The diffusivities of various dopants in Si and SiO_2 are shown as a function of temperature in Appendix VIII. Difficulty with profile control and the very high temperature requirement has led to diffusion being supplanted by ion implantation as a doping technique, as discussed in Section 5.1.4.

The trend of using larger Si wafers has changed many processing steps. For example, eight-inch and larger wafers are best handled in a vertical furnace (Fig. 5–1b) rather than the traditional horizontal furnace (Fig. 5–1a). Also, large wafers are often handled individually for a variety of deposition, etching, and implantation processes. Such single-wafer processing has led to development of robotic systems for fast and accurate wafer handling.

The distribution of impurities in the sample at any time during the diffusion can be calculated from a solution of the diffusion equation with appropriate boundary conditions. If the source of dopant atoms at the surface of the sample is limited (e.g., a given number of atoms deposited on the Si surface before diffusion), a gaussian distribution as described by Eq. (4–44)

Figure 5–2
Impurity concentration profile for fabricating a p-n junction by diffusion.

(for $x > 0$) is obtained. On the other hand, if the dopant atoms are supplied continuously, such that the concentration at the surface is maintained at a constant value, the distribution follows what is called a *complementary error function*. In Fig. 5–2, there is some point in the sample at which the introduced acceptor concentration just equals the background donor concentration in the originally n-type sample. This point is the location of the p-n junction. To the left of this point in the sample of Fig. 5–2, acceptor atoms predominate and the material is p-type, whereas to the right of the junction, the background donor atoms predominate and the material is n-type. The depth of the junction beneath the surface of the sample can be controlled by the time and temperature of the diffusion (Prob. 5.2).

In the horizontal diffusion furnace shown in Fig. 5–1a, Si wafers are placed in the tube during diffusion, and the impurity atoms are introduced into the gas which flows through the silica tube. Common impurity source materials for diffusions in Si are B_2O_3, BBr_3, and BCl_3 for boron; phosphorus sources include PH_3, P_2O_5, and $POCl_3$. Solid sources are placed in the silica tube upstream from the sample or in a separate heating zone of the furnace; gaseous sources can be metered directly into the gas flow system; and with liquid sources inert carrier gas is bubbled through the liquid before being introduced into the furnace tube. The Si wafers are held in a silica "boat" (Fig. 5–1a) which can be pushed into position in the furnace and removed by a silica rod.

It is important to remember the degree of cleanliness required in these processing steps. Since typical doping concentrations represent one part per million or less, cleanliness and purity of materials are critically important. Thus the impurity source and carrier gas must be extremely pure; the silica tube, sample holder, and pushrod must be cleaned and etched in hydrofluoric acid (HF) before use (once in use, the tube cleanliness can be maintained if no unwanted impurities are introduced); finally, the Si wafers themselves must undergo an elaborate cleaning procedure before diffusion, including a final etch containing HF to remove any unwanted SiO_2 from the surface.

5.1.3 Rapid Thermal Processing

Increasingly, many thermal steps formerly performed in furnaces are being done using what is called *rapid thermal processing* (RTP). This includes rapid thermal oxidation, annealing of ion implantation, and chemical vapor deposition, which are discussed in the following paragraphs. A simple RTP system is shown in Fig. 5–3. Instead of having a large batch of wafers in a conventional furnace where the temperature cannot be changed rapidly, a single wafer is held (face down to minimize particulates) on low-thermal-mass quartz pins, surrounded by a bank of high-intensity (tens of kW) tungsten–halogen infrared lamps, with gold-plated reflectors around them. By turning on the lamps, the high-intensity infrared radiation shines through the quartz chamber and is absorbed by the wafer, causing its temperature to rise *very* rapidly ($\sim50-100°C/s$). The processing temperature can be reached quickly, after the gas flows have been stabilized in the chamber. At the end

Figure 5–3
Schematic
diagram of a
rapid thermal
processor and
typical time–
temperature
profile.

of the process, the lamps are turned off, allowing the wafer temperature
to drop rapidly, once again because of the much lower thermal mass of
an RTP system compared to a furnace. In RTP, therefore, temperature is
essentially used as a "switch" to start or quench the reaction. Two critical
aspects of RTP are ensuring temperature uniformity across large wafers
and accurate temperature measurement, for example, with thermocouples
or pyrometers.

A key parameter in all thermal processing steps is the thermal budget, Dt. Generally speaking, we try to minimize this quantity because an
excessive Dt product leads to loss of control over compact doping profiles,
which is detrimental to ultra-small devices. In furnace processing, thermal
budgets are minimized by operating at as low a temperature as feasible so
that D is small. On the other hand, RTP operates at higher temperatures
($\sim$1000°C) but does so for only a few seconds (compared to minutes or
hours in a furnace).

5.1.4   Ion Implantation

A useful alternative to high-temperature diffusion is the direct implantation of energetic ions into the semiconductor. In this process a beam of
impurity ions is accelerated to kinetic energies ranging from several keV

Figure 5–4
Distributions
of implanted
impurities:
gaussian
distribution of
boron atoms about
a projected range
R_p (in this example,
a dose of 10^{14}
B atoms/cm^2
implanted at
140 keV).

to several MeV and is directed onto the surface of the semiconductor. As the impurity atoms enter the crystal, they give up their energy to the lattice in collisions and finally come to rest at some average penetration depth, called the *projected range*. Depending on the impurity and its implantation energy, the range in a given semiconductor may vary from a few hundred angstroms to about 1 μm. For most implantations the ions come to rest distributed almost evenly about the projected range R_p, as shown in Fig. 5–4. An implanted dose of ϕ ions/cm^2 is distributed approximately by a gaussian formula

$$N(x) = \frac{\phi}{\sqrt{2\pi}\Delta R_p} \exp\left[-\frac{1}{2}\left(\frac{x - R_p}{\Delta R_p}\right)^2\right] \quad (5\text{–}1a)$$

where ΔR_p, called the *straggle*, measures the half-width of the distribution at $e^{-1/2}$ of the peak (Fig. 5–4). Both R_p and ΔR_p increase with increasing implantation energy. These parameters are shown as a function of energy for various implant species into Si in Appendix IX.

Figure 5–5
Schematic diagram of an ion implantation system.

An ion implanter is shown schematically in Fig. 5–5. A gas containing the desired impurity is ionized within the *source* and is then extracted into the *acceleration tube*. After acceleration to the desired kinetic energy, the ions are passed through a *mass separator* to ensure that only the desired ion species enters the *drift tube*.[1] The ion beam is then focused and scanned electrostatically over the surface of the wafer in the *target chamber*. Repetitive scanning in a raster pattern provides exceptionally uniform doping of the wafer surface. The target chamber commonly includes automatic wafer-handling facilities to speed up the process of implanting many wafers per hour.

An obvious advantage of implantation is that it can be done at relatively low temperatures; this means that doping layers can be implanted without disturbing previously diffused regions. The ions can be blocked by metal or photoresist layers; therefore, the photolithographic techniques described in Section 5.1.6 can be used to define ion-implanted doping patterns. Very shallow (tenths of a micron) and well-defined doping layers can be achieved by this method. As we shall see in later chapters, many devices require thin doping regions and may be improved by ion implantation techniques. Furthermore, it is possible to implant impurities which do not diffuse conveniently into semiconductors.

One of the major advantages of implantation is the precise control of doping concentration it provides. Since the ion beam current can be measured accurately during implantation, a precise quantity of impurity can be introduced. This control over doping level, along with the uniformity of the implant over the wafer surface, make ion implantation particularly attractive for the fabrication of Si integrated circuits (Chapter 9).

One problem with this doping method is the lattice damage which results from collisions between the ions and the lattice atoms. However,

---

[1] In many ion implanters the mass separation occurs before the ions are accelerated to high energy.

most of this damage can be removed in Si by heating the crystal after the implantation. This process is called *annealing*. Although Si can be heated to temperatures in excess of 1000°C without difficulty, GaAs and some other compounds tend to dissociate at high temperatures. For example, As evaporation from the surface of GaAs during annealing damages the sample. Therefore, it is common to encapsulate the GaAs with a thin layer of silicon nitride during the anneal. Another approach to annealing either Si or compounds is to heat the sample only briefly (e.g., 10 s) using RTP, rather than a conventional furnace. Annealing leads to some unintended diffusion of the implanted species. It is desirable to minimize this diffusion by optimizing the annealing time and temperature. The profile after annealing is given by

$$N(x) = \frac{\phi}{\sqrt{2\pi}(\Delta R_p^2 + 2Dt)^{1/2}} \exp\left[-\frac{1}{2}\left(\frac{(x - R_p)^2}{\Delta R_p^2 + 2Dt}\right)\right] \quad (5-1b)$$

5.1.5 Chemical Vapor Deposition (CVD)

At various stages of device fabrication, thin films of dielectrics, semiconductors and metals have to be formed on the wafer and then patterned and etched. We have already discussed one important example of this involving thermal oxidation of Si. SiO_2 films can also be formed by *low pressure* $(\sim 100 \text{ mTorr})$[2] chemical vapor deposition (LPCVD) (Fig. 5–6) or plasma-enhanced CVD (PECVD). The key differences are that thermal oxidation consumes Si from the substrate, and very high temperatures are required, whereas CVD of SiO_2 does not consume Si from the substrate and can be done at much lower temperatures. The CVD process reacts a Si-containing gas such as SiH_4 with an oxygen-containing precursor, causing a chemical reaction, leading to the deposition of SiO_2 on the substrate. Being able to deposit SiO_2 is very important in certain applications. As a complicated

Figure 5–6
Low-pressure chemical vapor deposition (LPCVD) reactor.

[2]Torr or Torricelli = 1 mm Hg or 133 Pa.

device structure is built up, the Si substrate may not be available for reaction, or there may be metallization on the wafer that cannot withstand very high temperatures. In such cases, CVD is a necessary alternative.

Although we have used deposition of SiO_2 as an important example, LPCVD is also widely used to deposit other dielectrics such as silicon nitride (Si_3N_4), and polycrystalline or amorphous Si. It should also be clear that the VPE of Si or MOCVD of compound semiconductors discussed in Chapter 1 is really a special, more challenging example of CVD where not only must a film be deposited, but single-crystal growth must also be maintained.

5.1.6 Photolithography

Patterns corresponding to complex circuitry are formed on a wafer using *photolithography*. This involves first generating a *reticle* which is a transparent silica (quartz) plate containing the pattern (Fig. 5–7a). Opaque regions on the mask are made up of an ultraviolet (UV) light-absorbing layer, such as iron oxide. The reticle typically contains the patterns corresponding to a single *chip* or *die,* rather than the entire wafer (in which case it would be called a *mask*). It is usually created by a computer-controlled electron beam driven by the circuit layout data, using pattern generation software. A thin layer of electron beam sensitive material called electron beam resist is placed on the iron-oxide–covered quartz plate, and the resist is exposed by the electron beam. A resist is a thin organic polymer layer that undergoes chemical changes if it is exposed to energetic particles such as electrons or photons. The resist is exposed selectively, corresponding to the patterns that are required. After exposure, the resist is *developed* in a chemical solution. There are two types of resist. The developer is used to remove either the exposed (*positive* resist) or the unexposed (*negative* resist) material. The iron oxide layer is then selectively etched off in a plasma to generate the appropriate patterns. The reticle can be used repeatedly to pattern Si wafers. To make a typical integrated circuit, a dozen or more reticles are required, corresponding to different process steps.

Figure 5–7a
A photolithographic reticle used for one step in the processing of a 16-Mb dynamic random-access memory (DRAM). In a "stepper" projection exposure system, ultraviolet light shines through the glass plate and the image is projected onto the wafer to expose photoresist for one die in the array of circuits and then steps to the next. (Photograph courtesy of IBM Corp.)

(a)

The Si wafers are first covered with an UV light-sensitive organic material or photoemulsion called *photoresist* by dispensing the liquid resist onto the wafer and spinning it rapidly (~3000 rpm) to form a uniform coating (~0.5 μm). As mentioned above, there are two types of resist—negative, which forms the opposite polarity image on the wafer compared to that on the reticle, and positive (same polarity). Currently, positive resist has supplanted negative because it can achieve far better resolution, down to ~0.25 μm using UV light. The light shines on the resist-covered wafer through the reticle, causing the exposed regions to become acidified. Subsequently, the exposed wafers are developed in a basic solution of NaOH, which causes the exposed resist to etch away. Thereby, the pattern on the reticle is transferred to the die on the wafer. After the remaining resist is cured by baking at ~125°C in order to harden it, the appropriate process step can be performed, such as implanting dopants through windows in the resist pattern or plasma etching of the underlying layers.

The exposure of the wafers is achieved die-by-die in a step-and-repeat system called a *stepper* (Fig. 5–7b). As the name implies, the UV light shines selectively through the reticle onto a single die location. After the photoexposure is done, the wafer mechanically translates on a precisely controlled *x-y* translation stage to the next die location and is exposed again. It is very important to be able to precisely align the patterns on the reticle with respect to pre-existing patterns on the wafer, which is why these tools are also sometimes known as *mask aligners*. An advantage of such a "stepper" projection system is that refocusing and realignment can be done at each die to accommodate slight variations in surface flatness across the wafer. This is especially important in printing ultra-small linewidths over a very large wafer. The success of modern IC manufacture has depended on numerous advances in deep UV light sources, precision optical projection systems, techniques for registration between masking layers, and stepper design.

What makes photolithography (along with etching) so critical is that it obviously determines how small and closely packed the individual devices (e.g., transistors) can be made. We shall see that smaller devices operate better in terms of higher speed and lower power dissipation. What makes modern lithography so challenging is the fact that pattern dimensions are comparable to the wavelength of light that is used. Under these circumstances we cannot treat light propagation using simple geometrical ray optics; rather, the wave nature of light is manifested in terms of diffraction, which makes it harder to control the patterns. The *diffraction-limited minimum geometry* is given by

$$l_{min} = 0.8 \, \lambda/NA \qquad (5\text{–}2a)$$

where λ is the wavelength of the light and NA (~0.5) is the numerical aperture or "size" of the lens used in the aligner. This expression implies that for finer patterns, we should work with larger (and, therefore, more expensive) lenses and shorter wavelengths. As a result, smaller geometries

Figure 5–7b
Schematic
diagram of an
optical stepper.

(b)

require shorter wavelengths. This has led the push to replace UV mercury
lamp sources (0.365 μm), shown in Fig. 5–7b, with argon fluoride (ArF)
excimer lasers (λ = 0.193 μm). Novel exposure techniques employing
phase-shift masks, optical proximity correction, and off-axis illumination all
exploit Fourier optics to allow resolution near or below the dimension of the
wavelength being used. There is also interest in extreme ultraviolet (EUV)
sources (13 nm), which use a plasma to generate such short wavelengths,
for next-generation lithography. X-ray lithography involving even shorter
wavelengths has been the source of much research for many years, but does
not seem practical in a manufacturing environment. A promising advancement involves imprinting patterns in a photoresist using a physical pattern,
or mold, thereby overcoming the diffraction limits of optical lithography.

The other key parameter in lithography is the so-called *depth-of-focus* (DOF), which is given by

$$DOF = \frac{\lambda}{2(NA)^2} \qquad (5\text{--}2b)$$

The DOF tells us the range of distances around the focal plane where the image quality is sharp. Unfortunately, this expression implies that exposure with very short wavelengths leads to poor DOF. This is a big challenge because the topography or the "hills and valleys" on a chip during processing can be larger than the DOF allowed by the optics.

We must therefore add steps in the fabrication process to planarize the surface using *chemical mechanical polishing* (CMP). As the name implies, the planarizing process is partly chemical in nature (using a basic solution), and partly mechanical grinding of the layers using an abrasive slurry. As described in Section 1.3.3, CMP can be achieved using a slurry of fine SiO_2 particles in an NaOH solution.

The expression for diffraction-limited geometry [Eq. (5–2a)] explains why there is interest in electron beam lithography. The de Broglie relation states that the wavelength of a particle varies inversely with its momentum:

$$\lambda = \frac{h}{p} \qquad (5\text{--}2c)$$

Thus, more massive or energetic particles have shorter wavelengths. Electron beams are easily generated, focused, and deflected. Since a 10-keV electron has a wavelength of about 0.1 Å, the linewidth limits become the size of the focused beam and its interaction with the photoresist layer. It is possible to achieve linewidths of 0.1 μm by direct electron-beam writing on the wafer photoresist. Furthermore, the computer-controlled electron-beam exposure requires no masks. This capability allows extremely dense packing of circuit elements on the chip, but direct writing of complex patterns is slow. Because of the time required for electron-beam wafer exposure, it is usually advantageous to use electron-beam writing to make the reticle (Fig. 5–7a) and then to expose the wafer photoresist by using photons. Another approach being considered is electron projection lithography (EPL), using a mask, instead of steering a focused electron beam, in order to solve the throughput problem.

5.1.7 Etching

After the photoresist pattern is formed, it can be used as a mask to etch the material underneath. In the early days of Si technology, etching was done using wet chemicals. For example, dilute HF can be used to etch SiO_2 layers grown on a Si substrate with excellent *selectivity*. The term selectivity here refers to the fact that HF attacks SiO_2, but does not affect the Si substrate underneath or the photoresist mask. Although many wet etches are selective, they are unfortunately *isotropic,* which means that they etch as fast laterally as they etch vertically. This is unacceptable for ultra-small features. Hence, wet etching has been largely supplanted by dry, plasma-based etching which can be made both selective and *anisotropic* (etches vertically but not laterally along the surface). In modern IC processing the main use of wet chemical processing is in cleaning the wafers.

Plasmas are ubiquitous in IC processing. The most popular type of plasma-based etching is known as *reactive ion etching* (RIE) (Fig. 5–8). In a typical process, appropriate etch gases such as chlorofluorocarbons (CFCs) flow into the chamber at reduced pressure ($\sim 1-100$ mTorr), and a plasma is struck by applying an rf voltage across a cathode and an anode. The rf voltage accelerates the light electrons in the system to much higher kinetic energies (~ 10 eV) than the heavier ions. The high-energy electrons collide with neutral atoms and molecules to create ions and molecular fragments called radicals. The wafers are held on the rf powered cathode, while the grounded chamber walls act as the anode. From a study of plasma physics, we can show that although the bulk of the plasma is a highly conducting, equi-potential region, less conducting *sheath* regions form next to the two electrodes. It can also be shown that the sheath voltage next to the cathode can be increased by making the (powered) cathode smaller in area than the (grounded) anode. A high d-c voltage ($\sim 100-1000$ V) develops across the sheath next to the rf powered cathode, such that positive ions gain kinetic energy by being accelerated in this region, and bombard the wafer normal to the surface. This bombardment at normal incidence contributes a physical component to the etch that makes it anisotropic. Physical etching, however, is rather unselective. Simultaneously, the highly reactive radicals in the system give rise to a chemical etch component that is very selective, but not anisotropic. The result is that RIE achieves a good compromise between anisotropy and selectivity, and has become the mainstay of modern IC etch technology.

Figure 5–8
Reactive ion etcher. Single or multiple wafers are placed on the rf powered cathode to maximize the ion bombardment. Shown in the figure is a simple *diode* etcher in which we have just two electrodes. We can also use a third electrode to supply rf power separately to the etch gases in a *triode* etcher. The most commonly used rf frequency is 13.56 MHz, which is a frequency dedicated to industrial use so that there is minimal interference with radio communications.

5.1.8 Metallization

After the semiconductor devices are made by the processing methods described previously, they have to be connected to each other, and ultimately to the IC package, by metallization. Metal films are generally deposited by a physical vapor deposition technique such as evaporation (e.g., Au on GaAs) or sputtering (e.g., Al on Si). Sputtering of Al is achieved by immersing an Al target (typically alloyed with ~1% Si and ~4% Cu to improve the electrical and metallurgical properties of the Al, as described in Section 9.3.1) in an Ar plasma. Argon ions bombard the Al and physically dislodge Al atoms by momentum transfer (Fig. 5–9). Many of the Al atoms ejected from the target deposit on the Si wafers held in close proximity to the target. The Al is then patterned using the metallization reticle and subsequently etched by RIE. Finally, it is sintered at ~450°C for ~30 minutes to form a good electrical, ohmic contact to the Si.

Recently, for Si integrated circuits, there has been a shift from Al to lower resistivity Cu metallization. Copper cannot be deposited by sputtering. Instead, it is electroplated on the chips. Copper metallization introduces special challenges because Cu diffuses fast in Si, and acts as a deep trap. Hence, prior to the electroplating of Cu, a barrier metal such as Ti is first sputter deposited to block Cu diffusion into Si. The Ti also acts as a seed layer for Cu electrodeposition.

After the interconnection metallization is complete, a protective overcoat of silicon nitride is deposited using plasma-enhanced CVD. Then the individual integrated circuits can be separated by sawing or by scribing and breaking the wafer. The final steps of the process are mounting individual devices in appropriate packages and connecting leads to the Al contact

Figure 5–9
Aluminum sputtering by Ar$^+$ ions. The Ar$^+$ ions with energies of ~1–3 keV physically dislodge Al atoms which end up depositing on the Si wafers held in close proximity. The chamber pressures are kept low such that the mean free path of the ejected Al atoms is long compared to the target-to-wafer separation.

Mask A
(doping)

Mask B
(metallization)

1. Oxidize the Si sample

2. Apply a layer of positive
photoresist (PR)

3. Expose PR through
mask A

4. Remove exposed PR

5. Use RIE to remove
SiO$_2$ in windows

6. Implant boron through
windows in the PR and
SiO$_2$ layers

7. Remove PR and sputter
Al onto the surface

8. Using PR and mask B,
repeat steps 2–4; etch away
Al except in p-contact areas

SiO$_2$

n Si

PR

Ultraviolet

Mask

Exposed PR removed

Window

Implanted p region

n

Al

Si covered
with SiO$_2$

Al

Top view

Figure 5–10
Simplified description of steps in the fabrication of p-n junctions. For simplicity, only four diodes per
wafer are shown, and the relative thicknesses of the oxide, PR, and the Al layers are exaggerated.

regions. Very precise lead bonders are available for bonding Au or Al wire
(about one thousandth of an inch in diameter) to the device and then to the
package leads. This phase of device fabrication is called back-end processing,
and is discussed in more detail in Chapter 9.

The main steps in making p-n junctions using some of these unit processes
are illustrated in Fig. 5–10. Similarly, we will discuss how the key semiconductor devices are made using these same unit processes in subsequent chapters.

**5.2
EQUILIBRIUM
CONDITIONS**

In this chapter we wish to develop both a useful mathematical description
of the p-n junction and a strong qualitative understanding of its properties.
There must be some compromise in these two goals, since a complete mathematical treatment would obscure the essentially simple physical features

of junction operation, while a completely qualitative description would not be useful in making calculations. The approach, therefore, will be to describe the junction mathematically while neglecting small effects which add little to the basic solution. In Section 5.6 we shall include several deviations from the simple theory.

The mathematics of p-n junctions is greatly simplified for the case of the *step junction*, which has uniform p doping on one side of a sharp junction and uniform n doping on the other side. This model represents epitaxial junctions quite well; diffused or implanted junctions, however, are actually *graded* ($N_d - N_a$ varies over a significant distance on either side of the junction). After the basic ideas of junction theory are explored for the step junction, we can make the appropriate corrections to extend the theory to the graded junction. In these discussions we shall assume one-dimensional current flow in samples of uniform cross-sectional area.

In this section we investigate the properties of the step junction at equilibrium (i.e., with no external excitation and no net currents flowing in the device). We shall find that the difference in doping on each side of the junction causes a potential difference between the two types of material. This is a reasonable result, since we would expect some charge transfer because of diffusion between the p material (many holes) and the n material (many electrons). In addition, we shall find that there are four components of current which flow across the junction due to the drift and diffusion of electrons and holes. These four components combine to give zero net current for the equilibrium case. However, the application of bias to the junction increases some of these current components with respect to others, giving net current flow. If we understand the nature of these four current components, a sound view of p-n junction operation, with or without bias, will follow.

5.2.1 The Contact Potential

Let us consider separate regions of p- and n-type semiconductor material, brought together to form a junction (Fig. 5–11). This is not a practical way of forming a device, but this "thought experiment" does allow us to discover the requirements of equilibrium at a junction. Before they are joined, the n material has a large concentration of electrons and few holes, whereas the converse is true for the p material. Upon joining the two regions (Fig. 5–11), we expect diffusion of carriers to take place because of the large carrier concentration gradients at the junction. Thus holes diffuse from the p side into the n side, and electrons diffuse from n to p. The resulting diffusion current cannot build up indefinitely, however, because an opposing electric field is created at the junction (Fig. 5–11b). If the two regions were boxes of red air molecules and green molecules (perhaps due to appropriate types of pollution), eventually there would be a homogeneous mixture of the two after the boxes were joined. This cannot occur in the case of the charged particles in a p-n junction because of the development of space charge and the electric field $\mathscr{E}$. If we consider that electrons diffusing from n to p leave behind

Figure 5-11
Properties of
an equilibrium
p-n junction:
(a) isolated,
neutral regions
of p-type and
n-type material
and energy
bands for the
isolated regions;
(b) junction,
showing space
charge in the
transition region
W, the resulting
electric field
$\mathscr{E}$ and contact
potential V_0, and
the separation of
the energy bands;
(c) directions
of the four
components
of particle
flow within the
transition region,
and the resulting
current directions.

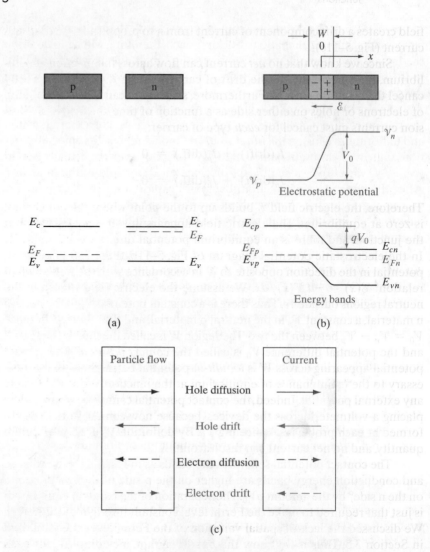

uncompensated[3] donor ions (N_d^+) in the n material, and holes leaving the p region leave behind uncompensated acceptors (N_a^-), it is easy to visualize the development of a region of positive space charge near the n side of the junction and negative charge near the p side. The resulting electric field is directed from the positive charge toward the negative charge. Thus $\mathscr{E}$ is in the direction opposite to that of diffusion current for each type of carrier (recall electron current is opposite to the direction of electron flow). Therefore, the

---

[3]We recall that neutrality is maintained in the bulk materials of Fig. 5-11a by the presence of one electron for each ionized donor ($n = N_d^+$) in the n material and one hole for each ionized acceptor ($p = N_a^-$) in the p material (neglecting minority carriers). Thus, if electrons leave n, some of the positive donor ions near the junction are left uncompensated, as in Fig. 5-11b. The donors and acceptors are fixed in the lattice, in contrast to the mobile electrons and holes.

field creates a drift component of current from n to p, opposing the diffusion current (Fig. 5–11c).

Since we know that no *net* current can flow across the junction at equilibrium, the current due to the drift of carriers in the $\mathscr{E}$ field must exactly cancel the diffusion current. Furthermore, since there can be no net buildup of electrons or holes on either side as a function of time, the drift and diffusion currents must cancel for *each* type of carrier:

$$J_p(\text{drift}) + J_p(\text{diff.}) = 0 \tag{5–3a}$$

$$J_n(\text{drift}) + J_n(\text{diff.}) = 0 \tag{5–3b}$$

Therefore, the electric field $\mathscr{E}$ builds up to the point where the net current is zero at equilibrium. The electric field appears in some region W about the junction, and there is an equilibrium potential difference V_0 across W. In the electrostatic potential diagram of Fig. 5–11b, there is a gradient in potential in the direction opposite to $\mathscr{E}$, in accordance with the fundamental relation[4] $\mathscr{E}(x) = -d\,\mathscr{V}(x)/dx$. We assume the electric field is zero in the neutral regions outside W. Thus there is a constant potential $\mathscr{V}_n$ in the neutral n material, a constant $\mathscr{V}_p$ in the neutral p material, and a potential difference $V_0 = \mathscr{V}_n - \mathscr{V}_p$ between the two. The region W is called the *transition region*,[5] and the potential difference V_0 is called the *contact potential*. The contact potential appearing across W is a *built-in* potential barrier, in that it is necessary to the maintenance of equilibrium at the junction; it does not imply any external potential. Indeed, the contact potential cannot be measured by placing a voltmeter across the devices, because new contact potentials are formed at each probe, just canceling V_0. By definition V_0 is an equilibrium quantity, and no net current can result from it.

The contact potential separates the bands as in Fig. 5–11b; the valence and conduction energy bands are higher on the p side of the junction than on the n side[6] by the amount qV_0. The separation of the bands at equilibrium is just that required to make the Fermi level constant throughout the device. We discussed the lack of spatial variation of the Fermi level at equilibrium in Section 3.5. Thus if we know the band diagram, including E_F, for each separate material (Fig. 5–11a), we can find the band separation for the junction at equilibrium simply by drawing a diagram such as Fig. 5–11b with the Fermi levels aligned.

[4]When we write $\mathscr{E}(x)$, we refer to the value of $\mathscr{E}$ as computed in the x-direction. This value will of course be negative, since it is directed opposite to the true direction of $\mathscr{E}$ as shown in Fig. 5–11b.

[5]Other names for this region are the *space charge region*, since space charge exists within W while neutrality is maintained outside this region, and the *depletion region*, since W is almost depleted of carriers compared with the rest of the crystal. The contact potential V_0 is also called the *diffusion potential*, since it represents a potential barrier which diffusing carriers must surmount in going from one side of the junction to the other.

[6]The electron energy diagram of Fig. 5–11b is related to the electrostatic potential diagram by $-q$, the negative charge on the electron. Since $\mathscr{V}_n$ is a higher potential than $\mathscr{V}_p$ by the amount V_0, the electron energies on the n side are *lower* than those on the p side by qV_0.

To obtain a quantitative relationship between V_0 and the doping concentrations on each side of the junction, we must use the requirements for equilibrium in the drift and diffusion current equations. For example, the drift and diffusion components of the hole current just cancel at equilibrium:

$$J_p(x) = q\left[\mu_p p(x)\mathscr{E}(x) - D_p\frac{dp(x)}{dx} \right] = 0 \qquad (5\text{--}4a)$$

This equation can be rearranged to obtain

$$\frac{\mu_p}{D_p}\mathscr{E}(x) = \frac{1}{p(x)}\frac{dp(x)}{dx} \qquad (5\text{--}4b)$$

where the x-direction is arbitrarily taken from p to n. The electric field can be written in terms of the gradient in the potential, $\mathscr{E}(x) = -d\mathcal{V}(x)/dx$, so that Eq. (5–4b) becomes

$$-\frac{q}{kT}\frac{d\mathcal{V}(x)}{dx} = \frac{1}{p(x)}\frac{dp(x)}{dx} \qquad (5\text{--}5)$$

with the use of the Einstein relation for μ_p/D_p. This equation can be solved by integration over the appropriate limits. In this case we are interested in the potential on either side of the junction, $\mathcal{V}_p$ and $\mathcal{V}_n$, and the hole concentration just at the edge of the transition region on either side, p_p and p_n. For a step junction it is reasonable to take the electron and hole concentration in the neutral regions outside the transition region as their equilibrium values. Since we have assumed a one-dimensional geometry, p and $\mathcal{V}$ can be taken reasonably as functions of x only. Integration of Eq. (5–5) gives

$$-\frac{q}{kT}\int_{\mathcal{V}_p}^{\mathcal{V}_n} d\mathcal{V} = \int_{p_p}^{p_n}\frac{1}{p} dp$$

$$-\frac{q}{kT}(\mathcal{V}_n - \mathcal{V}_p) = \ln p_n - \ln p_p = \ln\frac{p_n}{p_p} \qquad (5\text{--}6)$$

The potential difference $\mathcal{V}_n - \mathcal{V}_p$ is the contact potential V_0 (Fig. 5–11b). Thus we can write V_0 in terms of the equilibrium hole concentrations on either side of the junction:

$$V_0 = \frac{kT}{q}\ln\frac{p_p}{p_n} \qquad (5\text{--}7)$$

If we consider the step junction to be made up of material with N_a acceptors/cm^3 on the p side and a concentration of N_d donors on the n side, we can write Eq. (5–7) as

$$V_0 = \frac{kT}{q}\ln\frac{N_a}{n_i^2/N_d} = \frac{kT}{q}\ln\frac{N_a N_d}{n_i^2} \qquad (5\text{--}8)$$

by considering the majority carrier concentration to be the doping concentration on each side.

Another useful form of Eq. (5–7) is

$$\frac{p_p}{p_n} = e^{qV_0/kT} \tag{5-9}$$

By using the equilibrium condition $p_p n_p = n_i^2 = p_n n_n$, we can extend Eq. (5–9) to include the electron concentrations on either side of the junction:

$$\boxed{\frac{p_p}{p_n} = \frac{n_n}{n_p} = e^{qV_0/kT}} \tag{5-10}$$

This relation will be very valuable in calculation of the I–V characteristics of the junction.

An abrupt Si p-n junction has $N_a = 10^{18}\,\text{cm}^{-3}$ on one side and $N_d = 5 \times 10^{15}\,\text{cm}^{-3}$ on the other.   **EXAMPLE 5–1**

  (a) Calculate the Fermi level positions at 300 K in the p and n regions.

  (b) Draw an equilibrium band diagram for the junction and determine the contact potential V_0 from the diagram.

  (c) Compare the results of part (b) with V_0 as calculated from Eq. (5–8).

SOLUTION

(a) $E_{ip} - E_F = kT \ln \dfrac{p_p}{n_i} = 0.0259 \ln \dfrac{10^{18}}{(1.5 \times 10^{10})} = \mathbf{0.467\ eV}$

$E_F - E_{in} = kT \ln \dfrac{n_n}{n_i} = 0.0259 \ln \dfrac{5 \times 10^{15}}{(1.5 \times 10^{10})} = \mathbf{0.329\ eV}$

(b) $qV_0 = 0.467 + 0.329 = \mathbf{0.796\ eV}$

(c) $qV_0 = kT \ln \dfrac{N_a N_d}{n_i^2} = 0.0259 \ln \dfrac{5 \times 10^{33}}{2.25 \times 10^{20}} = \mathbf{0.796\ eV}$

5.2.2 Equilibrium Fermi Levels

We have observed that the Fermi level must be constant throughout the device at equilibrium. This observation can be easily related to the results of the previous section. Since we have assumed that p_n and p_p are given by their equilibrium values outside the transition region, we can write Eq. (5–9) in terms of the basic definitions of these quantities using Eq. (3–19):

$$\frac{p_p}{p_n} = e^{qV_0/kT} = \frac{N_v e^{-(E_{Fp}-E_{vp})/kT}}{N_v e^{-(E_{Fn}-E_{vn})/kT}} \tag{5–11a}$$

$$e^{qV_0/kT} = e^{(E_{Fn}-E_{Fp})/kT} e^{(E_{vp}-E_{vn})/kT} \tag{5–11b}$$

$$qV_0 = E_{vp} - E_{vn} \tag{5–12}$$

The Fermi level and valence band energies are written with subscripts to indicate the p side and the n side of the junction.

From Fig. 5–11b the energy bands on either side of the junction are separated by the contact potential V_0 times the electronic charge q; thus the energy difference $E_{vp} - E_{vn}$ is just qV_0. Equation (5–12) results from the fact that the Fermi levels on either side of the junction are equal at equilibrium ($E_{Fn} - E_{Fp} = 0$). When bias is applied to the junction, the potential barrier is raised or lowered from the value of the contact potential, and the Fermi levels on either side of the junction are shifted with respect to each other by an energy in electron volts numerically equal to the applied voltage in volts.

5.2.3 Space Charge at a Junction

Within the transition region, electrons and holes are in transit from one side of the junction to the other. Some electrons diffuse from n to p, and some are swept by the electric field from p to n (and conversely for holes); there are, however, very few carriers within the transition region at any given time, since the electric field serves to sweep out carriers which have wandered into W. To a good approximation, we can consider the space charge within the transition region as due only to the uncompensated donor and acceptor ions. The charge density within W is plotted in Fig. 5–12b. Neglecting carriers within the space charge region, the charge density on the n side is just q times the concentration of donor ions N_d, and the negative charge density on the p side is $-q$ times the concentration of acceptors N_a. The assumption of carrier depletion within W and neutrality outside W is known as the *depletion approximation*.

Figure 5–12
Space charge
and electric field
distribution within
the transition
region of a p-n
junction with
$N_d > N_a$:
(a) the transition
region, with
$x = 0$ defined at
the metallurgical
junction;
(b) charge
density within the
transition region,
neglecting the free
carriers; (c) the
electric field
distribution, where
the reference
direction for
$\mathscr{E}$ is arbitrarily
taken as the
+x-direction.

Since the dipole about the junction must have an equal number of charges on either side,[7] ($Q_+ = |Q_-|$), the transition region may extend into the p and n regions unequally, depending on the relative doping of the two sides. For example, if the p side is more lightly doped than the n side ($N_a < N_d$), the space charge region must extend farther into the p material than into the n, to "uncover" an equivalent amount of charge. For a sample of cross-sectional area A, the total uncompensated charge on either side of the junction is

$$qAx_{p0}N_a = qAx_{n0}N_d \qquad (5\text{--}13)$$

[7]A simple way of remembering this equal charge requirement is to note that electric flux lines must begin and end on charges of opposite sign. Therefore, if Q_+ and Q_- were not of equal magnitude, the electric field would not be contained within W but would extend farther into the p or n regions until the enclosed charges became equal.

where x_{p0} is the penetration of the space charge region into the p material, and x_{n0} is the penetration into n. The total width of the transition region (W) is the sum of x_{p0} and x_{n0}.

To calculate the electric field distribution within the transition region, we begin with *Poisson's equation,* which relates the gradient of the electric field to the local space charge at any point x:

$$\frac{d\mathscr{E}(x)}{dx} = \frac{q}{\epsilon}(p - n + N_d^+ - N_a^-) \tag{5-14}$$

This equation is greatly simplified within the transition region if we neglect the contribution of the carriers (p-n) to the space charge. With this approximation we have two regions of constant space charge:

$$\frac{d\mathscr{E}}{dx} = \frac{q}{\epsilon}N_d, \qquad 0 < x < x_{n0} \tag{5-15a}$$

$$\frac{d\mathscr{E}}{dx} = -\frac{q}{\epsilon}N_a, \qquad -x_{p0} < x < 0 \tag{5-15b}$$

assuming complete ionization of the impurities ($N_d^+ = N_d$) and ($N_a^- = N_a$). We can see from these two equations that a plot of $\mathscr{E}(x)$ vs. x within the transition region has two slopes, positive ($\mathscr{E}$ increasing with x) on the n side and negative ($\mathscr{E}$ becoming more negative as x increases) on the p side. There is some maximum value of the field $\mathscr{E}_0$ at $x = 0$ (the metallurgical junction between the p and n materials), and $\mathscr{E}(x)$ is everywhere negative within the transition region (Fig. 5–12c). These conclusions come from Gauss's law, but we could predict the qualitative features of Fig. 5–12 without equations. We expect the electric field $\mathscr{E}(x)$ to be negative throughout W, since we know that the $\mathscr{E}$ field actually points in the $-x$-direction, from n to p (i.e., from the positive charges of the transition region dipole toward the negative charges). The electric field is assumed to go to zero at the edges of the transition region, since we are neglecting any small $\mathscr{E}$ field in the neutral n or p regions. Finally, there must be a maximum $\mathscr{E}_0$ at the junction, since this point is between the charges Q_+ and Q_- on either side of the transition region. All the electric flux lines pass through the $x = 0$ plane, so this is the obvious point of maximum electric field.

The value of $\mathscr{E}_0$ can be found by integrating either part of Eq. (5–15) with appropriate limits (see Fig. 5–12c in choosing the limits of integration).

$$\int_{\mathscr{E}_0}^{0} d\mathscr{E} = \frac{q}{\epsilon}N_d \int_0^{x_{n0}} dx, \qquad 0 < x < x_{n0} \tag{5-16a}$$

$$\int_0^{\mathscr{E}_0} d\mathscr{E} = -\frac{q}{\epsilon}N_a \int_{-x_{p0}}^{0} dx, \qquad -x_{p0} < x < 0 \tag{5-16b}$$

Therefore, the maximum value of the electric field is

$$\mathscr{E}_0 = -\frac{q}{\epsilon}N_d x_{n0} = -\frac{q}{\epsilon}N_a x_{p0} \qquad (5\text{-}17)$$

It is simple to relate the electric field to the contact potential V_0, since the $\mathscr{E}$ field at any x is the negative of the potential gradient at that point:

$$\mathscr{E}(x) = -\frac{dV(x)}{dx} \quad \text{or} \quad -V_0 = \int_{-x_{p0}}^{x_{n0}} \mathscr{E}(x)dx \qquad (5\text{-}18)$$

Thus the negative of the contact potential is simply the area under the $\mathscr{E}(x)$ vs. x triangle. This relates the contact potential to the width of the depletion region:

$$V_0 = -\frac{1}{2}\mathscr{E}_0 W = \frac{1}{2}\frac{q}{\epsilon}N_d x_{n0} W \qquad (5\text{-}19)$$

Since the balance of charge requirement is $x_{n0}N_d = x_{p0}N_a$, and W is simply $x_{p0} + x_{n0}$, we can write $x_{n0} = WN_a/(N_a + N_d)$ in Eq. (5-19):

$$V_0 = \frac{1}{2}\frac{q}{\epsilon}\frac{N_a N_d}{N_a + N_d}W^2 \qquad (5\text{-}20)$$

By solving for W, we have an expression for the width of the transition region in terms of the contact potential, the doping concentrations, and known constants q and ϵ

$$\boxed{W = \left[\frac{2\epsilon V_0}{q}\left(\frac{N_a + N_d}{N_a N_d}\right)\right]^{1/2} = \left[\frac{2\epsilon V_0}{q}\left(\frac{1}{N_a} + \frac{1}{N_d}\right)\right]^{1/2}} \qquad (5\text{-}21)$$

There are several useful variations of Eq. (5-21); for example, V_0 can be written in terms of the doping concentrations with the aid of Eq. (5-8):

$$W = \left[\frac{2\epsilon kT}{q^2}\left(\ln\frac{N_a N_d}{n_i^2}\right)\left(\frac{1}{N_a} + \frac{1}{N_d}\right)\right]^{1/2} \qquad (5\text{-}22)$$

We can also calculate the penetration of the transition region into the n and p materials:

$$x_{p0} = \frac{WN_d}{N_a + N_d} = \frac{W}{1 + N_a/N_d} = \left\{\frac{2\epsilon V_0}{q}\left[\frac{N_d}{N_a(N_a + N_d)}\right]\right\}^{1/2} \qquad (5\text{-}23a)$$

$$x_{n0} = \frac{WN_a}{N_a + N_d} = \frac{W}{1 + N_d/N_a} = \left\{\frac{2\epsilon V_0}{q}\left[\frac{N_a}{N_d(N_a + N_d)}\right]\right\}^{1/2} \qquad (5\text{-}23b)$$

As expected, Eqs. (5-23) predict that the transition region extends farther into the side with the lighter doping. For example, if $N_a \ll N_d$, x_{p0} is large compared with x_{n0}. This agrees with our qualitative argument that a deep penetration is necessary in lightly doped material to "uncover" the same amount of space charge as for a short penetration into heavily doped material.

Another important result of Eq. (5–21) is that the transition width W varies as the square root of the potential across the region. In the derivation to this point, we have considered only the equilibrium contact potential V_0. In Section 5.3 we shall see that an applied voltage can increase or decrease the potential across the transition region by aiding or opposing the equilibrium electric field. Therefore, Eq. (5–21) predicts that an applied voltage will increase or decrease the width of the transition region as well.

EXAMPLE 5–2   The junction described in Example 5–1 has a circular cross section with a diameter of 10 μm. Calculate x_{n0}, x_{p0}, Q_+, and $\mathscr{E}_0$ for this junction at equilibrium (300 K). Sketch $\mathscr{E}(x)$ and charge density to scale, as in Fig. 5–12.

SOLUTION $A = \pi(5 \times 10^{-4})^2 = 7.85 \times 10^{-7}\,\text{cm}^2$

$$W = \left[\frac{2\epsilon V_0}{q}\left(\frac{1}{N_a} + \frac{1}{N_d}\right)\right]^{1/2}$$

$$= \left[\frac{2(11.8)(8.85 \times 10^{-14})(0.796)}{1.6 \times 10^{-19}}(10^{-18} + 2 \times 10^{-16})\right]^{1/2} = \mathbf{0.457\,\mu m}$$

$$x_{n0} = \frac{W}{1 + N_d/N_a} = \frac{0.457}{1 + 5 \times 10^{-3}} = \mathbf{0.455\ \mu m}$$

$$x_{p0} = \frac{0.457}{1 + 200} = \mathbf{2.27 \times 10^{-3}\,\mu m}$$

$$Q_+ = qAx_{n0}N_d = qAx_{p0}N_a = (1.6 \times 10^{-19})(7.85 \times 10^{-7})(2.27 \times 10^{11})$$

$$= \mathbf{2.85 \times 10^{-14}\,C}$$

$$\mathscr{E}_0 = -\frac{q}{\epsilon}x_{n0}N_d = -\frac{q}{\epsilon}x_{p0}N_a = \frac{1.6 \times 10^{-19}}{(11.8)(8.85 \times 10^{-14})}(2.27 \times 10^{11})$$

$$= \mathbf{-3.48 \times 10^4\,V/cm}$$

One useful feature of a p-n junction is that current flows quite freely in the p to n direction when the p region has a positive external voltage bias relative to n (forward bias and forward current), whereas virtually no current flows when p is made negative relative to n (reverse bias and reverse current). This asymmetry of the current flow makes the p-n junction diode very useful as a *rectifier*. While rectification is an important application, it is only the beginning of a host of uses for the biased junction. Biased p-n junctions can be used as voltage-variable capacitors, photocells, light emitters, and many more devices which are basic to modern electronics. Two or more junctions can be used to form transistors and controlled switches.

**5.3
FORWARD- AND
REVERSE-BIASED
JUNCTIONS;
STEADY STATE
CONDITIONS**

In this section we begin with a qualitative description of current flow in a biased junction. With the background of the previous section, the basic features of current flow are relatively simple to understand, and these qualitative concepts form the basis for the analytical description of forward and reverse currents in a junction.

5.3.1 Qualitative Description of Current Flow at a Junction

We assume that an applied voltage bias V appears across the transition region of the junction rather than in the neutral n and p regions. Of course, there will be some voltage drop in the neutral material, if a current flows through it. But in most p-n junction devices, the length of each region is small compared with its area, and the doping is usually moderate to heavy; thus the resistance is small in each neutral region, and only a small voltage drop can be maintained outside the space charge (transition) region. For almost all calculations it is valid to assume that an applied voltage appears entirely across the transition region. We shall take V to be positive when the external bias is positive on the p side relative to the n side.

Since an applied voltage changes the electrostatic potential barrier and thus the electric field within the transition region, we would expect changes in the various components of current at the junction (Fig. 5–13). In addition, the separation of the energy bands is affected by the applied bias, along with the width of the depletion region. Let us begin by examining qualitatively the effects of bias on the important features of the junction.

The *electrostatic potential barrier* at the junction is lowered by a forward bias V_f from the equilibrium contact potential V_0 to the smaller value $V_0 - V_f$. This lowering of the potential barrier occurs because a forward bias (p positive with respect to n) raises the electrostatic potential on the p side relative to the n side. For a reverse bias ($V = -V_r$) the opposite occurs; the electrostatic potential of the p side is depressed relative to the n side, and the potential barrier at the junction becomes larger ($V_0 + V_r$).

The *electric field* within the transition region can be deduced from the potential barrier. We notice that the field decreases with forward bias, since the applied electric field opposes the built-in field. With reverse bias the field at the junction is increased by the applied field, which is in the same direction as the equilibrium field.

The change in electric field at the junction calls for a change in the *transition region width W*, since it is still necessary that a proper number of positive

Figure 5–13
Effects of a bias at a p-n junction; transition region width and electric field, electrostatic potential, energy band diagram, and particle flow and current directions within W for (a) equilibrium, (b) forward bias, and (c) reverse bias. The electric fields vary linearly with position, as shown in Fig. 5–12, if the doping concentrations in the depletion regions are constant on either side of the junction. Since the electrostatic potential is obtained by integrating the (linearly varying) electric fields as shown in Eq. (5–18), the potential profiles (and band edges) vary as the square of distance from the depletion edges. Therefore, the shape of the band diagram in the depletion region is not linear, but consists of two parabolic curves that join smoothly.

and negative charges (in the form of uncompensated donor and acceptor ions) be exposed for a given value of the $\mathscr{E}$ field. Thus we would expect the width W to decrease under forward bias (smaller $\mathscr{E}$, fewer uncompensated charges) and to increase under reverse bias. Equations (5–21) and (5–23) can be used to calculate W, x_{p0}, and x_{n0} if V_0 is replaced by the new barrier height[8] $V_0 - V$.

The *separation of the energy bands* is a direct function of the electrostatic potential barrier at the junction. The height of the electron energy barrier is simply the electronic charge q times the height of the electrostatic potential barrier. Thus the bands are separated less $[q(V_0 - V_f)]$ under forward bias than at equilibrium, and more $[q(V_0 + V_r)]$ under reverse bias. We assume the Fermi level deep inside each neutral region is essentially the equilibrium value (we shall return to this assumption later); therefore, the shifting of the energy bands under bias implies a separation of the Fermi levels on either side of the junction, as mentioned in Section 5.2.2. Under forward bias, the Fermi level on the n side E_{Fn} is above E_{Fp} by the energy qV_f; for reverse bias, E_{Fp} is qV_r joules higher than E_{Fn}. *In energy units of electron volts, the Fermi levels in the two neutral regions are separated by an energy (eV) numerically equal to the applied voltage (V).*

The *diffusion current* is composed of majority carrier electrons on the n side surmounting the potential energy barrier to diffuse to the p side, and holes surmounting their barrier from p to n.[9] There is a distribution of energies for electrons in the n-side conduction band (Fig. 3–16), and some electrons in the high-energy "tail" of the distribution have enough energy to diffuse from n to p at equilibrium in spite of the barrier. With forward bias, however, the barrier is lowered (to $V_0 - V_f$), and many more electrons in the n-side conduction band have sufficient energy to diffuse from n to p over the smaller barrier. Therefore, the electron diffusion current can be quite large with forward bias. Similarly, more holes can diffuse from p to n under forward bias because of the lowered barrier. For reverse bias the barrier becomes so large $(V_0 + V_r)$ that virtually no electrons in the n-side conduction band or holes in the p-side valence band have enough energy to surmount it. Therefore, the diffusion current is usually negligible for reverse bias.

The *drift current* is relatively insensitive to the height of the potential barrier. This sounds strange at first, since we normally think in terms of material with ample carriers, and therefore we expect drift current to be simply proportional to the applied field. The reason for this apparent anomaly is the fact that the drift current is limited *not* by *how fast* carriers are swept down the barrier, *but* rather *how often*. For example, minority carrier electrons on the p side which wander into the transition region will be swept down the

---

[8]With bias applied to the junction, the 0 in the subscripts of x_{n0} and x_{p0} does not imply equilibrium. Instead, it signifies the origin of a new set of coordinates, $x_n = 0$ and $x_p = 0$, as defined later in Fig. 5–15.

[9]Remember that the potential energy barriers for electrons and holes are directed oppositely. The barrier for electrons is apparent from the energy band diagram, which is always drawn for electron energies. For holes, the potential energy barrier at the junction has the same shape as the electrostatic potential barrier (the conversion factor between electrostatic potential and hole energy is $+q$). A simple check of these two barrier directions can be made by asking the directions in which carriers are swept by the $\mathscr{E}$ field within the transition region—a hole is swept in the direction of $\mathscr{E}$, from n to p (swept down the potential "hill" for holes); an electron is swept opposite to $\mathscr{E}$, from p to n (swept down the potential energy "hill" for electrons).

barrier by the $\mathscr{E}$ field, giving rise to the electron component of drift current. However, this current is small not because of the size of the barrier, but because there are very few minority electrons in the p side to participate. Every electron on the p side which diffuses to the transition region will be swept down the potential energy hill, whether the hill is large or small. The electron drift current does not depend on how fast an individual electron is swept from p to n, but rather on how many electrons are swept down the barrier per second. Similar comments apply regarding the drift of minority holes from the n side to the p side of the junction. To a good approximation, therefore, the electron and hole drift currents at the junction are independent of the applied voltage.

The supply of minority carriers on each side of the junction required to participate in the drift component of current is generated by thermal excitation of electron–hole pairs (EHPs). For example, an EHP created near the junction on the p side provides a minority electron in the p material. If the EHP is generated within a diffusion length L_n of the transition region, this electron can diffuse to the junction and be swept down the barrier to the n side. The resulting current due to drift of generated carriers across the junction is commonly called the *generation current* since its magnitude depends entirely on the rate of generation of EHPs. As we shall discuss later, this generation current can be increased greatly by optical excitation of EHPs near the junction (the p-n junction *photodiode*).

The *total current* crossing the junction is composed of the sum of the diffusion and drift components. As Fig. 5–13 indicates, the electron and hole diffusion currents are both directed from p to n (although the particle flow directions are opposite to each other), and the drift currents are from n to p. The *net* current crossing the junction is zero at equilibrium, since the drift and diffusion components cancel for each type of carrier (the equilibrium electron and hole components need not be equal, as in Fig. 5–13, as long as the net hole current and the net electron current are each zero). Under reverse bias, both diffusion components are negligible because of the large barrier at the junction, and the only current is the relatively small (and essentially voltage-independent) generation current from n to p. This generation current is shown in Fig. 5–14, in a sketch of a typical *I–V* plot for a p-n junction. In this figure the positive direction for the current *I* is taken from p to n, and the applied voltage *V* is positive when the positive battery terminal is connected to p and the negative terminal to n. The only current flowing in this p-n junction diode for negative *V* is the small current *I*(gen.) due to carriers generated in the transition region or minority carriers which diffuse to the junction and are collected. The current at $V = 0$ (equilibrium) is zero since the generation and diffusion currents cancel:[10]

$$I = I(\text{diff.}) - |I(\text{gen.})| = 0 \text{ for } V = 0 \qquad (5\text{–}24)$$

[10]The total current *I* is the sum of the generation and diffusion components. However, these components are oppositely directed, with *I*(diff.) being positive and *I*(gen.) being negative for the chosen reference direction. To avoid confusion of signs, we use here the magnitude of the drift current $|I(\text{gen.})|$ and include its negative sign in Eq. (5–24). Thus, when we write the term $-|I(\text{gen.})|$, there is no doubt that the generation current is in the negative current direction. This approach emphasizes the fact that the two components of current add with opposite signs to give the total current.

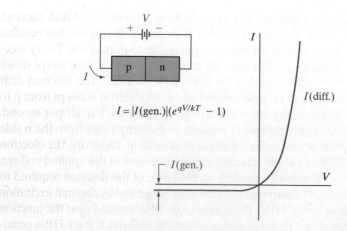

Figure 5–14
I–V characteristic
of a p-n junction.

$$I = |I(\text{gen.})|(e^{qV/kT} - 1)$$

As we shall see in the next section, an applied forward bias $V = V_f$ increases the probability that a carrier can diffuse across the junction, by the factor $\exp(qV_f/kT)$. Thus the diffusion current under forward bias is given by its equilibrium value multiplied by $\exp(qV/kT)$; similarly, for reverse bias the diffusion current is the equilibrium value reduced by the same factor, with $V = -V_r$. Since the equilibrium diffusion current is equal in magnitude to $|I(\text{gen.})|$, the diffusion current with applied bias is simply $|I(\text{gen.})| \exp(qV/kT)$. The total current I is then the diffusion current minus the absolute value of the generation current, which we will now refer to as I_0:

$$I = I_0(e^{qV/kT} - 1) \tag{5–25}$$

In Eq. (5–25) the applied voltage V can be positive or negative, $V = V_f$ or $V = -V_r$. When V is positive and greater than a few kT/q ($kT/q = 0.0259$ V at room temperature), the exponential term is much greater than unity. The current thus increases exponentially with forward bias. When V is negative (reverse bias), the exponential term approaches zero and the current is $-I_0$, which is in the n to p (negative) direction. This negative generation current is also called the *reverse saturation current*. The striking feature of Fig. 5–14 is the nonlinearity of the I–V characteristic. Current flows relatively freely in the forward direction of the diode, but almost no current flows in the reverse direction.

5.3.2 Carrier Injection

From the discussion in the previous section, we expect the minority carrier concentration on each side of a p-n junction to vary with the applied bias because of variations in the diffusion of carriers across the junction. The equilibrium ratio of hole concentrations on each side

$$\frac{p_p}{p_n} = e^{qV_0/kT} \tag{5–26}$$

becomes with bias (Fig. 5–13)

$$\frac{p(-x_{p0})}{p(x_{n0})} = e^{q(V_0 - V)/kT} \tag{5-27}$$

This equation uses the altered barrier $V_0 - V$ to relate the steady state hole concentrations on the two sides of the transition region with either forward or reverse bias (V positive or negative). For low-level injection we can neglect changes in the majority carrier concentrations. Although the absolute increase of the majority carrier concentration is equal to the increase of the minority carrier concentration in order to maintain space charge neutrality, the relative change in majority carrier concentration can be assumed to vary only slightly with bias compared with equilibrium values. With this simplification we can write the ratio of Eq. (5–26) to (5–27) as

$$\frac{p(x_{n0})}{p_n} = e^{qV/kT} \quad \text{taking } p(-x_{p0}) = p_p \tag{5-28}$$

With forward bias, Eq. (5–28) suggests a greatly increased minority carrier hole concentration at the edge of the transition region on the n side $p(x_{n0})$ than was the case at equilibrium. Conversely, the hole concentration $p(x_{n0})$ under reverse bias (V negative) is reduced below the equilibrium value p_n. The exponential increase of the hole concentration at x_{n0} with forward bias is an example of *minority carrier injection*. As Fig. 5–15 suggests, a forward bias V results in a steady state injection of excess holes into the n region and electrons into the p region. We can easily calculate the excess hole concentration Δp_n at the edge of the transition region x_{n0} by subtracting the equilibrium hole concentration from Eq. (5–28),

$$\boxed{\Delta p_n = p(x_{n0}) - p_n = p_n(e^{qV/kT} - 1)} \tag{5-29}$$

and similarly for excess electrons on the p side,

$$\boxed{\Delta n_p = n(-x_{p0}) - n_p = n_p(e^{qV/kT} - 1)} \tag{5-30}$$

From our study of diffusion of excess carriers in Section 4.4.4, we expect that injection leading to a steady concentration of Δp_n excess holes at x_{n0} will produce a *distribution* of excess holes in the n material. As the holes diffuse deeper into the n region, they recombine with electrons in the n material, and the resulting excess hole distribution is obtained as a solution of the diffusion equation, Eq. (4–34b). If the n region is long compared with the hole diffusion length L_p, the solution is exponential, as in Eq. (4–36). Similarly, the injected electrons in the p material diffuse and recombine, giving an exponential distribution of excess electrons. For convenience, let us define two new coordinates (Fig. 5–15): Distances measured in the x-direction in the n material from x_{n0} will be designated x_n; distances in the p material measured in the $-x$-direction with $-x_{p0}$ as the origin will

Figure 5–15
Forward-biased junction: (a) minority carrier distributions on the two sides of the transition region and definitions of distances x_n and x_p measured from the transition region edges; (b) variation of the quasi-Fermi levels with position.

be called x_p. This convention will simplify the mathematics considerably. We can write the diffusion equation as in Eq. (4–34) for each side of the junction and solve for the distributions of excess carriers (δn and δp) assuming long p and n regions:

$$\delta n(x_p) = \Delta n_p e^{-x_p/L_n} = n_p(e^{qV/kT} - 1)e^{-x_p/L_n} \qquad (5\text{–}31a)$$

$$\delta p(x_n) = \Delta p_n e^{-x_n/L_p} = p_n(e^{qV/kT} - 1)e^{-x_n/L_p} \qquad (5\text{–}31b)$$

The hole diffusion current at any point x_n in the n material can be calculated from Eq. (4–40):

$$I_p(x_n) = -qAD_p\frac{d\delta p(x_n)}{dx_n} = qA\frac{D_p}{L_p}\Delta p_n e^{-x_n/L_p} = qA\frac{D_p}{L_p}\delta p(x_n) \quad (5\text{–}32)$$

where A is the cross-sectional area of the junction. Thus the hole diffusion current at each position x_n is proportional to the excess hole concentration at that point.[11] The total hole current injected into the n material at the junction can be obtained simply by evaluating Eq. (5–32) at x_{n0}:

$$I_p(x_n = 0) = \frac{qAD_p}{L_p}\Delta p_n = \frac{qAD_p}{L_p}p_n(e^{qV/kT} - 1) \qquad (5\text{–}33)$$

By a similar analysis, the injection of electrons into the p material leads to an electron current at the junction of

$$I_n(x_p = 0) = -\frac{qAD_n}{L_n}\Delta n_p = -\frac{qAD_n}{L_n}n_p(e^{qV/kT} - 1) \qquad (5\text{–}34)$$

The minus sign in Eq. (5–34) means that the electron current is opposite to the x_p-direction; that is, the true direction of I_n is in the $+x$-direction, adding to I_p in the total current (Fig. 5–16). If we neglect recombination in the transition region, which is known as the Shockley ideal diode approximation, we can consider that each injected electron reaching $-x_{p0}$ must pass through x_{n0}. Thus the total diode current I at x_{n0} can be calculated as the sum of $I_p(x_n = 0)$ and $-I_n(x_p = 0)$. If we take the $+x$-direction as the reference direction for the total current I, we must use a minus sign with $I_n(x_p)$ to account for the fact that x_p is defined in the $-x$-direction:

$$I = I_p(x_n = 0) - I_n(x_p = 0) = \frac{qAD_p}{L_p}\Delta p_n + \frac{qAD_n}{L_n}\Delta n_p \qquad (5\text{–}35)$$

$$\boxed{I = qA\left(\frac{D_p}{L_p}p_n + \frac{D_n}{L_n}n_p\right)(e^{qV/kT} - 1) = I_0(e^{qV/kT} - 1)} \qquad (5\text{–}36)$$

Equation (5–36) is the *diode equation*, having the same form as the qualitative relation Eq. (5–25). Nothing in the derivation excludes the possibility that the bias voltage V can be negative; thus the diode equation describes the total current through the diode for either forward or reverse bias. We can calculate the current for reverse bias by letting $V = -V_r$:

$$I = qA\left(\frac{D_p}{L_p}p_n + \frac{D_n}{L_n}n_p\right)(e^{-qV_r/kT} - 1) \qquad (5\text{–}37\text{a})$$

If V_r is larger than a few kT/q, the total current is just the reverse saturation current

$$I = -qA\left(\frac{D_p}{L_p}p_n + \frac{D_n}{L_n}n_p\right) = -I_0 \qquad (5\text{–}37\text{b})$$

[11]With carrier injection due to bias, it is clear that the equilibrium Fermi levels cannot be used to describe carrier concentrations in the device. It is necessary to use the concept of quasi-Fermi levels, taking into account the spatial variations of the carrier concentrations.

Figure 5–16
Two methods for calculating junction current from the excess minority carrier distributions: (a) diffusion currents at the edges of the transition region; (b) charge in the distributions divided by the minority carrier lifetimes; (c) the diode equation.

(a)

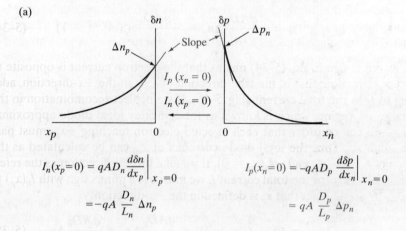

$$I_n(x_p=0) = qAD_n \frac{d\delta n}{dx_p}\bigg|_{x_p=0}$$

$$= -qA\frac{D_n}{L_n}\Delta n_p$$

$$I_p(x_n=0) = -qAD_p \frac{d\delta p}{dx_n}\bigg|_{x_n=0}$$

$$= qA\frac{D_p}{L_p}\Delta p_n$$

(b)

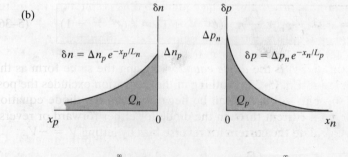

$$\delta n = \Delta n_p\, e^{-x_p/L_n}$$

$$\delta p = \Delta p_n\, e^{-x_n/L_p}$$

$$Q_n = -qA\int_0^\infty \delta n(x_p)\, dx_p$$

$$Q_p = qA\int_0^\infty \delta p(x_n)\, dx_n$$

$$I_n(x_p=0) = \frac{Q_n}{\tau_n} = \frac{-qAL_n}{\tau_n}\Delta n_p$$

$$I_p(x_n=0) = \frac{Q_p}{\tau_p} = \frac{qAL_p}{\tau_p}\Delta p_n$$

(c)

$$I = I_p(x_n=0) - I_n(x_p=0) = qA\left(\frac{D_p}{L_p}\Delta p_n + \frac{D_n}{L_n}\Delta n_p\right)$$

$$= qA\left(\frac{D_p p_n}{L_p} + \frac{D_n n_p}{L_n}\right)(e^{qV/kT}-1)$$

One implication of Eq. (5–36) is that the total current at the junction is dominated by injection of carriers from the more heavily doped side into the side with lesser doping. For example, if the p material is very heavily doped and the n region is lightly doped, the minority carrier concentration on the p side (n_p) is negligible compared with the minority carrier concentration on the n side (p_n). Thus the diode equation can be approximated by injection of holes only, as in Eq. (5–33). This means that the charge stored in the minority carrier distributions is due mostly to holes on the n side. For example, to double the hole current in this p^+-n junction one should not double the p^+ doping, but rather reduce the n-type doping by a factor of two. This structure is called a p^+-n junction, where the + superscript simply means heavy doping. Another characteristic of the p^+-n or n^+-p structure is that the transition region extends primarily into the lightly doped region, as we found in the discussion of Eq. (5–23). Having one side heavily doped is a useful arrangement for many practical devices, as we shall see in our discussions of switching diodes and transistors. This type of junction is common in devices which are fabricated by counterdoping. For example, an n-type Si sample with $N_d = 10^{14}\,cm^{-3}$ can be used as the substrate for an implanted or diffused junction. If the doping of the p region is greater than $10^{19}\,cm^{-3}$ (typical of diffused junctions), the structure is definitely p^+-n, with n_p more than five orders of magnitude smaller than p_n. Since this configuration is common in device technology, we shall return to it in much of the following discussion.

Figure 5–15b shows the quasi-Fermi levels as a function of position for a p-n junction in forward bias. The equilibrium E_F is split into the quasi-Fermi levels F_n and F_p which are separated within W by an energy qV caused by the applied bias, V. This energy represents the deviation from equilibrium (see Section 4.3.3). In forward bias in the depletion region we thus get

$$pn = n_i^2 e^{(F_n - F_p)/kT} = n_i^2 e^{(qV/kT)} \tag{5–38}$$

On either side of the junction, it is the minority carrier quasi-Fermi level that varies the most. The majority carrier concentration is not affected much, so the majority carrier quasi-Fermi level is close to the original E_F. Although there is some variation in E_F and F_p within W, it doesn't show up on the scale used in Fig. 5–15. Outside of the depletion regions, the quasi-Fermi levels for the minority carriers vary linearly and eventually merge with the Fermi levels. In contrast, the minority carrier concentrations decay exponentially with distance. In fact it takes many diffusion lengths for the quasi-Fermi level to cross E_i, where the minority carrier concentration is equal to the intrinsic carrier concentration, let alone approach E_F, where for example $\delta p(x_n) \simeq p_n$.

Another simple and instructive way of calculating the total current is to consider the injected current as supplying the carriers for the excess distributions (Fig. 5–16b). For example, $I_p(x_n = 0)$ must supply enough holes per second to maintain the steady state exponential distribution $\Delta p(x_n)$ as the holes recombine. The total positive charge stored in the excess carrier distribution at any instant of time is

$$Q_p = qA \int_0^\infty \delta p(x_n) dx_n = qA \Delta p_n \int_0^\infty e^{-x_n/L_p} dx_n = qAL_p \Delta p_n \quad (5\text{-}39)$$

The average lifetime of a hole in the n-type material is τ_p. Thus, on the average, this entire charge distribution recombines and must be replenished every τ_p seconds. The injected hole current at $x_n = 0$ needed to maintain the distribution is simply the total charge divided by the average time of replacement:

$$I_p(x_n = 0) = \frac{Q_p}{\tau_p} = qA\frac{L_p}{\tau_p}\Delta p_n = qA\frac{D_p}{L_p}\Delta p_n \quad (5\text{-}40)$$

using $D_p/L_p = L_p/\tau_p$.

This is the same result as Eq. (5-33), which was calculated from the diffusion currents. Similarly, we can calculate the negative charge stored in the distribution $\delta n(x_p)$ and divide by τ_n to obtain the injected electron current in the p material. This method, called the *charge control approximation*, illustrates the important fact that the minority carriers injected into either side of a p-n junction diffuse into the neutral material and recombine with the majority carriers. The minority carrier current [for example, $I_p(x_n)$] decreases exponentially with distance into the neutral region. Thus several diffusion lengths away from the junction, most of the total current is carried by the majority carriers. We shall discuss this point in more detail later in this section.

In summary, we can calculate the current at a p-n junction in two ways (Fig. 5-16): (a) from the slopes of the excess minority carrier distributions at the two edges of the transition regions and (b) from the steady state charge stored in each distribution. We add the hole current injected into the n material $I_p(x_n = 0)$ to the electron current injected into the p material $I_p(x_p = 0)$, after including a minus sign with $I_n(x_p)$ to conform with the conventional definition of positive current in the $+x$-direction. We are able to add these two currents because of the assumption that no recombination takes place within the transition region. Thus we effectively have the total electron and hole current at one point in the device (x_{n0}). Since the total current must be constant throughout the device (despite variations in the current components), I as described by Eq. (5-36) is the total current at every position x in the diode.

The drift of minority carriers can be neglected in the neutral regions *outside W*, because the minority carrier concentration is small compared with that of the majority carriers. If the minority carriers contribute to the total current at all, their contribution must be through diffusion (dependent on the *gradient* of the carrier concentration). Even a very small concentration of minority carriers can have an appreciable effect on the current if the spatial variation is large.

Calculation of the majority carrier currents in the two neutral regions is simple, once we have found the minority carrier current. Since the total current I must be constant throughout the device, the majority carrier component of current at any point is just the difference between I and the minority component (Fig. 5–17). For example, since $I_p(x_n)$ is proportional to the excess hole concentration at each position in the n material [Eq. (5–32)], it decreases exponentially in x_n with the decreasing $\delta p(x_n)$. Thus the electron component of current must increase appropriately with x_n to maintain the total current I. Far from the junction, the current in the n material is carried almost entirely by electrons. The physical explanation of this is that electrons must flow in from the n material (and ultimately from the negative terminal of the battery), to resupply electrons lost by recombination in the excess hole distribution near the junction. The electron current $I_n(x_n)$ includes sufficient electron flow to supply not only recombination near x_{n0}, but also injection of electrons into the p region. Of course, the flow of electrons in the n material toward the junction constitutes a current in the $+x$-direction, contributing to the total current I.

One question that still remains to be answered is whether the majority carrier current is due to drift or diffusion or both, at different points in the

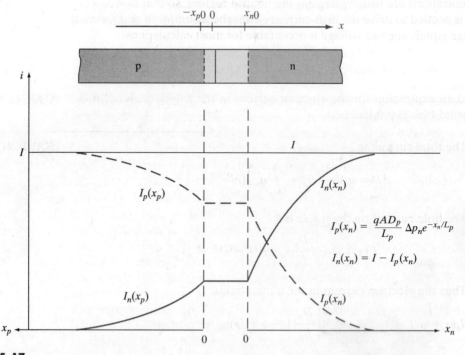

Figure 5–17
Electron and hole components of current in a forward-biased p-n junction. In this example, we have a higher injected minority hole current on the n side than electron current on the p side because we have a lower n doping than p doping.

diode. Near the junction (just outside of the depletion regions) the majority carrier concentration changes by exactly the same amount as minority carriers in order to maintain space charge neutrality. The majority carrier concentration can change rather fast, in a very short time scale known as the dielectric relaxation time, $\tau_D(=\rho\epsilon)$, where ρ is the resistivity and ϵ is the dielectric constant. The relaxation time τ_D is the analog of the RC time constant in a circuit. Very far away from the junction (more than 3 to 5 diffusion lengths), the minority carrier concentration decays to a low, constant background value. Hence, the majority carrier concentration also becomes independent of position. Here, clearly the only possible current component is majority carrier drift current. When approaching the junction there is a spatially varying majority (and minority) carrier concentration and the majority carrier current changes from pure drift to drift and diffusion, although drift always dominates for majority carriers except in cases of very high levels of injection. Throughout the diode, the total current due to majority and minority carriers at any cross section is kept constant.

We thus note that the electric field in the neutral regions cannot be zero as we previously assumed; otherwise, there would be no drift currents. Thus our assumption that all of the applied voltage appears across the transition region is not completely accurate. On the other hand, the majority carrier concentrations are usually large in the neutral regions, so that only a small field is needed to drive the drift currents. Thus the assumption that junction voltage equals applied voltage is acceptable for most calculations.

Find an expression for the electron current in the n-type material of a forward-biased p-n junction.

EXAMPLE 5–3

The total current is

SOLUTION

$$I = qA\left(\frac{D_p}{L_p}p_n + \frac{D_n}{L_n}n_p\right)(e^{qV/kT} - 1)$$

The hole current on the n side is

$$I_p(x_n) = qA\frac{D_p}{L_p}p_n e^{-x_n/L_p}(e^{qV/kT} - 1)$$

Thus the electron current in the n material is

$$I_n(x_n) = I - I_p(x_n) = qA\left[\frac{D_p}{L_p}(1 - e^{-x_n/L_p})p_n + \frac{D_n}{L_n}n_p\right](e^{qV/kT} - 1)$$

This expression includes the supplying of electrons for recombination with the injected holes, and the injection of electrons across the junction into the p side.

5.3.3 Reverse Bias

In our discussion of carrier injection and minority carrier distributions, we have primarily assumed forward bias. The distributions for reverse bias can be obtained from the same equations (Fig. 5–18), if a negative value of V is introduced. For example, if $V = -V_r$ (p negatively biased with respect to n), we can approximate Eq. (5–29) as

$$\Delta p_n = p_n(e^{q(-V_r)/kT} - 1) \simeq -p_n \quad \text{for } V_r \gg kT/q \quad (5\text{--}41)$$

and similarly $\Delta n_p \simeq -n_p$.

Thus for a reverse bias of more than a few tenths of a volt, the minority carrier concentration at each edge of the transition region becomes

(a)

(b)

Figure 5–18
Reverse-biased p-n junction: (a) minority carrier distributions near the reverse-biased junction; (b) variation of the quasi-Fermi levels.

essentially zero as the excess concentration approaches the negative of the equilibrium concentration. The excess minority carrier concentrations in the neutral regions are still given by Eq. (5–31), so that depletion of carriers below the equilibrium values extends approximately a diffusion length beyond each side of the transition region. This reverse-bias depletion of minority carriers can be thought of as *minority carrier extraction,* analogous to the injection of forward bias. Physically, extraction occurs because minority carriers at the edges of the depletion region are swept down the barrier at the junction to the other side and are not replaced by an opposing diffusion of carriers. For example, when holes at x_{n0} are swept across the junction to the p side by the $\mathscr{E}$ field, a gradient in the hole distribution in the n material exists, and holes in the n region diffuse toward the junction. The steady state hole distribution in the n region has the inverted exponential shape of Fig. 5–18a. It is important to remember that although the reverse saturation current occurs at the junction by drift of carriers down the barrier, this current is fed from each side by diffusion toward the junction of minority carriers in the neutral regions. The rate of carrier drift across the junction (reverse saturation current) depends on the rate at which holes arrive at x_{n0} (and electrons at x_{p0}) by diffusion from the neutral material. These minority carriers are supplied by thermal generation, and we can show that the expression for the reverse saturation current, Eq. (5–38), represents the rate at which carriers are generated thermally within a diffusion length of each side of the transition region.

In reverse bias, the quasi-Fermi levels split in the opposite sense than in forward bias (Fig. 5–18b). The F_n moves farther away from E_c (close to E_v) and F_p moves farther away from E_v, reflecting the fact that in reverse bias we have fewer carriers than in equilibrium, unlike the forward bias case where we have an excess of carriers. In reverse bias, in the depletion region, we have

$$pn = n_i^2 e^{(F_n - F_p)/kT} \approx 0 \tag{5–42}$$

It is interesting to note that the quasi-Fermi levels in reverse bias can go inside the bands. For example, F_p goes inside the conduction band on the n side of the depletion region. However, we must remember that F_p is a measure of the hole concentration, and should be correlated with the valence band edge, E_v, and not with E_c. Hence, the band diagram simply reflects the fact that we have very few holes in this region, even fewer than the already small equilibrium minority carrier hole concentration (Fig. 5–18a). Similar observations can be made about the electrons.

An abrupt Si p-n junction ($A = 10^{-4}\,\text{cm}^2$) has the following properties   **EXAMPLE 5–4**
at 300 K:

	p side	n side
	$N_a = 10^{17}\,\text{cm}^{-3}$	$N_d = 10^{15}$
	$\tau_n = 0.1\,\mu\text{s}$	$\tau_p = 10\,\mu\text{s}$

$$\mu_p = 200 \text{ cm}^2/\text{V}-\text{s} \qquad \mu_n = 1300$$
$$\mu_n = 700 \qquad \mu_p = 450$$

The junction is forward biased by 0.5 V. What is the forward current? What is the current at a reverse bias of –0.5 V?

SOLUTION

$$I = qA\left(\frac{D_p}{L_p}p_n + \frac{D_n}{L_n}n_p\right)(e^{qV/kT} - 1) = I_0(e^{qV/kT} - 1)$$

$$p_n = \frac{n_i^2}{n_n} = \frac{(1.5 \times 10^{10})^2}{10^{15}} = 2.25 \times 10^5 \text{ cm}^{-3}$$

$$n_p = \frac{n_i^2}{p_p} = \frac{(1.5 \times 10^{10})^2}{10^{17}} = 2.25 \times 10^3 \text{ cm}^{-3}$$

For minority carriers,

$$D_p = \frac{kT}{q}\mu_p = 0.0259 \times 450 = 11.66 \text{ cm}^2/\text{s on the n side}$$

$$D_n = \frac{kT}{q}\mu_n = 0.0259 \times 700 = 18.13 \text{ cm}^2/\text{s on the p side}$$

$$L_p = \sqrt{D_p\tau_p} = \sqrt{11.66 \times 10 \times 10^{-6}} = 1.08 \times 10^{-2} \text{ cm}$$
$$L_n = \sqrt{D_n\tau_n} = \sqrt{18.13 \times 0.1 \times 10^{-6}} = 1.35 \times 10^{-3} \text{ cm}$$
$$I_0 = qA\left(\frac{D_p}{L_p}p_n + \frac{D_n}{L_n}n_p\right)$$

$$= 1.6 \times 10^{-19} \times 0.0001\left(\frac{11.66}{0.0108}2.25 \times 10^5 + \frac{18.13}{0.00135}2.25 \times 10^3\right)$$

$$= 4.370 \times 10^{-15}\text{A}$$
$$I = I_0(e^{0.5/0.0259} - 1) \approx \mathbf{1.058 \times 10^{-6}\text{A} \text{ in forward bias.}}$$
$$I = -I_0 = \mathbf{-4.37 \times 10^{-15}\text{A} \text{ in reverse bias.}}$$

5.4
REVERSE-BIAS
BREAKDOWN

We have found that a p-n junction biased in the reverse direction exhibits a small, essentially voltage-independent saturation current. This is true until a critical reverse bias is reached, for which *reverse breakdown* occurs (Fig. 5–19). At this critical voltage (V_{br}) the reverse current through the diode increases sharply, and relatively large currents can flow with little further increase in voltage. The existence of a critical breakdown voltage introduces almost a right-angle appearance to the reverse characteristic of most diodes.

There is nothing inherently destructive about reverse breakdown. If the current is limited to a reasonable value by the external circuit, the p-n junction can be operated in reverse breakdown as safely as in the forward-bias

Figure 5–19
Reverse
breakdown in a
p-n junction.

condition. For example, the maximum reverse current which can flow in the device of Fig. 5–19 is $(E - V_{br})/R$; the series resistance R can be chosen to limit the current to a safe level for the particular diode used. If the current is not limited externally, the junction can be damaged by excessive reverse current, which overheats the device as the maximum power rating is exceeded. It is important to remember, however, that such destruction of the device is not necessarily due to mechanisms unique to reverse breakdown; similar results occur if the device passes excessive current in the forward direction.[12] As we shall see in Section 5.4.4, useful devices called *breakdown diodes* are designed to operate in the reverse breakdown regime of their characteristics.

Reverse breakdown can occur by two mechanisms, each of which requires a critical electric field in the junction transition region. The first mechanism, called the *Zener effect*, is operative at low voltages (up to a few volts reverse bias). If the breakdown occurs at higher voltages (from a few volts to thousands of volts), the mechanism is *avalanche breakdown*. We shall discuss these two mechanisms in this section.

5.4.1 Zener Breakdown

When a heavily doped junction is reverse biased, the energy bands become crossed at relatively low voltages (i.e., the n-side conduction band appears opposite the p-side valence band). As Fig. 5–20 indicates, the crossing of the bands aligns the large number of empty states in the n-side conduction

---

[12]The dissipated power (IV) in the junction is, of course, greater for a given current in the breakdown regime than it would be for the forward bias, simply because V is greater.

Figure 5–20
The Zener effect:
(a) heavily
doped junction
at equilibrium;
(b) reverse bias
with electron
tunneling from
p to n; (c) I–V
characteristic.

band opposite the many filled states of the p-side valence band. If the barrier separating these two bands is narrow, tunneling of electrons can occur, as discussed in Section 2.4.4. Tunneling of electrons from the p-side valence band to the n-side conduction band constitutes a reverse current from n to p; this is the *Zener effect*.

The basic requirements for tunneling current are a large number of electrons separated from a large number of empty states by a narrow barrier of finite height. Since the tunneling probability depends upon the width of the barrier (*d* in Fig. 5–20), it is important that the metallurgical junction be sharp and the doping high, so that the transition region *W* extends only a very short distance from each side of the junction. If the junction is not abrupt, or if either side of the junction is lightly doped, the transition region *W* will be too wide for tunneling.

As the bands are crossed (at a few tenths of a volt for a heavily doped junction), the tunneling distance *d* may be too large for appreciable tunneling. However, *d* becomes smaller as the reverse bias is increased, because the higher electric fields result in steeper slopes for the band edges. This assumes that the transition region width *W* does not increase appreciably with reverse bias. For low voltages and heavy doping on each side of the junction, this is a good assumption. However, if Zener breakdown does not occur with reverse bias of a few volts, avalanche breakdown will become dominant.

In the simple covalent bonding model (Fig. 3–1), the Zener effect can be thought of as *field ionization* of the host atoms at the junction. That is, the reverse bias of a heavily doped junction causes a large electric field within *W*; at a critical field strength, electrons participating in covalent bonds may be torn from the bonds by the field and accelerated to the n side of the junction. The electric field required for this type of ionization is on the order of 10^6 V/cm.

5.4.2 Avalanche Breakdown

For lightly doped junctions electron tunneling is negligible, and instead, the breakdown mechanism involves the *impact ionization* of host atoms by energetic carriers. Normal lattice-scattering events can result in the creation of

EHPs if the carrier being scattered has sufficient energy. For example, if the electric field $\mathscr{E}$ in the transition region is large, an electron entering from the p side may be accelerated to high enough kinetic energy to cause an ionizing collision with the lattice (Fig. 5–21a). A single such interaction results in *carrier multiplication*; the original electron and the generated electron are both swept to the n side of the junction, and the generated hole is swept to the p side (Fig. 5–21b). The degree of multiplication can become very high if carriers generated within the transition region also have ionizing collisions with the lattice. For example, an incoming electron may have a collision with the lattice and create an EHP; each of these carriers has a chance of creating a new EHP, and each of those can also create an EHP, and so forth (Fig. 5–21c).

Figure 5–21
Electron-hole pairs created by impact ionization: (a) band diagram of a p-n junction in reverse bias showing a (primary) electron gaining kinetic energy in the field of the depletion region, and creating a (secondary) electron–hole pair by impact ionization, the primary electron losing most of its kinetic energy in the process; (b) a single ionizing collision by an incoming electron in the depletion region of the junction; (c) primary, secondary, and tertiary collisions.

This is an *avalanche* process, since each incoming carrier can initiate the creation of a large number of new carriers.

We can make an approximate analysis of avalanche multiplication by assuming that a carrier of either type has a probability P of having an ionizing collision with the lattice while being accelerated a distance W through the transition region. Thus for n_{in} electrons entering from the p side, there will be Pn_{in} ionizing collisions and an EHP (secondary carriers) for each collision. After the Pn_{in} collisions by the primary electrons, we have the primary plus the secondary electrons, $n_{in}(1 + P)$. After a collision, each EHP moves effectively a distance of W within the transition region. For example, if an EHP is created at the center of the region, the electron drifts a distance $W/2$ to n and the hole $W/2$ to p. Thus the probability that an ionizing collision will occur due to the motion of the secondary carriers is still P in this simplified model. For $n_{in}P$ secondary pairs there will be $(n_{in}P)P$ ionizing collisions and $n_{in}P^2$ tertiary pairs. Summing up the total number of electrons out of the region at n after many collisions, we have

$$n_{out} = n_{in}(1 + P + P^2 + P^3 + \dots) \tag{5-43}$$

assuming no recombination. In a more comprehensive theory we would include recombination as well as different probabilities for ionizing collisions by electrons and holes. In our simple theory, the electron multiplication M_n is

$$M_n = \frac{n_{out}}{n_{in}} = 1 + P + P^2 + P^3 + \cdots = \frac{1}{1 - P} \tag{5-44a}$$

as can be verified by direct division. As the probability of ionization P approaches unity, the carrier multiplication (and therefore the reverse current through the junction) increases without limit. Actually, the limit on the current will be dictated by the external circuit.

The relation between multiplication and P was easy to write in Eq. (5–44a); however, the relation of P to parameters of the junction is much more complicated. Physically, we expect the ionization probability to increase with increasing electric field, and therefore to depend on the reverse bias. Measurements of carrier multiplication M in junctions near breakdown lead to an empirical relation

$$M = \frac{1}{1 - (V/V_{br})^n} \tag{5-44b}$$

where the exponent **n** varies from about 3 to 6, depending on the type of material used for the junction.

In general, the critical reverse voltage for breakdown increases with the band gap of the material, since more energy is required for an ionizing collision. Also, the peak electric field within W increases with increased doping on the more lightly doped side of the junction. Therefore, V_{br} decreases as the doping increases, as Fig. 5–22 indicates.

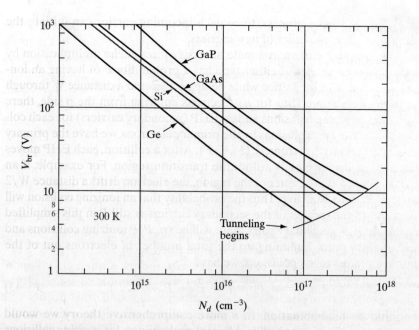

Figure 5–22
Variation of avalanche breakdown voltage in abrupt p^+-n junctions, as a function of donor concentration on the n side, for several semiconductors. [After S. M. Sze and G. Gibbons, *Applied Physics Letters*, vol. 8, p. 111 (1966).]

5.4.3 Rectifiers

The most obvious property of a p-n junction is its *unilateral* nature; that is, to a good approximation it conducts current in only one direction. We can think of an *ideal diode* as a short circuit when forward biased and as an open circuit when reverse biased (Fig. 5–23a). The p-n junction diode does not quite fit this description, but the I–V characteristics of many junctions can be approximated by the ideal diode in series with other circuit elements to form an equivalent circuit. For example, most forward-biased diodes exhibit an *offset voltage* E_0 (see Fig. 5–33), which can be approximated in a circuit model

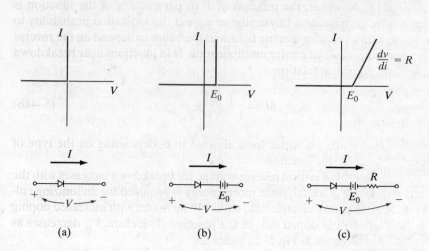

Figure 5–23
Piecewise-linear approximations of junction diode characteristics: (a) the ideal diode; (b) ideal diode with an offset voltage; (c) ideal diode with an offset voltage and a resistance to account for slope in the forward characteristic.

by a battery in series with the ideal diode (Fig. 5–23b). The series battery in the model keeps the ideal diode turned off for applied voltages less than E_0. From Section 5.6.1 we expect E_0 to be approximately the contact potential of the junction. In some cases the approximation to the actual diode characteristic is improved by adding a series resistor R to the circuit equivalent (Fig. 5–23c). The equivalent circuit approximations illustrated in Fig. 5–23 are called *piecewise-linear equivalents*, since the approximate characteristics are linear over specific ranges of voltage and current.

An ideal diode can be placed in series with an a-c voltage source to provide *rectification* of the signal. Since current can flow only in the forward direction through the diode, only the positive half-cycles of the input sine wave are passed. The output voltage is a *half-rectified sine wave*. Whereas the input sinusoid has zero average value, the rectified signal has a positive average value and therefore contains a d-c component. By appropriate filtering, this d-c level can be extracted from the rectified signal.

The unilateral nature of diodes is useful for many other circuit applications that require *waveshaping*. This involves alteration of a-c signals by passing only certain portions of the signal while blocking other portions.

Junction diodes designed for use as rectifiers should have I–V characteristics as close as possible to that of the ideal diode. The reverse current should be negligible, and the forward current should exhibit little voltage dependence (negligible *forward resistance R*). The reverse breakdown voltage should be large, and the offset voltage E_0 in the forward direction should be small. Unfortunately, not all of these requirements can be met by a single device; compromises must be made in the design of the junction to provide the best diode for the intended application.

From the theory derived in Section 5.3 we can easily list the various requirements for good rectifier junctions. *Band gap* is obviously an important consideration in choosing a material for rectifier diodes. Since n_i is small for large band gap materials, the reverse saturation current (which depends on thermally generated carriers) decreases with increasing E_g. A rectifier made with a wide band gap material can be operated at higher temperatures, because thermal excitation of EHPs is reduced by the increased band gap. Such temperature effects are critically important in rectifiers, which must carry large currents in the forward direction and are thereby subjected to appreciable heating. On the other hand, the contact potential and offset voltage E_0 generally increase with E_g. This drawback is usually outweighed by the advantages of low n_i; for example, Si is generally preferred over Ge for power rectifiers because of its wider band gap, lower leakage current, and higher breakdown voltage, as well as its more convenient fabrication properties.

The *doping concentration* on each side of the junction influences the avalanche breakdown voltage, the contact potential, and the series resistance of the diode. If the junction has one highly doped side and one lightly doped side (such as a p^+-n junction), the lightly doped region determines many of the properties of the junction. From Fig. 5–22 we see that a high-resistivity region should be used for at least one side of the junction to increase the breakdown voltage V_{br}. However, this approach tends to increase the forward resistance R of Fig. 5–23c, and therefore contributes to the problems of thermal effects due to I^2R heating. To reduce the resistance of the lightly doped region, it is necessary to make its area large and reduce its length. Therefore, the physical *geometry* of the diode is another important design variable. Limitations on the practical area for a diode include problems of obtaining uniform starting material and junction processing over large areas. Localized flaws in junction uniformity can cause premature reverse breakdown in a small region of the device. Similarly, the lightly doped region of the junction cannot be made arbitrarily short. One of the primary problems with a short, lightly doped region is an effect called *punch-through*. Since the transition region width W increases with reverse bias and extends primarily into the lightly doped region, it is possible for W to increase until it fills the entire length of this region (Prob. 5.30). The result of punch-through is a breakdown below the value of V_{br} expected from Fig. 5–22.

In devices designed for use at high reverse bias, care must be taken to avoid premature breakdown across the edge of the sample. This effect can be reduced by *beveling* the edge or by diffusing a *guard ring* to isolate the junction from the edge of the sample (Fig. 5–24). The electric field is lower at the beveled edge of the sample in Fig. 5–24b than it is in the main body of the device. Similarly, the junction at the lightly doped p guard ring of Fig. 5–24c breaks down at higher voltage than the p^+-n junction. Since the depletion region is wider in the p ring than in the p^+ region, the average electric field is smaller at the ring for a given diode reverse voltage.

In fabricating a p^+-n or a p-n^+ junction, it is common to terminate the lightly doped region with a heavily doped layer of the same type (Fig. 5–25a), to ease the problem of making ohmic contact to the device. The result is a p^+-n-n^+ structure with the p-n^+ layer serving as the active junction, or a p^+-n-n^+ device with an active p-n^+ junction. The lightly doped center region determines the avalanche breakdown voltage. If this region is short compared with the minority carrier diffusion length, the excess carrier injection for large forward currents can increase the conductivity of the region significantly. This type of *conductivity modulation*, which reduces the forward resistance R, can be very useful for high-current devices. On the other hand,

Figure 5–24
Beveled edge and guard ring to prevent edge breakdown under reverse bias: (a) diode with beveled edge; (b) closeup view of edge, showing reduction of depletion region near the level; (c) guard ring.

(a)   (b)   (c)

Figure 5–25
A p$^+$-n-n$^+$ junction
diode: (a) device
configuration;
(b) zero-bias
condition;
(c) reverse-biased
to punch-through.

a short, lightly doped center region can also lead to punch-through under reverse bias, as in Fig. 5–25c.

The mounting of a rectifier junction is critical to its ability to handle power. For diodes used in low-power circuits, glass or plastic encapsulation or a simple header mounting is adequate. However, high-current devices that must dissipate large amounts of heat require special mountings to transfer thermal energy away from the junction. A typical Si power rectifier is mounted on a molybdenum or tungsten disk to match the thermal expansion properties of the Si. This disk is fastened to a large stud of copper or other thermally conductive material that can be bolted to a heat sink with appropriate cooling.

5.4.4 The Breakdown Diode

As we discussed earlier in this section, the reverse-bias breakdown voltage of a junction can be varied by choice of junction doping concentrations. The breakdown mechanism is the Zener effect (tunneling) for abrupt junctions with extremely heavy doping; however, the more common breakdown is avalanche (impact ionization), typical of more lightly doped or graded junctions. By varying the doping we can fabricate diodes with specific breakdown voltages ranging from less than one volt to several hundred volts. If the junction is well designed, the breakdown will be sharp and the current after breakdown will be essentially independent of voltage (Fig. 5–26a). When a diode is designed for a specific breakdown voltage, it is called a *breakdown diode*. Such diodes are also called *Zener diodes*, despite the fact that the actual breakdown mechanism is usually the avalanche effect. This error in terminology is due to an early mistake in identifying the first observations of breakdown in p-n junctions.

Breakdown diodes can be used as *voltage regulators* in circuits with varying inputs. The 15-V breakdown diode of Fig. 5–26 holds the circuit output voltage v_0 constant at 15 V, while the input varies at voltages greater than 15 V. For example, if v_s is a rectified and filtered signal composed of a 17-V d-c component and a 1-V ripple variation above and below 17 V, the

Figure 5–26
A breakdown diode: (a) I–V characteristic; (b) application as a voltage regulator.

(a)   (b)

output v_0 will remain constant at 15 V. More complicated voltage regulator circuits can be designed using breakdown diodes, depending on the type of signal being regulated and the nature of the output load. In a similar application, such a device can be used as a *reference diode*; since the breakdown voltage of a particular diode is known, the voltage across it during breakdown can be used as a reference in circuits that require a known value of voltage.

We have considered the properties of p-n junctions under equilibrium conditions and with steady state current flow. Most of the basic concepts of junction devices can be obtained from these properties, except for the important behavior of junctions under transient or a-c conditions. Since most solid state devices are used for switching or for processing a-c signals, we cannot claim to understand p-n junctions without knowing at least the basics of time-dependent processes. Unfortunately, a complete analysis of these effects involves more mathematical manipulation than is appropriate for an introductory discussion. Basically, the problem involves solving the various current flow equations in two simultaneous variables, space and time. We can, however, obtain the basic results for several special cases which represent typical time-dependent applications of junction devices.

    In this section we investigate the important influence of excess carriers in transient and a-c problems. The switching of a diode from its forward state to its reverse state is analyzed to illustrate a typical transient problem. Finally, these concepts are applied to the case of small a-c signals to determine the equivalent capacitance of a p-n junction.

5.5
TRANSIENT AND A-C CONDITIONS

5.5.1 Time Variation of Stored Charge

Another look at the excess carrier distributions of a p-n junction under bias (e.g., Fig. 5–15) tells us that any change in current must lead to a change of charge stored in the carrier distributions. Since time is required in building up or depleting a charge distribution, however, the stored charge must inevitably lag behind the current in a time-dependent problem. This is inherently a capacitive effect, as we shall see in Section 5.5.4.

For a proper solution of a transient problem, we must use the time-dependent continuity equations, Eqs. (4–31). We can obtain each component of the current at position x and time t from these equations; for example, from Eq. (4–31a) we can write

$$-\frac{\partial J_p(x,t)}{\partial x} = q\frac{\delta p(x,t)}{\tau_p} + q\frac{\partial p(x,t)}{\partial t} \tag{5-45}$$

To obtain the instantaneous current density, we can integrate both sides at time t to obtain

$$J_p(0) - J_p(x) = q\int_0^x \left[\frac{\delta p(x,t)}{\tau_p} + \frac{p(x,t)}{\partial t}\right]dx \tag{5-46}$$

For injection into a long n region from a p^+ region, we can take the current at $x_n = 0$ to be all hole current, and J_p at $x_n = \infty$ to be zero. Then the total injected current, including time variations, is

$$i(t) = i_p(x_n = 0, t) = \frac{qA}{\tau_p}\int_0^\infty \delta p(x_n, t)dx_n + qA\frac{\partial}{\partial t}\int_0^\infty \delta p(x_n, t)dx_n$$

$$\boxed{i(t) = \frac{Q_p(t)}{\tau_p} + \frac{dQ_p(t)}{dt}} \tag{5-47}$$

This result indicates that the hole current injected across the p^+-n junction (and therefore approximately the total diode current) is determined by two charge storage effects: (1) the usual recombination term Q_p/τ_p in which the excess carrier distribution is replaced every τ_p seconds, and (2) a charge buildup (or depletion) term dQ_p/dt, which allows for the fact that the distribution of excess carriers can be increasing or decreasing in a time-dependent problem. For steady state the dQ_p/dt term is zero, and Eq. (5–47) reduces to Eq. (5–40), as expected. In fact, we could have written Eq. (5–47) intuitively rather than having obtained it from the continuity equation, since it is reasonable that the hole current injected at any given time must supply minority carriers for recombination and for whatever variations that occur in the total stored charge.

We can solve for the stored charge as a function of time for a given current transient. For example, the step turn-off transient (Fig. 5–27a), in which a current I is suddenly removed at $t = 0$, leaves the diode with stored charge. Since the excess holes in the n region must die out by recombination with the matching excess electron population, some time is required for $Q_p(t)$ to reach zero. Solving Eq. (5–47) with Laplace transforms, with $i(t > 0) = 0$ and $Q_p(0) = I\tau_p$, we obtain

Figure 5–27
Effects of a step
turn-off transient
in a p⁺-n diode:
(a) current
through the
diode; (b) decay
of stored charge
in the n-region;
(c) excess hole
distribution in
the n-region as
a function of
time during the
transient.

$$0 = \frac{1}{\tau_p} Q_p(s) + s Q_p(s) - I\tau_p$$

$$Q_p(s) = \frac{I\tau_p}{s + 1/\tau_p}$$

$$Q_p(t) = I\tau_p e^{-t/\tau_p} \tag{5–48}$$

As expected, the stored charge dies out exponentially from its initial value $I\tau_p$ with a time constant equal to the hole lifetime in the n material.

An important implication of Fig. 5–27 is that even though the current is suddenly terminated, the voltage across the junction persists until Q_p disappears. Since the excess hole concentration can be related to junction voltage by formulas derived in Section 5.3.2, we can presumably solve for $v(t)$. We already know that at any time during the transient, the excess hole concentration at $x_n = 0$ is

$$\Delta p_n(t) = p_n(e^{qv(t)/kT} - 1) \tag{5–49}$$

so that finding $\Delta p_n(t)$ will easily give us the transient voltage. Unfortunately, it is not simple to obtain $\Delta p_n(t)$ exactly from our expression for $Q_p(t)$. The problem is that the hole distribution does not remain in the convenient exponential form it has in steady state. As Fig. 5–27c suggests, the quantity $\delta p(x_n, t)$ becomes markedly nonexponential as the transient proceeds. For example, since the injected hole current is proportional to the gradient of the hole distribution at $x_n = 0$ (Fig. 5–16a), zero current implies zero gradient. Thus the slope of the distribution must be exactly zero at $x_n = 0$ throughout the transient.[13] This zero slope at the point of injection distorts the exponential distribution, particularly in the region near the junction. As time progresses in Fig. 5–27c, δp (and therefore δn) decreases as the excess electrons and holes recombine. To find the exact expression for $\delta p(x_n, t)$ during the transient would require a rather difficult solution of the time-dependent continuity equation.

---

[13]We notice that, while the magnitude of δp cannot change instantaneously, the slope must go to zero immediately. This can occur in a small region near the junction with negligible redistribution of charge at $t = 0$.

An approximate solution for $v(t)$ can be obtained by assuming an exponential distribution for δp at every instant during the decay. This type of *quasi-steady state* approximation neglects distortion due to the slope requirement at $x_n = 0$ and the effects of diffusion during the transient. Thus we would expect the calculation to give rather crude results. On the other hand, such a solution can give us a feeling for the variation of junction voltage during the transient. If we take

$$\delta p(x_n, t) = \Delta p_n(t)e^{-x_n/L_p} \tag{5–50}$$

we have for the stored charge at any instant

$$Q_p(t) = qA \int_0^\infty \Delta p_n(t)e^{-x_n/L_p}dx_n = qAL_p\Delta p_n(t) \tag{5–51}$$

Relating $\Delta p_n(t)$ to $v(t)$ by Eq. (5–49) we have

$$\Delta p_n(t) = p_n(e^{qv(t)/kT} - 1) = \frac{Q_p(t)}{qAL_p} \tag{5–52}$$

Thus in the quasi-steady state approximation, the junction voltage varies according to

$$v(t) = \frac{kT}{q}\ln\left(\frac{I\tau_p}{qAL_pp_n}e^{-t/\tau_p} + 1\right) \tag{5–53}$$

during the turn-off transient of Fig. 5–27. This analysis, while not accurate in its details, does indicate clearly that the voltage across a p-n junction cannot be changed instantaneously, and that stored charge can present a problem in a diode intended for switching applications.

Many of the problems of stored charge can be reduced by designing a p^+-n diode (for example) with a very narrow n region. If the n region is shorter than a hole diffusion length, very little charge is stored. Thus, little time is required to switch the diode on and off. This type of structure, called the *narrow base diode,* is considered in Prob. 5.40. The switching process can be made still faster by purposely adding recombination centers, such as Au atoms in Si, to increase the recombination rate.

5.5.2 Reverse Recovery Transient

In most switching applications a diode is switched from forward conduction to a reverse-biased state, and vice versa. The resulting stored charge transient is somewhat more complicated than for a simple turn-off transient, and therefore it requires slightly more analysis. An important result of this example is that a reverse current much larger than the normal reverse saturation current can flow in a junction during the time required for readjustment of the stored charge.

Let us assume a p⁺-n junction is driven by a square wave generator
that periodically switches from $+E$ to $-E$ volts (Fig. 5–28a). While E is
positive the diode is forward biased, and in steady state the current I_f flows
through the junction. If E is much larger than the small forward voltage of
the junction, the source voltage appears almost entirely across the resistor,

Figure 5–28
Storage delay
time in a p⁺-n
diode: (a) circuit
and input square
wave; (b) hole
distribution in
the n-region
as a function
of time during
the transient;
(c) variation
of current and
voltage with
time; (d) sketch of
transient current
and voltage on
the device I–V
characteristic.

and the current is approximately $i = I_f \simeq E/R$. After the generator voltage is reversed ($t > 0$), the current must initially reverse to $i = I_r \simeq -E/R$. The reason for this unusually large reverse current through the diode is that the stored charge (and hence the junction voltage) cannot be changed instantaneously. Therefore, just as the current is reversed, the junction voltage remains at the small forward-bias value it had before $t = 0$. A voltage loop equation then tells us that the large reverse current $-E/R$ must flow temporarily. While the current is negative through the junction, the slope of the $\delta p(x_n)$ distribution must be positive at $x_n = 0$.

As the stored charge is depleted from the neighborhood of the junction (Fig. 5–28b), we can find the junction voltage again from Eq. (5–49). As long as Δp_n is positive, the junction voltage $v(t)$ is positive and small; thus $i \simeq -E/R$ until Δp_n goes to zero. When the stored charge is depleted and Δp_n becomes negative, the junction exhibits a negative voltage. Since the reverse-bias voltage of a junction can be large, the source voltage begins to divide between R and the junction. As time proceeds, the magnitude of the reverse current becomes smaller as more of $-E$ appears across the reverse-biased junction, until finally the only current is the small reverse saturation current which is characteristic of the diode. The time t_{sd} required for the stored charge (and therefore the junction voltage) to become zero is called the *storage delay time*. This delay time is an important figure of merit in evaluating diodes for switching applications. It is usually desirable that t_{sd} be small compared with the switching times required (Fig. 5–29). The critical parameter determining t_{sd} is the carrier lifetime (τ_p for the example of the p^+-n junction). Since the recombination rate determines the speed with which excess holes can disappear from the n region, we would expect t_{sd} to

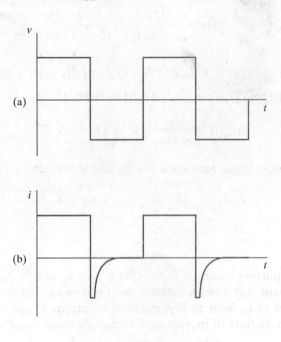

Figure 5–29
Effects of storage delay time on switching signal: (a) switching voltage; (b) diode current.

be proportional to τ_p. In fact, an exact analysis of the problem of Fig. 5–28 leads to the result

$$t_{sd} = \tau_p \left[erf^{-1} \left(\frac{I_f}{I_f + I_r} \right) \right]^2 \qquad (5\text{–}54)$$

where the error function (erf) is a tabulated function. Although the exact solution leading to Eq. (5–54) is too lengthy for us to consider here, an approximate result can be obtained from the quasi-steady state assumption.

Assume a p^+-n diode is biased in the forward direction, with a current I_f. At time $t = 0$ the current is switched to $-I_r$. Use the appropriate boundary conditions to solve Eq. (5–47) for $Q_p(t)$. Apply the quasi-steady state approximation to find the storage delay time t_{sd}.

EXAMPLE 5–5

From Eq. (5–47),

SOLUTION

$$i(t) = \frac{Q_p(t)}{\tau_p} + \frac{dQ_p(t)}{dt} \quad for\ t < 0, Q_p = I_f\tau_p$$

Using Laplace transforms,

$$-\frac{I_r}{s} = \frac{Q_p(s)}{\tau_p} + sQ_p(s) - I_f\tau_p$$

$$Q_p(s) = \frac{I_f\tau_p}{s + 1/\tau_p} - \frac{I_r}{s(s + 1/\tau_p)}$$

$$Q_p(t) = I_f\tau_p e^{-t/\tau_p} + I_r\tau_p(e^{-t/\tau_p} - 1) = \tau_p[-I_r + (I_f + I_r)e^{-t/\tau_p}]$$

Assuming that $Q_p(t) = qAL_p\Delta p_n(t)$ as in Eq. (5–52),

$$\Delta p_n(t) = \frac{\tau_p}{qAL_p} - [I_r + (I_f + I_r)e^{-t/\tau_p}]$$

This is set to equal zero when $t = t_{sd}$, and we obtain:

$$t_{sd} = -\tau_p \ln\left[\frac{I_r}{I_f + I_r}\right] = \tau_p \ln\left(1 + \frac{I_f}{I_r}\right)$$

An important result of Eq. (5–54) is that τ_p can be calculated in a straightforward way from a measurement of storage delay time. In fact, measurement of t_{sd} from an experimental arrangement such as Fig. 5–28a is a common method of measuring lifetimes. In some cases this is a more convenient technique than the photoconductive decay measurement discussed in Section 4.3.2.

As in the case of the turn-off transient of the previous section, the storage delay time can be reduced by introducing recombination centers into the diode material, thus reducing the carrier lifetimes, or by utilizing the narrow base diode configuration.

5.5.3 Switching Diodes

In discussing rectifiers we emphasized the importance of minimizing the reverse-bias current and the power losses under forward bias. In many applications, time response can be important as well. If a junction diode is to be used to switch rapidly from the conducting to the nonconducting state and back again, special consideration must be given to its charge control properties. We have discussed the equations governing the turn-on time and the reverse recovery time of a junction. From Eqs. (5–47) and (5–54) it is clear that a diode with fast switching properties must either store very little charge in the neutral regions for steady forward currents or have a very short carrier lifetime, or both.

As mentioned above, we can improve the switching speed of a diode by adding efficient recombination centers to the bulk material. For Si diodes, Au doping is useful for this purpose. To a good approximation the carrier lifetime varies with the reciprocal of the recombination center concentration. Thus, for example, a p^+-n Si diode may have $\tau_p = 1$ μs and a reverse recovery time of 0.1 μs before Au doping. If the addition of 10^{14} Au atoms/cm^3 reduces the lifetime to 0.1 μs and t_{sd} to 0.01 μs, 10^{15} cm^{-3} Au atoms could reduce τ_p to 0.01 μs and t_{sd} to 1 ns (10^{-9} s). This process cannot be continued indefinitely, however. The reverse current due to generation of carriers from the Au centers in the depletion region becomes appreciable with large Au concentration (Section 5.6.2). In addition, as the Au concentration approaches the lightest doping of the junction, the equilibrium carrier concentration of that region can be affected.

A second approach to improving the diode switching time is to make the lightly doped neutral region shorter than a minority carrier diffusion length. This is the *narrow base diode* (Prob. 5.40). In this case the stored charge for forward conduction is very small, since most of the injected carriers diffuse through the lightly doped region to the end contact. When such a diode is switched to reverse conduction, very little time is required to eliminate the stored charge in the narrow neutral region. The mathematics involved in Prob. 5.40 is particularly interesting, because it closely resembles the calculations we shall make in analyzing the bipolar junction transistor in Chapter 7.

5.5.4 Capacitance of p-n Junctions

There are basically two types of capacitance associated with a junction: (1) the *junction capacitance* due to the dipole in the transition region and

(2) the *charge storage capacitance* arising from the lagging behind of voltage as current changes, due to charge storage effects.[14] Both of these capacitances are important, and they must be considered in designing p-n junction devices for use with time-varying signals. The junction capacitance (1) is dominant under reverse-bias conditions, and the charge storage capacitance (2) is dominant when the junction is forward biased. In many applications of p-n junctions, the capacitance is a limiting factor in the usefulness of the device; on the other hand, there are important applications in which the capacitance discussed here can be useful in circuit applications and in providing important information about the structure of the p-n junction.

The junction capacitance of a diode is easy to visualize from the charge distribution in the transition region (Fig. 5–12). The uncompensated acceptor ions on the p side provide a negative charge, and an equal positive charge results from the ionized donors on the n side of the transition region. The capacitance of the resulting dipole is slightly more difficult to calculate than is the usual parallel plate capacitance, but we can obtain it in a few steps.

Instead of the common expression $C = |Q/V|$, which applies to capacitors in which charge is a linear function of voltage, we must use the more general definition

$$C = \left| \frac{dQ}{dV} \right| \tag{5–55}$$

since the charge Q on each side of the transition region varies nonlinearly with the applied voltage (Fig. 5–30a). We can demonstrate this nonlinear dependence by reviewing the equations for the width of the transition region (W) and the resulting charge. The equilibrium value of W was found in Eq. (5–21) to be

$$W = \left[\frac{2\epsilon V_0}{q} \left(\frac{N_a + N_d}{N_a N_d} \right) \right]^{1/2} \qquad (equilibrium) \tag{5–56}$$

Since we are dealing with the nonequilibrium case with voltage V applied, we must use the altered value of the electrostatic potential barrier ($V_0 - V$), as discussed in relation to Fig. 5–13. The proper expression for the width of the transition region is then

$$W = \left[\frac{2\epsilon (V_0 - V)}{q} \left(\frac{N_a + N_d}{N_a N_d} \right) \right]^{1/2} \qquad (with\ bias) \tag{5–57}$$

In this expression the applied voltage V can be either positive or negative to account for forward or reverse bias. As expected, the width of the transition region is increased for reverse bias and is decreased under forward bias.

---

[14]The capacitance (1) above is also referred to as the transition region capacitance or depletion layer capacitance; (2) is often called the diffusion capacitance.

Figure 5–30
Depletion capacitance of a junction: (a) p^+-n junction showing variation of depletion edge on n side with reverse bias. Electrically, the structure looks like a parallel plate capacitor whose dielectric is the depletion region, and the plates are the space charge neutral regions; (b) variation of depletion capacitance with reverse bias [Eq. (5–63)]. We neglect x_{p0} in the heavily doped p^+ material.

Since the uncompensated charge Q on each side of the junction varies with the transition region width, variations in the applied voltage result in corresponding variations in the charge, as required for a capacitor. The value of Q can be written in terms of the doping concentration and transition region width on each side of the junction (Fig. 5–12):

$$|Q| = qAx_{n0}N_d = qAx_{p0}N_a \qquad (5\text{–}58)$$

Relating the total width of the transition region W to the individual widths x_{n0} and x_{p0} from Eqs. (5–23) we have

$$x_{n0} = \frac{N_a}{N_a + N_d}W, \; x_{p0} = \frac{N_d}{N_a + N_d}W \qquad (5\text{--}59)$$

and therefore the charge on each side of the dipole is

$$|Q| = qA\frac{N_dN_a}{N_d + N_a}W = A\left[2q\epsilon(V_0 - V)\frac{N_dN_a}{N_d + N_a}\right]^{1/2} \qquad (5\text{--}60)$$

Thus the charge is indeed a nonlinear function of applied voltage. From this expression and the definition of capacitance in Eq. (5–55), we can calculate the junction capacitance C_j. Since the voltage that varies the charge in the transition region is the barrier height $(V_0 - V)$, we must take the derivative with respect to this potential difference:

$$C_j = \left|\frac{dQ}{d(V_0 - V)}\right| = \frac{A}{2}\left[\frac{2q\epsilon}{(V_0 - V)}\frac{N_dN_a}{N_d + N_a}\right]^{1/2} \qquad (5\text{--}61)$$

The quantity C_j is a *voltage-variable capacitance*, since C_j is proportional to $(V_0 - V)^{-1/2}$. There are several important applications for variable capacitors, including use in tuned circuits. The p-n junction device which makes use of the voltage-variable properties of C_j is called a *varactor*. We shall discuss this device further in Section 5.5.5.

Although the dipole charge is distributed in the transition region of the junction, the form of the parallel plate capacitor formula is obtained from the expressions for C_j and W (Fig. 5–30a):

$$C_j = \epsilon A\left[\frac{q}{2\epsilon(V_0 - V)}\frac{N_dN_a}{N_d + N_a}\right]^{1/2} = \frac{\epsilon A}{W} \qquad (5\text{--}62)$$

In analogy with the parallel plate capacitor, the transition region width W corresponds with the plate separation of the conventional capacitor.

In the case of an asymmetrically doped junction, the transition region extends primarily into the less heavily doped side, and the capacitance is determined by only one of the doping concentrations (Fig. 5–30a). For a p^+-n junction, $N_a \gg N_d$ and $x_{n0} \approx W$, while x_{p0} is negligible. The capacitance is then (Fig. 5–30b)

$$C_j = \frac{A}{2}\left[\frac{2q\epsilon}{V_0 - V}N_d\right]^{1/2} \quad \text{for } p^+\text{-}n \qquad (5\text{--}63)$$

It is therefore possible to obtain the doping concentration of the lightly doped n region from a measurement of capacitance. For example, in a reverse-biased junction the applied voltage $V = -V_r$ can be made much

Figure 5–31
Diffusion
capacitance as
a function of
forward bias in
long and short
diodes.

larger than the contact potential V_0, so that the latter becomes negligible. If the area of the junction can be measured, a reliable value of N_d results from a measurement of C_j. However, these equations were obtained by assuming a sharp step junction. Certain modifications must be made in the case of a graded junction (Section 5.6.4 and Prob. 5.42).

The junction capacitance dominates the reactance of a p-n junction under reverse bias; for forward bias, however, the charge storage, or diffusion capacitance, C_s becomes dominant. It has been recently shown[15] that the various time-dependent current components, as well as the boundary conditions, affect the diffusion capacitance in forward bias. We need to specify at which terminals the stored charges are extracted or "reclaimed" and where the relevant voltage drops occur. For *long* diodes whose dimensions are larger than the diffusion lengths, there is no diffusion capacitance. For a *short* diode, the reclaimable charge is two-thirds of the total stored charge. The diffusion capacitance due to stored holes on the n side of length c is:

$$C_s = \frac{dQ_p}{dV} = \frac{1}{3}\frac{q^2}{kT} Acp_n e^{qV/kT} \tag{5-64}$$

There is a similar contribution from the stored electrons on the p side (Fig. 5–31). In practice, most Si p-n junctions behave like short diodes, while laser diodes made in direct band gap (short lifetime) semiconductors often correspond to the long-diode case.

Similarly, we can determine the *a-c conductance* by allowing small changes in the current. For example, for a long diode, we get

$$G_s = \frac{dI}{dV} = \frac{qAL_p p_n}{\tau_p}\frac{d}{dV}(e^{qV/kT}) = \frac{q}{kT}I \tag{5-65}$$

[15]**Laux, S., and K. Hess,** "Revisiting the Analytic Theory of P-N Junction Impedance: Improvements Guided by Computer Simulation Leading to a New Equivalent Circuit," *IEEE Trans. Elec. Dev.* 46(2) (1999), 396.

For the diode of Example 5–4, what is the total depletion capacitance at –4 V?

EXAMPLE 5–6

SOLUTION

$$C_j = \sqrt{\epsilon} A \left[\frac{q}{2(V_0 - V)} \frac{N_d N_a}{N_d + N_a} \right]^{1/2}$$

$$= \sqrt{(8.85 \times 10^{-14} \times 11.8)(10^{-4})} \left[\frac{1.6 \times 10^{-19}}{2(0.695 + 4)} \left(\frac{10^{15} \times 10^{17}}{10^{15} + 10^{17}} \right) \right]^{1/2}$$

$$= 4.198 \times 10^{-13} \, \mathbf{F}$$

5.5.5 The Varactor Diode

The term *varactor* is a shortened form of *variable reactor*, referring to the voltage-variable capacitance of a reverse-biased p-n junction. The equations derived in Section 5.5.4 indicate that junction capacitance depends on the applied voltage and the design of the junction. In some cases a junction with fixed reverse bias may be used as a capacitance of a set value. More commonly the varactor diode is designed to exploit the voltage-variable properties of the junction capacitance. For example, a varactor (or a set of varactors) may be used in the tuning stage of a radio receiver to replace the bulky variable plate capacitor. The size of the resulting circuit can be greatly reduced, and its dependability is improved. Other applications of varactors include use in harmonic generation, microwave frequency multiplication, and active filters.

If the p-n junction is abrupt, the capacitance varies as the square root of the reverse bias V_r [Eq. (5–61)]. In a graded junction, however, the capacitance can usually be written in the form

$$C_j \propto V_r^{-n} \quad \text{for } V_r \gg V_0 \tag{5–66}$$

For example, in a linearly graded junction the exponent **n** is one-third (Prob. 5.42). Thus the voltage sensitivity of C_j is greater for an abrupt junction than for a linearly graded junction. For this reason, varactor diodes are often made by epitaxial growth techniques, or by ion implantation. The epitaxial layer and the substrate doping profile can be designed to obtain junctions for which the exponent **n** in Eq. (5–66) is greater than one-half. Such junctions are called *hyperabrupt junctions*.

In the set of doping profiles shown in Fig. 5–32, the junction is assumed p^+-n so that the depletion layer width W extends primarily into the n side. Three types of doping profiles on the n side are illustrated, with the donor distribution $N_d(x)$ given by Gx^m, where G is a constant and the exponent **m** is 0, 1, or $-\frac{3}{2}$. We can show (Prob. 5.42) that the exponent **n** in Eq. (5–66) is $1/(m + 2)$ for the p^+-n junction. Thus for the profiles of Fig. 5–32, **n** is $\frac{1}{2}$ for the abrupt junction and $\frac{1}{3}$ for the linearly graded junction. The hyperabrupt

Figure 5-32
Graded junction
profiles: linearly
graded, abrupt,
hyperabrupt.

Doping profiles

p^+ side: $N = N_a$
n side: $N = Gx^m$

Linearly graded, $\mathbf{m} = 1$

Abrupt, $\mathbf{m} = 0$

Hyperabrupt, $\mathbf{m} = -3/2$

junction[16] with $\mathbf{m} = -\frac{3}{2}$ is particularly interesting for certain varactor applications, since for this case $\mathbf{n} = 2$ and the capacitance is proportional to V_r^{-2}. When such a capacitor is used with an inductor L in a resonant circuit, the resonant frequency varies linearly with the voltage applied to the varactor.

$$\omega_r = \frac{1}{\sqrt{LC}} \propto \frac{1}{\sqrt{V_r^{-n}}} \propto V_r, \quad \text{for } \mathbf{n} = 2 \tag{5-67}$$

Because of the wide variety of C_j vs. V_r dependencies available by choosing doping profiles, varactor diodes can be designed for specific applications. For some high-frequency applications, varactors can be designed to exploit the forward-bias charge storage capacitance in short diodes.

**5.6
DEVIATIONS
FROM THE SIMPLE
THEORY**

The approach we have taken in studying p-n junctions has focused on the basic principles of operation, neglecting secondary effects. This allows for a relatively uncluttered view of carrier injection and other junction properties, and illuminates the essential features of diode operation. To complete the description, however, we must now fill in a few details which can affect the operation of junction devices under special circumstances.

Most of the deviations from the simple theory can be treated by fairly straightforward modifications of the basic equations. In this section we shall investigate the most important deviations and alter the theory wherever possible. In a few cases, we shall simply indicate the approach to be taken and the result. The most important alterations to the simple diode theory are the effects of contact potential and changes in majority carrier concentration on carrier injection, recombination and generation within the transition region, ohmic effects, and the effects of graded junctions.

---

[16]It is clear that $N_d(x)$ cannot become arbitrarily large at $x = 0$. However, the $m = -\frac{3}{2}$ profile can be approximated a short distance away from the junction.

5.6.1 Effects of Contact Potential on Carrier Injection

If the forward-bias $I–V$ characteristics of various semiconductor diodes are compared, it becomes clear that the band gap has an important influence on carrier injection. For example, Fig. 5–33 compares the low-temperature characteristics of heavily doped diodes having various band gaps. One obvious feature of this figure is that the $I–V$ characteristics appear "square"; that is, the current is very small until a critical forward bias is reached, and then the current increases rapidly. This is typical of exponentials plotted on such a scale. However, it is significant that the limiting voltage is slightly less than the value of the band gap in electron volts.

The reason for the small current at low voltages for these devices can be understood from a simple rearrangement of the diode equation. If we rewrite Eq. (5–36) for a forward-biased p^+-n diode (with $V \gg kT/q$) and include the exponential form for the minority carrier concentration p_n, we obtain

$$I = \frac{qAD_p}{L_p} p_n e^{qV/kT} = \frac{qAD_p}{L_p} N_v e^{[qV-(E_{Fn}-E_{vn})]/kT}. \qquad (5-68)$$

Hole injection into the n material is small if the forward bias V is much less than $(E_{Fn} - E_{vn})/q$. For a p^+-n diode, this quantity is essentially the contact potential, since the Fermi level is near the valence band on the p side. If the n region is also heavily doped, the contact potential is almost equal to the band gap (Fig. 5–34). This accounts for the dramatic increase in diode current near the band gap voltage in Fig. 5–33. Contributing to the small current at lower voltages is the fact that the minority carrier concentration $p_n = n_i^2/N_d$ is very small at low temperature (n_i small) and with heavy doping (N_d large).

Figure 5–33
$I–V$ characteristics of heavily doped p-n junction diodes at 77 K, illustrating the effects of contact potential on the forward current: (a) Ge, $E_g \simeq 0.7$ eV; (b) Si, $E_g \simeq 1.1$ eV; (c) GaAs, $E_g \simeq 1.4$ eV; (d) GaAsP, $E_g \simeq 1.9$ eV.

Figure 5–34
Examples of
contact potential
for a heavily
doped p-n
junction: (a) at
equilibrium;
(b) approaching
the maximum
forward bias
$V = V_0$.

(a)   (b)

The limiting forward bias across a p-n junction is equal to the contact potential, as in Fig. 5–34b. This effect is not predicted by the simple diode equation, for which the current increases exponentially with applied voltage. The reason this important result is excluded in the simple theory is that in Eq. (5–28) we neglect changes in the majority carrier concentrations on either side of the junction. This assumption is valid only for low injection levels; for large injected carrier concentrations, the excess majority carriers become important compared with the majority doping. For example, at low injection $\Delta n_p = \Delta p_p$ is important compared with the equilibrium minority electron concentration n_p, but is negligible compared with the majority hole concentration p_p; this was the basis for neglecting Δp_p in Eq. (5–28). For high injection levels, however, Δp_p can be comparable to p_p and we must write Eq. (5–27) in the form

$$\frac{p(-x_{p0})}{p(x_{n0})} = \frac{p_p + \Delta p_p}{p_n + \Delta p_n} = e^{q(V_0-V)/kT} = \frac{n_n + \Delta n_n}{n_p + \Delta n_p} \tag{5–69}$$

From Eq. (5–38), we get at either edge of the depletion region,

$$pn = p(-x_{p0})n(-x_{p0}) = p(x_{n0})n(x_{n0}) = n_i^2 e^{\frac{F_n-F_p}{kT}} = n_i^2 e^{qV/kT} \tag{5–70}$$

For example, at $-x_{po}$ we then get

$$(p_p + \Delta p_p)(n_p + \Delta n_p) = n_i^2 e^{qV/kT} \tag{5–71}$$

Keeping in mind that $\Delta p_p = \Delta n_p$, $n_p \ll \Delta n_p$, and in high-level injection $p_p < \Delta p_p$, we approximately get

$$\Delta n_p = n_i e^{qV/2kT} \tag{5–72}$$

The rest of the derivation is very similar to that in Section 5.3.2. Hence, the diode current in high-level injection scales as

$$I \propto e^{qV/2kT} \tag{5–73}$$

5.6.2 Recombination and Generation in the Transition Region

In analyzing the p-n junction, we have assumed that recombination and thermal generation of carriers occur primarily in the neutral p and n regions, outside the transition region. In this model, forward current in the diode is carried by recombination of excess minority carriers injected into each neutral region by the junction. Similarly, the reverse saturation current is due to the thermal generation of EHPs in the neutral regions and the subsequent diffusion of the generated minority carriers to the transition region, where they are swept to the other side by the field. In many devices this model is adequate; however, a more complete description of junction operation should include recombination and generation within the transition region itself.

When a junction is forward biased, the transition region contains excess carriers of both types, which are in transit from one side of the junction to the other. Unless the width of the transition region W is very small compared with the carrier diffusion lengths L_n and L_p, significant recombination can take place within W. An accurate calculation of this recombination current is complicated by the fact that the recombination rate, which depends on the carrier concentrations [Eq. (4–5)], varies with position within the transition region. Analysis of the recombination kinetics shows that the current due to recombination within W is proportional to n_i and increases with forward bias according to approximately $\exp(qV/2kT)$. On the other hand, current due to recombination in the neutral regions is proportional to p_n and n_p [Eq. (5–36)] and therefore to n_i^2/N_d and n_i^2/N_a, and increases according to $\exp(qV/kT)$. The diode equation can be modified to include this effect by including the parameter **n**:

$$\boxed{I = I'_0(e^{qV/\mathbf{n}kT} - 1)} \tag{5–74}$$

where **n** varies between 1 and 2, depending on the material and temperature. Since **n** determines the departure from the ideal diode characteristic, it is often called the *ideality factor*.

The ratio of the two currents

$$\frac{I(\text{recombination in neutral regions})}{I(\text{recombination in transition region})} \propto \frac{n_i^2 e^{qV/kT}}{n_i e^{qV/2kT}} \propto n_i e^{qV/2kT} \tag{5–75}$$

becomes small for wide band gap materials, low temperatures (small n_i), and for low voltage. Thus the forward current for low injection in a Si diode is likely to be dominated by recombination in the transition region, while a Ge diode may follow the usual diode equation. In either case, injection through W into the neutral regions becomes more important with increased voltage. Therefore, **n** in Eq. (5–74) may vary from ~2 at low voltage to ~1 at higher voltage.

Just as recombination within W can affect the forward characteristics, the reverse current through a junction can be influenced by carrier *generation* in the transition region. We found in Section 5.3.3 that the reverse saturation current can be accounted for by the thermal generation of EHPs within a diffusion length of either side of the transition region. The generated minority carriers diffuse to the transition region, where they are swept to the other side of the junction by the electric field (Fig. 5–35). However, carrier generation can take place within the transition region itself. If W is small compared with L_n or L_p, band-to-band generation of EHPs within the transition region is not important compared with generation in the neutral regions. However, the lack of free carriers within the space charge of the transition region can create a current due to the net generation of carriers by *emission from recombination centers*. Of the four generation–recombination processes depicted in Fig. 5–36, the two capture rates R_n and R_p are negligible within W because of the very small carrier concentrations in the reverse-bias space charge region. Therefore, a recombination level E_r near the center of the band gap can provide carriers through the thermal generation rates G_n and G_p. Each recombination center alternately emits an electron and a hole; physically, this means that an electron at E_r is thermally excited to the conduction band (G_n) and a valence band electron is subsequently excited thermally to the empty state on the recombination level, leaving a hole behind in the valence band (G_p). The process can then be repeated over and over, providing electrons for the conduction band and holes for the valence band. Normally, these emission processes are exactly balanced by the corresponding capture processes R_n and R_p. However, in the reverse-bias transition region, generated carriers are swept out before recombination can occur, and net generation results.

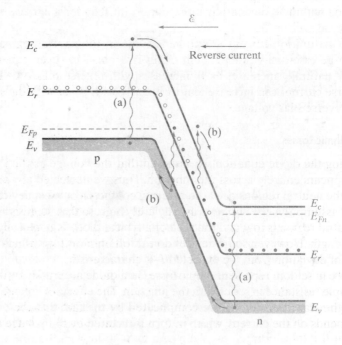

Figure 5–35
Current in a reverse-biased p-n junction due to thermal generation of carriers by (a) band-to-band EHP generation, and (b) generation from a recombination level.

Figure 5–36
Capture and generation of carriers at a recombination center: (a) capture and generation of electrons and holes; (b) hole capture and generation processes redrawn in terms of valence band electron excitation to E_r (hole generation) and electron deexcitation from E_r to E_v (hole capture by E_r).

Of course, the importance of thermal generation within W depends on the temperature and the nature of the recombination centers. A level near the middle of the band gap is most effective, since for such centers neither G_n nor G_p requires thermal excitation of an electron over more than about half the band gap. If no recombination level is available, this type of generation is negligible. However, in most materials recombination centers exist near the middle of the gap due to trace impurities or lattice defects. Generation from centers within W is most important in materials with large band gaps, for which band-to-band generation in the neutral regions is small. Thus for Si, generation within W is generally more important than for a narrower band gap material such as Ge.

The saturation current due to generation in the neutral regions was found to be essentially independent of reverse bias. However, generation within W naturally increases as W increases with reverse bias. As a result, the reverse current can increase almost linearly with W, or with the square root of reverse-bias voltage.

5.6.3 Ohmic Losses

In deriving the diode equation we assumed that the voltage applied to the device appears entirely across the junction. Thus we neglected any voltage drop in the neutral regions or at the external contacts. For most devices this is a valid assumption; the doping is usually fairly high, so that the resistivity of each neutral region is low, and the area of a typical diode is large compared with its length. However, some devices do exhibit ohmic effects, which cause significant deviation from the expected I–V characteristic.

We can seldom represent ohmic losses in a diode accurately by including a simple resistance in series with the junction. The effects of voltage drops outside the transition region are complicated by the fact that the voltage drop depends on the current, which in turn is dictated by the voltage across the junction. For example, if we represent the series resistance of the p and n regions by R_p and R_n, respectively, we can write the junction voltage V as

$$V = V_a - I[R_p(I) + R_n(I)] \tag{5-76}$$

where V_a is the external voltage applied to the device. As the current increases, there is an increasing voltage drop in R_p and R_n, and the junction voltage V decreases. This reduction in V lowers the level of injection so that the current increases more slowly with increased bias. A further complication in calculating the ohmic loss is that the conductivity of each neutral region increases with increasing carrier injection. Since the effects of Eq. (5–76) are most pronounced at high injection levels, this *conductivity modulation* by the injected excess carriers can reduce R_p and R_n significantly.

Ohmic losses are purposely avoided in properly designed devices by appropriate choices of doping and geometry. Therefore, deviations of the current generally appear only for very high currents, outside the normal operating range of the device.

Figure 5–37 shows the forward and reverse current–voltage character-istics of a p-n junction on a semilog scale, both for an ideal Shockley diode as well as for non-ideal devices. For an ideal forward-biased diode, we get a straight line on a semilog plot reflecting the exponential dependence of current on voltage. On the other hand, taking into account all the second-order effects discussed in Section 5.6, we see various regions of operation. At low current levels, we see the enhanced generation–recombination current, leading to a higher diode ideality factor (**n** = 2). For moderate currents, we get ideal low-level injection and diffusion-limited current (**n** = 1). At higher currents, we get high-level injection and **n** = 2, while at even higher currents, the ohmic drops in the space charge neutral regions become important.

Similarly, in reverse bias, in an ideal diode, we have a constant, volt-age-independent reverse saturation current. However, in actuality, we get an enhanced, voltage-dependent generation–recombination leakage current. At very high reverse biases, the diode breaks down reversibly due to avalanche or Zener effects.

5.6.4 Graded Junctions

While the abrupt junction approximation accurately describes the proper-ties of many epitaxially grown junctions, it is often inadequate in analyzing diffused or implanted junction devices. For shallow diffusions, in which the diffused impurity profile is very steep (Fig. 5–38a), the abrupt approximation is usually acceptable. If the impurity profile is spread out into the sample, however, a graded junction can result (Fig. 5–38b). Several of the expressions we have derived for the abrupt junction must be modified for this case (see Section 5.5.5).

The graded junction problem can be solved analytically if, for example, we make a linear approximation of the net impurity distribution near the

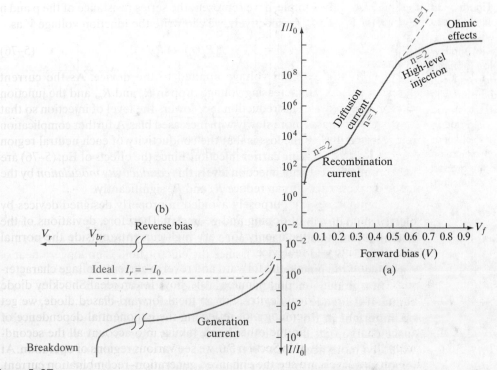

Figure 5–37
Forward and reverse current–voltage characteristics plotted on semilog scales, with current normalized with respect to saturation current, I_0; (a) the ideal forward characteristic is an exponential with an ideality factor n = 1 (dashed straight line on log-linear plot). The actual forward characteristics of a typical diode (solid line) have four regimes of operation; (b) ideal reverse characteristic (dashed line) is a voltage-independent current = $-I_0$. Actual leakage characteristics (solid line) are higher due to generation in the depletion region, and also show breakdown at high voltages.

junction (Fig. 5–38c). We assume that the graded region can be described approximately by

$$N_d - N_a = Gx \qquad (5\text{–}77)$$

where G is a grade constant giving the slope of the net impurity distribution.

In Poisson's equation [Eq. (5–14)], the linear approximation becomes

$$\frac{d\mathscr{E}}{dx} = \frac{q}{\epsilon}(p - n + N_d^+ - N_a^-) \simeq \frac{q}{\epsilon}Gx \qquad (5\text{–}78)$$

within the transition region. In this approximation we assume complete ionization of the impurities and neglect the carrier concentrations in the transition region, as before. The net space charge varies linearly over W, and the

(a)

(b)

(c)

electric field distribution is therefore parabolic. The expressions for contact potential and junction capacitance are different from the abrupt junction case (Fig. 5–39 and Prob. 5.42), since the electric field is no longer linear on each side of the junction.

In a graded junction the usual depletion approximation is often inaccurate. If the grade constant G is small, the carrier concentrations (p-n) can be important in Eq. (5–78). Similarly, the usual assumption of negligible space charge outside the transition region is questionable for small G. It would be more accurate to refer to the regions just outside the transition region as quasi-neutral rather than neutral. Thus the edges of the transition region are not sharp as Fig. 5–39 implies but are spread out in x. These effects

(a)

(b)

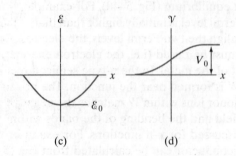

(c)

(d)

complicate calculations of junction properties, and a computer must be used in solving the problem accurately.

Most of the conclusions we have made regarding carrier injection, recombination and generation currents, and other properties are qualitatively applicable to graded junctions, with some alterations in the functional form of the resulting equations. Therefore, we can apply most of our basic concepts of junction theory to reasonably graded junctions as long as we remember that certain modifications should be made in accurate computations.

Many of the useful properties of a p-n junction can be achieved by simply forming an appropriate metal–semiconductor contact. This approach is obviously attractive because of its simplicity of fabrication; also, as we shall see in this section, metal–semiconductor junctions are particularly useful when high-speed rectification is required. On the other hand, we also must be able to form nonrectifying (ohmic) contacts to semiconductors. Therefore, this section deals with both rectifying and ohmic contacts.

5.7 METAL– SEMICONDUCTOR JUNCTIONS

5.7.1 Schottky Barriers

In Section 2.2.1 we discussed the work function $q\Phi_m$ of a metal in a vacuum. An energy of $q\Phi_m$ is required to remove an electron at the Fermi level to the vacuum outside the metal. Typical values of Φ_m for very clean surfaces are 4.3 V for Al and 4.8 V for Au. When negative charges are brought near the metal surface, positive (image) charges are induced in the metal. When this image force is combined with an applied electric field, the effective work function is somewhat reduced. Such barrier lowering is called the *Schottky effect*, and this terminology is carried over to the discussion of potential barriers arising in metal–semiconductor contacts. Although the Schottky effect is only a part of the explanation of metal–semiconductor contacts, rectifying contacts are generally referred to as *Schottky barrier diodes*. In this section we shall see how such barriers arise in metal–semiconductor contacts. First we consider barriers in ideal metal–semiconductor junctions, and then in Section 5.7.4 we will include effects which alter the barrier height.

When a metal with work function $q\Phi_m$ is brought in contact with a semiconductor having a work function $q\Phi_s$, charge transfer occurs until the Fermi levels align at equilibrium (Fig. 5–40). For example, when $\Phi_m > \Phi_s$, the semiconductor Fermi level is initially higher than that of the metal before contact is made. To align the two Fermi levels, the electrostatic potential of the semiconductor must be raised (i.e., the electron energies must be lowered) relative to that of the metal. In the n-type semiconductor of Fig. 5–40 a depletion region W is formed near the junction. The positive charge due to uncompensated donor ions within W matches the negative charge on the metal. The electric field and the bending of the bands within W are similar to effects already discussed for p-n junctions. For example, the depletion width W in the semiconductor can be calculated from Eq. (5–21) by using

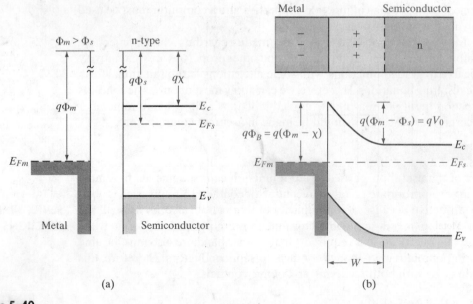

Figure 5–40
A Schottky barrier formed by contacting an n-type semiconductor with a metal having a larger work function: (a) band diagrams for the metal and the semiconductor before joining; (b) equilibrium band diagram for the junction.

the p^+-n approximation (i.e., by assuming the negative charge in the dipole as a thin sheet of charge to the left of the junction). Similarly, the junction capacitance is $A\epsilon_s/W$, as in the p^+-n junction.[17]

The equilibrium contact potential V_0, which prevents further net electron diffusion from the semiconductor conduction band into the metal, is the difference in work function potentials $\Phi_m - \Phi_s$. The potential barrier height Φ_B for electron injection from the metal into the semiconductor conduction band is $\Phi_m - \chi$, where $q\chi$ (called the *electron affinity*) is measured from the vacuum level to the semiconductor conduction band edge. The equilibrium potential difference V_0 can be decreased or increased by the application of either forward- or reverse-bias voltage, as in the p-n junction.

Figure 5–41 illustrates a Schottky barrier on a p-type semiconductor, with $\Phi_m < \Phi_s$. In this case aligning the Fermi levels at equilibrium requires a positive charge on the metal side and a negative charge on the semiconductor side of the junction. The negative charge is accommodated by a depletion region W in which ionized acceptors (N_a^-) are left uncompensated by holes. The potential barrier V_0 retarding hole diffusion from the semiconductor to the metal is $\Phi_s - \Phi_m$, and as before this barrier can be raised or lowered

[17]While the properties of the Schottky barrier depletion region are similar to those of the p^+-n region, it is clear that the analogy does not include forward-bias hole injection, which is dominant for the p^+-n region, but not for the contact of Fig. 5–40.

Figure 5–41
A Schottky barrier between a p-type semiconductor and a metal having a smaller work function: (a) band diagrams before joining; (b) band diagram for the junction at equilibrium.

by the application of voltage across the junction. In visualizing the barrier for holes, we recall from Fig. 5–11 that the electrostatic potential barrier for positive charge is opposite to the barrier on the electron energy diagram.

The two other cases of ideal metal–semiconductor contacts ($\Phi_m < \Phi_s$ for n-type semiconductors, and $\Phi_m > \Phi_s$ for p-type) result in nonrectifying contacts. We will save treatment of these cases for Section 5.7.3, where ohmic contacts are discussed.

5.7.2 Rectifying Contacts

When a forward-bias voltage V is applied to the Schottky barrier of Fig. 5–40b, the contact potential is reduced from V_0 to $V_0 - V$ (Fig. 5–42a). As a result, electrons in the semiconductor conduction band can diffuse across the depletion region to the metal. This gives rise to a forward current (metal to semiconductor) through the junction. Conversely, a reverse bias increases the barrier to $V_0 + V_r$, and electron flow from semiconductor to metal becomes negligible. In either case flow of electrons from the metal to the semiconductor is retarded by the barrier $\Phi_m - \chi$. The resulting diode equation is similar in form to that of the p-n junction

$$I = I_0(e^{qV/kT} - 1) \qquad (5\text{–}79)$$

as Fig. 5–42c suggests. In this case the reverse saturation current I_0 is not simply derived as it was for the p-n junction. One important feature we can

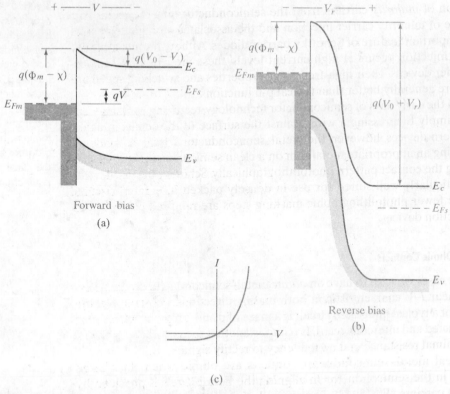

Figure 5–42
Effects of forward and reverse bias on the junction of Fig. 5–40: (a) forward bias; (b) reverse bias; (c) typical current–voltage characteristic.

predict intuitively, however, is that the saturation current should depend upon the size of the barrier Φ_B for electron injection from the metal into the semiconductor. This barrier (which is $\Phi_m - \chi$ for the ideal case shown in Fig. 5–42) is unaffected by the bias voltage. We expect the probability of an electron in the metal surmounting this barrier to be given by a Boltzmann factor. Thus

$$I_0 \propto e^{-q\Phi_B/kT} \tag{5–80}$$

The diode equation (5–79) applies also to the metal–p-type semiconductor junction of Fig. 5–41. In this case forward voltage is defined with the semiconductor biased positively with respect to the metal. Forward current increases as this voltage lowers the potential barrier to $V_0 - V$ and holes flow from the semiconductor to the metal. Of course, a reverse voltage increases the barrier for hole flow and the current becomes negligible.

In both of these cases the Schottky barrier diode is rectifying, with easy current flow in the forward direction and little current in the reverse direction. We also note that the forward current in each case is due to the injection of *majority* carriers from the semiconductor into the metal. The absence of minority carrier injection and the associated storage delay time is an important feature of Schottky barrier diodes. Although some minority carrier injection occurs at high current levels, these are essentially majority carrier devices. Their high-frequency properties and switching speed are therefore generally better than typical p-n junctions.

In the early days of semiconductor technology, rectifying contacts were made simply by pressing a wire against the surface of the semiconductor. In modern devices, however, the metal–semiconductor contact is made by depositing an appropriate metal film on a clean semiconductor surface and defining the contact pattern photolithographically. Schottky barrier devices are particularly well suited for use in densely packed integrated circuits, because fewer photolithographic masking steps are required compared to p-n junction devices.

5.7.3 Ohmic Contacts

In many cases we wish to have an *ohmic* metal–semiconductor contact, having a linear I–V characteristic in both biasing directions. For example, the surface of a typical integrated circuit is a maze of p and n regions, which must be contacted and interconnected. It is important that such contacts be ohmic, with minimal resistance and no tendency to rectify signals.

Ideal metal–semiconductor contacts are ohmic when the charge induced in the semiconductor in aligning the Fermi levels is provided by majority carriers (Fig. 5–43). For example, in the $\Phi_m < \Phi_s$ (n-type) case of Fig. 5–43a, the Fermi levels are aligned at equilibrium by transferring electrons from the metal to the semiconductor. This raises the semiconductor electron energies (lowers the electrostatic potential) relative to the metal at equilibrium (Fig. 5–43b). In this case the barrier to electron flow between the metal and the semiconductor is small and easily overcome by a small voltage. Similarly, the case $\Phi_m > \Phi_s$ (p-type) results in easy hole flow across the junction (Fig. 5–43d). Unlike the rectifying contacts discussed previously, no depletion region occurs in the semiconductor in these cases since the electrostatic potential difference required to align the Fermi levels at equilibrium calls for accumulation of majority carriers in the semiconductor.

A practical method for forming ohmic contacts is by doping the semiconductor heavily in the contact region. Thus if a barrier exists at the interface, the depletion width is small enough to allow carriers to tunnel through the barrier. For example, Au containing a small percentage of Sb can be alloyed to n-type Si, forming an n^+ layer at the semiconductor surface and an excellent ohmic contact. Similarly, p-type material requires a p^+ surface layer in contact with the metal. In the case of Al on p-type Si, the metal contact also provides the acceptor dopant. Thus the required p^+ surface layer is formed during a brief heat treatment of the contact after the Al is deposited.

Figure 5–43
Ohmic metal–semiconductor contacts: (a) $\Phi_m < \Phi_s$ for an n-type semiconductor, and (b) the equilibrium band diagram for the junction; (c) $\Phi_m > \Phi_s$ for a p-type semiconductor, and (d) the junction at equilibrium.

5.7.4 Typical Schottky Barriers

The discussion of ideal metal–semiconductor contacts does not include certain effects of the junction between the two dissimilar materials. Unlike a p-n junction, which occurs within a single crystal, a Schottky barrier junction includes a termination of the semiconductor crystal. The semiconductor surface contains *surface states* due to incomplete covalent bonds and other effects, which can lead to charges at the metal–semiconductor interface. Furthermore, the contact is seldom an atomically sharp discontinuity between the semiconductor crystal and the metal. There is typically a thin interfacial layer, which is neither semiconductor nor metal. For example, silicon crystals are covered by a thin (10–20 Å) oxide layer even after etching or cleaving in atmospheric conditions. Therefore, deposition of a metal on such a Si surface leaves a glassy interfacial layer at the junction. Although electrons can tunnel through this thin layer, it does affect the barrier to current transport through the junction.

Because of surface states, the interfacial layer, microscopic clusters of metal–semiconductor phases, and other effects, it is difficult to fabricate junctions with barriers near the ideal values predicted from the work functions of the two isolated materials. Therefore, measured barrier heights are used in device design. In compound semiconductors the interfacial layer introduces states in the semiconductor band gap that pin the Fermi level at a fixed position, regardless of the metal used (Fig. 5–44). For example, a collection of interface states located 0.7~0.9 eV below the conduction band pins E_F at the surface of n-type GaAs, and the Schottky barrier height is determined from this pinning effect rather than by the work function of the metal. An interesting case is n-type InAs (Fig. 5–44b), in which E_F at the interface is pinned *above* the conduction band edge. As a result, ohmic

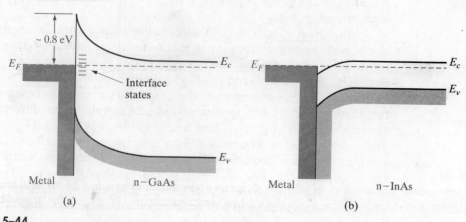

Figure 5–44
Fermi level pinning by interface states in compound semiconductors: (a) E_F is pinned near E_c − 0.8 eV in n-type GaAs, regardless of the choice of metal; (b) E_F is pinned above E_c in n-type InAs, providing an excellent ohmic contact.

contact to n-type InAs can be made by depositing virtually any metal on the surface. For Si, good Schottky barriers are formed by various metals, such as Au or Pt. In the case of Pt, heat treatment results in a platinum silicide layer, which provides a reliable Schottky barrier with $\Phi_B \approx 0.85$ V on n-type Si.

A full treatment of Schottky barrier diodes results in a forward current equation of the form

$$I = ABT^2 e^{-q\Phi_B/kT} e^{qV/nkT} \tag{5-81}$$

where B is a constant containing parameters of the junction properties and **n** is a number between 1 and 2, similar to the ideality factor in Eq. (5–74) but arising from different reasons. The mathematics of this derivation is similar to that of *thermionic emission,* and the factor B corresponds to an effective Richardson constant in the thermionic problem.

5.8 HETERO-JUNCTIONS

Thus far we have discussed p-n junctions formed within a single semiconductor (*homojunctions*) and junctions between a metal and a semiconductor. The third important class of junctions consist of those between two lattice-matched semiconductors with different band gaps (*heterojunctions*). We discussed lattice-matching in Section 1.4.1. The interface between two such semiconductors may be virtually free of defects, and continuous crystals containing single or multiple heterojunctions can be formed. The availability of heterojunctions and multilayer structures in compound semiconductors opens a broad range of possibilities for device development. We will discuss many of these applications in later chapters, including heterojunction bipolar transistors, field-effect transistors, and semiconductor lasers.

When semiconductors of different band gaps, work functions, and electron affinities are brought together to form a junction, we expect discontinuities in the energy bands as the Fermi levels line up at equilibrium (Fig. 5–45). The discontinuities in the conduction band ΔE_c and the valence band ΔE_v accommodate the difference in band gap between the two semiconductors ΔE_g. In an ideal case, ΔE_c would be the difference in electron affinities $q(\chi_2 - \chi_1)$, and ΔE_v would be found from $\Delta E_g - \Delta E_c$. This is known as the Anderson affinity rule. In practice, the band discontinuities are found experimentally for particular semiconductor pairs. For example, in the commonly used system GaAs–AlGaAs (see Figs. 3–6 and 3–13), the direct band gap difference ΔE_g^Γ between the wider band gap AlGaAs and the narrower band gap GaAs is apportioned approximately $\frac{2}{3}$ in the conduction band and $\frac{1}{3}$ in the valence band for the heterojunction. The built-in contact potential is divided between the two semiconductors as required to align the Fermi levels at equilibrium. The resulting depletion region on each side of the heterojunction and the amount of built-in potential on each side (making up the contact potential V_0) are found by solving Poisson's equation with the boundary condition of continuous electric flux density, $\epsilon_1 \mathscr{E}_1 = \epsilon_2 \mathscr{E}_2$ at the junction. The barrier that electrons must overcome in moving from the n side to the p side may be quite different from the barrier for holes moving from p to n. The depletion region on each side is analogous to that described in

(a)

$$\Delta E_g = E_{g1} - E_{g2}$$
$$= \Delta E_c + \Delta E_v$$

Figure 5–45
An ideal heterojunction between a p-type, wide band gap semiconductor and an n-type narrower band gap semiconductor:
(a) band diagrams before joining; (b) band discontinuities and band bending at equilibrium.

(b)

$$qV_0 = q(V_{01} + V_{02})$$

$$\frac{V_{01}}{V_{02}} = \frac{\epsilon_2 N_{d2}}{\epsilon_1 N_{a1}}$$

Eq. (5–23), except that we must account for the different dielectric constants in the two semiconductors.

To draw the band diagram for any semiconductor device involving homojunctions or heterojunctions, we need material parameters such as the band gap and the electron affinity which depend on the semiconductor material but not on the doping, and the work function which depends on the semiconductor as well as the doping. The electron affinity and work function are referenced to the vacuum level. The true vacuum level (or global vacuum level), E_{vac}, is the potential energy reference when an electron is taken out of the semiconductor to infinity, where it sees no forces. Hence, the true vacuum level is a constant (Fig. 5–45). That introduces an apparent contradiction, however, because looking at the band bending in a semiconductor device, it seems to imply that the electron affinity in the semiconductor changes as a function of position, which is impossible because the electron affinity is a material parameter. Therefore, we need to introduce the new concept of the local vacuum level, E_{vac} (loc), which varies along with and parallel to the conduction band edge, thereby keeping the electron affinity constant. The local vacuum level tracks the potential energy of an electron if it is moved just outside of the semiconductor, but not far away. The difference between the local and global vacuum levels is due to the electrical work done against the fringing electric fields of the depletion region, and is equal to the potential energy qV_0 due to the built-in contact potential V_0 in equilibrium. This potential energy can, of course, be modified by an applied bias.

To draw the band diagram for a heterojunction accurately, we must not only use the proper values for the band discontinuities but also account for the band bending in the junction. To do this, we must solve Poisson's equation across the heterojunction, taking into account the details of doping and space charge, which generally requires a computer solution. We can, however, sketch an approximate diagram without a detailed calculation. Given the experimental band offsets ΔE_v and ΔE_c, we can proceed as follows:

1. Align the Fermi level with the two semiconductor bands separated. Leave space for the transition region.

$$E_c \rule{2cm}{0.4pt} \qquad \rule{2cm}{0.4pt}$$
$$E_F \text{-----------------}$$

$$E_v \rule{2cm}{0.4pt}$$

2. The metallurgical junction ($x = 0$) is located near the more heavily doped side. At $x = 0$ put ΔE_v and ΔE_c, separated by the appropriate band gaps.

3. Connect the conduction band and valence band regions, keeping the band gap constant in each material.

Steps 2 and 3 of this procedure are where the exact band bending is important and must be obtained by solving Poisson's equation. In step 2 we must use the band offset values ΔE_c and ΔE_v for the specific pair of semiconductors in the heterojunction.

For heterojunctions in the GaAs–AlGaAs system, the direct (Γ) band gap difference ΔE_g^{Γ} is accommodated approximately $\frac{2}{3}$ in the conduction band and $\frac{1}{3}$ in the valence band. For an Al composition of 0.3, the AlGaAs is direct (see Fig. 3–6) with $\Delta E_g^{\Gamma} = 1.85$ eV. Sketch the band diagrams for two heterojunction cases: N^+-Al$_{0.3}$Ga$_{0.7}$As on n-type GaAs, and N^+-Al$_{0.3}$Ga$_{0.7}$As on p^+-GaAs.[18]

EXAMPLE 5–7

Taking $\Delta E_g = 1.85 - 1.43 = 0.42$ eV, the band offsets are $\Delta E_c = 0.28$ eV and $\Delta E_v = 0.14$ eV. In each case we draw the equilibrium Fermi level, add the appropriate bands far from the junction, add the band offsets while estimating the relative amounts of band bending and position of $x = 0$ for the particular doping on the two sides, and finally sketch the band edges so that E_g is maintained in each separate semiconductor right up to the heterojunction at $x = 0$.

SOLUTION

[18]In discussing heterojunctions, it is common to use a capital N or P to designate the wide band gap material.

A particularly important example of a heterojunction is shown in Figure 5–46, in which heavily n-type AlGaAs is grown on lightly doped GaAs. In this example the discontinuity in the conduction band allows electrons to spill over from the N⁺-AlGaAs into the GaAs, where they become trapped in the potential well. As a result, electrons collect on the GaAs side of the heterojunction and move the Fermi level above the conduction band in the GaAs near the interface. These electrons are confined in a narrow potential well in the GaAs conduction band. If we construct a device in which conduction occurs parallel to the interface, the electrons in such a potential well form a *two-dimensional electron gas* with very interesting device properties. As we shall see in Chapter 6, electron conduction in such a potential well can result in very high mobility electrons. This high mobility is due to the fact that the electrons in this well

Figure 5–46
A heterojunction
between
N^+-AlGaAs and
lightly doped
GaAs, illustrating
the potential
well for electrons
formed in the
GaAs conduction
band. If this well
is sufficiently thin,
discrete states
(such as E_1 and
E_2) are formed,
as discussed in
Section 2.4.3.

come from the AlGaAs, and not from doping in the GaAs. As a result, there is negligible impurity scattering in the GaAs well, and the mobility is controlled almost entirely by lattice scattering (phonons). At low temperatures, where phonon scattering is low, the mobility in this region can be very high. If the band bending in the GaAs conduction band is strong enough, the potential well may be extremely narrow, so that discrete states such as E_1 and E_2 in Fig. 5–46 are formed. We will return to this example in Chapter 6.

Another obvious feature of Fig. 5–46 is that the concept of a contact potential barrier qV_0 for both electrons and holes in a homojunction is no longer valid for the heterojunction. In Fig. 5–46 the barrier for electrons qV_n is smaller than the barrier for holes qV_p. This property of a heterojunction can be used to alter the relative injection of electrons and holes, as we shall see in Section 7.9.

5.1 Diodes and other semiconductor devices are made by combinations of steps such as oxidation, selective doping (via implant or diffusion), and the deposition of various insulators or metals in concert with etching, using patterns formed by photolithography.

SUMMARY

5.2 When we bring p- and n-type semiconductors into contact to make a p-n junction diode, carriers diffuse across the junction until we get a flat Fermi level in equilibrium. A *built-in junction potential barrier* is formed between the p and n sides, which reflects the voltage drop across the depletion region. This is a *dynamic* equilibrium, in which there is a continual diffusion of electrons from the n to the p side (and holes from p to n), but at a reduced rate over the potential barrier, and these fluxes are cancelled by opposing flows of minority carriers diffusing to the depletion edges and getting swept across the junction.

5.3 The electrostatics of the depletion region are determined by solving the Poisson's equation. For uniformly doped *abrupt* step junctions we get *linearly varying electric fields* that are highest at the metallurgical junction. We get a wider depletion region on the more lightly doped side and equal and opposite depletion charges on the two sides of the junction.

5.4 For an *ideal Shockley diode,* one assumes *negligible generation–recombination inside the depletion region.* In forward bias, the built-in potential barrier is lowered, making it exponentially easier for majority carriers, to diffuse across.

5.5 The opposing minority carrier fluxes are unaffected because they are limited by how *often* the few minority carriers diffuse to the depletion edges. Far from the junction, the current is carried by drift of the majority carriers, which are injected across the junction to the other side, where, as minority carriers, they give rise to diffusion currents.

5.6 In reverse bias, for ideal diodes, the *voltage-independent* reverse current is due to the collection of thermally generated minority carriers on either side diffusing to the depletion region and then being swept across. The current flow from n to p is small and is the basis of diode rectifiers.

5.7 For high reverse biases, diodes undergo (reversible) breakdown due to quantum mechanical *tunneling* (*Zener* mechanism) across a narrow depletion region for very heavily doped junctions or due to *impact ionization* or *avalanche* multiplication of carriers in a wider depletion region for lightly doped junctions. For narrow diodes, there can also be punch-through from one contact to the other.

5.8 Varying the bias leads to diode switching; the diode transient behavior can be found by solving the continuity equation, for example, using Laplace transforms, with suitable initial and boundary conditions.

5.9 Small signal capacitance in a semiconductor device is caused by a *change* in the charge storage as a function of bias. There are two components of diode capacitance: *depletion capacitance,* due to exposed dopant charges in the depletion region (dominates in reverse bias); and *diffusion capacitance,* due to stored excess mobile carriers (dominates in forward bias).

5.10 *Real diodes* can deviate from Shockley "ideal" diodes, which have negligible generation–recombination in the depletion region. *Generation–recombination* in the depletion region increases the diode ideality factor **n** from 1 to 2 in forward bias and introduces a roughly square root voltage dependence of reverse leakage current.

5.11 *High-level carrier injection* for large forward bias, in which the injected minority carrier concentration is comparable to the background majority carrier concentration, also makes **n** = 2. *Series resistance* effects play a role as well for higher currents.

5.12 Graded junctions, where the doping concentrations on either side are not constant, are qualitatively similar to abrupt junctions, but are harder to analyze. They have different C–V than abrupt junctions have.

5.13 Metal–semiconductor junctions behave as *Schottky diodes* (if the Fermi level alignments are such that there is a depletion of majority carriers in the semiconductor) or *ohmic contacts* (if there is no depletion region formed in the semiconductor).

5.14 Junctions between dissimilar semiconductors are called *heterojunctions*. With respect to a vacuum reference level, one looks at the conduction band edges (electron affinities) and band gaps to determine the band offsets and at the Fermi levels (work functions) to determine the direction of carrier transfer. Electrons flow from the high to low Fermi level regions, and holes flow the opposite way.

5.1 A 900-nm oxide is grown on (100) Si in wet oxygen at 1100°C (see Appendix VI). **PROBLEMS** How long does it take to grow the first 200 nm, the next 300 nm, and the final 400 nm?

A square window (1 mm × 1 mm) is etched in this oxide, and the wafer is reoxidized at 1150°C in wet oxygen such that the oxide thickness *outside* of the window region increases to 2000 nm. Draw a cross section of the wafer and mark off all the thicknesses, dimensions, and oxide–Si interfaces relative to the original Si surface. Calculate the step heights in Si and in the oxide at the edge of the window.

5.2 When impurities are diffused into a sample from an unlimited source such that the surface concentration N_0 is held constant, the impurity distribution (profile) is given by

$$N(x, t) = N_0 \, \text{erfc}\left(\frac{x}{2\sqrt{Dt}}\right)$$

where D is the diffusion coefficient for the impurity, t is the diffusion time, and erfc is the complementary error function.

If a certain number of impurities are placed in a thin layer on the surface before diffusion, and if no impurities are added and none escape during diffusion, a gaussian distribution is obtained:

$$N(x, t) = \frac{N_s}{\sqrt{\pi Dt}} e^{-(x/2\sqrt{Dt})^2}$$

where N_s is the quantity of impurity placed on the surface (atoms/cm^2) prior to $t = 0$. Notice that this expression differs from Eq. (4–44) by a factor of two. Why?

Figure P5–2 gives curves of the complementary error function and gaussian factors for the variable u, which in our case is $x/2\sqrt{Dt}$. Assume that boron is diffused into n-type Si (uniform $N_d = 5 \times 10^{16}$ cm^{-3}) at 1000°C for 30 minutes. The diffusion coefficient for B in Si at this temperature is $D = 3 \times 10^{-14}$ cm^2/s.

(a) Plot $N_a(x)$ after the diffusion, assuming that the surface concentration is held constant at $N_0 = 5 \times 10^{20}$ cm^{-3}. Locate the position of the junction below the surface.

(b) Plot $N_a(x)$ after the diffusion, assuming that B is deposited in a thin layer on the surface prior to diffusion ($N_s = 5 \times 10^{13}$ cm^{-2}), and no additional B atoms are available during the diffusion. Locate the junction for this case.

Figure P5-2

$$u = \frac{x}{2\sqrt{Dt}}$$

Hint: Plot the curves on five-cycle semilog paper, with an abscissa varying from zero to $\frac{1}{2}$ µm. In plotting $N_a(x)$, choose values of x that are simple multiples of $2\sqrt{Dt}$.

5.3 Assuming a constant (unlimited) source diffusion of P at 1000°C into p-type Si ($N_a = 2 \times 10^{16}\,\mathrm{cm}^{-3}$), calculate the time required to achieve a junction depth of 1 micron. See the equations in Prob. 5.2 and data in Appendices VII and VIII.

5.4 In an ion implanter, dopant implantation of energetic B ion is done into a Si substrate with 2 µm oxide thickness, such that the peak B concentration becomes $5 \times 10^{18}/\mathrm{cm}^3$ at 0.4 µm distance from the surface. For this projected range, what will be the energy and corresponding straggle? What will be the value of implant dose and beam current, if the scanning is done for 100 cm^2 area with 30 sec implant time.

5.5 Silicon is implanted with P ions at 200 keV to a dose of $2.1 \times 10^{14}\,\mathrm{cm}^{-2}$. Calculate and plot the P distribution on a semilog plot as in Fig. 5–4.

5.6 We are interested in patterning the structure shown in Fig. P5–6. Design the mask aligner optics in terms of the numerical aperture of the lens and the wavelength of the source.

5.7 In a p^+-n Si junction, the n side has a donor concentration of 10^{16} cm^{-3}. If $n_i = 10^{10}$ cm^{-3}, relative dielectric constant $\epsilon_r = 12$, calculate the depletion width at a reverse bias of 100 V? What is the electric field at the mid-point of the depletion region on the n side? (*Hint:* Remember that p^+ means very heavily doped!)

5.8 A semiconductor with a band gap of 0.8 eV and an intrinsic carrier concentration of 10^{12} cm^{-3} is doped with 10^{18} cm^{-3} donors on the left half and 10^{17} cm^{-3} acceptors on the right half. Draw the equilibrium band diagram. Calculate the junction potential and the position of the Fermi level, and indicate them on the band diagram. Suppose an electron at the conduction band edge on the p side goes over the n side without scattering. Assuming parabolic band structure, calculate its wavevector there. The effective mass of the carriers is $0.2m_0$.

5.9 An abrupt Si junction (area = 0.0001 cm^2) has the following parameters:

n side	p side
$N_d = 5 \times 10^{17}$ cm^{-3}	$N_a = 10^{17}$ cm^{-3}

Draw and label the band diagram, and calculate the difference between the Fermi level and the intrinsic Fermi level on both sides. Calculate the built-in potential at the junction in equilibrium and the depletion width. What is the *total number* of exposed acceptors in the depletion region?

5.10 A p-n junction diode has a doping concentration of 10^{16} cm^{-3} on the p side, and is very highly doped on the n side. The intrinsic carrier concentration is 10^9 cm^{-3}, band gap is 2 eV, and $\epsilon_r = 15$. Sketch the band diagram for a reverse bias of 2 V, and calculate the values of band edges with respect to the quasi-Fermi levels far from the junction. Calculate the depletion charge per cm^2 on the n side. If an electron at the conduction band edge on the p side goes over to the n side without scattering, calculate its velocity. Electron and hole effective masses = $0.4m_0$.

5.11 In a p-n junction, the n-side doping is five times the p-side doping. The intrinsic carrier concentration = 10^{11} cm^{-3} and band gap is 2 eV at 100°C. If the built-in junction potential is 0.65 V, what is the doping on the p side? If the relative dielectric constant of this semiconductor is 10, what is the depletion capacitance at 2 V reverse bias for a diode of cross-sectional area of 0.5 cm²? Draw a **qualitatively** correct sketch of the band diagram and label the depletion widths and voltage drops for this bias.

5.12 For three p-n junction diode samples A, B, and C, acceptor and donor carrier concentrations are the same of $10^{15}/cm^3$ and $10^{18}/cm^3$, respectively. Find the contact potentials for these three devices at temp 300 K. Intrinsic carrier concentrations for the three samples are $1.5 \times 10^{10}/cm^3$, $2 \times 10^{10}/cm^3$, and $2 \times 10^{6}/cm^3$. Comment on the comparison of estimated contact potentials.

5.13 In a p⁺-n junction the hole diffusion current in the neutral n material is given by Eq. (5–32). What are the electron diffusion and electron drift components of current at point x_n in the neutral n region?

5.14 An abrupt Si p-n junction has $N_a = 10^{17}\,cm^{-3}$ on the p side and $N_d = 10^{16}\,cm^{-3}$ on the n side. At 300 K, (a) calculate the Fermi levels, draw an equilibrium band diagram, and find V_0 from the diagram; (b) compare the result from (a) with V_0 calculated from Eq. (5–8).

5.15 Boron is implanted into an n-type Si sample ($N_d = 10^{16}\,cm^{-3}$), forming an abrupt junction of square cross section with area $= 2 \times 10^{-3}\,cm^2$. Assume that the acceptor concentration in the p-type region is $N_a = 4 \times 10^{18}\,cm^{-3}$. Calculate $V_0, x_{n0}, x_{p0}, Q_+,$ and E_0 for this junction at equilibrium (300 K). Sketch $\mathscr{E}$ and the charge density to scale, as in Fig. 5–12.

5.16 In a p-n junction diode acceptor, donor and intrinsic carrier concentrations are $10^{17}/cm^3$, $10^{18}/cm^3$, and $10^{10}/cm^3$, respectively. The relative dielectric constant for the material of the diode is 12. The diffusion coefficients are $D_n = 49\,cm^2/sec$ and $D_p = 18\,cm^2/sec$, respectively. Electron and hole carrier lifetimes are the same, 25 ns. Under forward bias of 0.2 V, calculate the electron diffusion current density at a distance of twice of the diffusion length.

5.17 A Si n⁺p junction has an acceptor doping of $2 \times 10^{17}/cm^3$ on the p side and cross-sectional area of $10^{-2}\,cm^2$. If majority carrier lifetime is 10 ns and corresponding diffusion coefficient is 400 cm²/sec, estimate the current density under a reverse bias of 0.3 V at 300 K temperature.

5.18 Estimate the expressions for developed electric field of a p-n junction where the space charge profile at depletion region is given as $p(x) = q.h(2x+3)$, where x is a distance of the device from physical contact at $x = 0$ and h is a constant.

5.19 (a) A Si p⁺-n junction $10^{-2}\,cm^2$ in area has $N_d = 10^{15}\,cm^{-3}$ doping on the n side. Calculate the junction capacitance with a reverse bias of 10 V.

(b) An abrupt p⁺-n junction is formed in Si with a donor doping of $N_d = 10^{15}\,cm^{-3}$. What is the depletion region thickness W just prior to avalanche breakdown?

5.20 In a p^+n junction diode, which side penetration depth will be larger? Estimate and compare the ratio of the penetration depths on both sides of the junction if the acceptor concentration is twice than that for the donor concentration. Compare the generated electric fields on both sides also.

5.21 For a Si p^+n junction of area 2×10^{-4} cm², calculate the depletion width, the peak electric field, and the depletion capacitance under 60 V of reverse bias with the following diode specifications:

p side	n side
$N_a = 10^{19}$/cm³	$N_d = 10^{16}$/cm³
$T_p = 10$ ns	$T_n = 0.1$ ns
$\mu_p = 800$ cm²/V-sec	$\mu_n = 1250$ cm²/V-sec
$\mu_n = 200$ cm²/V-sec	$\mu_p = 1400$ cm²/V-sec

5.22 In a simple p-n diode, if the diffusion coefficent for holes is twice than that for the electrons, the minority carrier concentration at n side is twice than that in p side, and the diffusion coefficent for holes is also twice of that for the electrons, calculate the injection efficiency for this diode at $x_n = 0$.

5.23 An abrupt Si p-n junction diode with area $= 10^{-4}$ cm² has $N_a = 10^{17}$/cm³ and $N_d = 10^{18}$/cm³. The diode has FB of 1 V. The mobility's for electrons and holes are $\mu n = 1350$ cm²/v-sec, $\mu_p = 400$ cm²/v-sec, and $\tau_p = \tau_n = 10$ ns.

(a) Find the excess carrier concentration.

(b) Find the electron and hole concentration at $x = 2 L_n$ and $2 L_p$.

5.24 A Si p-n junction with cross-sectional area $A = 0.001$ cm² is formed with $N_a = 10^{15}$ cm^{-3} and $N_d = 10^{20}$ cm^{-3}. Calculate:

(a) Contact potential, V_0.

(b) Space-charge width at equilibrium (zero bias).

(c) Current with a forward bias of 0.7 V. Assume that the current is diffusion dominated. Assume $\mu_n = 1500$ cm²/V-s, $\mu_p = 450$ cm²/V-s, and $\tau_n = \tau_q = 2.5$ ms. Which carries most of the current, electrons or holes, and why? If you wanted to double the electron current, what should you do?

5.25 Suppose in a p^+n diode the n region and the p region thickness are 20 μm and 5μm, respectively. What will be the RB applied to obtain a breakdown for this diode? [Given: $\epsilon = 11.8, Nd = 10^{15}$/cm³]

5.26 In a p-n junction diode operating under certain reverse bias V_r, if V_r is increased to 3 V_r, what will be the impact on the following parameters?

(a) Depletion width

(b) Contact potential

(c) Junction capacitance

(d) Probability of breakdown

5.27 We make a Si bar with a p-type doping of 2×10^{16} cm^{-3} on the left half and a p-type doping of 10^{18} cm^{-3} on the right side. Sketch the equilibrium band diagram, with precise values marked off, *far* from the doping transition at 600 K when the intrinsic carrier concentration is 10^{16} cm^{-3}. (*Note:* This is p type on both sides. Such a junction is known as a *high–low junction* rather than a p-n junction. Observe that the doping level is comparable to n_i on the left side! Do not worry about the exact details right near the doping transition!)

5.28 Assume that an abrupt Si p-n junction with area 10^{-4} cm^2 has $N_a = 10^{17}$ cm^{-3} on the p side and $N_d = 10^{17}$ cm^{-3} on the n side. The diode has a forward bias of 0.7 V. Using mobility values from Fig. 3–23 and assuming that $\tau_n = \tau_p = 1$ μs, plot I_p and I_n vs. distance on a diagram such as Fig. 5–17, including both sides of the junction. Neglect recombination within W.

5.29 In a p$^+$n diode reverse biased at 5 V, the generated capacitance is 20 pF. If the doping of the p side is doubled and the bias is change to 20 V, what will be the change in capacitance? If now the bias is changed to 100 V, then what will be the change?

5.30 A Ge p$^+$n junction diode has donor doping of 2×10^{15}/cm^3 and relative permittivity 16. What will be the minimum thickness of n region that will ensure avalanche breakdown at 300 V reverse bias voltage?

5.31 Calculate the capacitance for the following Ge p$^+$n junction for two reverse bias voltages of 1 and 3 V. [Given: $N_d = 10^{16}$/cm^3, $N_a = 10^{18}$/cm^3, area $= 10^{-4}$ cm^2, ni, Ge $= 2 \times 10^{10}$/cm^3]

5.32 We assumed in Section 5.2.3 that carriers are excluded within W and that the semiconductor is neutral outside W. This is known as the *depletion approximation*. Obviously, such a sharp transition is unrealistic. In fact, the space charge varies over a distance of several *Debye lengths*, given by

$$L_D = \left[\frac{\epsilon_s kT}{q^2 N_d} \right]^{1/2} \quad \text{on the n side.}$$

Calculate the Debye length on the n side for Si junctions having $N_a = 10^{18}$ cm^{-3} on the p side and $N_d = 10^{14}, 10^{16}$, and 10^{18} cm^{-3} on the n side and compare with the size of W in each case.

5.33 A Si p-n junction diode with area $= 10^4$ cm^2 has $N_a = 10^{17}$/cm^3 and $N_d = 10^{17}$/cm^3.

(a) Find the reverse saturation current, given $\mu n = 1500$ cm^2/v-sec, $\mu p = 450$ cm^2/v-sec, and $\tau_p = \tau_n = 2$ ns.

(b) With the ideality factor n = 1.5 and FB of 0.2 V, calculate the forward current.

5.34 Holes are injected in a p^+n diode with an n region width similar to hole diffusion length L_p. Excess holes at n side varies linearly from $\triangle p_n$ (at $x_n=0$) to zero (at $x_n=L_p$). Solve the diffusion equation to find the excess hole concentration.

5.35 Soive for the electron carrier concentration and current density at the p region for narrow base diode with high recombination at the edges of depletion n region.

5.36 Consider an n^+p junction under reverse bias of 5 V. Let $N_a = 5 \times 10^{17}$ cm^{-3}. Find the reverse current density due to diffusion. [Given: $D_n = 10$ cm^2/sec, $L_n = 45\mu$m]

5.37 The diode of Fig. 5–23c is used in a simple half-wave rectifier circuit in which the diode is placed in series with a load resistor. Assume that the diode offset voltage E_0 is 0.4 V and that $R = dv/di = 400\,\Omega$. For a load resistor of 1 $k\Omega$ and a sinusoidal input of 2 sin ωt, sketch the output voltage (across the load resistor) over two cycles.

5.38 The ideality factor **n** can be used to describe the relative importance of recombination within the transition region and the neutral region. Calculate and plot the $I-V$ characteristics of a diode, using Eq. (5–74) for values of the ideality factor of 1.0, 1.2, 1.4, 1.6, 1.8, and 2.0.

$$A = 100 \ \mu\text{m}^2, N_a = 10^{19} \ \text{cm}^{-3}, \text{and}$$
$$N_d = 10^{19} \ \text{cm}^{-3}; \tau_n = \tau_p = \mu\text{s}$$

5.39 Assume holes are injected from a p^+-n junction into a short n region of length l. If $\delta p(x_n)$ varies linearly from Δpn at $x_n = 0$ to zero at the ohmic contact $(x_n = l)$, find the steady state charge in the excess hole distribution Q_p and the current I.

5.40 Assume that a p^+-n diode is built with an n region width l smaller than a hole diffusion length $(l < L_p)$. This is the so-called *narrow base diode*. Since for this case holes are injected into a short n region under forward bias, we cannot use the assumption $\delta p(x_n = \infty) = 0$ in Eq. (4–35). Instead, we must use as a boundary condition the fact that $\delta p = 0$ at $x_n = l$.

(a) Solve the diffusion equation to obtain

$$\delta p(x_n) = \frac{\Delta p_n[e^{(l-x_n)/L_p} - e^{(x_n-l)/L_p}]}{e^{l/L_p} - e^{-l/L_p}}$$

(b) Show that the current in the diode is

$$I = \left(\frac{qAD_pp_n}{L_p} \ \text{ctnh} \ \frac{l}{L_p}\right)(e^{qV/kT} - 1)$$

5.41 Given the narrow base diode result (Prob. 5.40), (a) calculate the current due to recombination in the n region, and (b) show that the current due to recombination at the ohmic contact is

$$I(\text{ohmic contact}) = \left(\frac{qAD_pp_n}{L_p}\right)\operatorname{csch}\frac{l}{L_p}\left(e^{qV/kT} - 1\right)$$

5.42 Assume that a p^+-n junction is built with a graded n region in which the doping is described by $N_d(x) = Gx^m$. The depletion region ($W \cong x_{n0}$) extends from essentially the junction at $x = 0$ to a point W within the n region. The singularity at $x = 0$ for negative $\mathbf{m}$ can be neglected.

(a) Integrate Gauss's law across the depletion region to obtain the maximum value of the electric field $\mathscr{E}_0 = -qGW^{(m+1)}/\epsilon(m + 1)$.

(b) Find the expression for (x), and use the result to obtain $V_0 - V = qGW^{(m+2)}/\epsilon(m + 2)$.

(c) Find the charge Q due to ionized donors in the depletion region; write Q explicitly in terms of $(V_0 - V)$.

(d) Using the results of (c), take the derivative $dQ/d(V_0 - V)$ to show that the capacitance is

$$C_j = A\left[\frac{qG\epsilon^{(m+1)}}{(m + 2)(V_0 - V)}\right]^{1/(m+2)}$$

5.43 We deposit a metal with a work function of 4.6 eV on Si (electron affinity of 4 eV) and acceptor doping level of 10^{18} cm^{-3}. Draw the equilibrium band diagram and mark off the Fermi level, the band edges, and the vacuum level. Is this a Schottky or ohmic contact, and why? By how much should the metal work function be altered to change the type of contact? Explain with reference to the band diagram.

5.44 Design an ohmic contact for n-type GaAs using InAs, with an intervening graded InGaAs region (see Fig. 5–44).

5.45 A Schottky barrier is formed between a metal having a work function of 4.3 eV and p-type Si (electron affinity = 4 eV). The acceptor doping in the Si is 10^{17} cm^{-3}.

(a) Draw the equilibrium band diagram, showing a numerical value for qV_0.

(b) Draw the band diagram with 0.3 V forward bias. Repeat for 2 V reverse bias.

5.46 We want to make a Schottky diode on one surface of an n-type semiconductor, and an ohmic contact on the other side. The electron affinity is 5 eV, band gap is 1.5 eV, and the Fermi potential is 0.25 eV? What should be values of work functions of the two metals? (Give your answer as greater than or less than certain values.) Sketch the band diagram of the structure.

5.47 A semiconductor heterojunction is made between the following materials, A and B, with the following parameters:

	E_G (eV)	χ (eV)	Doping (cm^{-3})	Length (μm)	$L_{n,p}$ (μm)	n_i (cm^{-3})	$\tau_{n,p}$ (μs)
A:	2	4	$N_A = 10^{20}$	0.5	10	10^8	10
B:	1	5	$N_D = 10^{16}$	0.1	100	10^{10}	1

Draw the equilibrium band diagram, marking off the band edge energies and E_F, with respect to the vacuum level.

Calculate the current density if the junction is forward biased such that the minority concentrations are increased *by a factor* of 10^6.

(*Hint: Use appropriate approximations.* There is a lot of extraneous information here; the answer is very simple. Remember that this is a p$^+$-n junction, and the length of the semiconductors is $\ll$ diffusion length; the minority carrier concentration is zero at the ohmic contacts at both ends of the device.)

5.48 A p-n junction diode has a doping concentration of 10^{17} cm^{-3} on the p- side, and double that on the n side. The intrinsic carrier concentration is 10^{11} cm^{-3}, band gap is 2 eV, and $\epsilon_r = 15$. Sketch the band diagram in equilibrium, and mark off the values of band edges with respect to the Fermi level and the depletion widths on both sides.

Repeat the above for a heterojunction, where the band gap on the n side is reduced to 1 eV, and the electron affinity on the n side is 4 eV. Other parameters are kept the same. Band offsets are the same for conduction and valence bands across the heterojunction.

Very useful applets for understanding diode operation are available at https://nanohub.org/resources/animations **READING LIST**

Campbell, S. A. *The Science and Engineering of Microelectronic Fabrication*, 2d ed. NY: Oxford, 2001.

Chang, L. L., and L. Esaki. "Semiconductor Quantum Heterostructures." *Physics Today* 45 (October 1992): 36–43.

Muller, R. S., and T. I. Kamins. *Device Electronics for Integrated Circuits.* New York: Wiley, 1986.

Neamen, D. A. *Semiconductor Physics and Devices: Basic Principles.* Homewood, IL: Irwin, 1992.

Pierret, R. F. *Semiconductor Device Fundamentals.* Reading, MA: Addison-Wesley, 1996.

Plummer, J. D., M. D. Deal, and P. B. Griffin. *Silicon VLSI Technology.* Upper Saddle River, NJ: Prentice Hall, 2000.

Shockley, W. "The Theory of p-n Junctions in Semiconductors and p-n Junction Transistors." *Bell Syst. Tech. J.* 28 (1949), 435.

Wolf, S., and R. N. Tauber. *Silicon Processing for the VLSI Era*, 2d ed. Sunset Beach, CA: Lattice Press, 2000.

Wolfe, C. M., G. E. Stillman, and N. Holonyak, Jr. *Physical Properties of Semiconductors.* Englewood Cliffs, NJ: Prentice Hall, 1989.

SELF QUIZ   **Question 1**

Consider a forward-biased *ideal* (abrupt junction, no recombination or generation in the depletion region) long p-n junction diode under forward bias. On the following graph, sketch and label the total current I_{total}, the total electron current $I_{n,total}$, and the total hole current $I_{p,total}$ as a function of position throughout the entire device. The value of each has been given at the n-side edge of the depletion region for reference. (*Hint:* The excess carrier concentrations are essentially pinned to zero at the contacts.)

Question 2

(a) Consider (1) a long p-n junction diode with the ohmic contact on the n side, $x_{contact,1} \gg L_p$, and (2) a short p-n junction diode with the ohmic contact on the n-side well within a diffusion length of the depletion region, $x_{contact,2} < L_p$. Given the indicated excess hole (equals electron) concentration at the n-side edge of the depletion region Δp for both diodes, sketch the excess hole concentrations as a function of position $\delta p(x_n)$ within the region for the two cases on the following graph, and label them (1) and (2) accordingly.

(b) Consistent with your answers to part (a), sketch the hole (diffusion) currents within the region for the same two diodes on the following graph, and label them (1) and (2) again. The value of the hole current at the edge of the depletion region for the long diode $I_{p,1}(x_n = 0)$ is provided for reference.

Question 3

Consider two Si p-n junction diodes, one long and one short (contacts within a diffusion length of the depletion region) but otherwise identical. Under identical forward-bias voltage, which diode would have greater current flow?

Question 4

If the depletion capacitance of a p-n junction diode is $C_{d,o}$ at equilibrium and the contact potential is 0.5 V, how much reverse-bias voltage would have to be applied to reduce the depletion capacitance to $0.5\,C_{d,o}$?

Question 5

(a) What is the difference between depletion and diffusion capacitance in a diode? Which one dominates in forward bias and why? In reverse bias?

(b) Why is it meaningful to define small signal capacitance and conductance in semiconductor devices such as diodes? How are they defined?

Question 6

We grow a pseudomorphic heterostructure consisting of an epitaxial film with lattice constant of 6 Å and band gap of 2 eV on a thick substrate with lattice constant of 4 Å and band gap of 1 eV. Both the substrate and epitaxial layer have a cubic crystal structure in the unstrained state. If 60% of the band edge discontinuity is in the conduction band, sketch a simplified band diagram of this heterostructure. Also, qualitatively show a 2-D view of the crystal structure in relation to the band diagram.

Question 7

(a) In the space below, sketch the equilibrium band diagram resulting from bringing together the illustrated metal and lightly doped semiconductor indicating the Fermi level; the conduction band and valence band offsets from the Fermi level at the metal–semiconductor interface in terms of $q\Phi_m$, $q\Phi_s$, $q\chi$, and/or E_g; any band bending in the semiconductor in terms of $q\Phi_m$, $q\Phi_s$, $q\chi$, and/or E_g; and (qualitatively) any charge depletion or accumulation layer. Assume no interface traps.

(b)   Is this a Schottky contact or an ohmic contact?

Question 8

Calculate the electron concentration of an n type semiconductor whose conductivity is 15 s/n and electron mobility is 25×10^{-4} m²/Vs. Assume $\sigma = 9$ s/m and $un = 40 \times 10^{-4}$ m²/Vs.

Question 9

The resistivities of p region and n region of a silicon diode is 5 W/cm and 3 W/cm. Calculate the contact potential and potential energy barrier. Assume standard values of the parameters at 300 K.

Question 10

In a pn juction diode when it is forward biased the diode current is 0.5 mA when the applied voltage is 300 mV and 16 mA when the applied voltage is 600 mV. Determine η.

Chapter 6
Field-Effect Transistors

OBJECTIVES

1. Derive I–V characteristics of JFETs, MESFETs, and HEMTs
2. Determine MOS C–V behavior and threshold voltage; study leakage characteristics of gate dielectrics
3. Understand MOSFET band diagrams, and linear and saturation behavior
4. Understand "effective" channel mobility, body effect, and subthreshold slopes
5. Analyze second-order effects—DIBL, GIDL, charge sharing, and V_T roll-off

The modern era of semiconductor electronics was ushered in by the invention of the bipolar transistor in 1948 by Bardeen, Brattain, and Shockley at the Bell Telephone Laboratories. This device, along with its field-effect counterpart, has had an enormous impact on virtually every area of modern life. In this chapter we will learn about the operation, applications, and fabrication of the field-effect transistor (FET).

The FET comes in several forms. In a *junction* FET (called a *JFET*) the control (*gate*) voltage varies the depletion width of a reverse-biased p-n junction. A similar device results if the junction is replaced by a Schottky barrier (*metal – semiconductor* FET, called a *MESFET*). Alternatively, the metal gate electrode may be separated from the semiconductor by an insulator (*metal–insulator–semiconductor* FET, called a *MISFET*). A common special case of this type uses an oxide layer as the insulator (*MOSFET*).

In Chapter 5 we found that two dominant features of p-n junctions are the injection of minority carriers with forward bias and a variation of the depletion width W with reverse bias. These two p-n junction properties are used in two important types of transistors. The *bipolar junction transistor (BJT)* discussed in Chapter 7 uses the injection of minority carriers across a forward-biased junction, and the JFET discussed in this chapter depends on control of a junction depletion width under reverse bias. The FET is a majority carrier device, and is therefore often called a *unipolar* transistor. The BJT, on the other hand, operates by the injection and collection of *minority* carriers. Since the action of both electrons and holes is important in this device, it is called a *bipolar* transistor. Like its bipolar counterpart, the FET is a three-terminal device in which the current through two terminals is controlled at the third. Unlike the BJT, however, field-effect devices are controlled by a voltage at the third terminal rather than by a current.

      The history of BJTs and FETs is rather interesting. It was the FET that was proposed first in 1930 by Lilienfeld, but he never got it to work because he did not fully appreciate the role of surface defects or surface states. In the process of trying to demonstrate experimentally such a FET, Bardeen and Brattain somewhat serendipitously invented the first bipolar transistor, the Ge point contact transistor. This major breakthrough was rapidly followed by Shockley's extension of the concept to the BJT. It was only much later, after the problem of surface states was resolved by growing an oxide insulator on Si, that the first MOSFET was demonstrated in 1960 by Kahng and Atalla. Although the BJT reigned supreme in the early days of semiconductor-integrated electronics, it has been gradually supplanted in most applications by the Si MOSFET. The main reason is, unlike BJTs, the various types of FET are characterized by a high *input impedance*, since the control voltage is applied to a reverse-biased junction or Schottky barrier, or across an insulator. These devices are particularly well suited for controlled switching between a conducting state and a nonconducting state, and are therefore useful in digital circuits. They are also suitable for integration of many devices on a single chip, as we shall see in Chapter 9. In fact, billions of MOS transistors are commonly used together in semiconductor memory devices and microprocessors.

6.1
TRANSISTOR
OPERATION

We begin this section with a general discussion of amplification and switching, the basic circuit functions performed by transistors. The transistor is a three-terminal device with the important feature that the current through two terminals can be controlled by small changes we make in the current or voltage at the third terminal. This control feature allows us to amplify small a-c signals or to switch the device from an *on* state to an *off* state and back. These two operations, *amplification* and *switching*, are the basis of a host of electronic functions. This section provides a brief introduction to these operations, as a foundation for understanding both bipolar and field-effect transistors.

6.1.1 The Load Line

Consider a two-terminal device (Fig. 6-1a) that has a nonlinear *I–V* characteristic, as in Fig. 6–1b. We might determine this curve experimentally by measuring the current for various applied voltages. When such a device is biased with the simple battery–resistor combination shown in the figure,

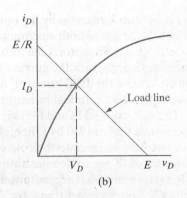

Figure 6–1
A two-terminal
nonlinear device:
(a) biasing circuit;
(b) I–V
characteristic and
load line.

(a)   (b)

steady state values of I_D and V_D are attained. To find these values we begin by writing a loop equation around the circuit:[1]

$$E = i_D R + v_D \tag{6–1}$$

This gives us one equation describing the circuit, but it contains two unknowns (i_D and v_D). Fortunately, we have another equation of the form $i_D = f(v_D)$ in the curve of Fig. 6–1b, giving us two equations with two unknowns. The steady state current and voltage are found by a simultaneous solution of these two equations. However, since one equation is analytical and the other is graphical, we must first put them into the same form. It is easy to make the linear equation (6–1) graphical, so we plot it on Fig. 6–1b to find the simultaneous solution. The end points of the line described by Eq. (6–1) are at E when $i_D = 0$ and at E/R when $v_D = 0$. The two graphs cross at $v_D = V_D$ and $i_D = I_D$, the steady state values of current and voltage for the device with this biasing circuit.

Now let's add a third terminal which somehow controls the I–V characteristic of the device (Fig. 6-2a). For example, assume that the device current–voltage curve can be moved up the current axis by increasing the control voltage as in Fig. 6–2b. This results in a family of $i_D - v_D$ curves, depending upon the choice of v_G. We can still write the loop equation (6–1) and draw it on the set of curves, but now the simultaneous solution depends on the value of v_G. In the example of Fig. 6–2, V_G is 0.5 V and the d-c values of I_D and V_D are found at the intersection to be 10 mA and 5 V, respectively. Whatever the value of the control voltage v_G at the third terminal, values of I_D and V_D are obtained from points along the line representing Eq. (6–1). This is called the *load line*.

6.1.2 Amplification and Switching

If an a-c source is added to the control voltage, we can achieve large variations in i_D by making small changes in v_G. For example, as v_G varies about its

---

[1]We use i_D to symbolize the total current, I_D for the d-c value, and i_d for the a-c component. A similar scheme is used for other currents and voltages.

Figure 6–2
A three-terminal nonlinear device that can be controlled by the voltage at the third terminal v_G: (a) biasing circuit; (b) I–V characteristic and load line. If $V_G = 0.5$ V, the d-c values of I_D and V_D are as shown by the dashed lines.

d-c value by 0.25 V in Fig. 6–2, v_d varies about its d-c value V_D by 2 V. Thus the amplification of the a-c signal is $2/0.25 = 8$. If the curves for equal changes in v_G are equally spaced on the i_D axis, a faithful amplified version of the small control signal can be obtained. This type of voltage-controlled amplification is typical of FETs. For bipolar transistors, a small control current is used to achieve large changes in the device current, achieving current amplification.

Another important circuit function of transistors is the controlled switching of the device off and on. In the example of Fig. 6–2, we can switch from the bottom of the load line ($i_D = 0$) to almost the top ($i_D \simeq E/R$) by appropriate changes in v_G. This type of switching with control at a third terminal is particularly useful in digital circuits.

**6.2
THE JUNCTION
FET**

In a *junction FET (JFET)* the voltage-variable depletion region width of a junction is used to control the effective cross-sectional area of a conducting *channel*. In the device of Fig. 6–3, the current I_D flows through an n-type channel between two p^+ regions. A reverse bias between these p^+ regions and the channel causes the depletion regions to intrude into the n material, and therefore the effective width of the channel can be restricted. Since the resistivity of the channel region is fixed by its doping, the channel resistance varies with changes in the effective cross-sectional area. By analogy, the variable depletion regions serve as the two doors of a gate, which open and close on the conducting channel.

In Fig. 6–3 electrons in the n-type channel drift from left to right, opposite to current flow. The end of the channel from which electrons flow is called the *source*, and the end toward which they flow is called the *drain*. The p^+ regions are called *gates*. If the channel were p type, holes would flow from

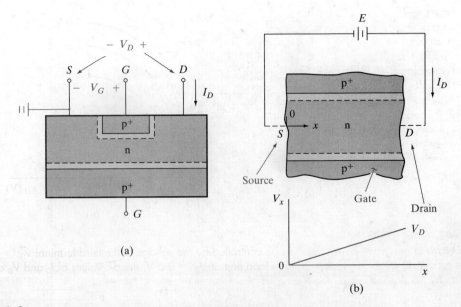

Figure 6-3
Simplified cross-sectional view of a junction FET: (a) transistor geometry; (b) detail of the channel and voltage variation along the channel with $V_G = 0$ and small I_D.

the source to the drain, in the same direction as the current flow, and the gate regions would be n^+. It is common practice to connect the two gate regions electrically; therefore, the voltage V_G refers to the potential from each gate region G to the source S. Since the conductivity of the heavily doped p^+ regions is high, we can assume that the potential is uniform throughout each gate. In the lightly doped channel material, however, the potential varies with position (Fig. 6–3b). If the channel of Fig. 6–3 is considered as a distributed resistor carrying a current I_D it is clear that the voltage from the drain end of the channel D to the source electrode S must be greater than the voltage from a point near the source end to S. For low values of current we can assume a linear variation of voltage V_x in the channel, varying from V_D at the drain end to zero at the source end (Fig. 6–3b).

6.2.1 Pinch-off and Saturation

In Fig. 6–4 we consider the channel in a simplified way by neglecting voltage drops between the source and drain electrodes and the respective ends of the channel. For example, we assume that the potential at the drain end of the channel is the same as the potential at the electrode D. This is a good approximation if the source and drain regions are relatively large, so that there is little resistance between the ends of the channel and the electrodes. In Fig. 6–4 the gates are short circuited to the source ($V_G = 0$), such that the potential at $x = 0$ is the same as the potential everywhere in the gate regions. For very small currents, the widths of the depletion regions are

Figure 6–4
Depletion regions
in the channel
of a JFET with
zero gate bias
for several values
of V_D: (a) linear
range; (b) near
pinch-off;
(c) beyond
pinch-off.

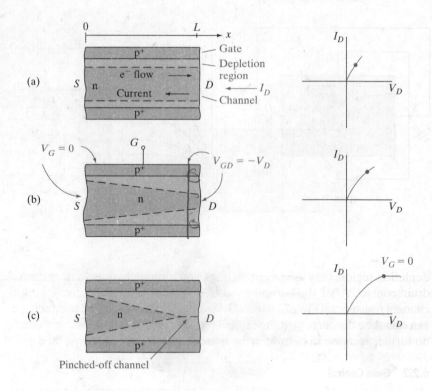

close to the equilibrium values (Fig. 6–4a). As the current I_D is increased, however, it becomes important that V_x is large near the drain end and small near the source end of the channel. Since the reverse bias across each point in the gate-to-channel junction is simply V_x when V_G is zero, we can estimate the shape of the depletion regions as in Fig. 6–4b. The reverse bias is relatively large near the drain ($V_{GD} = -V_D$) and decreases toward zero near the source. As a result, the depletion region intrudes into the channel near the drain, and the effective channel area is constricted.

Since the resistance of the constricted channel is higher, the I–V plot for the channel begins to depart from the straight line that was valid at low current levels. As the voltage V_D and current I_D are increased still further, the channel region near the drain becomes more constricted by the depletion regions and the channel resistance continues to increase. As V_D is increased, there must be some bias voltage at which the depletion regions meet near the drain and essentially *pinch-off* the channel (Fig. 6–4c). When this happens, the current I_D cannot increase significantly with further increase in V_D. Beyond pinch-off the current is *saturated* approximately at its value at pinch-off.[2] Once electrons from the channel enter the electric field of the

---

[2]*Saturation* is used by device engineers in more different contexts than any other word is used. We have discussed velocity saturation, the reverse saturation current of a junction, and, now, the saturation of FET characteristics. In Chapter 7, we will discuss the saturation of a BJT. The student has probably also reached saturation by now in trying to absorb these various meanings!

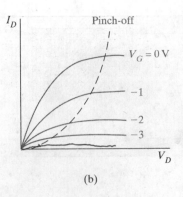

(a)

(b)

Figure 6–5
Effects of a
negative gate
bias: (a) increase
of depletion
region widths with
V_G negative;
(b) family of
current–voltage
curves for the
channels as V_G is
varied.

depletion region, they are swept through and ultimately flow to the positive drain contact. After the current saturates beyond pinch-off, the differential channel resistance dV_D/dI_D becomes very high. To a good approximation, we can calculate the current at the critical pinch-off voltage and assume there is no further increase in current as V_D is increased.

6.2.2 Gate Control

The effect of a negative gate bias $-V_G$ is to increase the resistance of the channel and induce pinch-off at a lower value of current (Fig. 6–5). Since the depletion regions are larger with V_G negative, the effective channel width is smaller and its resistance is higher in the low-current range of the characteristic. Therefore, the slopes of the I_D vs. V_D curves below pinch-off become smaller as the gate voltage is made more negative (Fig. 6–5b). The pinch-off condition is reached at a lower drain-to-source voltage, and the saturation current is lower than for the case of zero gate bias. As V_G is varied, a family of curves is obtained for the I–V characteristic of the channel, as in Fig. 6–5b.

Beyond the pinch-off voltage the drain current I_D is controlled by V_G. By varying the gate bias we can obtain amplification of an a-c signal. Since the input control voltage V_G appears across the reverse-biased gate junctions, the input impedance of the device is high.

We can calculate the pinch-off voltage rather simply by representing the channel in the approximate form of Fig. 6–6. If the channel is symmetrical and the effects of the gates are the same in each half of the channel region, we can restrict our attention to the channel half-width $h(x)$, measured from the center line ($y = 0$). The metallurgical half-width of the channel (i.e., neglecting the depletion region) is a. We can find the pinch-off voltage by calculating the reverse bias between the n channel and the p$^+$ gate at the drain end of the channel ($x = L$). For simplicity we shall assume that the channel width at the drain decreases uniformly as the reverse bias increases

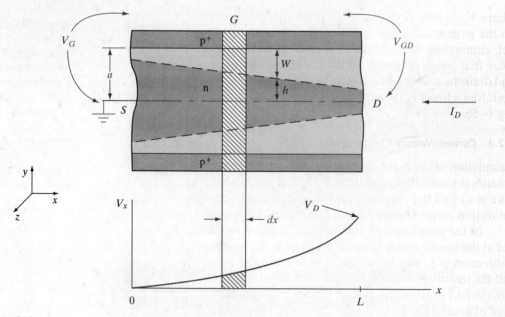

Figure 6–6
Simplified diagram of the channel with definitions of dimensions and differential volume for calculations.

to pinch-off. If the reverse bias between the gate and the drain is $-V_{GD}$, the width of the depletion region at $x = L$ can be found from Eq. (5–57):

$$W(x = L) = \left[\frac{2\epsilon(-V_{GD})}{qN_d}\right]^{1/2} \quad (V_{GD} \text{ negative}) \qquad (6\text{–}2)$$

In this expression we assume the equilibrium contact potential V_0 is negligible compared with V_{GD} and the depletion region extends primarily into the channel for the p^+-n junction. Including V_0 is left for Prob. 6.1.

Pinch-off occurs at the drain end of the channel when

$$h(x = L) = a - W(x = L) = 0 \qquad (6\text{–}3)$$

that is, when $W(x = L) = a$. If we define the value of $-V_{GD}$ at pinch-off as V_p, we have

$$\left[\frac{2\epsilon V_P}{qN_d}\right]^{1/2} = a$$

$$\boxed{V_P = \frac{qa^2N_d}{2\epsilon}} \qquad (6\text{–}4)$$

The pinch-off voltage V_p is a positive number; its relation to V_D and V_G is

$$V_P = -V_{GD}(\text{pinch-off}) = -V_G + V_D \qquad (6\text{–}5)$$

where V_G is zero or negative for proper device operation. A forward bias on the gate would cause hole injection from the p$^+$ regions into the channel, eliminating the field-effect control of the device. From Eq. (6–5) it is clear that pinch-off results from a combination of gate-to-source voltage and drain-to-source voltage. Pinch-off is reached at a lower value of V_D (and therefore a lower I_D) when a negative gate bias is applied, in agreement with Fig. 6–5b.

6.2.3 Current–Voltage Characteristics

Calculation of the exact channel current is complicated, although the mathematics is relatively straightforward below pinch-off. The approach we shall take is to find the expression for I_D just at pinch-off, and then assume the saturation current beyond pinch-off remains fairly constant at this value.

In the coordinate system defined in Fig. 6–6, the center of the channel at the source end is taken as the origin. The length of the channel in the x-direction is L, and the depth of channel in the z-direction is Z. We shall call the resistivity of the n-type channel material ρ (valid only in the neutral n material, outside the depletion regions). If we consider the differential volume of neutral channel material $Z2h(x)dx$, the resistance of the volume element is $\rho dx/Z2h(x)$ [see Eq. (3–44)]. Since the current does not change with distance along the channel, I_D is related to the differential voltage change in the element dV_x by the conductance of the element:

$$I_D = \frac{Z2h(x)}{\rho} \frac{dV_x}{dx} \tag{6-6}$$

The term $2h(x)$ is the channel width at x.

The half-width of the channel at point x depends on the local reverse bias between gate and channel $-V_{Gx}$:

$$h(x) = a - W(x) = a - \left[\frac{2\epsilon(-V_{Gx})}{qN_d}\right]^{1/2} = a\left[1 - \left(\frac{V_x - V_G}{V_P}\right)^{1/2}\right] \tag{6-7}$$

since $V_{Gx} = V_G - V_x$ and $V_p = qa^2N_d/2\epsilon$. Implicit in Eq. (6–7) is the assumption that the expression for $W(x)$ can be obtained by a simple extension of Eq. (6–2) to point x in the channel. This is called the *gradual channel approximation*; it is valid if $h(x)$ does not vary abruptly in any element dx.

The voltage V_{Gx} will be negative since the gate voltage V_G is chosen zero or negative for proper operation. Substituting Eq. (6–7) into Eq. (6–6), we have

$$\frac{2Za}{\rho}\left[1 - \left(\frac{V_x - V_G}{V_P}\right)^{1/2}\right]dV_x = I_D dx \tag{6-8}$$

We can solve this equation to obtain

$$I_D = G_0 V_P\left[\frac{V_D}{V_P} + \frac{2}{3}\left(-\frac{V_G}{V_P}\right)^{3/2} - \frac{2}{3}\left(\frac{V_D - V_G}{V_P}\right)^{3/2}\right] \tag{6-9}$$

where V_G is negative and $G_0 \equiv 2aZ/\rho L$ is the conductance of the channel for negligible $W(x)$, that is, with no gate voltage and low values of I_D. This equation is valid only up to pinch-off, where $V_D - V_G = V_P$. If we assume the saturation current remains essentially constant at its value at pinch-off, we have

$$I_D(\text{sat.}) = G_0 V_P \left[\frac{V_D}{V_P} + \frac{2}{3}\left(-\frac{V_G}{V_P}\right)^{3/2} - \frac{2}{3} \right]$$

$$= G_0 V_P \left[\frac{V_G}{V_P} + \frac{2}{3}\left(-\frac{V_G}{V_P}\right)^{3/2} + \frac{1}{3} \right]$$

(6–10)

where

$$\frac{V_D}{V_P} = 1 + \frac{V_G}{V_P}$$

The resulting family of I–V curves for the channel agrees with the results we predicted qualitatively (Fig. 6–5b). The saturation current is greatest when V_G is zero and becomes smaller as V_G is made negative.

We can represent the device biased in the saturation region by an equivalent circuit where changes in drain current are related to gate voltage changes by

$$g_m(\text{sat.}) = \frac{\partial I_D(\text{sat.})}{\partial V_G} = G_0 \left[1 - \left(-\frac{V_G}{V_P}\right)^{1/2} \right]$$

(6–11)

The quantity g_m is the *mutual transconductance*, with units (A/V) called siemens (S), sometimes called mhos. As a figure of merit for FET devices it is common to describe the transconductance per unit channel width Z. This quantity g_m/Z is usually given in units of millisiemens per millimeter.

It is found experimentally that a square-law characteristic closely approximates the drain current in saturation:

$$I_D(\text{sat.}) \simeq I_{DSS}\left(1 + \frac{V_G}{V_P} \right)^2, \quad (V_G \text{ negative})$$

(6–12)

where I_{DSS} is the saturated drain current with $V_G = 0$.

The appearance of a constant value of channel resistivity (in the G_0 term) in Eqs. (6–9)–(6–11) implies that the electron mobility is constant. As mentioned in Section 3.4.4, electron velocity saturation at high fields may make this assumption invalid. This is particularly likely for very short channels, where even moderate drain voltage can result in a high field along the channel. Another departure from the ideal model results from the fact that the effective channel length decreases as the drain voltage is increased beyond pinch-off, as Fig. 6–4c suggests. In short channel devices this effect can cause I_D to increase beyond pinch-off, since L appears in the denominator of Eq. (6–10), in G_0. Therefore, the assumption of constant saturation current is not valid for very short channel devices.

The depletion of the channel discussed above for a JFET can be accomplished by the use of a reverse-biased Schottky barrier instead of a p-n junction. The resulting device is called a MESFET, indicating that a metal–semiconductor junction is used. This device is useful in high-speed digital or microwave circuits, where the simplicity of Schottky barriers allows fabrication to close geometrical tolerances. There are particular speed advantages for MESFET devices in III–V compounds such as GaAs or InP, which have higher mobilities and carrier drift velocities than Si.

6.3.1 The GaAs MESFET

Figure 6–7 shows schematically a simple MESFET in GaAs. The substrate is undoped or doped with chromium, which has an energy level near the center of the GaAs band gap. In either case the Fermi level is near the center of the gap, resulting in very high resistivity material ($\sim 10^8$ Ω-cm) generally called *semi-insulating* GaAs. On this nonconducting substrate a thin layer of lightly doped n-type GaAs is grown epitaxially, to form the channel region of the FET.[3] The photolithographic processing consists of defining patterns in the metal layers for source and drain ohmic contacts (e.g., Au–Ge) and for the Schottky barrier gate (e.g., Al). By reverse biasing the Schottky gate, the channel can be depleted to the semi-insulating substrate, and the resulting *I–V* characteristics are similar to the JFET device.

By using GaAs instead of Si, a higher electron mobility is available (see Appendix III), and furthermore GaAs can be operated at higher temperatures (and therefore higher power levels). Since no diffusions are involved in Fig. 6–7, close geometrical tolerances can be achieved and the MESFET can be made very small. Gate lengths $L \lesssim 50$ nm are common in these devices. This is important at high frequencies, since drift time and capacitances must be kept to a minimum.

It is possible to avoid the epitaxial growth of the n-type layer and the etched isolation in Fig. 6–7 by using ion implantation. Starting with a semi-insulating GaAs substrate, a thin n-type layer at the surface of each transistor region can be formed by implanting Si or a column VI donor impurity such

**6.3
THE METAL–
SEMICONDUCTOR
FET**

Figure 6–7
GaAs MESFET
formed on an
n-type GaAs
layer grown
epitaxially on a
semi-insulating
substrate. Common
metals for the
Schottky gate
in GaAs are Al
or alloys of Ti,
W, and Au. The
ohmic source and
drain contacts
may be an alloy
of Au and Ge. In
this example the
device is isolated
from others on
the same chip by
etching through
the n region to
the semi-insulating
substrate.

[3]In many cases, a high-resistivity GaAs epitaxial layer (called a *buffer layer*) is grown between the two layers shown in Fig. 6–7.

as Se. This implantation requires an anneal to remove the radiation damage, but the epitaxial growth step is eliminated. In either the fully implanted device or the epitaxial device of Fig. 6–7, the source and drain contacts may be improved by further n^+ implantation in these regions. Because of the relative simplicity of implanted GaAs MESFETs and the isolation between devices provided by the semi-insulating substrate, these structures are commonly used in GaAs integrated circuits.

6.3.2 The High Electron Mobility Transistor (HEMT)

Since the metal–semiconductor field effect transistor (MESFET) is compatible with the use of III–V compounds, it is possible to exploit the band gap engineering available with heterojunctions in these materials. In order to maintain high transconductance in a MESFET, the channel conductivity must be as high as possible. Obviously, the conductivity can be increased by increasing the doping in the channel and thus the carrier concentration. However, increased doping also causes increased scattering by the ionized impurities, which leads to a degradation of mobility (see Fig. 3–23). What is needed is a way of creating a high electron concentration in the channel of a MESFET by some means other than doping. A clever approach to this requirement is to grow a thin undoped well (e.g., GaAs) bounded by wider band gap, doped barriers (e.g., AlGaAs). This configuration, called *modulation doping*, results in conductive GaAs when electrons from the doped AlGaAs barriers fall into the well and become trapped there, as shown in Fig. 6–8a. Since the donors are in the AlGaAs rather than the GaAs, there is no impurity scattering of electrons in the well. If a MESFET is constructed with the channel along the GaAs well (perpendicular to the page in Fig. 6–8), we can take advantage of this reduced scattering and

Figure 6–8
(a) Simplified view of modulation doping, showing only the conduction band. Electrons in the donor-doped AlGaAs fall into the GaAs potential well and become trapped. As a result, the undoped GaAs becomes n type, without the scattering by ionized donors which is typical of bulk n-type material.
(b) Use of a single AlGaAs/GaAs heterojunction to trap electrons in the undoped GaAs. The thin sheet of charge due to free electrons at the interface forms a two-dimensional electron gas (2-DEG), which can be exploited in HEMT devices.

resulting higher mobility. The effect is especially strong at low temperature where lattice (phonon) scattering is also low. This device is called a *modulation doped field-effect transistor* (MODFET) and is also called a *high electron mobility transistor* (HEMT).

In Fig. 6–8a we have left out the band bending expected at the AlGaAs/GaAs interfaces. Based upon the discussion in Section 5.8, we expect the electrons to accumulate at the corners of the well due to band bending at the heterojunction. In fact, only one heterojunction is required to trap electrons, as shown in Fig. 6–8b. Generally, the donors in the AlGaAs layer are purposely separated from the interface by ~100 Å. Using this configuration, we can achieve a high electron concentration in the channel while retaining high mobility, since the GaAs channel region is spatially separated from the ionized impurities which provide the free carriers.

In Fig. 6–8b, mobile electrons generated by the donors in the AlGaAs diffuse into the small band gap GaAs layer, and they are prevented from returning to the AlGaAs by the potential barrier at the AlGaAs/GaAs interface. The electrons in the (almost) triangular well form a two-dimensional electron gas (sometimes abbreviated 2-DEG). Sheet carrier densities as high as $10^{12}\,cm^{-2}$ can be obtained at a single interface such as that shown in Fig. 6–8b. Ionized impurity scattering is greatly reduced simply by separating the electrons from the donors. Also, screening effects due to the extremely high density of the two-dimensional electron gas can reduce ionized impurity scattering further. In properly designed structures, the electron transport approaches that of bulk GaAs with no impurities, so that mobility is limited by lattice scattering. As a result, mobilities above 250,000 cm²/V-s at 77 K and 2,000,000 cm²/V-s at 4 K can be achieved.

The advantages of a HEMT are its ability to locate a large electron density (~10^{12} cm^{-2}) in a very thin layer (< 100 Å thick) very close to the gate while simultaneously eliminating ionized impurity scattering. The AlGaAs layer in a HEMT is fully depleted under normal operating conditions, and since the electrons are confined to the heterojunction, device behavior closely resembles that of a MOSFET. The advantages of the HEMT over the Si MOSFET are the higher mobility and maximum electron velocity in GaAs compared with Si, and the smoother interfaces possible with an AlGaAs/GaAs heterojunction compared with the Si/SiO$_2$ interface. The high performance of the HEMT translates into an extremely high cutoff frequency, and devices with fast access times.

Although we have discussed the HEMT in terms of the AlGaAs/GaAs heterojunction, other materials are also promising, such as the InGaAsP/InP system. A motivation for avoiding $Al_xGa_{1-x}As$ is the presence of a deep-level defect called the DX center for $x > 0.2$, which traps electrons and impairs the HEMT operation. Since very thin layers are involved, materials with slight lattice mismatch can be grown to form *pseudomorphic* HEMTs. An example of such a system is the use of a thin layer of InGaAs grown pseudomorphically on GaAs, followed by AlGaAs. An advantage of this system is that a useful band discontinuity can be achieved using AlGaAs of low enough Al composition to avoid the DX center problem.

The HEMT, or MODFET, is also referred to as a *two-dimensional electron gas FET* (*2-DEG FET*, or *TEGFET*) to emphasize the fact that conduction along the channel occurs in a thin sheet of charge. The device has also been called a *separately doped FET (SEDFET)*, to emphasize the fact that the doping occurs in a separate region from the channel.

6.3.3 Short Channel Effects

As mentioned in Section 6.2.3, a variety of modifications to the simple theory of JFET and MESFET operation must be made when the channel length is small (typically < 1 μm). In the past, these short channel effects would be considered unusual, but now it is common to encounter FET devices in which these effects dominate the $I-V$ characteristics. For example, high-field effects occur when 1 V appears across a channel length of 1 μm (10^{-4} cm), giving an electric field of 10 kV/cm.

A simple piecewise-linear approximation to the velocity–field curve assumes a constant mobility (linear) dependence up to some critical field $\mathscr{E}_c$ and a constant saturation velocity v_s for higher fields. For Si a better approximation is

$$v_d = \frac{\mu\mathscr{E}}{1 + \mu\mathscr{E}/v_s} \tag{6-13}$$

where μ is the low-field mobility. These two approximations are shown in Fig. 6–9a. If we assume that the electrons passing through the channel drift with a constant saturation velocity v_s, the current takes a simple form

$$I_D = qnv_sA = qN_dv_sZh \tag{6-14}$$

where h is a slow function of V_G. In this case the saturated current follows the velocity saturation, and does not require a true pinch-off in the sense of depletion regions meeting at some point in the channel. In the saturated velocity case, the transconductance g_m is essentially constant, in contrast with the constant mobility case described by Eq. (6–11). As shown in Fig. 6–9b, the $I_D - V_D$ curves are more evenly spaced if constant saturation velocity dominates, compared with the V_G-dependent spacing shown in Fig. 6–5b for the long-channel constant-mobility case.

Most devices operate with characteristics intermediate between the constant mobility and the constant velocity regimes. Depending on the details of the field distribution, it is possible to divide up the channel into regions dominated by the two extreme cases, or to use an approximation such as Eq. (6–13).

Another important short channel effect, described in Section 6.2.3, is the reduction in effective channel length after pinch-off as the drain voltage is increased. This effect is not significant in long-channel devices, since the change in L due to intrusion of the depletion region is a minor fraction of the total channel length. In short channel devices, however, the effective channel length can be substantially shortened, leading to a slope in the saturated $I-V$

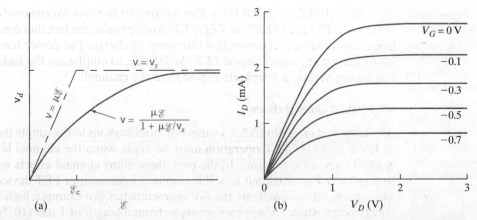

Figure 6–9
Effects of electron velocity saturation at high electric fields: (a) approximations to the saturation of drift velocity with increasing field; (b) drain current–voltage characteristics for the saturated velocity case, showing almost equally spaced curves with increasing gate voltage.

characteristic that is analogous to the Early (base-width narrowing) effect in bipolar transistors discussed in Section 7.7.2.

**6.4
THE METAL–
INSULATOR–
SEMICONDUCTOR
FET**

One of the most widely used electronic devices, particularly in digital integrated circuits, is the *metal–insulator–semiconductor (MIS) transistor*. In this device the channel current is controlled by a voltage applied at a gate electrode that is isolated from the channel by an insulator. The resulting device may be referred to generically as an insulated-gate field-effect transistor (IGFET). However, since most such devices are made using silicon for the semiconductor, SiO_2 or other oxides for the insulator, and metal or heavily doped polysilicon for the gate electrode, the term *MOS field-effect transistor* (MOSFET) is commonly used.

6.4.1 Basic Operation and Fabrication

The basic MOS transistor is illustrated in Fig. 6–10a for the case of an enhancement-mode n-channel device formed on a p-type Si substrate. The n^+ source and drain regions are diffused or implanted into a relatively lightly doped p-type substrate, and a thin oxide layer separates the conducting gate from the Si surface. No current flows from drain to source without a conducting n channel between them. This can be understood clearly by looking at the band diagram of the MOSFET in equilibrium along the channel (Fig. 6–10a). The Fermi level is flat in equilibrium. The conduction band is close to the Fermi level in the n^+ source/drain, while the valence band is closer to the Fermi level in the p-type material. Hence, there is a potential barrier for an electron to go from the source to the drain, corresponding to the built-in potential of the back-to-back p-n junctions between the source and drain.

Figure 6–10
An enhancement-type n-channel MOSFET: (a) isometric view of device and equilibrium band diagram along channel; (b) drain current–voltage output characteristics as a function of gate voltage.

(a)

(b)

When a positive voltage is applied to the gate relative to the substrate (which is connected to the source in this case), positive charges are in effect deposited on the gate metal. In response, negative charges are induced in the underlying Si, by the formation of a depletion region and a thin surface region containing mobile electrons. These induced electrons form the channel of the FET, and allow current to flow from drain to source. As Fig. 6–10b suggests, the effect of the gate voltage is to vary the conductance of this induced channel for low drain-to-source voltage, analogous to the JFET case. Since electrons are electrostatically induced in the p-type channel region, the channel becomes less p-type, and therefore the valence band moves down, farther away from the Fermi level. This obviously reduces the barrier for electrons between the source, the channel, and the drain. If the barrier is reduced sufficiently by applying a gate voltage in excess of what is known as the *threshold voltage,* V_T, there is significant current flow from the source to the drain. Thus, one view of a MOSFET is that it is a gate-controlled potential barrier. It is very important to have high-quality, low-leakage p-n junctions in order to ensure a low off-state leakage in the MOSFET. For a given value of V_G there will be some drain voltage V_D for which the current becomes saturated, after which it remains essentially constant.

The threshold voltage V_T is the minimum gate voltage required to induce the channel. In general, the positive gate voltage of an n-channel device (such as that shown in Fig. 6–11) must be larger than some value V_T before a conducting channel is induced. Similarly, a p-channel device (made on an n-type substrate with p-type source and drain implants or diffusions) requires a gate voltage more negative than some threshold value to induce the required positive charge (mobile holes) in the channel. There are exceptions to this general rule, however, as we shall see. For example, some n-channel devices have a channel already with zero gate voltage, and in fact a negative gate voltage is required to turn the device off. Such a "normally on" device is called a *depletion-mode* transistor, since gate voltage is used to deplete a channel which exists at equilibrium. The more common MOS transistor is "normally off" with zero gate voltage, and operates in the *enhancement mode* by applying gate voltage large enough to induce a conducting channel.

An alternative view of a MOSFET is that it is a gate-controlled resistor. If the (positive) gate voltage exceeds the threshold voltage in an n-channel device, electrons are induced in the p-type substrate. Since this channel is connected to the n^+ source and drain regions, the structure looks electrically like an induced n-type resistor. As the gate voltage increases, more electron charge is induced in the channel and, therefore, the channel becomes more conducting. The drain current initially increases linearly with the drain bias (the *linear* regime) (Fig. 6–10b). As more drain current flows in the channel, however, there is more ohmic voltage drop along the channel such that the channel potential varies from zero near the grounded source to whatever the applied drain potential is near the drain end of the channel. Hence, the voltage difference between the gate and the channel reduces from V_G near the source to $(V_G - V_D)$ near the drain end. Once the drain bias is increased to the point that $(V_G - V_D) = V_T$, threshold is barely maintained near the drain end, and the channel is said to be pinched off. Increasing the drain bias beyond this point (V_D (sat.)) causes the point at which the channel gets pinched off to move more and more into the channel, closer to the source end (Fig. 6–11c). Electrons in the channel are pulled into the pinch-off region and travel at the saturation drift velocity because of the very high longitudinal electric field along the channel. Now, the drain current is said to be in the *saturation* region because it does not increase with drain bias significantly (Fig. 6–10b). Actually, there is a slight increase of drain current with drain bias due to

Figure 6–11
n-channel
MOSFET cross
sections under
different operating
conditions:
(a) linear region
for $V_G > V_T$ and
$V_D < (V_G - V_T)$;
(b) onset of
saturation
at pinch-off,
$V_G > V_T$ and
$V_D = (V_G - V_T)$;
(c) strong
saturation,
$V_G > V_T$ and
$V_D > (V_G - V_T)$.

various effects such as channel length modulation and drain-induced barrier lowering (DIBL) that will be discussed in Section 6.5.10.

The MOS transistor is particularly useful in digital circuits, in which it is switched from the "off" state (no conducting channel) to the "on" state. The control of drain current is obtained at a gate electrode which is insulated from the source and drain by the oxide. Thus the d-c input impedance of an MOS circuit can be very large.

Both n-channel and p-channel MOS transistors are in common usage. The n-channel type illustrated in Fig. 6–10 is generally preferred because it takes advantage of the fact that the electron mobility in Si is larger than the mobility of holes. In much of the discussion to follow we will use the n-channel (p-type substrate) example, although the p-channel case will be kept in mind also.

Let us give a very simplified description of how such an n-channel MOSFET can be fabricated. A much more detailed discussion is given in Section 9.3.1. An ultra-thin (~ few Angstroms) dry thermal silicon dioxide is grown on the p-type substrate, followed by deposition of a so-called high-k dielectric such as HfO_2. This serves as the gate insulator between the conducting gate and the channel. We cover it with a metal electrode which is then patterned to form the gates, and etched anisotropically by reactive ion etching (RIE) to achieve vertical walls (Section 5.1.7). The gate itself is used as an implant mask for an n^+ implant which forms the source/drain junctions abutted to the gate edges, but is blocked from the channel region. Such a scheme is called a *self-aligned process* because we did not have to use a separate lithography step for the source/drain formation. Self-alignment is simple and is very useful because we thereby guarantee that there will be some overlap of the gate with the source/drain but not too much overlap. The advantages of this are discussed in Section 6.5.8. The implanted dopants must be annealed for reasons discussed in Section 5.1.4. Finally, the MOSFETs have to be properly interconnected according to the circuit layout, using metallization. This involves LPCVD of an oxide dielectric, etching contact holes by RIE, depositing a suitable metal such as Cu, patterning and etching it.

As shown in Fig. 6–10a, the MOSFET is surrounded on all sides by a thick SiO_2 layer. This layer provides critical electrical isolation between adjacent transistors on an integrated circuit. We shall see in Section 9.3.1 that such *isolation* or *field* regions can be formed by *Shallow Trench Isolation (STI)*. Shallow grooves or trenches are etched in the substrate using RIE, and a thermal oxide is grown to passivate the surface and fill up the trench with LPCVD of SiO_2. The reason why a thick field oxide layer leads to electrical isolation is discussed in Section 6.5.5.

6.4.2 The Ideal MOS Capacitor

The surface effects that arise in an apparently simple MOS structure are actually quite complicated. Although many of these effects are beyond the scope of this discussion, we will be able to identify those which control typical MOS transistor operation. We begin by considering an uncomplicated idealized case, and then include effects encountered in real surfaces in the next section.

Some important definitions are made in the energy band diagram of Fig. 6–12a. The work function characteristic of the metal (see Section 2.2.1) can be defined in terms of the energy required to move an electron from the Fermi level to outside the metal. In MOS work it is more convenient to use a *modified work function* $q\Phi_m$ for the metal–oxide interface. The energy $q\Phi_m$ is measured from the metal Fermi level to the conduction band of the oxide.[4] Similarly, $q\Phi_s$ is the modified work function at the semiconductor–oxide interface. In this idealized case we assume that $\Phi_m = \Phi_s$, so there is no difference in the two work functions. Another quantity that will be useful in later discussions is $q\phi_F$, which measures the position of the Fermi level below the intrinsic level E_i for the semiconductor. This quantity indicates how strongly p-type the semiconductor is [see Eq. (3–25)].

The MOS structure of Fig. 6–12a is essentially a capacitor in which one plate is a semiconductor. If we apply a negative voltage between the metal and the semiconductor (Fig. 6–12b), we effectively deposit a negative charge on the metal. In response, we expect an equal net positive charge to accumulate at the surface of the semiconductor. In the case of a p-type substrate this occurs by *hole accumulation* at the semiconductor–oxide interface.

Since the applied negative voltage *depresses* the electrostatic potential of the metal relative to the semiconductor, the electron energies are *raised* in the metal relative to the semiconductor.[5] As a result, the Fermi level for the metal E_{Fm} lies above its equilibrium position by qV, where V is the applied voltage.

Since Φ_m and Φ_s do not change with applied voltage, moving E_{Fm} up in energy relative to E_{Fs} causes a tilt in the oxide conduction band. We expect such a tilt since an electric field causes a gradient in E_i (and similarly in E_v and E_c) as described in Section 4.4.2:

$$\mathscr{E}(x) = \frac{1}{q}\frac{dE_i}{dx} \qquad \text{(see 4–26)}$$

The energy bands of the semiconductor bend near the interface to accommodate the accumulation of holes. Since

$$p = n_i e^{(E_i - E_F)/kT} \qquad \text{(see 3–25)}$$

it is clear that an increase in hole concentration implies an increase in $E_i - E_F$ at the semiconductor surface.

Since no current passes through the MOS structure, there can be no variation in the Fermi level within the semiconductor. Therefore, if $E_i - E_F$ is to increase, it must occur by E_i moving up in energy near the surface.

---

[4]On the MOS band diagrams of this section, we show a break in the electron energy scale leading to the insulator conduction band, since the band gap of SiO$_2$ (or other typical insulators) is much greater than that of the Si.

[5]Recall that an electrostatic potential diagram is drawn for positive test charges, in contrast to an electron energy diagram, which is drawn for negative charges.

Figure 6–12
Band diagram for
the ideal MOS
structure at:
(a) equilibrium;
(b) negative
voltage causes
hole accumulation
in the p-type
semiconductor;
(c) positive
voltage depletes
holes from the
semiconductor
surface; (d) a
larger positive
voltage causes
inversion—an
"n-type" layer at
the semiconductor
surface.

(a)

$(V = 0)$

$q\Phi_m$

$q\Phi_s$

E_c

E_i

$q\phi_F$

E_{Fs}

E_v

E_{Fm}

Metal   Oxide   Semiconductor

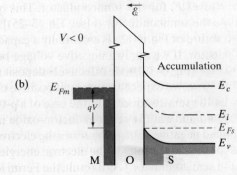

(b)

$V < 0$

Accumulation

E_{Fm}

qV

E_c

E_i

E_{Fs}

E_v

M   O   S

(c)

$V > 0$

Depletion

E_c

E_i

E_{Fs}

E_v

E_{Fm}

qV

M   O   S

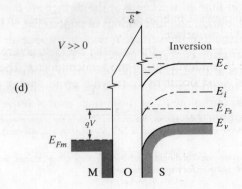

(d)

$V \gg 0$

Inversion

E_c

E_i

E_{Fs}

E_v

E_{Fm}

qV

M   O   S

The result is a bending of the semiconductor bands near the interface. We notice in Fig. 6–12b that the Fermi level near the interface lies closer to the valence band, indicating a larger hole concentration than that arising from the doping of the p-type semiconductor.

In Fig. 6–12c we apply a positive voltage from the metal to the semiconductor. This raises the potential of the metal, lowering the metal Fermi level by qV relative to its equilibrium position. As a result, the oxide conduction band is again tilted. We notice that the slope of this band, obtained by simply moving the metal side down relative to the semiconductor side, is in the proper direction for the applied field, according to Eq. (4–26).

The positive voltage deposits positive charge on the metal and calls for a corresponding net negative charge at the surface of the semiconductor. Such a negative charge in p-type material arises from *depletion* of holes from the region near the surface, leaving behind uncompensated ionized acceptors. This is analogous to the depletion region at a p-n junction discussed in Section 5.2.3. In the depleted region the hole concentration decreases, moving E_i closer to E_F, and bending the bands down near the semiconductor surface.

If we continue to increase the positive voltage, the bands at the semiconductor surface bend down more strongly. In fact, a sufficiently large voltage can bend E_i *below* E_F (Fig. 6–12d). This is a particularly interesting case, since $E_F \gg E_i$ implies a large electron concentration in the conduction band.

The region near the semiconductor surface in this case has conduction properties typical of n-type material, with an electron concentration given by Eq. (3–25a). This n-type surface layer is formed not by doping, but instead by *inversion* of the originally p-type semiconductor due to the applied voltage. This inverted layer, separated from the underlying p-type material by a depletion region, is the key to MOS transistor operation.

We should take a closer look at the inversion region, since it becomes the conducting channel in the FET. In Fig. 6–13 we define a potential ϕ at any point x, measured relative to the equilibrium position of E_i. The energy $q\phi$ tells us the extent of band bending at x, and $q\phi_s$ represents the band bending at the surface. We notice that $\phi_s = 0$ is the *flat band* condition for this ideal MOS case (i.e., the bands look like Fig. 6–12a). When $\phi_s < 0$, the bands bend up at the surface, and we have hole accumulation (Fig. 6–12b). Similarly, when $\phi_s > 0$, we have depletion (Fig. 6–12c). Finally, when ϕ_s is positive and larger than ϕ_F the bands at the surface are bent down such that $E_i(x = 0)$ lies below E_F, and inversion is obtained (Fig. 6–12d).

While it is true that the surface is inverted whenever ϕ_s is larger than ϕ_F, a practical criterion is needed to tell us whether a true n-type conducting channel exists at the surface. The best criterion for *strong inversion* is that the surface should be as strongly n-type as the substrate is p type. That is, E_i should lie as far below E_F at the surface as it is above E_F far from the surface. This condition occurs when

$$\phi_s(\text{inv.}) = 2\phi_F = 2\frac{kT}{q}\ln\frac{N_a}{n_i} \qquad (6\text{–}15)$$

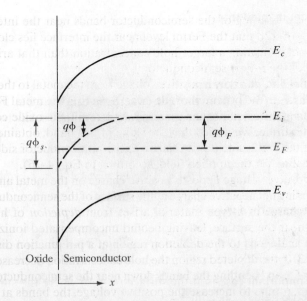

Figure 6–13
Bending of the
semiconductor
bands at the
onset of strong
inversion: The
surface potential
ϕ_s is twice the
value of ϕ_F in the
neutral p material.

A surface potential of ϕ_F is required to bend the bands down to the intrinsic condition at the surface ($E_i = E_F$), and E_i must then be depressed another $q\phi_F$ at the surface to obtain the condition we call strong inversion.

The electron and hole concentrations are related to the potential $\phi(x)$ defined in Fig. 6–13. Since the equilibrium electron concentration is

$$n_0 = n_i e^{(E_F - E_i)/kT} = n_i e^{-q\phi_F/kT} \qquad (6\text{–}16)$$

we can easily relate the electron concentration at any x to this value:

$$n = n_i e^{-q(\phi_F - \phi)/kT} = n_0 e^{q\phi/kT} \qquad (6\text{–}17)$$

and similarly for holes:

$$p_0 = n_i e^{q\phi_F/kT} \qquad (6\text{–}18a)$$

$$p = p_0 e^{-q\phi/kT} \qquad (6\text{–}18b)$$

at any x. We could combine these equations with Poisson's equation (6–19) and the usual charge density expression (6–20) to solve for $\phi(x)$:

$$\frac{\partial^2 \phi}{\partial x^2} = -\frac{\rho(x)}{\epsilon_s} \qquad (6\text{–}19)$$

$$\rho(x) = q(N_d^+ - N_a^- + p - n) \qquad (6\text{–}20)$$

Let us solve this equation to determine the total integrated charge per unit area, Q_s, as a function of the surface potential, ϕ_s. Substituting Eqs. (6–16), (6–17), and (6–18) for the electron and hole concentrations in Eqs. (6–19) and (6–20), we get

$$\frac{\partial^2 \phi}{\partial x^2} = \frac{\partial}{\partial x}\left(\frac{\partial \phi}{\partial x}\right) = -\frac{q}{\epsilon_s}\left[p_0\left(e^{\frac{-q\phi}{kT}} - 1\right) - n_0\left(e^{\frac{q\phi}{kT}} - 1\right)\right] \qquad (6\text{–}21)$$

It should be kept in mind that

$$\frac{-\partial \phi}{\partial x}$$

is the electric field, $\mathscr{E}$, at a depth x.

Integrating Eq. (6–21) from the bulk (where the bands are flat, the electric fields are zero, and the carrier concentrations are determined solely by the doping), toward the surface, we get

$$\int_0^{\frac{\partial \phi}{\partial x}} \left(\frac{\partial \phi}{\partial x} \right) d\left(\frac{\partial \phi}{\partial x} \right) = -\frac{q}{\varepsilon_s} \int_0^{\phi} \left[p_0 \left(e^{\frac{-q\phi}{kT}} - 1 \right) - n_0 \left(e^{\frac{q\phi}{kT}} - 1 \right) \right] d\phi \quad (6\text{--}22)$$

After integration, we then get

$$\mathscr{E}^2 = \left(\frac{2kT\, p_0}{\epsilon_s} \right) \left[\left(e^{\frac{-q\phi}{kT}} + \frac{q\phi}{kT} - 1 \right) + \frac{n_0}{p_0} \left(e^{\frac{q\phi}{kT}} - \frac{q\phi}{kT} - 1 \right) \right] \quad (6\text{--}23)$$

A particularly important case is at the surface ($x = 0$) where the surface perpendicular electric field, $\mathscr{E}_s$, becomes

$$\mathscr{E}_s = \frac{\sqrt{2}kT}{qL_D} \left[\left(e^{\frac{-q\phi_s}{kT}} + \frac{q\phi_s}{kT} - 1 \right) + \frac{n_0}{p_0} \left(e^{\frac{q\phi_s}{kT}} - \frac{q\phi_s}{kT} - 1 \right) \right]^{\frac{1}{2}} \quad (6\text{--}24)$$

where we have introduced a new term, the *Debye screening length*,

$$L_D = \sqrt{\frac{\epsilon_s kT}{q^2 p_0}} \quad (6\text{--}25)$$

The Debye length is a very important concept in semiconductors. It gives us an idea of the distance scale in which charge imbalances are screened or smeared out. For example, if we think of inserting a positively charged sphere in an n-type semiconductor we know that the mobile electrons will crowd around the sphere. If we move away from the sphere by several Debye lengths, the positively charged sphere and the negative electron cloud will look like a neutral entity. Not surprisingly, L_D depends inversely on doping because the higher the carrier concentration, the more easily screening takes place. For n-type material we should use n_0 in Eq. (6–25).

By using Gauss's law at the surface, we can relate the integrated space charge per unit area to the electric displacement, keeping in mind that the electric field or displacement deep in the substrate is zero.

$$Q_s = -\epsilon_s \mathscr{E}_s \quad (6\text{--}26)$$

The space charge density per unit area Q_s in Eq. (6–26) is plotted as a function of the surface potential ϕ_s in Fig. 6–14. We see from Eq. (6–24) and Fig. 6–14 that when the surface potential is zero (flat band conditions), the net space charge is zero. This is because the fixed dopant charges are cancelled by the mobile carrier charges at flat band. When the surface potential is negative, it attracts and forms an accumulation layer of the majority carrier holes at the

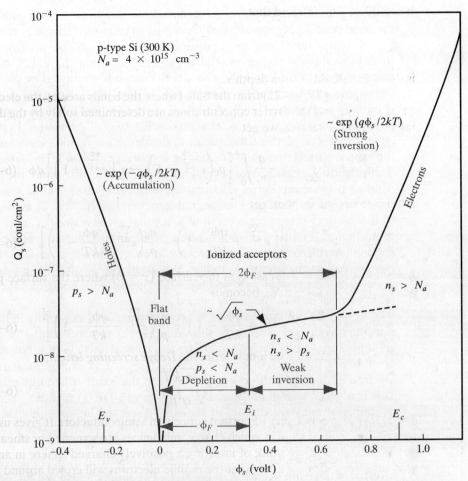

Figure 6–14

Variation of space-charge density in the semiconductor as a function of the surface potential ϕ_s for p-type silicon with $N_a = 4 \times 10^{15}$ cm^{-3} at room temperature. p_s and n_s are the hole and electron concentrations at the surface, ϕ_F is the potential difference between the Fermi level and the intrinsic level of the bulk. (Garrett and Brattain, Phys. Rev., 99, 376 (1955).)

surface. The first term in Eq. (6–24) is the dominant one, and the accumulation space charge increases very strongly (exponentially) with negative surface potential. It is easy to see why by looking at Eq. (6–18), which gives the surface hole concentration in a p-type semiconductor as a function of surface potential. Since the band bending decreases as a function of depth, the integrated accumulation charge involves averaging over depth and introduces a factor of 2 in the exponent. Mathematically, this is due to the square root in Eq. (6–24). It must be noted that since this charge is due to the mobile majority carriers (holes in this case), the charge piles up near the oxide–silicon interface, since typical accumulation layer thicknesses are ~ 20 nm. Also, because of the exponential dependence of accumulation charge on surface potential, the band bending is generally small or is said to be *pinned* to nearly zero.

On the other hand, for a positive surface potential, we see from Eq. (6–24) that initially the second (linear) term is the dominant one. Although the exponential term $\exp(q\phi_s/kT)$ is very large, it is multiplied by the ratio of the minority to majority carrier concentration which is very small, and is initially negligible. Hence, the space charge for small positive surface potentials increases as $\sim \sqrt{\phi_s}$ as shown in Fig. 6–14. As discussed in detail later in this section, this corresponds to the depletion region charge due to the exposed, fixed immobile dopants (acceptors in this case). The depletion width typically extends over several hundred nm. At some point, the band bending is twice the Fermi potential ϕ_F, which is enough for the onset of strong inversion. Now, the exponential term $\exp(q\phi_s(\text{inv.})/kT)$ multiplied by the minority carrier concentration n_0 is equal to the majority carrier concentration p_0. Hence, for band bending beyond this point, it becomes the dominant term. As in the case of accumulation, the mobile inversion charge now increases very strongly with bias, as indicated by Eq. (6–17) and shown in Fig. 6–14. The typical inversion layer thicknesses are ~ 5 nm, and the surface potential now is essentially pinned at $2\phi_F$.

It may be pointed out that in accumulation, and especially in inversion, the carriers are confined in the x-direction in narrow, essentially triangular potential wells, causing quantum mechanical particle-in-a-box states or subbands, similar to those discussed in Chapter 2. However, the carriers are free in the other directions (parallel to the oxide–silicon interface). This leads to a two-dimensional electron gas (2-DEG) or hole gas, with a "staircase" constant density of states, as discussed in Appendix IV. The detailed analysis of these effects is, unfortunately, beyond the scope of our discussion here.

The charge distribution, electric field, and electrostatic potential for the inverted surface are sketched in Fig. 6–15. For simplicity we use the depletion approximation of Chapter 5 in this figure, assuming complete depletion for $0 < x < W$, and neutral material for $x > W$. In this approximation the charge per unit area[6] due to uncompensated acceptors in the depletion region is $-qN_aW$. The positive charge Q_m on the metal is balanced by the negative charge Q_s in the semiconductor, which is the depletion layer charge plus the charge due to the inversion region Q_n:

$$Q_m = -Q_s = qN_aW - Q_n \qquad (6\text{–}27)$$

The width of the inversion region is exaggerated in Fig. 6–15 for illustrative purposes. Actually, the width of this region is generally less than 100 Å. Thus we have neglected it in sketching the electric field and potential distribution. In the potential distribution diagram we see that an applied voltage V

[6]In this chapter, we will use charge per unit area (Q) and capacitance per unit area (C) to avoid repeating A throughout the discussion.

Figure 6–15
Approximate distributions of charge, electric field, and electrostatic potential in the ideal MOS capacitor in inversion. The relative width of the inverted region is exaggerated for illustrative purposes, but is neglected in the field and potential diagrams. The slopes of the band edges reflect the electric fields in the gate dielectric and the semiconductor channel. The product of the perpendicular electric field and dielectric constant (known as the displacement) is continuous across the dielectric–semiconductor interface if there are no charges at the interface, according to Maxwell's boundary conditions.

appears partially across the insulator (V_i) and partially across the depletion region of the semiconductor (ϕ_s):

$$V = V_i + \phi_s \qquad (6\text{--}28)$$

The voltage across the insulator is obviously related to the charge on either side, divided by the capacitance:

$$V_i = \frac{-Q_s d}{\epsilon_i} = \frac{-Q_s}{C_i} \qquad (6\text{--}29)$$

where ϵ_i is permittivity of the insulator and C_i is the insulator capacitance per unit area. The charge Q_s will be negative for the n channel, giving a positive V_i.

Using the depletion approximation, we can solve for W as a function of ϕ_s (Prob. 6.7). The result is the same as would be obtained for an n⁺-p junction in Chapter 5, for which the depletion region extends almost entirely into the p region:

$$W = \left[\frac{2\epsilon_s \phi_s}{qN_a}\right]^{1/2} \qquad (6\text{--}30)$$

This depletion region grows with increased voltage across the capacitor until strong inversion is reached. After that, further increases in voltage result in stronger inversion rather than in more depletion. Thus the maximum value of the depletion width is

$$W_m = \left[\frac{2\epsilon_s \phi_s(\text{inv.})}{qN_a}\right]^{1/2} = 2\left[\frac{\epsilon_s kT \ln(N_a/n_i)}{q^2 N_a}\right]^{1/2} \qquad (6\text{--}31)$$

using Eq. (6–15). We know the quantities in this expression, so W_m can be calculated.

The charge per unit area in the depletion region Q_d at strong inversion is[7]

$$Q_d = -qN_a W_m = -2(\epsilon_s q N_a \phi_F)^{1/2} \qquad (6\text{--}32)$$

The applied voltage must be large enough to create this depletion charge plus the surface potential ϕ_s (inv.). The *threshold* voltage required for strong inversion, using Eqs. (6–15), (6–28), and (6–29), is

$$V_T = -\frac{Q_d}{C_i} + 2\phi_F \quad (\textit{ideal case}) \qquad (6\text{--}33)$$

This assumes the negative charge at the semiconductor surface Q_s at inversion is mostly due to the depletion charge Q_d. The threshold voltage represents the minimum voltage required to achieve strong inversion, and is an extremely important quantity for MOS transistors. We will see in the next section that other terms must be added to this expression for real MOS structures.

---

[7]In the p-channel (n-type substrate) case, for which ϕ_F is negative, we use $Q_d = +qN_d W_m = 2(\epsilon_s q N_d|\phi_F|)^{1/2}$.

The capacitance–voltage characteristics of this ideal MOS structure (Fig. 6–16) vary depending on whether the semiconductor surface is in accumulation, depletion, or inversion.

Since the capacitance for MOSFETs is voltage dependent, we must use the more general expression in Eq. (5–55) for the voltage-dependent semiconductor capacitance,

$$C_s = \frac{dQ}{dV} = \frac{dQ_s}{d\phi_s} \qquad (6\text{–}34)$$

Actually, if one looks at the electrical equivalent circuit of a MOS capacitor or MOSFET, it is the series combination of a fixed, voltage-independent gate oxide (insulator) capacitance, and a voltage-dependent semiconductor capacitance [defined according to Eq. (6–34)], such that the overall MOS capacitance becomes voltage dependent. The semiconductor capacitance itself can be determined from the slope of the Q_s vs. ϕ_s plot (Fig. 6–14). It is clear that the semiconductor capacitance in accumulation is very high because the slope is so steep; that is, the accumulation charge changes a lot with surface potential. Hence, the series capacitance in accumulation is basically the insulator capacitance, C_i. Since, for negative voltage, holes are accumulated at the surface (Fig. 6–12b), the MOS structure appears almost like a parallel-plate capacitor, dominated by the insulator properties $C_i = \epsilon_i/d$ (point 1 in Fig. 6–16). As the voltage becomes less negative, the semiconductor surface is depleted. Thus a depletion-layer capacitance C_d is added in series with C_i:

$$C_d = \frac{\epsilon_s}{W} \qquad (6\text{–}35)$$

Figure 6–16
Capacitance–voltage relation for an n-channel (p-substrate) MOS capacitor. The dashed curve for $V > V_T$ is observed at high measurement frequencies. The flat band voltage V_{FB} will be discussed in Section 6.4.3. When the semiconductor is in depletion, the semiconductor capacitance C_s is denoted as C_d.

where ϵ_s is the semiconductor permittivity and W is the width of the depletion layer from Eq. (6–30). The total capacitance is

$$C = \frac{C_i C_d}{C_i + C_d} \tag{6–36}$$

The capacitance decreases as W grows from flat band (point 2), past weak inversion (point 3), until finally strong inversion is reached at V_T (point 4). In the depletion region, the small signal semiconductor capacitance is given by the same formula [Eq. (6–34)] which gives the variation of the (depletion) space charge with surface potential. Since the charge increases as $\sim\sqrt{\phi_s}$, the depletion capacitance will obviously decrease as $1/\sqrt{\phi_s}$, exactly as for the depletion capacitance of a p-n junction [see Eq. (5–63)].

After inversion is reached, the small signal capacitance depends on whether the measurements are made at high (typically ~ 1 MHz) or low (typically $\sim 1-100$ Hz) frequency, where "high" and "low" are with respect to the generation–recombination rate of the minority carriers in the inversion layer. If the gate voltage is varied rapidly, the charge in the inversion layer cannot change in response, and thus does not contribute to the small signal a-c capacitance. Hence, the semiconductor capacitance is at a minimum, corresponding to a maximum depletion width.

On the other hand, if the gate bias is changed slowly, there is time for minority carriers to be generated in the bulk, drift across the depletion region to the inversion layer, or go back to the substrate and recombine. Now, the semiconductor capacitance, using the same Eq. (6–34), is very large because we saw in Fig. 6–14 that the inversion charge increases exponentially with ϕ_s. Hence, the low frequency MOS series capacitance in strong inversion is basically C_i once again (point 5).

What is the frequency dependence of the capacitance in accumulation (Fig. 6–12a)? We get a very high capacitance both at low and high frequencies because the majority carriers in the accumulation layer can respond much faster than minority carriers. While minority carriers respond on the time scale of generation–recombination times (typically hundreds of microseconds in Si), majority carriers respond on the time scale of the dielectric relaxation time, $\tau_D = \rho\epsilon$, where ρ is the resistivity and ϵ is the permittivity. τ_D is analogous to the RC time constant of a system, and is small for the majority carriers ($\sim 10^{-13}$ s). As an interesting aside, it may be pointed out that in inversion, although the high-frequency capacitance for MOS capacitors is low, it is high ($= C_i$) for MOSFETs because now the inversion charge can flow in readily and very fast ($\sim\tau_D$) from the source/drain regions rather than having to be created by generation–recombination in the bulk.

6.4.3 Effects of Real Surfaces

When MOS devices are made using typical materials (e.g., metal-high-k/SiO_2–Si), departures from the ideal case described in the previous section can strongly affect V_T and other properties. First, there is a work function

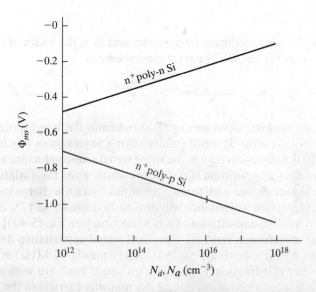

Figure 6–17
Variation of the metal–semiconductor work function potential difference Φ_{ms} with substrate doping concentration, for n^+ poly-Si.

difference between the metal gate and substrate, which depends on the substrate doping. Second, there are inevitably charges at the Si-high-k/SiO$_2$ interface and within the oxide which must be taken into account.

Work Function Difference. We expect Φ_s to vary depending on the doping of the semiconductor. Figure 6–17 illustrates the work function potential difference $\Phi_{ms} = \Phi_m - \Phi_s$ for n^+ polysilicon on Si as the doping is varied. For other metal electrodes, the work function of that metal, Φ_m, must be used. We note that Φ_{ms} is always negative for this case, and is most negative for heavily doped p-type Si (i.e., for E_F close to the valence band).

If we try to construct an equilibrium diagram with Φ_{ms} negative (Fig. 6–18a), we find that in aligning E_F we must include a tilt in the oxide conduction band (implying an electric field). Thus the metal is positively charged and the semiconductor surface is negatively charged at equilibrium, to accommodate the work function difference. As a result, the bands bend down near the semiconductor surface. In fact, if Φ_{ms} is sufficiently negative, an inversion region can exist with no external voltage applied. To obtain the *flat band* condition pictured in Fig. 6–18b, we must apply a negative voltage to the metal ($V_{FB} = \Phi_{ms}$).

Interface Charge. In addition to the work function difference, the equilibrium MOS structure is affected by charges in the insulator and at the semiconductor-oxide interface (Fig. 6–19). For example, alkali metal ions (particularly Na$^+$) can be incorporated inadvertently in the oxide during growth or subsequent processing steps. Since sodium is a common contaminant, it is necessary to use extremely clean chemicals, water, gases, and processing environment to minimize its effect on dielectric layers. Sodium ions introduce positive charges (Q_m) in the oxide, which in turn induce negative charges in the semiconductor. The effect of such positive ionic charges in the oxide depends

(a)   Equilibrium
      V = 0

(b)   Flat band
      $V = V_{FB} = \Phi_{ms}$

upon the number of ions involved and their distance from the semiconductor surface (Prob. 6.14). The negative charge induced in the semiconductor is greater if the Na$^+$ ions are near the interface than if they are farther away. The effect of this ionic charge on threshold voltage is complicated by the fact that Na$^+$ ions are relatively mobile in SiO$_2$, particularly at elevated temperatures, and can thus drift in an applied electric field. Obviously, a device with V_T dependent on its past history of voltage bias is unacceptable. Fortunately, Na contamination of the oxide can be reduced to tolerable levels by proper care in processing. The oxide also contains trapped charges (Q_{ot}) due to imperfections in the SiO$_2$.

Q_m Mobile ionic charge
Q_{ot} Oxide trapped charge
Q_f Oxide fixed charge
Q_{it} Interface trap charge

(a)

(b)

$$V = V_{FB} = -\frac{Q_i}{C_i}$$

In addition to oxide charges, a set of positive charges arises from *interface states* at the Si−SiO₂ interface. These charges, which we will call Q_{it}, result from the sudden termination of the semiconductor crystal lattice at the oxide interface. Near the interface is a transition layer (SiO$_x$) containing fixed charges (Q_f). As oxidation takes place in forming the SiO₂ layer, Si is removed from the surface and reacts with the oxygen. When the oxidation is stopped, some ionic Si is left near the interface. These ions, along with uncompleted Si bonds at the surface, result in a sheet of positive charge Q_f near the interface. This charge depends on oxidation rate and subsequent heat treatment, and also on crystal orientation. For carefully treated Si−SiO₂ interfaces, typical charge densities due to Q_{it} and Q_f are about 10^{10} charges/cm² for samples with {100} surfaces. The interface charge density is about a factor of ten higher on {111} surfaces. That is why MOS devices are generally made on {100} Si.

For simplicity we will include the various oxide and interface charges in an *effective* positive charge at the interface Q_i(C/cm²). The effect of this charge is to induce an equivalent negative charge in the semiconductor. Thus an additional component must be added to the flat band voltage:

$$V_{FB} = \Phi_{ms} - \frac{Q_i}{C_i} \qquad (6\text{--}37)$$

Since the difference in work function and the positive interface charge both tend to bend the bands down at the semiconductor surface, a negative voltage must be applied to the metal relative to the semiconductor to achieve the flat band condition of Fig. 6–19b.

6.4.4 Threshold Voltage

The voltage required to achieve flat band should be added to the threshold voltage equation (6–33) obtained for the ideal MOS structure (for which we assumed a zero flat band voltage):

$$\boxed{V_T = \Phi_{ms} - \frac{Q_i}{C_i} - \frac{Q_d}{C_i} + 2\phi_F} \qquad (6\text{--}38)$$

Thus the voltage required to create strong inversion must be large enough to first achieve the flat band condition (Φ_{ms} and Q_i/C_i terms), then accommodate the charge in the depletion region (Q_d/C_i), and finally to induce the inverted region ($2\phi_F$). This equation accounts for the dominant threshold voltage effects in typical MOS devices. It can be used for both n-type and p-type substrates[8] if appropriate signs are included for each term (Fig. 6–20). Typically Φ_{ms} is negative, although its value varies as in Fig. 6–17. The interface charge is positive, so the contribution of the $-Q_i/C_i$ term is negative for either substrate type. On the other hand, the charge in the depletion region is negative for ionized acceptors (p-type substrate, n-channel device) and is positive for

---

[8]It is important to remember that n-channel devices are made on p-type substrates and that p-channel devices have n-type substrates.

Figure 6–20
Influence of materials parameters on threshold voltage: (a) the threshold voltage equation indicating signs of the various contributions; (b) variation of V_T with substrate doping for n-channel and p-channel n^+ poly-SiO$_2$–Si devices.

$V_T =$	Φ_{ms}	$-\dfrac{Q_i}{C_i}$	$-\dfrac{Q_d}{C_i}$	$+ 2\phi_F$
(a)	(−)	(−)	(+) n channel (−) p channel	(+) n channel (−) p channel

ionized donors (n-type substrate, p channel). Also, the term ϕ_F, which is defined as $(E_i - E_F)/q$ in the neutral substrate, can be positive or negative, depending on the conductivity type of the substrate. Considering the signs in Fig. 6–20, we see that all four terms give negative contributions in the p-channel case. Thus we expect negative threshold voltages for typical p-channel devices. On the other hand, n-channel devices may have either positive or negative threshold voltages, depending on the relative values of terms in Eq. (6–38).

All terms in Eq. (6–38) except Q_i/C_i depend on the doping in the substrate. The terms Φ_{ms} and ϕ_F have relatively small variations as E_F is moved up or down by the doping. Large changes can occur in Q_d, which varies with the square root of the doping impurity concentration as in Eq. (6–32). We illustrate the variation of threshold voltage with substrate doping in Fig. 6–20. As expected from Eq. (6–38), V_T is always negative for the p-channel case. In the n-channel case, the negative flat band voltage terms can dominate for lightly doped p-type substrates, resulting in a negative threshold voltage. However, for more heavily doped substrates, the increasing contribution of N_a to the Q_d term dominates, and V_T becomes positive.

We should pause here and consider what positive or negative V_T means for the two cases. In a p-channel device we expect to apply a negative voltage from metal to semiconductor in order to induce the positive charges in the channel. In this case a negative threshold voltage means that the negative voltage we apply must be larger than V_T in order to achieve strong inversion. In the n-channel case we expect to apply a positive voltage to the metal to induce the channel. Thus a positive value for V_T means the applied voltage must be larger than this threshold value to obtain strong inversion and a conducting n channel. On the other hand, a negative V_T in this case means that a channel exists at $V = 0$ due to the Φ_{ms} and Q_i effects (Figs. 6–18 and 6–19), and we must apply a negative voltage V_T to turn the device off. Since lightly doped substrates are desirable to maintain a high breakdown voltage for the drain junction, Fig. 6–20 suggests that V_T will be negative for n-channel devices made by standard processing. This tendency for the formation of depletion mode (normally on) n-channel transistors is a problem which must be dealt with by special fabrication methods to be described in Section 6.5.5.

6.4.5 MOS Capacitance–Voltage Analysis

Let us see how the various parameters of a MOS device such as insulator thickness, substrate doping, and V_T can be determined from the C–V characteristics (Fig. 6–21a). First, the shape of the C–V curve depends upon the

---

An n$^+$-polysilicon-gate n-channel MOS transistor is made on a p-type Si substrate with $N_a = 5 \times 10^{15}$ cm^{-3}. The SiO$_2$ thickness is 100 Å in the gate region, and the effective interface charge Q_i is 4×10^{10} q C/cm^2. Find C_i and C_{min} on the C–V characteristics, and find W_m, V_{FB}, and V_T.

EXAMPLE 6–1

$$\phi_F = \frac{kT}{q} \ln \frac{N_a}{n_i} = 0.0259 \ln \frac{5 \times 10^{15}}{1.5 \times 10^{10}} = 0.329 \text{ eV}$$

SOLUTION

$$W_m = 2 \left[\frac{\epsilon_s \phi_F}{q N_a} \right]^{1/2} = 2 \left[\frac{11.8 \times 8.85 \times 10^{-14} \times 0.329}{1.6 \times 10^{-19} \times 5 \times 10^{15}} \right]^{1/2}$$

$$= 4.15 \times 10^{-5} \text{ cm} = \textbf{0.415 μm}$$

From Fig. 6–17, $\Phi_{ms} \cong -0.95$ V, and we have

$$Q_i = 4 \times 10^{10} \times 1.6 \times 10^{-19} = 6.4 \times 10^{-9} \text{ C/cm}^2$$

$$C_i = \frac{\epsilon_i}{d} = \frac{3.9 \times 8.85 \times 10^{-14}}{0.1 \times 10^{-5}} = 3.45 \times 10^{-7} \text{ F/cm}^2$$

$$V_{FB} = \Phi_{ms} - Q_i/C_i = -0.95 - 6.4 \times 10^{-9}/3.45 \times 10^{-7} = \textbf{-0.969 V}$$

$$Q_d = -q N_a W_m = -1.6 \times 10^{-19} \times 5 \times 10^{15} \times 4.15 \times 10^{-5}$$

$$= -3.32 \times 10^{-8} \text{ C/cm}^2$$

$$V_T = V_{FB} - \frac{Q_d}{C_i} + 2h_F = -0.969 + \frac{3.32 \times 10^{-8}}{3.45 \times 10^{-7}} + 0.658 = \textbf{-0.215 V}$$

$$C_d = \frac{\epsilon_s}{W_m} = \frac{11.8 \times 8.85 \times 10^{-14}}{4.15 \times 10^{-5}} = 2.5 \times 10^{-8} \text{ F/cm}$$

$$C_{min} = \frac{C_i C_d}{C_i + C_d} = \frac{3.45 \times 10^{-7} \times 2.5 \times 10^{-8}}{3.45 \times 10^{-7} + 2.5 \times 10^{-8}} = \textbf{2.33} \times \textbf{10}^{-8} \textbf{ F/cm}^2$$

Figure 6–21
Fast interface state
determination:
(a) High-frequency
and low-frequency
C–V curves
showing impact
of fast interface
states; (b) energy
levels in the band
gap due to fast
interface states;
(c) equivalent
circuit of MOS
structure showing
capacitance
components due
to gate oxide (C_i),
depletion layer in
the channel (C_d),
and fast interface
states (C_{it}).

(a)

(b)

(c)

type of substrate doping. If the high-frequency capacitance is large for negative gate biases and small for positive biases, it is a p-type substrate, and vice versa. From the low-frequency C–V curve for p-type material, as the gate bias is made more positive (or less negative), the capacitance goes down slowly in depletion and then rises rapidly in inversion. As a result, the low-frequency C–V is not quite symmetric in shape. For n-type substrates, the C–V curves would be the mirror image of Fig. 6–21.

The capacitance $C_i = \epsilon_i/d$ in accumulation or strong inversion (at low frequencies) gives us the insulator thickness, d. The minimum MOS capacitance, C_{min}, is the series combination of C_i and the minimum depletion capacitance, $C_{dmin} = \epsilon_s/W_m$, corresponding to the maximum depletion width. We can in principle use the measurement of C_{min} to determine the substrate doping. However, from Eq. (6–31) we see that the dependence of W_m on N_a is complicated, and we get a transcendental equation which can only be solved numerically. Actually, an approximate, iterative solution exists which gives us N_a in terms of the minimum depletion capacitance, C_{dmin}.

$$N_a = 10^{[30.388 + 1.683 \log C_{dmin} - 0.03177(\log C_{dmin})^2]} \tag{6–39}$$

where C_{dmin} is in F/cm^2.

Once the substrate doping is obtained, we can determine the flat band capacitance from it. It can be shown that the semiconductor capacitance at flat band C_{FB} (point 2 in Fig. 6–16) is determined from the Debye length capacitance

$$C_{debye} = \frac{\epsilon_s}{L_D} \tag{6–40}$$

where the Debye length is dependent on doping as described in Eq. (6–25). The overall MOS flat band capacitance, C_{FB}, is the series combination of C_{debye} and C_i. We can thus determine V_{FB} corresponding to the C_{FB}. Once C_i, V_{FB}, and substrate doping are obtained, all terms in the V_T expression (Eq. 6–38) are known. Interestingly, the threshold voltage V_T does not correspond to exactly the minimum of the C–V characteristics, C_{min}, but a slightly higher capacitance marked as point 4 in Fig. 6–16. In fact, it corresponds to the series combination of C_i and $2C_{dmin}$, rather than the series combination of C_i and C_{dmin}. The reason for this is that when we change the gate bias around strong inversion, the change of charge in the semiconductor is the sum of the change in depletion charge and the mobile inversion charge, where the two are equal in magnitude at the onset of strong inversion.

We can also determine MOS parameters such as the *fast interface state* density, D_{it}, and mobile ion charges, Q_m, from C–V measurements (Figs. 6–21b,c and 6–22). The term fast interface state refers to the fact that these defects can change their charge state relatively fast in response to changes of the gate bias. As the surface potential in a MOS device is varied, the fast interface states or traps in the band gap can move above or below the Fermi level in response to the bias, because their positions relative to the band edges are fixed (Fig. 6–21b). Keeping in mind the property of

Figure 6–22
Mobile ion determination: (a) movement of mobile ions due to positive and negative bias-temperature stress; (b) C–V characteristics under positive (dashed line) and negative (solid line) bias-temperature.

the Fermi–Dirac distribution that energy levels below the Fermi level have a high probability of occupancy by electrons, while levels above the Fermi level tend to be empty, we see that a fast interface state moving above the Fermi level would tend to give up its trapped electron to the semiconductor (or equivalently capture a hole). Conversely, the same fast interface state below the Fermi level captures an electron (or gives up a hole). It obviously makes sense to talk in terms of electrons or holes, depending on which is the majority carrier in the semiconductor. Since charge storage results in capacitance, the fast interface states give rise to a capacitance which is in parallel with the depletion capacitance in the channel (and hence is additive), and this combination is in series with the insulator capacitance C_i. The fast interface states can keep pace with low frequency variations of the gate bias (~ 1–1000 Hz), but not at extremely high frequencies (~ 1 MHz). So the fast interface states contribute to the low frequency capacitance C_{LF}, but not the high-frequency capacitance C_{HF}. Clearly, from the difference between the two, we ought to be able to compute the fast interface state density. Although we will not do the detailed derivation here, it can be shown that

$$D_{it} = \frac{1}{q}\left(\frac{C_i C_{LF}}{C_i - C_{LF}} - \frac{C_i C_{HF}}{C_i - C_{HF}}\right) \text{cm}^{-2}\text{eV}^{-1} \qquad (6\text{--}41)$$

While the fast interface states can respond quickly to voltage changes, the fixed oxide charges Q_f, as the name implies, do not change their charge state regardless of the gate bias or surface potential. As mentioned above, the effect of these charges on the flat band and threshold voltage depends not only on the number of charges but also their location relative to the oxide–silicon interface (Fig. 6–22a). Hence, we must take a weighted sum of these charges, counting charges closer to the oxide–silicon interface more heavily than those that are farther away. This position dependence is the basis of what is called the *bias-temperature stress test* for measuring the mobile ion content, Q_m. We heat up the MOS device to ~200–300°C (to make the ions more mobile) and apply a positive gate bias to generate a field of ~1 MV/cm within the oxide. After cooling the capacitor to room temperature, the C–V characteristics are measured. We have seen how V_{FB} can be determined from the C–V curve, using Eq. (6–40) and C_i. V_{FB} is also given by Eq. (6–37). The positive bias repels positive mobile ions such as Na$^+$ to the oxide–silicon interface so that they contribute fully to a flat band voltage we can call V_{FB}^+. Next, the capacitor is heated up again, a negative bias is applied so that the ions drift to the gate electrode, and another C–V measurement is made. Now, the mobile ions are too far away to affect the semiconductor band bending, but induce an equal and opposite charge on the gate electrode. From the resulting C–V, the new flat band, V_{FB}^-, is determined. From the difference of the two flat band voltages, we can determine the mobile ion content using

$$Q_m = C_i(V_{FB}^- - V_{FB}^+) \qquad (6\text{--}42)$$

6.4.6 Time-Dependent Capacitance Measurements

During C–V measurements, if the gate bias is varied rapidly from accumulation to inversion, the depletion width can momentarily become greater than the theoretical maximum for gate biases beyond V_T. This phenomenon is known as *deep depletion*, and causes the MOS capacitance to drop below the theoretical minimum, C_{min}, for a transient period. After a time period characteristic of the minority carrier lifetime, which determines the rate of generation of the minority carriers in the MOS device, the depletion width collapses back to the theoretical maximum and the capacitance recovers to C_{min} (Fig. 6–23). This capacitance transient, C–t, forms the basis of a powerful technique to measure the lifetime, known as the Zerbst technique.

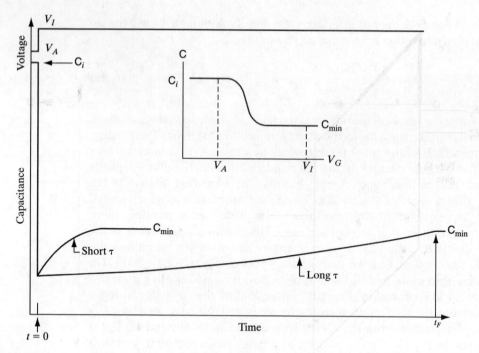

Figure 6–23
Time-dependent MOS capacitance (C_{HF}) due to the application of a step voltage V_A (which puts the capacitor in accumulation) to V_I (which puts the capacitor in inversion).

6.4.7   Current–Voltage Characteristics of MOS Gate Oxides

An ideal gate insulator does not conduct any current, but for real insulators there can be some leakage current which varies with the voltage or electric field across the gate oxide. By looking at the band diagram of the MOS system perpendicular to the oxide–silicon interface (Fig. 6–24), we see that for electrons in the conduction band, there is a barrier, $\Delta E_c (= 3.1 \text{ eV})$. Although electrons with energy less than this barrier cannot go through the oxide classically, it was discussed in Chapter 2 that quantum mechanically electrons can tunnel through a barrier, especially if the barrier thickness is sufficiently small. The detailed calculation of the *Fowler–Nordheim tunneling* current for electrons going from the Si conduction band to the conduction band of SiO_2, and then having the electrons "hop" along in the oxide to the gate electrode, involves solving the Schrödinger equation for the electron wavefunction. The Fowler–Nordheim tunneling current I_{FN} can be expressed as a function of the electric field in the gate oxide:

$$I_{FN} \propto \mathscr{E}_{ox}^2 \, \exp\!\left(\frac{-B}{\mathscr{E}_{ox}}\right) \tag{6–43}$$

where B is a constant depending on m_n^* and the barrier height.

Fowler–Nordheim tunneling

Direct tunneling

(a)

$$J_{FN} = \frac{I_{FN}}{\text{Capacitor area}}$$

(b)

Figure 6–24

Current–voltage characteristics of gate oxides: (a) Fowler–Nordheim and direct tunneling through thin gate oxides; (b) plot of Fowler–Nordheim tunneling leakage current as a function of electric field across the oxide.

As gate oxides are made thinner in successive generations of MOSFETs, the tunneling barrier in the gate oxide becomes so thin that the electrons in the conduction band of Si can tunnel through the gate oxide and emerge in the gate, without having to go via the conduction band of the gate oxide. This is known as *direct tunneling* rather than Fowler–Nordheim tunneling. The overall physics is similar, but some of the details are different. For instance, Fowler–Nordheim tunneling involves a triangular barrier, while direct tunneling is through a trapezoidal barrier (Fig. 6–24a). Such tunneling currents are becoming a major problem in modern devices because the useful feature of high input impedance for MOS devices is degraded.

It is necessary to increase the gate capacitance in successive generations of MOSFETs in order to increase the drain current, as discussed later in Section 6.5. One can achieve higher C_i by using insulators with a dielectric constant higher than SiO_2 instead of reducing the gate oxide thickness, d, as can be seen from Eq. (6–29). The advantage of not reducing d too much is that it keeps the tunneling barrier wide, and the gate oxide field low, thereby keeping the gate tunneling leakage current low [Eq. (6–43)]. Such high dielectric constant insulators such as hafnium dioxide, HfO_2, are also known as high-k gate dielectrics because k is also sometimes used as a symbol for dielectric constant.

Prolonged charge transport through gate oxides can ultimately cause catastrophic electrical breakdown of the oxides. This is known as *Time-Dependent Dielectric Breakdown (TDDB)*. One of the popular models that explains this degradation involves electrons tunneling into the conduction band of the gate oxide from the negative electrode (cathode), then gaining energy from the electric field, thus becoming "hot" electrons in the gate oxide. If they gain sufficient energy, they can cause impact ionization within the oxide and create electron–hole pairs (EHPs). The electrons are accelerated toward the (positive) Si substrate, while the holes travel toward the gate. However, electron and hole mobilities are extremely small in SiO_2. Hole mobilities are particularly low (~ 0.01 cm^2/Vs). Hence, there is a great propensity for these impact-generated holes to be trapped at defect sites within the oxide, near the cathode. The resulting band diagram (Fig. 6–25) is altered by this sheet of trapped positive charge, which causes the internal electric field between this point and the gate to increase. A similar distortion of the electric field near the Si anode is created by the trapped impact-generated electrons. However, the steepest slope in Fig. 6–25, and therefore the highest field, is near the gate. As a result, the barrier for electron tunneling from the gate into the oxide is reduced. More electrons can tunnel into the oxide, and cause more impact ionization. We get a positive feedback effect that can lead to a runaway TDDB process.

With high-k gate dielectrics, other degradation mechanisms occur, such as Negative Bias Temperature Instability (NBTI) in PMOSFETs. The negative gate voltage that must be applied to turn the PMOSFET on causes breakage of Si-H bonds near the gate dielectric interface and hole trapping in the gate dielectric. Similarly, one can have PBTI in NMOSFETs, although those effects are experimentally found to be less severe.

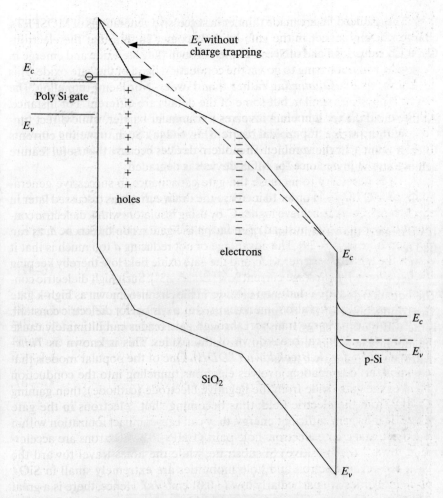

Figure 6–25
Time-dependent dielectric breakdown of oxides: Band diagram of a MOS device showing the band edges in the polysilicon gate, oxide, and Si substrate. Trapped holes and electrons in the oxide distort the band edges, and increase the electric field in the oxide near the gate. The tunneling barrier width is seen to be less than if there were no charge trapping (dashed line).

The MOS transistor is also called a surface field-effect transistor, since it depends on control of current through a thin channel at the surface of the semiconductor (Fig. 6–10). When an inversion region is formed under the gate, current can flow from drain to source (for an n-channel device). In this section we analyze the conductance of this channel and find the $I_D - V_D$ characteristics as a function of gate voltage V_G. As in the JFET case, we will find these characteristics below saturation and then assume I_D remains essentially constant above saturation.

6.5 THE MOS FIELD-EFFECT TRANSISTOR

6.5.1 Output Characteristics

The applied gate voltage V_G is accounted for by Eq. (6–28) plus the voltage required to achieve flat band:

$$V_G = V_{FB} - \frac{Q_s}{C_i} + \phi_s \qquad (6\text{–}44)$$

The induced charge Q_s in the semiconductor is composed of mobile charge Q_n and fixed charge in the depletion region Q_d. Substituting $Q_n + Q_d$ for Q_s, we can solve for the mobile charge:

$$Q_n = -C_i\left[V_G - \left(V_{FB} + \phi_s - \frac{Q_d}{C_i}\right)\right] \tag{6-45}$$

At threshold the term in brackets can be written $V_G - V_T$ from Eq. (6–38).

With a voltage V_D applied, there is a voltage rise V_x from the source to each point x in the channel. Thus the potential $\phi_s(x)$ is that required to achieve strong inversion ($2\phi_F$) plus the voltage V_x:

$$Q_n = -C_i\left[V_G - V_{FB} - 2\phi_F - V_x - \frac{1}{C_i}\sqrt{2q\,\epsilon_s N_a(2\phi_F + V_x)}\right] \tag{6-46}$$

If we neglect the variation of $Q_d(x)$ with bias V_x, Eq. (6–46) can be simplified to

$$Q_n(x) = -C_i(V_G - V_T - V_x) \tag{6-47}$$

This equation describes the mobile charge in the channel at point x (Fig. 6-26). The conductance of the differential element dx is $\bar{\mu}_n Q_n(x)Z/dx$, where Z is the width of the channel and $\bar{\mu}_n$ is a *surface* electron mobility (indicating the mobility in a thin region near the surface is not the same as in the bulk material). At point x we have

$$I_D dx = \bar{\mu}_n Z |Q_n(x)| dV_x \tag{6-48}$$

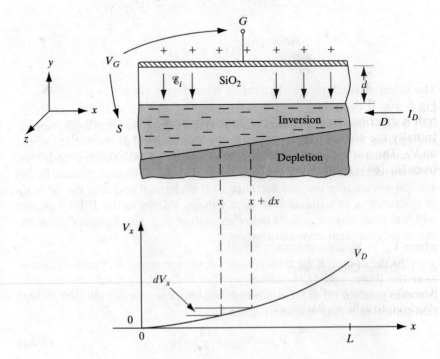

Figure 6–26
Schematic view of the n-channel region of a MOS transistor under bias below pinch-off, and the variation of voltage V_x along the conducting channel.

Integrating from source to drain,

$$\int_0^L I_D dx = \bar{\mu}_n Z C_i \int_0^{V_D} (V_G - V_T - V_x) dV_x$$

$$I_D = \frac{\bar{\mu}_n Z C_i}{L}[(V_G - V_T)V_D - \tfrac{1}{2}V_D^2] \tag{6-49}$$

where

$$\frac{\bar{\mu}_n Z C_i}{L} = k_N$$

determines the conductance and transconductance of the n-channel MOSFET [see Eqs. (6–51) and (6–54)].

In this analysis the depletion charge Q_d in the threshold voltage V_T is simply the value with no drain current. This is an approximation, since $Q_d(x)$ varies considerably when V_D is applied, to reflect the variation in V_x (see Fig. 6–26b). However, Eq. (6–49) is a fairly accurate description of drain current for low values of V_D, and is often used in approximate design calculations because of its simplicity. A more accurate and general expression is obtained by including the variation of $Q_d(x)$. Performing the integration of Eq. (6–48) using Eq. (6–46) for $Q_n(x)$, one obtains

$$I_D = \frac{\bar{\mu}_n Z C_i}{L} \left\{ (V_G - V_{FB} - 2\phi_F - \tfrac{1}{2}V_D)V_D \right.$$

$$\left. - \frac{2}{3} \frac{\sqrt{2\epsilon_s q N_a}}{C_i} [(V_D + 2\phi_F)^{3/2} - (2\phi_F)^{3/2}] \right\} \tag{6-50}$$

The drain characteristics that result from these questions are shown in Fig. 6–10c. If the gate voltage is above threshold ($V_G > V_T$), the drain current is described by Eq. (6–50) or approximately by Eq. (6–49) for low V_D. Initially the channel appears as an essentially linear resistor, dependent on V_G. The conductance of the channel in this linear region can be obtained from Eq. (6–49) with $V_D \ll (V_G - V_T)$:

$$g = \frac{\partial I_D}{\partial V_D} \cong \frac{Z}{L}\bar{\mu}_n C_i(V_G - V_T) \tag{6-51}$$

where $V_G > V_T$ for a channel to exist.

As the drain voltage is increased, the voltage across the oxide decreases near the drain, and Q_n becomes smaller there. As a result the channel becomes pinched off at the drain end, and the current saturates. The saturation condition is approximately given by

$$V_D(\text{sat.}) \cong V_G - V_T \tag{6-52}$$

The drain current at saturation remains essentially constant for larger values of drain voltage. Substituting Eq. (6–52) into Eq. (6–49), we obtain

$$I_D(\text{sat.}) \cong \tfrac{1}{2}\bar{\mu}_n C_i \frac{Z}{L}(V_G - V_T)^2 = \frac{Z}{2L}\bar{\mu}_n C_i V_D^2(\text{sat.}) \qquad (6\text{–}53)$$

for the approximate value of drain current at saturation.

The transconductance in the saturation range can be obtained approximately by differentiating Eq. (6–53) with respect to the gate voltage:

$$g_m(\text{sat.}) = \frac{\partial I_D(\text{sat.})}{\partial V_G} \cong \frac{Z}{L}\bar{\mu}_n C_i(V_G - V_T) \qquad (6\text{–}54)$$

The derivations presented here are based on the n-channel device. For the p-channel enhancement transistor the voltages V_D, V_G, and V_T are negative, and current flows from source to drain (Fig. 6–27).

6.5.2 Transfer Characteristics

The output characteristics plot the drain current as a function of the drain bias, with gate bias as a parameter (Fig. 6–27). On the other hand, the *transfer* characteristics plot the output drain current as a function of the input gate bias, for fixed drain bias (Fig. 6–28a). Clearly, in the linear region, I_D vs. V_G should be a straight line from Eq. (6–49). The intercept of this line on the V_G

Figure 6–27
Drain current–voltage characteristics for enhancement transistors:
(a) for n-channel V_D, V_G, V_T, and I_D are positive;
(b) for p-channel all these quantities are negative.

axis is the linear region threshold voltage, V_T(lin.), and the slope (divided by the applied V_D) gives us the linear value of k_N, k_N (lin.), of the n-channel MOSFET. If we look at actual data, however, we see that while the characteristics are approximately linear at low gate bias, at high gate biases the drain current increases sub-linearly. The transconductance, g_m(lin.), in the linear region can be obtained by differentiating the right-hand side of Eq. (6–49) with respect to gate bias. The g_m (lin.) is plotted as a function of V_G in Fig. 6–28b. It may be noted that the transconductance is zero below V_T because there is little drain current. It goes through a maximum at the point of inflection of the $I_D - V_G$ curve, and then decreases. This decrease is due to two factors that will be discussed in Sections 6.5.3 and 6.5.8: degradation of the effective channel mobility as a function of increasing transverse electric field across the gate oxide, and source/drain series resistance.

For the transfer characteristics in the saturation region, since Eq. (6–53) shows a quadratic dependence of I_D on V_G, we get a linear behavior by

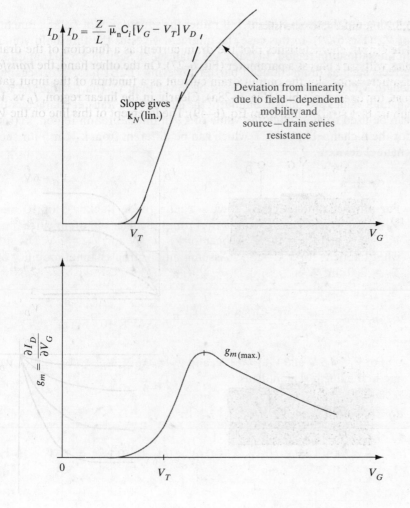

$$I_D = \frac{Z}{L} \bar{\mu}_n C_i [V_G - V_T] V_D ,$$

Slope gives k_N(lin.)

Deviation from linearity due to field−dependent mobility and source−drain series resistance

V_T V_G

$g_{m (max.)}$

0 V_T V_G

$g_m = \left.\dfrac{\partial I_D}{\partial V_G}\right|$

Figure 6–28
Linear region transfer characteristics: (a) plot of drain current vs. gate voltage for MOSFETs in the linear region; (b) transconductance as a function of gate bias.

Figure 6–29
Saturation
region transfer
characteristics:
plot of square
root of the
drain current
vs. gate voltage
for MOSFETs.

plotting not the drain current, but rather the square root of I_D, as a function of V_G (Fig. 6–29). In this case the intercept gives us the threshold voltage in the saturation region, $V_T(\text{sat.})$. We shall see in Section 6.5.10 that due to effects such as drain-induced barrier lowering (DIBL), for short channel length MOSFETs the V_T (sat.) can be lower than V_T (lin.), while the long channel values are similar. Similarly, the slope of the transfer characteristics can be used to determine the value of k_N in the saturation region, $k_N(\text{sat.})$ for the n-channel MOSFET, which can be different from k_N (lin.) for short channel devices.

EXAMPLE 6–2   For an n-channel MOSFET with a gate oxide thickness of 10 nm, $V_T = 0.6$ V, and $Z = 25\ \mu\text{m}, L = 1\ \mu\text{m}$. Calculate the drain current at $V_G = 5$ V and $V_D = 0.1$ V. Repeat for $V_G = 3$ V and $V_D = 5$ V. Discuss what happens for $V_D = 7$ V. Assume an electron channel mobility of $\bar{\mu}_n = 200\ \text{cm}^2/\text{V-s}$.

SOLUTION

$$C_i = \frac{\epsilon_i}{d} = \frac{(3.9)(8.85 \times 10^{-14})}{10^{-6}} = 3.45 \times 10^{-7}\,\text{F/cm}^2$$

For $V_G = 5$ V and $V_D = 0.1$ V, and $V_T = 0.6$ V, $V_D < (V_G - V_T)$, we are in the linear region. Thus,

$$I_D = \frac{Z}{L}\bar{\mu}_n C_i\left[(V_G - V_T)V_D - \frac{1}{2}V_D^2\right]$$

$$= \frac{25}{1}(200)(3.45 \times 10^{-7})\left[(5 - 0.6) \times 0.1 - \frac{1}{2}(0.1)^2\right] = \mathbf{7.51 \times 10^{-4}\,A}$$

For $V_G = 3$ V, $V_D = 5$ V, $V_D(\text{sat.}) = V_G - V_T = 3 - 0.6 = 2.4$ V

$$I_D = \frac{Z}{L}\bar{u}_n\bar{\iota}_i\left[(V_G - V_T)V_D(\text{sat.}) - \frac{1}{2}V_D^2(\text{sat.})\right]$$

$$= \frac{25}{1}(200)(3.45 \times 10^{-7})\left[(2.4)^2 - \frac{1}{2}(2.4)^2\right] = \mathbf{4.97 \times 10^{-3} A}$$

For $V_D = 7$ V, I_D will not increase, because we are in the saturation region.

6.5.3 Mobility Models

The mobility of carriers in the channel of a MOSFET is lower than in bulk semiconductors because there are additional scattering mechanisms. Since carriers in the channel are very close to the semiconductor–oxide interface, they are scattered by surface roughness and by coulombic interaction with fixed charges in the gate oxide. When the carriers travel in the inversion layer from the source to the drain, they encounter microscopic roughness on an atomistic scale at the oxide–silicon interface and undergo scattering because, as discussed in Section 3.4.1, any deviation from a perfectly periodic crystal potential results in scattering. This mobility degradation increases with the gate bias because a higher gate bias draws the carriers closer to the oxide–silicon interface, where they are more influenced by the interfacial roughness.

It is very interesting to note that if we plot the effective carrier mobility in the MOSFET as a function of the average transverse electric field in the middle of the inversion layer, we get what is known as a "universal" mobility degradation curve for any MOSFET, which is independent of the technology or device structural parameters such as oxide thickness and channel doping (Fig. 6–30). We can apply Gauss's law to the region marked by the colored

Figure 6–30
Inversion layer electron mobility vs. effective transverse field, at various temperatures. The triangles, circles, and squares refer to different MOSFETs with different gate oxide thicknesses and channel dopings. (After Sabnis and Clemens, *IEEE IEDM*, 1979.)

Figure 6–31
Determination of effective transverse field. Idealized charge distribution and transverse electric field in the inversion layer and depletion layer, as a function of depth in the channel of a MOSFET. The region to which we apply Gauss's law is shown in color.

box in Fig. 6–31, which encloses all the depletion charge and half of the inversion charge in the channel. We see that the average transverse field in the middle of the inversion region is given by

$$\mathscr{E}_{eff} = \frac{1}{\epsilon_s}\left(Q_d + \frac{1}{2}Q_n\right) \qquad (6\text{–}55a)$$

While this model works quite well for electrons, for reasons that are not clearly understood at present, it has to be modified slightly for holes in the sense that the average transverse field must now be defined as

$$\mathscr{E}_{eff} = \frac{1}{\epsilon_s}\left(Q_d + \frac{1}{3}Q_n\right) \qquad (6\text{–}55b)$$

This degradation of mobility with gate bias is often compactly described by writing the drain current expression as

$$I_D = \frac{\bar{\mu}_n Z C_i}{L\{1 + \theta(V_G - V_T)\}}\left[(V_G - V_T)V_D - \frac{1}{2}V_D^2\right] \qquad (6\text{–}56)$$

where θ is called the *mobility degradation parameter*. Because of the additional $(V_G - V_T)$ term in the denominator, the drain current increases sublinearly with gate bias for high gate voltages.

In addition to this dependence of the channel mobility on gate bias or transverse electric field, there is also a strong dependence on drain bias or the longitudinal electric field. As shown in Fig. 3–24, the carrier drift velocity increases linearly with electric field (ohmic behavior) until the field reaches $\mathscr{E}_{sat}$; in other words, the mobility is constant up to $\mathscr{E}_{sat}$. After this, the velocity saturates at v_s, and it can no longer be described in terms of mobility. These effects can be described as:

$$v = \mu\mathscr{E} \text{ for } \mathscr{E} < \mathscr{E}_{sat} \tag{6-57}$$

$$\text{and } v = v_s \text{ for } \mathscr{E} > \mathscr{E}_{sat} \tag{6-58}$$

The maximum longitudinal electric field near the drain end of the channel is approximately given by the voltage drop along the pinch-off region $(V_D - V_D(\text{sat.}))$, divided by the length of the pinch-off region, ΔL:

$$\mathscr{E}_{max} = \left(\frac{V_D - V_D(\text{sat.})}{\Delta L}\right) \tag{6-59}$$

From a two-dimensional solution of the Poisson equation near the drain end, one can show that the pinch-off region ΔL shown in Fig. 6–11c is approximately equal to $\sqrt{(3dx_j)}$, where d is the gate oxide thickness and x_j is the source/drain junction depth. The factor of 3 is due to the ratio of the dielectric constant for Si to that of SiO_2.

6.5.4 Short Channel MOSFET I–V Characteristics

In short channel devices, the analysis has to be somewhat modified. As mentioned in the previous section, the effective channel mobility decreases with increasing transverse electric field perpendicular to the gate oxide (i.e., the gate bias). Furthermore, for very high longitudinal electric fields in the pinch-off region, the carrier velocity saturates (Fig. 3–24). For short channel lengths, the carriers travel at the saturation velocity over most of the channel. In that case, the drain current is given by the width times the channel charge per unit area times the saturation velocity:

$$I_D(\text{sat.}) \approx ZC_i(V_G - V_T)v_s \tag{6-60}$$

As a result, the saturation drain current does not increase quadratically with $(V_G - V_T)$ as shown in Eq. (6–53), but rather shows a linear dependence (note the equal spacing of curves in Fig. 6–32). Due to the advances in Si device processing, particularly photolithography, MOSFETs used in modern integrated circuits tend to have short channels, and are commonly described by Eq. (6–60) rather than Eq. (6–53).

Current-generation nanoscale MOSFET channel lengths have been scaled down so aggressively that we have entered a different regime of operation where there are very few scattering events in the channel. This is known as the ballistic or quasi-ballistic regime. [The terminology comes from the analogy with launching electrons in the channel where they travel unimpeded like ballistic missiles.] Under these conditions, the current is not limited by velocity saturation (which is caused by optical phonon scattering) in the pinch-off region near the drain, as described in Eq. (6–60). Instead, the current is limited by how rapidly the carriers can be supplied *by the*

Figure 6–32
Experimental
output
characteristics
of n-channel
and p-channel
MOSFETs with
0.1-μm channel
lengths. The curves
exhibit almost
equal spacing,
indicating a linear
dependence of
I_D on V_G, rather
than a quadratic
dependence. We
also see that I_D
is not constant
but increases
somewhat with V_D
in the saturation
region. The
p-channel devices
have lower
currents because
hole mobilities
are lower than
electron mobilities.

Figure 6–32 Experimental output characteristics of n-channel and p-channel MOSFETs with 0.1-μm channel lengths. The curves exhibit almost equal spacing, indicating a linear dependence of I_D on V_G, rather than a quadratic dependence. We also see that I_D is not constant but increases somewhat with V_D in the saturation region. The p-channel devices have lower currents because hole mobilities are lower than electron mobilities.

source. This is known as source-injection limited transport. Under these conditions, the drain current is given by

$$I_D(\text{sat.}) \approx \{(1 - r)/(1 + r)\}\ ZC_i(V_G - V_T)\ \mathrm{v}_{inj} \qquad (6\text{--}61)$$

where r is the reflection coefficient of the electron wavefunction near the top of the channel potential barrier near the source (Fig. 6–33), and v_{inj} is effective source-injection velocity. v_{inj} is related to the random thermal velocity, v_{th}, of the carriers in the source. At high carrier concentrations in the channel, v_{inj} approaches a higher velocity. v_F, which is the velocity of the carriers near the Fermi level. An analysis of the physics by Natori and Lundstrom has shown that the backscattering or the reflection coefficient r is related to the low field mobility in the channel. The higher the mobility, the longer is the mean free path, leading to a lower r and higher source-injection-limited drain current. This model of transport of carriers in a nanoscale device treats electrons being transmitted as waves in an electron waveguide, and is known as the Landauer-Buttiker formalism. This is a powerful and different way of treating transport in nanoscale devices where scattering is negligible, and the concept of mobility (which is determined by scattering) is suspect. The Landauer approach treats conductance in terms of *transmission* of the electron waves.

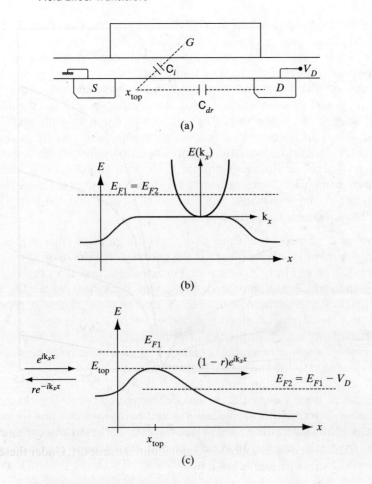

Figure 6–33
(a) Source-injection-limited quasi-ballistic MOSFET. The gate capacitance and drain-to-channel capacitance compete from control of the potential barrier near the source end of the channel at x_{top}. (b) Channel potential profile for MOSFET in equilibrium, and superimposed parabolic $E(k)$ band structure; (c) Channel potential profile with drain at V_D showing partial transmission of electron waves over "top of barrier."

6.5.5 Control of Threshold Voltage

Since the threshold voltage determines the requirements for turning the MOS transistor on or off, it is very important to be able to adjust V_T in designing the device. For example, if the transistor is to be used in a circuit driven by a 3-V battery, it is clear that a 4-V threshold voltage is unacceptable. Some applications require not only a low value of V_T, but also a precisely controlled value to match other devices in the circuit.

All of the terms in Eq. (6–38) can be controlled to some extent. The work function potential difference Φ_{ms} is determined by choice of the gate conductor material; ϕ_F depends on the substrate doping; Q_i can be reduced by proper oxidation methods and by using Si grown in the (100) orientation; Q_d can be adjusted by doping of the substrate; and C_i depends on the thickness and dielectric constant of the insulator. We shall discuss here several methods of controlling these quantities in device fabrication.

Choice of Gate Electrode. Since V_T depends on Φ_{ms}, the choice of the gate electrode material (i.e., the gate electrode work function) has an impact on the threshold voltage. When MOSFETs were first made in the 1960s, they used Al gates. However, since Al has a low melting point, it precluded the use of a self-aligned source/drain technology because that required a high temperature source/drain implant anneal after the gate formation. Hence, Al was supplanted by n^+ doped LPCVD polysilicon *refractory* (high melting point) gates, where the Fermi level lines up with the conduction band edge in Si. While this works quite well for n-channel MOSFETs, we shall see in Section 9.3.1 that it can create problems for p-channel MOSFETs. Therefore, sometimes, a p^+ doped polysilicon gate is used for p-channel devices. Refractory metal gates with suitable work functions are now being used as replacements for doped polysilicon. One attractive candidate is tungsten, whose work function is such that the Fermi level happens to lie near the midgap of Si.

Control of C_i. Since a low value of V_T and a high drive current is usually desired, a thin oxide layer is used in the gate region to increase $C_i = \epsilon_i/d$ in Eq. (6–38). From Fig. 6–20 we see that increasing C_i makes V_T less negative for p-channel devices and less positive for n channel with $-Q_d > Q_i$. For practical considerations, the high-k gate oxide thickness is generally 10–100 Å (1–10 nm) in modern devices having submicron gate length. An example of such a device is shown in Fig. 6–34. The gate oxide, easily observable in this micrograph, is high-k. The interfacial layer between the crystalline silicon and the high-k is also observable.

Although a low threshold voltage is desirable in the gate region of a transistor, a large value of V_T is needed between devices. For example, if a number of transistors are interconnected on a single Si chip, we do not want inversion layers to be formed inadvertently between devices (generally called the *field*). One way to avoid such parasitic channels is to increase V_T in the field by using a very thick oxide using STI. Figure 6–35 illustrates a transistor with a gate oxide 10 nm thick and a field oxide of 0.5 μm.

Threshold Adjustment by Ion Implantation. The most valuable tool for controlling threshold voltage is ion implantation (Section 5.1.4). Since very precise quantities of impurity can be introduced by this method, it is possible to maintain close control of V_T. The negatively charged boron acceptors serve to reduce the effects of the positive depletion charge Q_d. As a result, V_T becomes less negative. Similarly, a shallow boron implant into the p-type substrate of an n-channel transistor can make V_T positive, as required for an enhancement device.

If the implantation is performed at higher energy, or into the bare Si instead of through an oxide layer, the impurity distribution lies deeper below the surface. In such cases the essentially gaussian impurity concentration profile cannot be approximated by a spike at the Si surface. Therefore, effects of distributed charge on the Q_d term of Eq. (6–38) must be considered. Calculations of the effects on V_T in this case are more complicated, and the shift of threshold voltage with implantation dose is often obtained empirically instead.

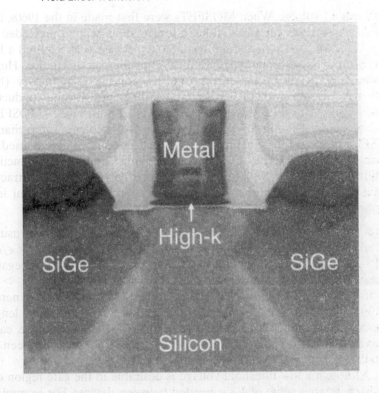

Figure 6–34
Cross section of a MOSFET. This high resolution transmission electron micrograph of a silicon Metal–Oxide Semiconductor Field Effect Transistor shows the silicon channel and metal gate separated by a thin silicon high-k gate dielectric. This 45nm PMOS metal gate transistor was made using gate-last or replacement metal gate process flow. (Photograph courtesy of Intel.)

The implantation energy required for shallow V_T adjustment implants is low (50–100 keV), and relatively low doses are needed. A typical V_T adjustment requires only about 10 s of implantation for each wafer, and therefore this procedure is compatible with large-scale production requirements.

If the implantation is continued to higher doses, V_T can be moved past zero to the *depletion-mode* condition (Fig. 6–36). This capability provides considerable flexibility to the integrated-circuit designer, by allowing enhancement- and depletion-mode devices to be incorporated on the same chip. For example, a depletion-mode transistor can be used instead of a resistor as a load element for the enhancement device. Thus an array of MOS transistors can be fabricated in an IC layout, with some adjusted by implantation to have the desired enhancement-mode V_T and others implanted to become depletion loads.

As mentioned, V_T control is important not only in the MOSFETs but also in the isolation or field regions. In addition to using a thick field oxide, we can do a *channel stop implant* (so called because it stops turning on a parasitic channel in the isolation regions) selectively in the isolation regions under the field oxide (Fig. 6–34). Generally, a B channel stop implant is used for n-channel devices. (It must be noted that such an acceptor implant will

Boron implant through gate oxide
(before polysilicon gate formation)

(a)

(b)

Figure 6–35
Thin oxide in the gate region and thick oxide in the field between transistors for V_T control (not to scale).

raise the field thresholds for n-channel MOSFETs made in a p-substrate, but will *decrease* the field thresholds for p-MOSFETs made in an n-substrate).

6.5.6 Substrate Bias Effects—the "Body" Effect

In the derivation of Eq. (6–49) for current along the channel, we assumed that the source S was connected to the substrate B (Fig. 6–27). In fact, it

For a p-channel transistor with a gate oxide thickness of 10 nm, calcu-late the boron ion dose $F_B(\text{B}^+ \text{ ions/cm}^2)$ required to reduce V_T from -1.1 V to -0.5 V. Assume that the implanted acceptors form a sheet of negative charge just below the Si surface. If, instead of a shallow B implant, it was a much broader distribution, how would the V_T calculation change? Assuming a boron ion beam current of 10^{-5} A, and supposing that the area scanned by the ion beam is 650 cm², how long does this implant take?

EXAMPLE 6–3

Since the B negative ions are assumed to form a sheet of charge just below the gate oxide, they affect the fixed oxide charge term in V_{FB}. Thus,

SOLUTION

$$C_i = \frac{\epsilon_i}{d} = \frac{(3.9)(8.85 \times 10^{-14})}{10^{-6}} = 3.45 \times 10^{-7}\,\text{F/cm}^2$$

$$-0.5 = -1.1 + \frac{qF_B}{C_i}$$

$$F_B = \frac{3.45 \times 10^{-7}}{1.6 \times 10^{-19}}(0.6) = 1.3 \times 10^{12}\,\text{cm}^{-2}$$

If the B distribution is deeper, we cannot assume it to be a sheet charge in V_{FB}. If it is approximately *constant over the maximum deple-tion width*, we should instead change the substrate doping term in the expression for V_T. Otherwise, the calculation has to be done by numeri-cally solving Poisson's equation in the depletion region, with a varying doping concentration corresponding to the B distribution, to obtain the voltage drop in the semiconductor.

For a beam current of 10 μA scanned over a 650-cm² target area,

$$\frac{10^{-5}(\text{C/s})}{650\,\text{cm}^2}\,t(s) = 1.3 \times 10^{12}\,(\text{ions/cm}^2) \times 1.6 \times 10^{-19}\,(\text{C/ion})$$

The implant time is $t = 13.5$ s.

is possible to apply a voltage between S and B (Fig. 6–37). With a reverse bias between the substrate and the source (V_B negative for an n-channel device), the source-channel junction potential barrier (Fig. 6–10b) is increased. Clearly, the gate must be biased more positively than for the grounded substrate, to lower the source-channel potential barrier suffi-ciently to create an inversion layer. This causes the threshold voltage to increase with (reverse) substrate bias—this is known as the body effect. The new V_T is given by adding a voltage drop $-V_B$ between the gate and the substrate (Fig. 6–37) to the $2\phi_F$ term in the grounded substrate case, so that Eq. (6–38) should be changed.

However, since the V_T is defined not with respect to the substrate, but rather with respect to the grounded source, we need to add the V_B term at the end, and the V_B terms cancel out. The net result is that the depletion region in the channel is widened and the threshold gate voltage required to achieve inversion must be increased to accommodate the larger Q'_d.

$$V'_T = \Phi_{ms} - \frac{Q_i}{C_i} - \frac{Q'_d}{C_i} + (2\phi_F - V_B) + V_B \qquad (6\text{–}62a)$$

$$Q'_d = -[2\epsilon_s q N_a (2\phi_F - V_B)]^{1/2} \qquad (6\text{–}62b)$$

The change in threshold voltage due to the substrate bias is

$$\Delta V_T = \frac{\sqrt{2\epsilon_s q N_a}}{C_i}[(2\phi_F - V_B)^{1/2} - (2\phi_F)^{1/2}] \qquad (6\text{–}63a)$$

If the substrate bias V_B is much larger than $2\phi_F$ (typically ~0.6 V), the threshold voltage is dominated by V_B and

$$\Delta V_T \cong \frac{\sqrt{2\epsilon_s q N_a}}{C_i}(-V_B)^{1/2} \quad (\text{n channel}) \qquad (6\text{–}63b)$$

where V_B will be negative for the n-channel case. As the substrate bias is increased, the threshold voltage becomes more positive. The effect of this bias becomes more dramatic as the substrate doping is increased, since ΔV_T is also proportional to $\sqrt{N_a}$. For a p-channel device the bulk-to-source

Figure 6–37
Threshold voltage dependence on substrate bias resulting from application of a voltage V_B from the substrate (i.e., bulk) to the source. For n channel, V_B must be zero or negative to avoid forward bias of the source junction. For p channel, V_B must be zero or positive.

voltage V_B is positive to achieve a reverse bias, and the approximate change ΔV_T for $V_B \gg 2\phi_F$ is

$$\Delta V_T \cong -\frac{\sqrt{2\epsilon_s q N_d}}{C_i} V_B^{1/2} \quad \text{(p channel)} \qquad (6\text{–}64)$$

Thus the p-channel threshold voltage becomes more negative with substrate bias.

The substrate bias effect (also called the *body effect*) increases V_T for either type of device. This effect can be used to raise the threshold voltage of a marginally enhancement device ($V_T \sim 0$) to a somewhat larger and more manageable value. This can be an asset for n-channel devices particularly (see Fig. 6–20). The effect can present problems, however, in MOS integrated circuits for which it is impractical to connect each source region to the substrate. In these cases, possible V_T shifts due to the body effect must be taken into account in the circuit design.

6.5.7 Subthreshold Characteristics

If we look at the drain current expression [Eq. (6–53)], it appears that the current abruptly goes to zero as soon as V_G is reduced to V_T. In reality, there is still some drain conduction below threshold, and this is known as *subthreshold conduction*. This current is due to weak inversion in the channel between flat band and threshold (for band bending between zero and $2\phi_F$), which leads to a diffusion current from source to drain. The drain current in the subthreshold region is equal to

$$I_D = \mu(C_d + C_{it})\frac{Z}{L}\left(\frac{kT}{q}\right)^2\left(1 - e^{\frac{-qV_D}{kT}}\right)\left(e^{\frac{q(V_G-V_T)}{c_r kT}}\right) \qquad (6\text{–}65)$$

where

$$c_r = \left[1 + \frac{C_d + C_{it}}{C_i}\right]$$

It can be seen that I_D depends exponentially on gate bias, V_G. However, V_D has little influence once V_D exceeds a few kT/q. Obviously, if we plot $\ln I_D$ as a function of gate bias V_G, we should get a linear behavior in the subthreshold regime, as shown in Fig. 6–38a. The slope of this line (or more precisely the reciprocal of the slope) is known as the subthreshold slope, S, which has typical values of ~ 70 mV/decade at room temperature for state-of-the-art MOSFETs. This means that a change in the input V_G of 70 mV will change the output I_D by an order of magnitude. Clearly, the smaller the value of S, the better the transistor is as a switch. A small value of S means a small change in the input bias can modulate the output current considerably. It can be shown that the expression for S is given by

$$S = \frac{dV_G}{d(\log I_D)} = \ln 10 \frac{dV_G}{d(\ln I_D)} = 2.3\frac{kT}{q}\left[1 + \frac{C_d + C_{it}}{C_i}\right] \qquad (6\text{–}66)$$

Here, the factor $\ln 10 \,(= 2.3)$ is introduced to change from $\log_{10}$ to natural logarithm, ln. This equation can be understood by looking at the electrical equivalent circuit of the MOSFET in terms of the capacitors (Fig. 6–38b). Between the gate and the substrate, we find the gate capacitance, C_i, in series with the parallel combination of the depletion capacitance in the channel, C_d, and the fast interface state capacitance, $C_{it} = qD_{it}$. The expression in brackets in Eq. (6–66) is simply the capacitor divider ratio which tells us

Figure 6–38
Subthreshold conduction in MOSFETs: (a) semilog plot of I_D vs. V_G; (b) equivalent circuit showing capacitor divider which determines subthreshold slope.

what fraction of the applied gate bias, V_G, appears at the Si–SiO$_2$ interface as the surface potential. Ultimately, it is the surface potential that is responsible for modulating the barrier between source and drain, and therefore the drain current. Hence, S is a measure of the efficacy of the gate potential in modulating I_D. From Eq. (6–66), we observe that S is improved by reducing the gate oxide thickness, which is reasonable because if the gate electrode is closer to the channel, the gate control is obviously better. The value of S is higher for heavy channel doping (which increases the depletion capacitance) or if the silicon–oxide interface has many fast interface states.

For a very small gate voltage, the subthreshold current is reduced to the leakage current of the source/drain junctions. This determines the off-state leakage current, and therefore the standby power dissipation in many complementary MOS (CMOS) circuits involving both n-channel and p-channel MOSFETs. It also underlines the importance of having high-quality source/drain junctions. From the subthreshold characteristics, it can be seen that if the V_T of a MOSFET is too low, it cannot be turned off fully at $V_G = 0$. Also, unavoidable statistical variations of V_T cause drastic variations of the subthreshold leakage current. On the other hand, if V_T is too high, one sacrifices drive current, which depends on the difference between the power supply voltage and V_T. For these reasons, the V_T of MOSFETs has historically been designed to be ~0.7 V. However, with the recent advent of various types of low-voltage, low-power portable electronics, there are new challenges in device and circuit design to optimize speed and power dissipation.

6.5.8 Equivalent Circuit for the MOSFET

When we attempt to draw an equivalent circuit of a MOSFET, we find that in addition to the intrinsic MOSFET itself, there are a variety of parasitic elements associated with it. An important addition to the gate capacitance is the so-called *Miller overlap capacitance* due to the overlap between the gate and the drain region (Fig. 6–39). This capacitance is particularly problematic because it represents a feedback path between the output drain terminal and the input gate terminal. One can measure the Miller capacitance at high-frequency by holding the gate at ground ($V_G = 0$) so that an inversion layer is not formed in the channel. Thereby, most of the measured capacitance between gate and drain is due to the Miller capacitance, rather than the gate capacitance C_i. It is possible to minimize this capacitance by using a so-called *self-aligned gate*. In this process, the gate itself is used to mask the source/drain implants, thereby achieving alignment. Even in this design, however, there is still a certain amount of overlap because of the lateral straggle or spread of the implanted dopants underneath the gate, further exacerbated by the lateral diffusion which occurs during high temperature annealing. This spread of the source/drain junctions under the gate edge determines what is called the channel length reduction, ΔL_R (Fig. 6–40). Hence, we get the electrical or "effective" channel length, L_{eff}, in terms of the physical gate length, L as

$$L_{eff} = L - \Delta L_R \qquad (6\text{–}67)$$

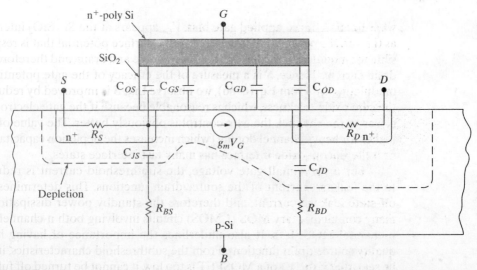

Figure 6–39
Equivalent circuit of a MOSFET, showing the passive capacitive and resistive components. The gate capacitance C_i is the sum of the distributed capacitances from the gate to the source end of the channel (C_{GS}) and the drain end (C_{GD}). In addition, we have an overlap capacitance (where the gate electrode overlaps the source/drain junctions) from the gate-to-source (C_{OS}) and gate-to-drain (C_{OD}). C_{OD} is also known as the Miller overlap capacitance. We also have p-n junction depletion capacitances associated with the source (C_{JS}) and drain (C_{JD}). The parasitic resistances include the source/drain series resistances (R_S and R_D), and the resistances in the substrate between the bulk contact and the source and drain (R_{BS} and R_{BD}). The drain current can be modeled as a (gate) voltage-controlled constant-current source.

There can also be a width reduction, ΔZ, which changes the effective width, Z_{eff}, from the physical width Z of the MOSFET. The width reduction results from the electrical isolation regions that are formed around all transistors, generally by LOCOS. The LOCOS isolation technique is discussed in Section 9.3.1.

Another very important parameter in the equivalent circuit is the source/drain series resistance, $R_{SD} = (R_S + R_D)$, because it degrades the drain current and transconductance. For a certain applied drain bias to the source/drain terminals, part of the applied voltage is "wasted" as an ohmic voltage drop across these resistances, depending on the drain current (or gate bias). Hence, the actual drain voltage applied to the intrinsic MOSFET itself is less; this causes I_D to increase sub-linearly with V_G.

We can determine R_{SD}, along with ΔL_R, from the overall resistance of the MOSFET in the linear region,

$$\left(\frac{V_D}{I_D}\right)$$

This corresponds to the intrinsic channel impedance R_{Ch}, plus the source-drain resistance R_{SD}. Modifying Eq. (6–51) we get

$$\frac{V_D}{I_D} = R_{Ch} + R_{SD} = \frac{L - \Delta L_R}{Z - \Delta Z} \frac{1}{\bar{\mu}_n C_i (V_G - V_T)} + R_{SD} \quad (6\text{–}68)$$

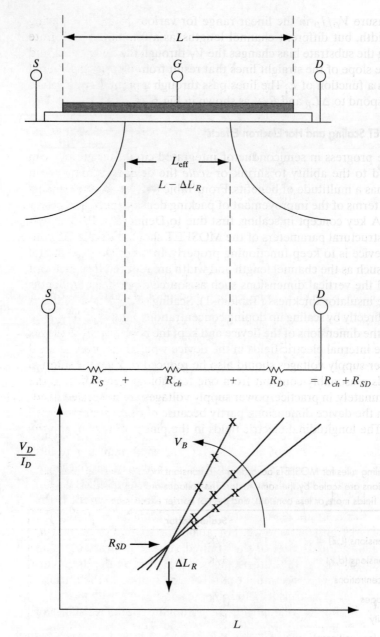

Figure 6–40
Determination of length reduction and source/drain series resistance in a MOSFET. The overall resistance of a MOSFET in the linear region is plotted as a function of channel length, for various substrate biases. The X's mark data points for three different physical gate lengths L.

We can measure V_D/I_D in the linear range for various MOSFETs having the same width, but different channel lengths, as a function of substrate bias. Varying the substrate bias changes the V_T through the body effect, and therefore the slope of the straight lines that result from plotting the overall resistance as a function of L. The lines pass through a point, having values which correspond to ΔL_R and R_{SD}, as shown in Fig. 6–40.

6.5.9 MOSFET Scaling and Hot Electron Effects

Much of the progress in semiconductor integrated circuit technology can be attributed to the ability to shrink or *scale* the devices. Scaling down MOSFETs has a multitude of benefits. From Table 6–1, we see the benefits of scaling in terms of the improvement of packing density, speed and power dissipation. A key concept in scaling, first due to Dennard at IBM, is that the various structural parameters of the MOSFET should be scaled in concert if the device is to keep functioning properly. In other words, if lateral dimensions such as the channel length and width are reduced by a factor of K, so should the vertical dimensions such as source/drain junction depths (x_j) and gate insulator thickness (Table 6–1). Scaling of depletion widths is achieved indirectly by scaling up doping concentrations. However, if we simply reduced the dimensions of the device and kept the power supply voltages the same, the internal electric fields in the device would increase. For ideal scaling, power supply voltages should also be reduced to keep the internal electric fields reasonably constant from one technology generation to the next. Unfortunately, in practice, power supply voltages are not scaled hand-in-hand with the device dimensions, partly because of other system-related constraints. The longitudinal electric fields in the pinch-off region, and the

Table 6–1 Scaling rules for MOSFETs according to a constant factor K. The horizontal and vertical dimensions are scaled by the same factor. The voltages are also scaled to keep the internal electric fields more or less constant, and the hot carrier effects manageable.

	Scaling factor
Surface dimensions (L,Z)	$1/K$
Vertical dimensions (d,x_j)	$1/K$
Impurity concentrations	K
Current, voltages	$1/K$
Current density	K
Capacitance (per unit area)	K
Transconductance	1
Circuit delay Time	$1/K$
Power dissipation	$1/K^2$
Power density	1
Power-delay product	$1/K^3$

transverse electric fields across the gate oxide, increase with MOSFET scaling. A variety of problems then arise which are generically known as hot
electron effects and short channel effects (Fig. 6–41).

   When an electron travels from the source to the drain along the channel, it gains kinetic energy at the expense of electrostatic potential energy in
the pinch-off region, and becomes a "hot" electron. At the conduction band
edge, the electron has potential energy only; as it gains more kinetic energy, it
moves higher up in the conduction band. A few of the electrons can become
energetic enough to surmount the 3.1-eV potential barrier between the Si
channel and the gate oxide (Fig. 6–25). Some of these injected hot electrons can go through the gate oxide and be collected as gate current, thereby
reducing the input impedance. More importantly, some of these electrons can
be trapped in the gate oxide as fixed oxide charges. According to Eq. (6–37),
this increases the flat band voltage, and therefore the V_T. In addition, these
energetic hot carriers can rupture Si–H bonds that exist at the Si–SiO$_2$ interface, creating fast interface states that degrade MOSFET parameters such
as transconductance and subthreshold slope, with stress. The results of such
hot carrier degradation are shown in Fig. 6–42, where we see the increase
of V_T and decrease of slope, and therefore transconductance, with stress.
The solution to this problem is to use what is known as a *lightly doped drain*
(LDD). As discussed in more detail in Section 9.3.1, by reducing the doping

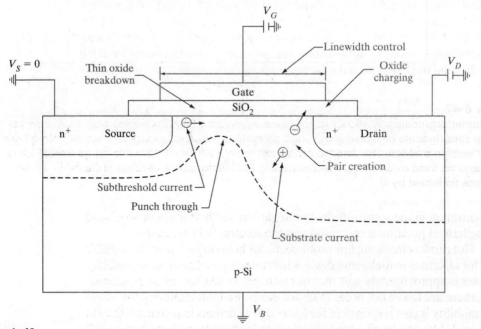

Figure 6–41
Short channel effects in MOSFETs. As MOSFETs are scaled down, potential problems due to short
channel effects include hot carrier generation (electron–hole pair creation) in the pinch-off region, punch-
through breakdown between source and drain, and thin gate oxide breakdown.

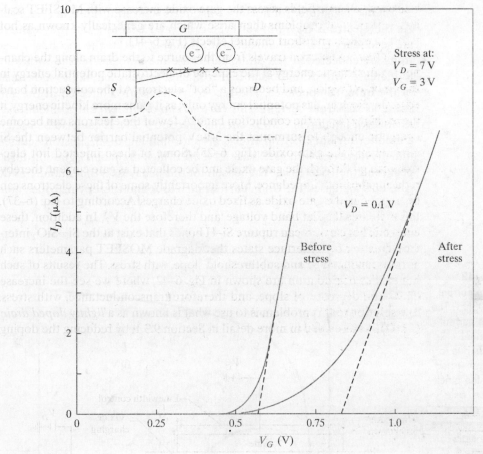

Figure 6–42

Hot carrier degradation in MOSFETs. The linear region transfer characteristics before and after hot carrier stress indicate an increase of V_T and decrease of transconductance (or channel mobility) due to hot electron damage. The damage can be due to hot electron injection into the gate oxide which increases the fixed oxide charge, and increasing fast interface state densities at the oxide–silicon interface (indicated by x).

concentration in the source/drain, the depletion width at the reverse-biased drain-channel junction is increased and the electric field is reduced.

Hot carrier effects are less problematic for holes in p-channel MOSFETs than for electrons in n-channel devices for two reasons. The channel mobility of holes is approximately half that of electrons; hence, for the same electric field, there are fewer hot holes than hot electrons. Unfortunately, the lower hole mobility is also responsible for lower drive currents in p channel than in n channel. Also, the barrier for hole injection in the valence band between Si and SiO_2 is higher (5 eV) than for electrons in the conduction band (3.1 eV), as shown in Fig. 6–25. Hence, while LDD is mandatory for n channel, it is often not used for p-channel devices.

One "signature" for hot electron effects is substrate current (Fig. 6–43). As the electrons travel toward the drain and become hot, they can create secondary EHPs by impact ionization (Fig. 6–41). The secondary electrons are collected at the drain, and cause the drain current in saturation to increase with drain bias at high voltages, thereby leading to a decrease of the output impedance. The secondary holes are collected at the substrate as substrate current. This current can create circuit problems such as noise or latchup in CMOS circuits (Section 9.3.1). It can also be used as a monitor for hot electron effects. As shown in Fig. 6–43, substrate current initially increases with gate bias (for a fixed, high drain bias), goes through a peak, and then decreases. The reason for this behavior is that initially, as the gate bias increases, the drain current increases and thereby provides more

Figure 6–43
Substrate current in a MOSFET. The substrate current in n-channel MOSFETs due to impact-generated holes in the pinch-off region, as a function of gate bias. The substrate current initially increases with V_G, because of the corresponding increase of I_D. However, for even higher V_G the MOSFET goes from the saturation to the linear region, and the high electric fields in the pinch-off region decrease, causing less impact ionization. (After Kamata, et al., Jpn. J. Appl. Phys., 15 (1976), 1127.)

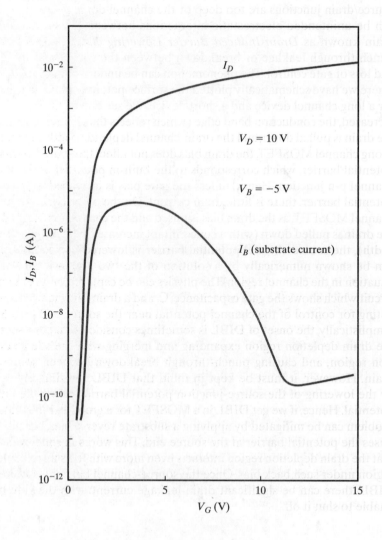

primary carriers into the pinch-off region for impact ionization. However, for even higher gate bias, the MOSFET goes from the saturation region into the linear region when the fixed V_D drops below $V_D(\text{sat.}) = (V_G - V_T)$. The longitudinal electric field in the pinch-off region drops, thereby reducing the impact ionization rates. Hot electron reliability studies are done under "worst case" conditions of peak substrate current. These are generally done under accelerated conditions of higher-than-normal operating voltages so that if there are any potential problems, they show up in a reasonable time period. The degradation data is then extrapolated to the actual operating conditions.

6.5.10 Drain-Induced Barrier Lowering

If small channel length MOSFETs are not scaled properly, and the source/drain junctions are too deep or the channel doping is too low, there can be unintended electrostatic interactions between the source and the drain known as *Drain-Induced Barrier Lowering (DIBL)*. This leads to punch-through leakage or breakdown between the source and the drain, and loss of gate control. The phenomenon can be understood from Fig. 6–44, where we have schematically plotted the surface potential along the channel for a long channel device and a short device. We see that as the drain bias is increased, the conduction band edge (which reflects the electron energies) in the drain is pulled down, and the drain-channel depletion width expands. For a long channel MOSFET, the drain bias does not affect the source-to-channel potential barrier, which corresponds to the built-in potential of the source-channel p-n junction. Hence, unless the gate bias is increased to lower this potential barrier, there is little drain current. On the other hand, for a short channel MOSFET, as the drain bias is raised and the conduction band edge in the drain is pulled down (with a concomitant increase of the drain depletion width), the source-channel potential barrier is lowered due to DIBL. This can be shown numerically by a solution of the two-dimensional Poisson' equation in the channel region. The physics can be captured by an equivalent circuit which shows the gate capacitance, C_i and a drain capacitance C_{dr} competing for control of the channel potential near the source end (Fig. 6–33). Simplistically, the onset of DIBL is sometimes considered to correspond to the drain depletion region expanding and merging with the source depletion region, and causing punch-through breakdown between source and drain. However, it must be kept in mind that DIBL is ultimately caused by the lowering of the source-junction potential barrier below the built-in potential. Hence, if we get DIBL in a MOSFET for a grounded substrate, the problem can be mitigated by applying a substrate reverse bias, because that raises the potential barrier at the source end. This works in spite of the fact that the drain depletion region interacts even more with the source depletion region under such back bias. Once the source-channel barrier is lowered by DIBL, there can be significant drain leakage current, with the gate being unable to shut it off.

Figure 6–44
Drain-induced barrier lowering in MOSFETs. Cross sections and potential distribution along the channel for a long channel and short channel MOSFET.

What are the solutions to this problem? The source/drain junctions must be made sufficiently shallow (i.e., scaled properly) as the channel lengths are reduced, to prevent DIBL. Secondly, the channel doping must be made sufficiently high to prevent the drain from being able to control the source junction. This is achieved by performing what is known as an *anti-punch-through* implant in the channel. Sometimes, instead of such an implant throughout the channel (which can have undesirable consequences such as raising the V_T or the body effect), a localized implant is done only near the source/drains. These are known as *halo* or *pocket* implants. The higher doping reduces the source/drain depletion widths and prevents their interaction.

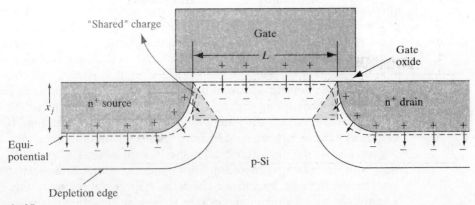

Figure 6–45
Short channel effect in a MOSFET. Cross-sectional view of MOSFET along the length showing depletion charge sharing (colored regions) between the gate, source, and drain.

For short channel MOSFETs, DIBL is related to the electrical modulation of the channel length in the pinch-off region, ΔL. Since the drain current is inversely proportional to the electrical channel length, we get

$$I_D \propto \frac{1}{L - \Delta L} = \frac{1}{L}\left(1 + \frac{\Delta L}{L}\right) \qquad (6\text{–}69)$$

for small pinch-off regions, ΔL. We assume that the fractional change in the channel length is proportional to the drain bias,

$$\frac{\Delta L}{L} = \lambda V_D \qquad (6\text{–}70)$$

where λ is the *channel length modulation parameter*. Hence, in the saturation region, the expression for the drain current becomes

$$I_D = \frac{Z}{2L}\,\bar{\mu}_n C_i (V_G - V_T)^2 (1 + \lambda V_D) \qquad (6\text{–}71)$$

This leads to a slope in the output characteristics, or a lowering of the output impedance (Fig. 6–32).

6.5.11 Short Channel Effect and Narrow Width Effect

If we plot the threshold voltage as a function of channel length in MOSFETs, we find that V_T decreases with L for very small geometries. This effect is called the *short channel effect (SCE)*, and is somewhat similar to DIBL. The mechanism is due to something called *charge sharing* between the source/drain and the gate (Fig. 6–45).[9] From the equation for the

[9]L. Yau, "A simple theory to predict the threshold voltage of short-channel IGFETs," Solid-State Electronics, 17 (1974): 1059.

threshold voltage (6–38), we notice that one of the terms is the depletion charge under the gate.

The equipotential lines in Fig. 6–45 designating the depletion regions curve around the contours of the source/drain junctions. Keeping in mind that the electric field lines are perpendicular to the equipotential contours, we see that the depletion charges that are physically underneath the gate in the approximately triangular regions near the source/drains have their field lines terminate not on the gate, but instead on the source/drains. Hence, electrically these depletion charges are "shared" with the source and drain regions and should not be counted in the V_T expression, Eq. (6–38). We can deal with this effect by replacing the orginal Q_d in the rectangular region underneath the gate by a lower Q_d in the trapezoidal region in Fig. 6–45. Clearly, for a long channel device, the triangular depletion charge regions near the source and drain are a very small fraction of the total depletion charge underneath the gate. However, as the channel lengths are reduced, the shared charge becomes a larger fraction of the total, and this results in a V_T *roll-off* as a function of L (Fig. 6–46). This is important because it is hard to control the channel lengths precisely in manufacturing. The channel length variations then lead to problems with V_T control.

In the last several years, another effect has been observed in n-channel MOSFETs with decreasing L. The V_T initially goes up before it goes down due to the short channel effect. This phenomenon has been dubbed the *reverse short channel effect (RSCE)*, and is due to interactions between Si point defects that are created during the source/drain implant and the B doping in the channel, causing the B to pile up near the source and drains, and thus raise the V_T.

Another related effect in MOSFETs is the *narrow width effect*, where the V_T goes up as the channel width Z is reduced for very narrow devices (Fig. 6–46). This can be understood from Fig. 6–47, where some of the depletion charges under the LOCOS isolation regions have field lines electrically terminating on the gate. Unlike the SCE, where the effective depletion

Figure 6–46
Roll-off of V_T with decreasing channel length, and increase of V_T with decreasing width.

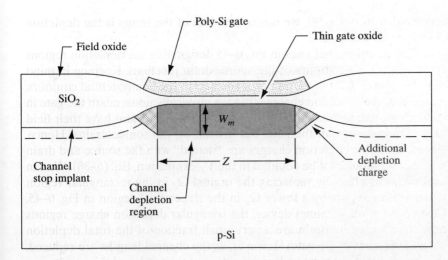

Figure 6–47
Narrow width effect in a MOSFET. Cross-sectional view of MOSFET along the width, showing additional depletion charge (colored regions) underneath the field or the LOCOS isolation regions.

charge is reduced due to charge sharing with the source/drain, here the depletion charge belonging to the gate is increased. The effect is not important for very wide devices, but becomes quite important as the widths are reduced below 1 μm.

6.5.12 Gate-Induced Drain Leakage

If we examine the subthreshold characteristics shown in Fig. 6–38, we find that as the gate voltage is reduced below V_T, the subthreshold current drops and then bottoms out at a level determined by the source/drain diode leakage. However, for even more negative gate biases we find that the off-state leakage current actually goes up as we try to turn off the MOSFET more for high V_D; this is known as *gate-induced drain leakage (GIDL)*. The same effect is seen at a fixed gate bias of near zero, for increasing drain bias. The reason for GIDL can be understood from Fig. 6–48, where we show the band diagram as a function of depth in the region where the gate overlaps the drain junction. As the gate is made more negative (or alternatively, for a fixed gate bias, the drain is made more positive), a depletion region forms in the n-type drain. Since the drain doping is high, the depletion widths tend to be narrow. If the band bending is more than the band gap E_g across a narrow depletion region, the conditions are conducive to band-to-band tunneling in this region, thereby creating EHPs. The electrons then go to the drain as GIDL. It must be emphasized that this tunneling is not through the gate oxide (Section 6.4.7), but entirely in the Si drain region. For GIDL to occur, the drain doping level should be moderate ($\sim 10^{18} \text{ cm}^{-3}$). If it is much lower than this, the depletion widths and tunneling barriers are too wide. On the other hand, if the doping in the drain is very high, most of the voltage drops in the gate oxide, and the band bending in the Si drain region drops below

Figure 6–48
Gate-induced
drain leakage in
MOSFETs. The
band diagram
for the location
shown in color
is plotted as a
function of depth
in the gate–drain
overlap region,
indicating band-
to-band tunneling
and creation of
electron–hole
pairs in the drain
region in the Si
substrate.

Figure 6–48
Gate-induced drain leakage in MOSFETs. The band diagram for the location shown in color is plotted as a function of depth in the gate–drain overlap region, indicating band-to-band tunneling and creation of electron–hole pairs in the drain region in the Si substrate.

the value E_g. GIDL is an important factor in limiting the off-state leakage current in state-of-the-art MOSFETs.

6.6 ADVANCED MOSFET STRUCTURES

6.6.1 Metal Gate-High-k

As described above, the Si MOSFET with thermally grown SiO_2 gate dielectric with its high-quality interface, and heavily doped polysilicon gate electrode has been the workhorse in this field for decades. However, due to the problems of tunneling leakage currents in ultra-thin SiO_2 gate dielectrics, in recent years there has been a shift to high-k gate dielectrics such as HfO_2 which can be made physically thicker without sacrificing gate capacitance, $C_i = \epsilon_i/d$. Generally, higher dielectric constant materials have lower band gaps than SiO_2. Hence, the band offsets in the conduction and valence bands may also be lower between these high-k gate dielectrics and Si. Thus, while the gate dielectric tunnel barriers may be wider, the heights of the barriers may be lower than for SiO_2 on Si. Another complication is that the electrical interfaces between the high-k dielectrics and Si are worse than between thermally grown SiO_2 and Si, leading to degraded channel mobilities. Hence, it is common to grow a thin interfacial SiO_2 layer between the high-k dielectric and the Si channel in order to recover the high effective channel mobilities.

A common technique for deposition of such high-k dielectrics is atomic layer deposition (ALD). Atomic layer deposition is a type of CVD where one alternately cycles in a self-limiting fashion between two types of gas precursors that are needed to grow the material. For instance, to grow hafnia (HfO_2), in one cycle we saturate the Si surface with a monolayer of a Hf-containing precursor, after which the precursor will not adsorb under the selected conditions of susbtrate temperature and gas pressure. We flush out the Hf precursor, and flow in the oxygen-containing precursor (H_2O) which will complete the growth of a monolayer of HfO_2. Then, we go to the next cycle by flushing out the H_2O, and flowing in the HF precursor. Thus, we achieve *digital* control over the layer thicknesses where the growth depends on the number of the growth cycles rather than the growth time, as in conventional CVD. Such control is particulary important for ultra-thin gate dielectrics.

In addition to a shift from SiO_2 to high-k dielectrics, there has been a shift from doped polysilicon gates to metal gates with appropriate work functions. As seen in Eq. (6–38), this can be used to engineer the flat band voltage, and thus the V_T of a MOSFET. This is sometimes referred to as gate work function engineering. It is interesting that in some ways, things have come full circle. The first MOSFETs were made with Al gates, which were supplanted by refractory polysilicon gates which could be patterned to form masks for the self-aligned source-drain implants and high temperature anneals. We have now gone back to metal gates, using refractory materials.

In some MOSFET fabrication flows, in order to be able to integrate the high-k dielectrics which cannot survive the high process temperatures of source-drain anneals, the source-drains are formed first with a *dummy*, sacrificial gate electrode. This gate electrode is then etched off, the high-k dielectric deposited, and the metal gate formed. Such processes have been dubbed the *gate-last* process.

In addition to engineering the gate stack, one must carefully design the source/drain junctions, the channel doping profile, and the contact metallurgy on the various electrodes to reduce resistance. Those details are discussed in Section 9.3.1.

6.6.2 Enhanced Channel Mobility Materials and Strained Si FETs

The HEMT described in Section 6.3.2 is capable of high-frequency operation and high drive currents because of the high carrier mobilities in the III–V channel. However, the device tends to suffer from high gate leakage currents and, therefore, low input impedance because of the use of Schottky gates which tend to be leakier than MOS gates. Unfortunately, high-quality native thermal oxides such as SiO_2 on Si cannot be grown on III–V materials. With the advent of deposited high-k gate dielectrics on Si MOSFETs, there was a similar move toward depositing high-k gate dielectrics on high electron mobility compound semiconductors such as InGaAs, to make III–V NMOSFETs with better performance than Si. Most III–V semiconductors unfortunately have low hole mobilties; hence, for PMOSFETs, Ge is a better choice since it has a hole mobility four times that of Si.

A more careful examination of the problem, however, reveals that the movement to high mobility channels may not always be justified. The drive current in a MOSFET can be somewhat simplistically considered to be proportional to the product of carrier density in the channel times the carrier velocity. The carrier velocity in these high mobility channel materials is expected to be higher than in Si because it is *inversely* proportional to the lower conductivity effective mass [Eq. (3–36)]. Unfortunately, the carrier density, which depends on the density of states in the channel, is *directly* proportional to the density-of-states effective mass in a 2-D system such as an inversion layer [Eq. (IV–10b) in Appendix IV]. Hence, there is a cancellation of the effective mass terms in the drive current expression. This is known as the *density-of-states bottleneck* in these high mobility channels. In addition, the highest doping densities in the source-drains of such high channel mobility materials are sometimes not as high as in Si, leading to higher source-drain access resistance. Finally, we find that many semiconductors with low effective mass have low band gaps. [Simplistically, this is because low effective masses are associated with high band curvature, which generally implies *wider* bands due to larger overlap of wavefunctions, and *lower band gaps.*] The low band gaps cause high off-state leakage currents in MOSFETs, which is particularly problematic for low power logic circuits. Nevertheless, a more detailed analysis shows that under some circumstances, these high channel mobility MOSFETs can indeed outperform Si.

Another approach to improving carrier mobilities is to introduce mechanical strain in the semiconductors. For instance, in Si if uniaxial *tensile* strain is introduced in *one* direction, or biaxial strain in two directions, in order to break the cubic symmetry of the unit cell, it breaks the six-fold degeneracy of the conduction band minima in the [100] directions near the X point (Fig. 3–10a). In bulk Si, for transport in any of the [100] directions, we get a contribution from two ellipsoidal valleys with high m_l, and four valleys with low m_t, as described in Example 3–6. Under biaxial tensile strain, there is a contraction of the planes in the third direction, and the two valleys in this direction are lowered in energy and are preferentially occupied. For transport in the plane of tensile strain, both these valleys have the lower transverse effective mass, m_t, leading to an enhancement of the electron mobility (Fig. 6–49). There is also reduced inter-valley scattering, leading to a higher scattering mean free time and higher mobility [Eq. (3–40a)]. Similar enhancements in hole mobility are achievable with *compressive* strain in Si.

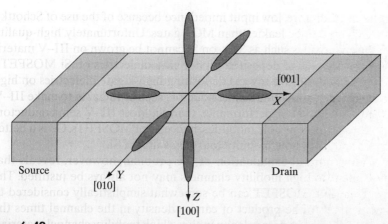

Figure 6–49
Energy ellipsoids in Si shown with respect to MOSFET made on (100) Si. Confinement by the inversion layer potential in the vertical direction lowers the two valleys in the Z-direction; tensile strain lowers them even more, reducing scattering between the valleys. Also, since these ellipsoids have the lower m_t in the transport direction from source-to-drain, there is enhancement of mobility and drain current.

These effects can be exploited in strained Si channels to enhance MOSFET drive currents, although there are additional complications due to carrier confinement in the inversion layers. One way to introduce biaxial tensile strain in Si is to epitaxially grow it on relaxed, larger lattice constant SiGe buffer layers grown on a Si substrate [see Fig. 1–14]. Alternatively, uni-axial tensile strain can introduced by judicious deposition of *stressor* layers of silicon nitride on the Si MOSFETs. Similarly, process-induced compressive strain is created in Si MOSFETs by etching trenches in the source-drain regions and re-filling them with larger lattice constant SiGe layers.

6.6.3   SOI MOSFETs and FinFETs

In the previous section, we discussed some of the problems, such as leakage due to punch-through, in short channel MOSFETs in bulk Si. It is also important to recognize that most of the current flow in the MOSFET is restricted to a thin layer comparable to the inversion layer thickness (~10 nm) near the surface, and most of the bulk Si substrate acts merely as mechanical support for the MOSFET, and has no electrical function whatsoever. These considerations led to the development of the Silicon-on-Insulator MOSFET (SOI MOSFET) shown in Fig. 6.50(a) made in a thin (~10 − 100 nm) Si single crystal film on an insulating Buried OXide (BOX) layer (~100 nm thick) on a bulk Si substrate.

Since SiO_2 can easily be grown on Si substrates, it serves as an attractive insulator for subsequent growth of thin-film Si. Since polycrystalline Si can be deposited directly over SiO_2, devices can be made in thin poly-Si films. However, to avoid grain boundaries and other defects typical of

Figure 6–50
(a) Silicon on
insulator. Both
n-channel and
p-channel
enhancement
transistors are
made in islands
of Si film on
the insulating
substrate. These
devices can be
interconnected
for CMOS
applications.
(b) FinFET and
comparison to
planar MOSFET;
(c) scanning
electron
micrograph
of multiple
fin 22 nm tri-gate
FETs connected
in parallel to
increase the
effective width
(Photograph
courtesy of Intel.).

polycrystalline material, a variety of techniques have been developed to grow single-crystal Si on oxide. For example, the oxide layer can be formed beneath the surface of a Si wafer by high-dose oxygen implantation. The thin Si layer remaining on the surface above the implanted oxide is usually about 0.1 μm thick, and can be used as the thin film for CMOS or other device fabrication. This process is called *separation by implantation of oxygen (SIMOX)*. In some cases a thicker Si film is grown epitaxially on the SIMOX wafer, using the thin Si crystalline layer over the oxide as a seed for the epitaxy. Another approach for making SOI is to place two oxidized Si wafers face to face, and thermally bond the oxide layers by high temperature annealing in a furnace. One of the wafers is then chemically etched back almost completely, leaving a fraction of a micron of single-crystal Si material on top of the SiO_2. This approach is known as *Bond-and-Etch-back* SOI (BE-SOI). Since it is challenging to etch off about 600 μm of Si and stop controllably so as to leave about a micron of Si, an initial p^+ implanted layer is often used to act as an etch stop near the end of the chemical etch. The chemical recipe that is used for etching Si has a much lower etch rate in a p^+ layer than in lightly doped Si. Another approach known as *Smart Cut* is a modification of BE-SOI using very high dose H implantation into one of the oxidized Si wafers, such that the peak of the H profile is about a micron below the Si surface. During the high temperature annealing step, the H atoms coalesce to form tiny H bubbles which cause a thin layer of Si to cleave off from the implanted wafer, leaving the Si layer bonded to the oxidized Si surface. This way, we do not have to chemically etch off one Si wafer for every BE-SOI wafer. If properly done, the cleaved-off Si wafer has a fairly smooth surface and can be reused.

Another suitable substrate for such devices is silicon-on-sapphire (SOS). Epitaxial Si films can be grown on crystalline sapphire (Al_2O_3) substrates by chemical vapor deposition (e.g., the pyrolysis of silane), with typical film thickness of about 1 μm. This is sometimes referred to as SOI-SOS (a term which can elicit a laugh in an otherwise serious discussion).

The thin SOI film can be patterned by standard photolithographic techniques into islands for each transistor, making electrical isolation of adjacent MOSFETs simpler than for bulk Si. Implantation of p^+ and n^+ areas into these islands for source and drain regions result in the MOS devices. Since the film is so thin, the source and drain regions can be made to extend entirely through the film to the insulating substrate. As a result, the junction capacitance is reduced to the very small capacitance associated with the sidewalls between the source/drain and the channel region. In addition, since interconnections between devices pass over the insulating substrate, the usual interconnection–Si substrate capacitance is reduced (along with the possibility of parasitic induced channels in the field between devices). These capacitance reductions improve considerably the high-frequency operation and power consumption of circuits using such devices.

The electrostatic behavior of the SOI MOSFET in saturation is improved, because the thinness of the channel layer means the gate exerts better control of the channel potential than the drain, compared to a bulk MOSFET. Therefore problems such as DIBL are reduced. Since the leakage paths in the bulk Si far from gate control are blocked by the BOX layer, the off-state leakage is lower in SOI MOSFETs, and the channel lengths can be controlled more aggressively. In *fully-depleted* extremely thin channel ($\sim$10 nm) SOI MOSFETs, where the channel depletion layer can extend throughout the SOI film under typical gate biases, it is possible to leave the channel undoped and still avoid punch-through, and achieve the required V_T by choosing the gate work function appropriately. Undoped channels have the advantage of having high carrier mobility due to reduced ionized impurity scattering, and less V_T variations. In a scaled bulk MOSFET, the total number of dopants in the channel, which is equal to the doping density times channel volume (= width $\times$ length $\times$ depletion width), is quite small and susceptible to statistical *dopant number fluctuations,* leading to V_T variability. An undoped channel SOI MOSFET avoids this problem.

As discussed, the top gate in an SOI MOSFET improves control of the channel potential compared to bulk devices and leads to better scalability. The electrostatic control can be improved further if multiple gates can be incorporated to control the channel potential. An elegant way to achieve this is to etch thin *fins* of height h and width w in the SOI film, deposit high-k gate dielectrics on the fins, pattern gates over them, and use the gate as a *self-aligned* mask to implant source-drains in the fin, adjacent to the gate (Fig. 6–50b). Notice that this a non-planar 3-D geometry of the MOSFET, where the channel is mostly on the two vertical sidewalls of the fins. The effective width of a so-called FinFET is $(2h + w)$ times the number of parallel fins. The two self-aligned gates on the sidewalls improve electrostatic control even more than a top-gated SOI MOSFET. Variations of the FinFET are known as multiple gate FETs (MuGFETs) or tri-gate FETs.

The SOI approach does not suffer from the latchup problem of bulk CMOS discussed in Chapter 9 because there is no p-n-p-n thyristor from the power supply to ground. For circuits requiring high speeds, low standby power due to the elimination of junction leakage to the substrate, and alphaparticle radiation (from cosmic rays and radioactive impurities) tolerance due to the elimination of the Si substrate, the extra expense of preparing SOI substrates is compensated by increased performance.

SUMMARY

6.1 *Three-terminal active* devices capable of *power gain* are key to the switching and amplification of electronic signals. The *input impedance* is (desirably) high for voltage-controlled FETs and low for current-controlled bipolar junction transistors. The power gain of the a-c signal comes from the d-c power supply. It is also desirable to have a high output impedance and a linear dependence of output current with respect to input voltage (or current).

6.2 Field effect devices such as the JFETs (or MESFETs and HEMTs) use a reverse-biased p-n junction (or Schottky diode) as a *gate* to control the undepleted part of a *channel* and thereby modulate the current flow between a *source* (*S*) of carriers and a *drain* (*D*) of carriers.

6.3 The *MOSFET* uses an oxide-isolated gate (MOS capacitor) that has a very high input impedance to modulate the barrier between *S* and *D* and to change the conductivity of the channel.

6.4 An enhancement-mode NMOSFET has a p-type channel between the n^+ source and the drain regions. At the *flat band conditions* (V_{FB}), there is no band bending as a function of depth in the channel. A gate bias more negative than V_{FB} causes exponentially more holes to be accumulated near the surface with band bending.

6.5 More positive gate voltages initially repel the majority carrier holes and create a *depletion* region. Then, above the *threshold voltage* (V_T), they attract minority carrier electrons near the surface and *invert* the surface, thereby forming a conductive channel between source and drain. PMOSFETs have the opposite polarities.

6.6 The V_T can be increased by increasing the channel doping and the gate oxide thickness (lower C_i). It is also affected by V_{FB}, which depends on the gate work function and oxide charges, and increases with substrate reverse bias (*body effect*) as well.

6.7 The overall MOS capacitance is the series combination of a fixed gate capacitance C_i and the voltage-dependent semiconductor capacitance in the channel. The inversion charge per unit area is approximately $C_i(V_G - V_T)$.

6.8 For long channel MOSFETs, initially I_D increases *linearly* with V_D, and then it *saturates* once the inversion channel is *pinched off* near the drain end.

6.9 There is a quadratic dependence of I_D on V_G for long channel MOSFETs. For *short channel* devices that operate in the *velocity-saturated region* or *source-injection regime*, the dependence of I_D on V_G is approximately linear.

6.10 For short L, $I_{Dsat.}$ often increases slightly with V_D due to various short channel effects, leading to a decrease of output impedance. Short channel effects include *drain-induced barrier lowering* (*DIBL*) and *charge sharing*, which leads to V_T *roll-off* with L.

6.11 There is some conduction below V_T, characterized by a subthreshold slope, that is a measure of the effectiveness of the MOSFET as a switch.

6.12 Conduction above V_T in the channel inversion region reflects an *effective channel mobility* lower than that in bulk due to *surface roughness scattering*, and increasingly so at higher V_G.

6.13 In highly scaled MOSFETs, there can be *gate-tunneling* leakage currents (mitigated by high-k dielectrics) and *hot electron* (and, to a lesser extent, hole) effects, mitigated by lower power supply voltages and lightly doped drains (*LDDs*). The resulting high-S/D parasitic series resistance is minimized by Self-Aligned siLICIDEs (*SALICIDE*), described in Chapter 9.

PROBLEMS

6.1 Assume the JFET shown in Fig. 6–6 is Si and has p^+ regions doped with 10^{18} acceptors/cm^3 and a channel with 10^{16} donors/cm^3. If the channel half-width a is 1 μm, compare V_P with V_0. What voltage V_{GD} is required to cause pinch-off when V_0 is included? With $V_G = -3$ V, at what value of V_D does the current saturate?

6.2 If the ratio $Z/L = 10$ for the JFET of Prob. 6.1, and $\mu_n = 1000$ cm^2/V-s, calculate $I_D(\text{sat.})$ for $V_G = 0, -2, -4$, and -6V. Plot $I_D(\text{sat.})$ vs. $V_D(\text{sat.})$.

6.3 For the JFET of Prob. 6.2, plot I_D vs. V_D for the same four values of V_G. Terminate each plot at the point of saturation.

6.4 Use Eqs. (6–9) and (6–10) to calculate and plot $I_D(V_D, V_G)$ at 300 K for a Si JFET with $a = 1000$ Å, $N_d = 7 \times 10^{17}$ cm^{-3}, $Z = 100$ μm, and $L = 5$ μm. Allow V_D to range from 0 to 5 V, and allow V_G to take on the values 0, $-1, -2, -3, -4$, and -5 V.

6.5 Use the field-dependent mobility expression to calculate and plot $I_D(V_D, V_G)$ for the Si JFET described in Prob. 6.4 for gate lengths of 0.25, 0.50, 1.0, 2.0, and 5.0 μm and a gate voltage of 0 V. The field-dependent mobility model of Eq. (8–12) takes the form

$$\mu(\mathscr{E}) = \frac{v_d}{\mathscr{E}} = \frac{\mu_0}{1 + (\mu\mathscr{E}/v_s)}$$

where μ_0 is the low-field mobility (as given in Fig. 3–23) and v_s is the saturation velocity (10^7 cm/s). Assume that $\mathscr{E} = V_D/L$, and assume that the drain current saturates when it reaches a maximum. Discuss the advantages of having a short gate length device.

6.6 Consider a n-channel JFET. Draw the transfer characteristics curve. Show that the drain current is independent of drain voltage after pinch off. If the donor concentration increases in the substrate, then how will it affect the drain current?

6.7 Show that the width of the depletion region in Fig. 6–15 is given by Eq. (6–30). Assume the carriers are completely swept out within W, as was done in Section 5.2.3.

6.8 Sketch the low and high-frequency behavior (and explain the difference) of an MOS capacitor with a high-k gate dielectric ($\epsilon_r = 25$) on an n-type semiconductor ($\epsilon_r = 10$, $n_i = 10^{13}$ cm^{-3}). Mark off the accumulation, depletion, inversion regions, and the approximate location of the flat band and threshold voltages. If the high-frequency capacitance is 250 nF/cm^2 in accumulation and 50 nF/cm^2 in inversion, calculate the dielectric thickness and the depletion width in inversion.

6.9 Sketch the low and high-frequency $C–V$ behavior (and explain any difference) of an MOS capacitor with a high-k gate dielectric ($\epsilon_r = 25$) on a p-type Si substrate doped at 10^{17} cm^{-3}. Label the accumulation, depletion, inversion regions. If the high-frequency capacitance is 2 μF/cm^2 in accumulation, calculate the dielectric thickness and the minimum high-frequency capacitance.

6.10 A CMOS capacitor with n$^+$ Poly Si as metal gate has 100 nm thick oxide (SiO$_2$) layer, 1.5×10^{16}/cm^3 substrate carrier density, 8×10^{-8} C/cm^2 oxide layer charge density, and -6×10^{-8} C/cm^2 depletion layer charge density. Find

(a) the oxide capacitance,

(b) the maximum depletion width,

(c) the modified work function.

[Given: ϵ_r (SiO$_2$) = 3.9, $\epsilon_0 = 8.854*10^{-14}$ F/cm]

6.11 An Al-gate p-channel MOS transistor is made on an n-type Si substrate with $N_d = 5 \times 10^{17}$ cm^{-3}. The SiO$_2$ thickness is 100 Å in the gate region, $\phi_{ms} = -0.15$V, and the effective interface charge Q_i is 5×10^{10} qC/cm^2. Find W_m, V_{FB}, and V_T. Sketch the $C–V$ curve for this device and give important numbers for the scale.

6.12 Use Eq. (6–50) to calculate and plot $I_D(V_D, V_G)$ at 300 K for an n-channel Si MOSFET with an oxide thickness $d = 200$ Å, a channel mobility $\bar{\mu}_n = 1000$ cm^2/V-s, $Z = 100$ μm, $L = 5$ μm, and N_a of 10^{14}, 10^{15}, 10^{16}, and 10^{17} cm^{-3}. Allow V_D to range from 0 to 5 V and allow V_G to take on values of 0, 1, 2, 3, 4, and 5 V. Assume that $Q_i = 5 \times 10^{11}$ q C/cm^2.

6.13 In Prob. 6.2, find the threshold voltage V_T for the MOS structure. How much AL has to be doped in the substrate in order to achieve 20% reduction in the present threshold voltage of the structure?

6.14 A MOS capacitor is made with n^+ Poly Si gate. Si substrate carrier density is $2 \times 10^{16}/\text{cm}^3$, and the oxide region thickness is 80 nm. Find the flat band voltage (V_{FB}) of the structure, where the oxide charge density is 2×10^9 C/cm² and $\phi_{ms} = -0.90$ V.

6.15 Redraw Figs. 6–12, 6–13, and 6–15 for the p-channel case (n-type substrate).

6.16 Calculate the V_T of an MOS capacitor where we deposit a high-k gate dielectric, HfO_2, whose relative dielectric constant is 25, on a *novel* p-type semiconductor whose electron affinity is 4 eV, band gap is 1.5 eV, relative dielectric constant is 10, and intrinsic carrier concentration is 10^{12} cm⁻³. The gate is made of a metal whose work function is 5 eV, gate oxide thickness is 100 Å, and N_A is 10^{18} cm⁻³ and that has a fixed oxide charge of 5×10^{10} q C/cm². At V_T, what are the electron and hole concentrations at the oxide–semiconductor interface and deep in the substrate? Sketch a labeled band diagram normal to the surface at V_T, and mark off the relevant values on the basis of the numbers given.

Sketch the *low- and high*-frequency C–V characteristics of this capacitor, and explain their differences. How would the characteristics change *at large negative gate bias* if we doubled the oxide thickness? How about if we doubled the substrate doping?

6.17 A Si MOS capacitor has the high-frequency C–V curve shown in Fig. P6–17 normalized to the capacitance in strong accumulation. Determine the oxide

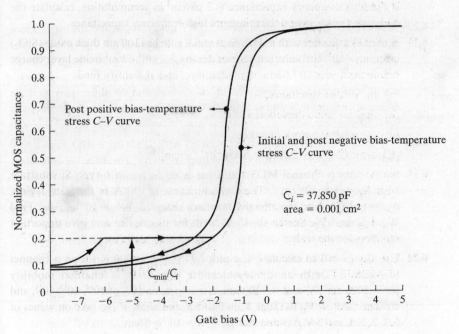

Figure P6–17

thickness and substrate doping assuming a gate-to-substrate work function difference of -0.35 V.

6.18 For the capacitor in Prob. 6.17, determine the initial flat band voltage.

6.19 For the capacitor in Prob. 6.17, determine the fixed oxide charge, Q_i, and the mobile ion content.

6.20 Sketch the cross section of a n-channel enhancement-mode Si MOSFET. It has a channel length of 2 μm, width of 5 μm, high-k gate dielectric of thickness 10 nm, with a relative dielectric constant of 25, and substrate doping of 10^{18} cm^{-3}. If the threshold voltage is 0.5 V, calculate the flat band voltage. For a gate bias of 3V, what is the *total* approximate inversion charge under the channel? Sketch the band diagram as a function of depth in the middle of the channel under this condition, specifying the value of the band edges to the Fermi level deep in the bulk and at the interface with the gate dielectric.

For a drain bias of 0.1 V, calculate the drain current. The mobility of electrons is 1000 cm^2/V-s and the effective mobility of holes is 200 cm^2/V-s. Repeat the calculation of drain current using a "charge control" approach by dividing the inversion charge by the transit time for carriers to go from source to drain.

6.21 Calculate V_T of a Si n-channel MOSFET with $\phi_{ms} = -0.25$ V, 100 nm gate oxide thickness, $N_A = 10^{17}$/cm^3, and oxide charge density 5×10^{18} C/cm^2 for a substrate bias of -2 V. $(QD = 6 \times 10^{-8}$ C/cm$^2)$ If the channel mobility is $\mu_n = 250$ cm^2/V-sec, then what will be the drive current for a 50-nm channel MOSFET with gate bias at 2 V working at saturation region? The length of the MOSFET is 2 μm.

6.22 A M-SiO$_2$-SI MOSFET turns on with 0.7 V gate voltage, and the capacitance generates 1 μF/cm^2. Calculate the overdrive voltage for $V_G = V_D = 3$ V when the channel length is 70 nm. Suppose in this structure the Fermi level is 0.365 eV below the intrinsic level in the substrate, and the substrate is doped with 2×10^{16}/cm^3 acceptor doping. Now, calculate the drain saturation current if the effective channel mobility is 550 cm^2/V-sec and carrier saturation velocity is 0.5×10^7 cm/sec.

6.23 A p-channel enhancement-mode MOSFET with 50 nm thick HfO$_2$ high-k gate dielectric $(\epsilon_r = 25)$ has a threshold voltage of -0.6V. The effective hole channel mobility is 150 cm^2/V-s. What is the drive current for a 50 μm wide and 2 μm long device at $V_G = -3$V and $V_D = -0.05$V? What is the saturation current at this gate bias? Sketch a cross section of the device schematically showing the inversion layer if gate and drain are both at -3V. Below that sketch qualitatively the variation of channel potential with position.

6.24 For a long channel nMOSFET with $V_T = 1$ V, calculate the V_G required for an I_D(sat.) of 0.1 mA and V_D(sat.) of 5 V. Calculate the small-signal output conductance g and the transconductance g_m(sat.) at $V_D = 10$ V. Sketch the cross section of this MOSFET, and schematically show the inversion charge and depletion charge distributions for $V_D = 1$ V, 5 V, and 10 V.

Recalculate the new I_D for $V_G - V_T = 3$ V and $V_D = 4$ V.

6.25 Calculate the V_T of a Si n-channel MOSFET for a gate-to-substrate work function difference $\phi_{ms} = -1.5$ eV, gate oxide thickness $= 100$ Å, $N_A = 10^{18}$ cm^{-3}, and fixed oxide charge of $5 \times 10^{10} q$ C/cm^2, for a substrate bias of -2.5 V. At V_T, what are the electron and hole concentrations at the oxide–Si interface and deep in the substrate? Sketch a labeled band diagram normal to the surface at V_T, showing the Fermi potential.

6.26 Calculate the V_T of a Si n-channel MOSFET for an n$^+$-polysilicon gate with gate oxide thickness = 100 Å, $N_a = 10^{18}$ cm^{-3}, and a fixed oxide charge of $5 \times 10^{10} q$ C/cm^2.

6.27 For a n-channel MOSFET with gate oxide thickness of 30 nm, threshold voltage of 0.7 V, $Z = 30$ μm, and length of the device is 0.9 μm, calculate the drain current for $V_G = 3$ V and $V_D = 0.2$ V. Assume that the electron channel mobility is 200 cm^2/V-sec, what will be the required drain current to drive the MOS in saturation region?

6.28 For the MOSFET characteristics shown in Fig. P6–28, calculate:

Figure P6–28

1. Linear V_T and k_N
2. Saturation V_T and k_N

   Assume channel mobility $\bar{\mu}_n = 500$ cm^2/V – s and $V_{FB} = 0$.

6.29 For Prob. 6.28, calculate the gate oxide thickness and substrate doping, either graphically or iteratively.

6.30 For a n-channel MOSFET with gate oxide thickness of 20 nm, calculate the required phosphorous (P ions/cm^2) to be doped to reduce the threshold voltage from 1.5 V to 1 V. If the P ion implantation takes place for 15 seconds with a beam current of amount 10^{-6} Amp, then what scan area will be covered by the implanted beam?

6.31 In Prob. 6.5, calculate the depletion charge (Q_D) and the threshold voltage (V_T). Now suppose a reverse bias of 0.4 V is applied between the substrate and the source, how will it affect the V_T due to evolved substrate bias effect?

6.32 Plot I_D vs. V_D with several values of V_G for a thin-oxide p-channel transistor with a 10-μm oxide and $V_T = -1.1$ V. Assume that I_D(sat.) remains constant beyond pinch-off. Assume that $\bar{\mu}_p = 200$ cm^2/V-s, and $Z = 10L$.

6.33 A typical figure of merit for high-frequency operation of MOS transistors is the cutoff frequency $f_c = g_m/2\pi C_G LZ$, where the gate capacitance C_G is essentially C_i over most of the voltage range. Express f_c above pinch-off in terms of materials parameters and device dimensions, and calculate f_c for the transistor of Prob. 6.32, with $L = 1$ μm.

6.34 When an MOS transistor is biased with $V_D > V_D$(sat.), the effective channel length is reduced by ΔL and the current I'_D is larger than I_D(sat.), as shown in Fig. 6–32. Assuming that the depleted region ΔL is described by an expression similar to Eq. (6–30) with $V_D - V_D$(sat.) for the voltage across ΔL, show that the conductance beyond saturation is

$$g'_D = \frac{\partial I'_D}{\partial V_D} = I_D(\text{sat.}) \frac{\partial}{\partial V_D}\left(\frac{L}{L - \Delta L}\right)$$

and find the expression for g'_D in terms of V_D.

6.35 From Fig. 6–44, it is clear that the depletion regions of the source and drain junctions can meet for short channels, a condition called *punch-through*. Assume that the source and drain regions of an n-channel Si MOSFET are doped with 10^{20} donors/cm^3 and the 1-μm-long channel is doped with 10^{16} acceptors/cm^3. If the source and substrate are grounded, what drain voltage will cause punch-through?

READING LIST   Very useful applets for understanding device operation are available at **https://nanohub.org/resources/animations**

Information about MOS devices used in integrated circuits can be found at **http://public.itrs.net/**

Hu, C. "Modern Semiconductor Devices for Integrated Circuits," available free online.

Kahng, D. "A Historical Perspective on the Development of MOS Transistors and Related Devices," *IEEE Trans. Elec. Dev.*, ED-23 (1976): 655.

Muller, R. S., and T. I. Kamins. *Device Electronics for Integrated Circuits.* New York: Wiley, 1986.

Neamen, D. A. *Semiconductor Physics and Devices: Basic Principles.* Homewood, IL: Irwin, 2003.

Pierret, R. F. *Field Effect Devices.* Reading, MA: Addison-Wesley, 1990.

Sah, C. T. "Characteristics of the Metal–Oxide Semiconductor Transistors," *IEEE Trans. Elec. Dev.,* ED-11 (1964): 324.

Sah, C. T. "Evolution of the MOS Transistor–From Conception to VLSI," *Proceedings of the IEEE* 76 (October 1988): 1280–1326.

Schroder, D. K. *Modular Series on Solid State Devices: Advanced MOS Devices.* Reading, MA: Addison-Wesley, 1987.

Shockley, W., and G. Pearson. "Modulation of Conductance of Thin Films of Semiconductors by Surface Charges," *Phys. Rev.* 74 (1948): 232.

Sze, S. M. *Physics of Semiconductor Devices.* New York: Wiley, 1981.

Taur, Y., and T.H. Ning. *Fundamentals of Modern VLSI Devices.* Cambridge: Cambridge Unversity Press, 1998.

Tsividis, Y. *Operation and Modeling of the MOS Transistor.* Boston: McGraw-Hill College, 1998.

SELF QUIZ

Question 1

(a) What is the main distinction between an active device and a passive device?

(b) If a device has power gain, where is the higher energy of the a-c signal at the output coming from?

(c) What is the distinction between a current-controlled vs. voltage-controlled three-terminal active device? Which is preferable?

Question 2

For parts (a) through (c) below, consider the following low-frequency gate capacitance (per unit area) vs. gate voltage characteristic for a metal gate n-channel MOSFET.

(a) On the below figure label the *approximate* regions or points of

- weak inversion (1)
- flat band (2)
- strong inversion (3)
- accumulation (4)
- threshold (5)
- depletion (6)

(b) What is the oxide capacitance per unit area?_____ $\mu F/cm^2$

(c) On the curve below, sketch the high-frequency curves for this MOSFET with grounded source/drain.

Question 3

Label—in the "answer" space provided *above* the figure—the following MOS capacitor band diagrams as corresponding to accumulation, weak inversion, depletion, strong inversion, flat band, or threshold. Use each possibility only once.

Question 4

Consider the following MOSFET characteristic.

(a) Is this an n-channel or p-channel device?

(b) Does this appear to be a long channel or short channel device?

(c) What is the apparent threshold voltage V_T?

(d) Is this a depletion-mode or enhancement-mode MOSFET?

Question 5

Is the subthreshold slope of a MOSFET decreased (improved) by:

(a) Increasing or decreasing the oxide thickness?

(b) Increasing or decreasing the substrate doping?

For each of these two methods, name one thing/factor/effect that limits the extent to which the method can be used to reduce subthreshold swing.

Question 6

Would increasing the device temperature increase, decrease, or leave unchanged (circle the correct answers):

(a) the reverse saturation current of a p-n diode?

increase / decrease / unchanged

(b) the subthreshold source-to-drain leakage current of MOSFET?

increase / decrease / unchanged

Question 7

Assuming no interface charge due to defects and/or traps, would decreasing the oxide thickness/increasing the oxide capacitance of an n-channel MOSFET *increase, decrease,* or leave essentially *unchanged* the following parameters (circle the correct answers):

(a) the flat band voltage, V_{FB}?

increase / decrease / unchanged

(b) the threshold voltage, V_T?

increase / decrease / unchanged

(c) the subthreshold slope?

increase / decrease / unchanged

Question 8

Consider the following MOSFET characteristic.

(a) What is the transconductance g_m at $V_D = -1.0$ V (in units of mhos)?
(b) What is the apparent threshold voltage at $V_D = -1.0$ V?
(c) Does this MOSFET appear to be a long channel or short channel device?
(d) Is this an n-channel or p-channel device?
(e) Is this a depletion-mode or enhancement-mode MOSFET?

Question 9

A senior in electrical and computer engineering in a device fabrication course presented the following characteristics as those of an n-channel MOSFET that he had fabricated and characterized at a temperature of 300 K.

(a) If we were to believe this student, would this be *normally on/depletion mode* or a *normally off/enhancement -mode* MOSFET? Circle one choice below.

normally off / normally on

(b) If we were to believe this student, would this MOSFET appear to be a *long channel* or *short channel* device? Circle one.

long channel / short channel

(c) If we were to believe this student, what would be the *subthreshold slope/swing*, *S*, of this MOSFET?

(d) This student, however, was subsequently expelled from the university for falsifying this data, leaving him with nothing to show for his years at school but huge college loan debts. What *clearly* physically unrealistic aspect of these MOSFET characteristics (besides less than smooth curves) should have drawn suspicion?

Question 10

Consider the mos system with the following parameters:

$Qms = -0.7$ v, $tox = 100$A, $Na = 1.4 \times 10^{15}$ cm^(−3), $Qox = 2.6 \times 10^{(-9)}$ c/cm

Determine the threshold voltage under 0 bias $T = 300$ K. Assume Eox and Esi.

Question 11

Calculate the drain current of an N-Mos transistor with the following parameters:

$$Bn = 60 \text{ uA/V2}, Vgs = 1.2 \text{ V}, Vds = 1.4 \text{ V}, Vt0 = 0.5 \text{ V}.$$

Question 12

Calculate the channel resistance of a transistor with the following specifications:

$$Bn = 65 \text{ uA/V2}, Vgs = 1 \text{ V}, Vt0 = 0.5 \text{ V}.$$

Question 13

Assuming full scalling calculate the current scale if as N-Mos transistor is scaled by a factor by 2. If $Bn = 45\text{uA/V2}, Vgs = 1 \text{ V}, Vds = 2 \text{ V}, Vt0 = 0.5 \text{ V}.$

Chapter 7

Bipolar Junction Transistors

OBJECTIVES

1. Analyze BJT band diagrams and understand current gain, base transport factor, and emitter injection efficiency
2. Discuss the Ebers–Moll coupled diode model, equivalent circuits, cutoff, saturation, and active regions
3. Develop the Gummel–Poon charge control model for second-order effects—Early effect, high-level injection
4. Study HBTs and other advanced BJTs

We begin this chapter with a qualitative discussion of charge transport in a *bipolar junction transistor (BJT)*, to establish a sound physical understanding of its operation. Then we shall investigate carefully the charge distributions in the transistor and relate the three terminal currents to the physical characteristics of the device. Our aim is to gain a solid understanding of the current flow and control of the transistor and to discover the most important secondary effects that influence its operation. We shall discuss the properties of the transistor with proper biasing for amplification and then consider the effects of more general biasing, as encountered in switching circuits.

In this chapter we shall use the p-n-p transistor for most illustrations. The main advantage of the p-n-p for discussing transistor action is that hole flow and current are in the same direction. This makes the various mechanisms of charge transport somewhat easier to visualize in a preliminary explanation. Once these basic ideas are established for the p-n-p device, it is simple to relate them to the more widely used transistor, the n-p-n.

The bipolar transistor is basically a simple device, and this section is devoted to a simple and largely qualitative view of BJT operation. We will deal with the details of these transistors in the following sections, but first we must define some terms and gain physical understanding of how carriers are transported through the device. Then we can discuss how the current through two terminals can be controlled by small changes in the current at a third terminal.

7.1 FUNDAMENTALS OF BJT OPERATION

Figure 7–1
External control
of the current in
a reverse-biased
p-n junction:
(a) optical
generation;
(b) junction *I–V*
characteristics as
a function of EHP
generation;
(c) minority
carrier injection
by a hypothetical
device.

(a) (b) (c)

Let us begin the discussion of bipolar transistors by considering the reverse-biased p-n junction diode of Fig. 7–1. According to the theory of Chapter 5, the reverse saturation current through this diode depends on the rate at which minority carriers are generated in the neighborhood of the junction. We found, for example, that the reverse current due to holes being swept from n to p is essentially independent of the size of the junction $\mathscr{E}$ field and hence is independent of the reverse bias. The reason given was that the hole current depends on how often minority holes are generated by EHP creation within a diffusion length of the junction—not upon how fast a particular hole is swept across the depletion layer by the field. As a result, it is possible to increase the reverse current through the diode by increasing the rate of EHP generation (Fig. 7–1b). One convenient method for accomplishing this is optical excitation of EHPs with light ($h\nu > E_g$), as in Section 4.3. With steady photoexcitation the reverse current will still be essentially independent of bias voltage, and if the dark saturation current is negligible, the reverse current is directly proportional to the optical generation rate g_{op}.

The example of external control of current through a junction by optical generation raises an interesting question: Is it possible to inject minority carriers into the neighborhood of the junction *electrically* instead of optically? If so, we could control the junction reverse current simply by varying the rate of minority carrier injection. For example, let us consider a hypothetical *hole injection device* as in Fig. 7–1c. If we can inject holes at a predetermined rate into the n side of the junction, the effect on the junction current will resemble the effects of optical generation. The current from n to p will depend on the hole injection rate and will be essentially independent of the bias voltage. There are several obvious advantages to such an external control of a current; for example, the current through the reverse-biased junction would vary very little if the load resistor R_L were changed, since the magnitude of the junction voltage is relatively unimportant. Therefore, such an arrangement should be a good approximation to a controllable constant current source.

A convenient hole injection device is a forward-biased p$^+$-n junction. According to Section 5.3.2, the current in such a junction is due primarily to holes injected from the p$^+$ region into the n material. If we make the n side

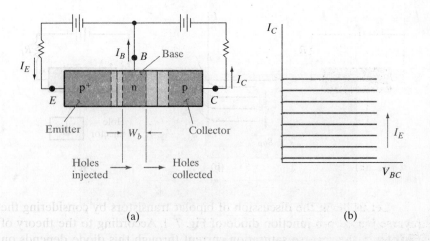

(a)   (b)

Figure 7-2
A p-n-p transistor: (a) schematic representation of a p-n-p device with a forward-biased emitter junction and a reverse-biased collector junction; (b) I–V characteristics of the reverse-biased n-p junction as a function of emitter current.

of the forward-biased junction the same as the n side of the reverse-biased junction, the p$^+$-n-p structure of Fig. 7–2 results. With this configuration, injection of holes from the p$^+$-n junction into the center n region supplies the minority carrier holes to participate in the reverse current through the n-p junction. Of course, it is important that the injected holes do not recombine in the n region before they can diffuse to the depletion layer of the reverse-biased junction. Thus we must make the n region narrow compared with a hole diffusion length.

The structure we have described is a p-n-p BJT. The forward-biased junction that injects holes into the center n region is called the *emitter junction*, and the reverse-biased junction that collects the injected holes is called the *collector junction*. The p$^+$ region, which serves as the source of injected holes, is called the *emitter*, and the p region into which the holes are swept by the reverse-biased junction is called the *collector*. The center n region is called the *base*, for reasons which will become clear in Section 7.3, when we discuss the historical development of transistor fabrication. The biasing arrangement in Fig. 7–2 is called the *common base* configuration, since the base electrode B is common to the emitter and collector circuits.

To have a good p-n-p transistor, we would prefer that almost all the holes injected by the emitter into the base be collected. Thus the n-type base region should be narrow, and the hole lifetime τ_p should be long. This requirement is summed up by specifying $W_b \ll L_p$, where W_b is the length of the *neutral* n material of the base (measured between the depletion regions of the emitter and collector junctions) and L_p is the diffusion length for holes in the base $(D_p\tau_p)^{1/2}$. With this requirement satisfied, an average hole injected at the emitter junction will diffuse to the depletion region of the collector junction without recombination in the base. A second requirement is that the current I_E crossing the emitter junction should be composed almost entirely of holes injected into the base, rather than electrons crossing from base to emitter. This requirement is satisfied by doping the base region lightly compared with the emitter, so that the p$^+$-n emitter junction of Fig. 7–2 results.

Figure 7–3
Summary of hole
and electron
flow in a p-n-p
transistor with
proper biasing:
(1) injected
holes lost to
recombination
in the base; (2)
holes reaching
the reverse-biased
collector junction;
(3) thermally
generated
electrons and
holes making
up the reverse
saturation
current of the
collector junction;
(4) electrons
supplied by the
base contact for
recombination
with holes;
(5) electrons
injected across the
forward-biased
emitter junction.

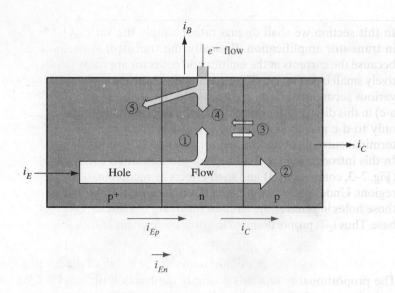

Figure 7–3
Summary of hole and electron flow in a p-n-p transistor with proper biasing: (1) injected holes lost to recombination in the base; (2) holes reaching the reverse-biased collector junction; (3) thermally generated electrons and holes making up the reverse saturation current of the collector junction; (4) electrons supplied by the base contact for recombination with holes; (5) electrons injected across the forward-biased emitter junction.

It is clear that current I_E flows into the emitter of a properly biased p-n-p transistor and that I_C flows out at the collector, since the direction of hole flow is from the emitter to collector. However, the base current I_B requires a bit more thought. In a good transistor the base current will be very small since I_E is essentially hole current, and the collected hole current I_C is almost equal to I_E. There must be some base current, however, due to requirements of electron flow into the n-type base region (Fig. 7–3). We can account for I_B physically by three dominant mechanisms:

(a)   There must be some recombination of injected holes with electrons in the base, even with $W_b \ll L_p$. The electrons lost to recombination must be resupplied through the base contact.

(b)   Some electrons will be injected from n to p in the forward-biased emitter junction, even if the emitter is heavily doped compared with the base. These electrons must also be supplied by I_B.

(c)   Some electrons are swept into the base at the reverse-biased collector junction due to thermal generation in the collector. This small current reduces I_B by supplying electrons to the base.

The dominant sources of the base current are (a) recombination in the base and (b) injection into the emitter region. Both of these effects can be greatly reduced by device design, as we shall see. In a well-designed transistor, I_B will be a very small fraction (perhaps one-hundredth) of I_E.

In an n-p-n transistor the three current directions are reversed, since electrons flow from the emitter to collector and holes must be supplied to the base. The physical mechanisms for operation of the n-p-n can be understood simply by reversing the roles of electrons and holes in the p-n-p discussion.

In this section we shall discuss rather simply the various factors involved in transistor amplification. Basically, the transistor is useful in amplifiers because the currents at the emitter and collector are controllable by the relatively small base current. The essential mechanisms are easy to understand if various secondary effects are neglected. We shall use total current (d-c plus a-c) in this discussion, with the understanding that the simple analysis applies only to d-c and to small-signal a-c at low frequencies. We can relate the terminal currents of the transistor i_E, i_B, and i_C by several important factors. In this introduction we shall neglect the saturation current at the collector (Fig. 7–3, component 3) and such effects as recombination in the transition regions. Under these assumptions, the collector current is made up entirely of those holes injected at the emitter, which are not lost to recombination in the base. Thus i_C is proportional to the hole component of the emitter current i_{Ep}:

$$i_C = Bi_{Ep} \tag{7–1}$$

The proportionality factor B is simply the fraction of injected holes which make it across the base to the collector; B is called the *base transport factor*. The total emitter current i_E is made up of the hole component i_{Ep} and the electron component i_{En}, due to electrons injected from the base to emitter (component 5 in Fig. 7–3). The *emitter injection efficiency* γ is

$$\gamma = \frac{i_{Ep}}{i_{En} + i_{Ep}} \tag{7–2}$$

For an efficient transistor we would like B and γ to be very near unity; that is, the emitter current should be due mostly to holes ($\gamma \simeq 1$), and most of the injected holes should eventually participate in the collector current ($B \simeq 1$). The relation between the collector and emitter currents is

$$\frac{i_C}{i_E} = \frac{Bi_{Ep}}{i_{En} + i_{Ep}} = B\gamma \equiv \alpha \tag{7–3}$$

The product $B\gamma$ is defined as the factor α, called the *current transfer ratio*, which represents the emitter-to-collector current amplification. There is no real amplification between these currents, since α is smaller than unity. On the other hand, the relation between i_C and i_B is more promising for amplification.

In accounting for the base current, we must include the rates at which electrons are lost from the base by injection across the emitter junction (i_{En}) and the rate of electron recombination with holes in the base. In each case, the lost electrons must be resupplied through the base current i_B. If the fraction of injected holes making it across the base *without* recombination is B, it follows that $(1-B)$ is the fraction *recombining* in the base. Thus the base current is

$$i_B = i_{En} + (1-B)i_{Ep} \tag{7–4}$$

neglecting the collector saturation current. The relation between the collector and base currents is found from Eqs. (7–1) and (7–4):

$$\frac{i_C}{i_B} = \frac{Bi_{Ep}}{i_{En} + (1 - B)i_{Ep}} = \frac{B[i_{Ep}/(i_{En} + i_{Ep})]}{1 - B[i_{Ep}/(i_{En} + i_{Ep})]} \tag{7–5}$$

$$\boxed{\frac{i_C}{i_B} = \frac{B\gamma}{1 - B\gamma} = \frac{\alpha}{1 - \alpha} \equiv \beta} \tag{7–6}$$

The factor β relating the collector current to the base current is the *base-to-collector current amplification factor*.[1] Since α is near unity, it is clear that β can be large for a good transistor, and the collector current is large compared with the base current.

It remains to be shown that the collector current i_C can be controlled by variations in the small current i_B. In the discussion to this point, we have indicated control of i_C by the emitter current i_E, with the base current characterized as a small side effect. In fact, we can show from space charge neutrality arguments that i_B can indeed be used to determine the magnitude of i_C. Let us consider the transistor of Fig. 7–4, in which i_B is determined by a biasing circuit. For simplicity, we shall assume unity emitter injection efficiency and negligible collector saturation current. Since the n-type base region is electrostatically neutral between the two transition regions, the presence of

Figure 7–4
Example of amplification in a common-emitter transistor circuit: (a) biasing circuit; (b) addition of an a-c variation of base current i_b to the d-c value of I_B, resulting in an a-c component i_c.

$\tau_p = 10 \ \mu s$

$\tau_t = 0.1 \ \mu s$

$\dfrac{i_C}{i_B} = \beta = \dfrac{\tau_p}{\tau_t} = 100$

Neglecting v_{BE}

$I_B = \dfrac{5 \ V}{50 \ k\Omega} = 0.1 \ mA$

$I_C = \beta I_B = 10 \ mA$

---

[1] α is also called the *common-base current gain*; β is also called the *common-emitter current gain*.

excess holes in transit from emitter to collector calls for compensating excess electrons from the base contact. However, there is an important difference in the times that electrons and holes spend in the base. The average excess hole spends a time τ_t, defined as the *transit time* from the emitter to collector. Since the base width W_b is made small compared with L_p, this transit time is much less than the average hole lifetime τ_p in the base.[2] On the other hand, an average excess electron supplied from the base contact spends τ_p seconds in the base supplying space charge neutrality during the lifetime of an average excess hole. While the average electron waits τ_p seconds for recombination, many individual holes can enter and leave the base region, each with an average transit time τ_t. In particular, for each electron entering from the base contact, τ_p/τ_t holes can pass from the emitter to collector while maintaining space charge neutrality. Thus the ratio of collector current to base current is simply

$$\frac{i_C}{i_B} = \beta = \frac{\tau_p}{\tau_t} \tag{7-7}$$

for $\gamma = 1$ and negligible collector saturation current.

If the electron supply to the base (i_B) is restricted, the traffic of holes from the emitter to base is correspondingly reduced. This can be argued simply by supposing that the hole injection does continue despite the restriction on electrons from the base contact. The result would be a net buildup of positive charge in the base and a loss of forward bias (and therefore a loss of hole injection) at the emitter junction. Clearly, the supply of electrons through i_B can be used to raise or lower the hole flow from emitter to collector.

The base current is controlled independently in Fig. 7–4. This is called a *common-emitter* circuit, since the emitter electrode is common to the base and collector circuits. The emitter junction is clearly forward biased by the battery in the base circuit. The voltage drop in the forward-biased emitter junction is small, however, so that almost all of the voltage from the collector to emitter appears across the reverse-biased collector junction. Since v_{BE} is small for the forward-biased junction, we can neglect it and approximate the base current as 5 V/50 kΩ = 0.1 mA. If τ_p = 10 µs and τ_t = 0.1 µs, β for the transistor is 100 and the collector current I_C is 10 mA. It is important to note that i_c is determined by β and the base current, rather than by the battery and resistor in the collector circuit (as long as these are of reasonable values to maintain a reverse-biased collector junction). In this example 5 V of the

---

[2]This difference between average hole lifetime before recombination (τ_p) and the average time a hole spends in transit across the base (τ_t) may be confusing at first. How can the lifetime be longer than the time a hole actually spends in transit? The answer depends on the fact that holes are indistinguishable in the recombination kinetics. Think of an analogy with a shooting gallery, in which a good marksman fires slowly at a line of quickly moving ducks. Although many individual ducks make it across the firing line without being hit, the lifetime of an *average* duck within the firing line is determined by the time between shots. We can speak of the lifetime of an average duck because they are essentially indistinguishable. Similarly, the rate of recombination in the base (and therefore i_B) depends on the average lifetime τ_p and the distribution of the indistinguishable holes in the base region.

collector circuit battery voltage appears across the 500 Ω resistor, and 5 V serves to reverse bias the collector junction.

If a small a-c current i_b is superimposed on the steady state base current of Fig. 7–4a, a corresponding a-c current i_c appears in the collector circuit. The time-varying portion of the collector current will be i_b multiplied by the factor β, and current gain results.

We have neglected a number of important properties of the transistor in this introductory discussion, and many of these properties will be treated in detail below. We have established, however, the fundamental basis of operation for the bipolar transistor and have indicated in a simplified way how it can be used to produce current gain in an electronic circuit.

EXAMPLE 7–1

(a) Show that Eq. (7–7) is valid from arguments of the steady state replacement of stored charge. Assume that $\tau_n = \tau_p$.

(b) What is the steady state charge $Q_n = Q_p$ due to excess electrons and holes in the neutral base region for the transistor of Fig. 7–4?

SOLUTION

(a) In steady state there are excess electrons and holes in the base. The charge in the electron distribution Q_n is replaced every τ_p seconds. Thus $i_B = Q_n/\tau_p$. The charge in the hole distribution Q_p is collected every τ_t seconds, and $i_C = Q_p/\tau_t$. For space charge neutrality, $Q_n = Q_p$, and

$$\frac{i_C}{i_B} = \frac{Q_n/\tau_t}{Q_n/\tau_p} = \frac{\tau_p}{\tau_t}$$

(b) $Q_n = Q_p = i_C\tau_t = i_B\tau_p = 10^{-9}\,\text{C}.$

7.3
BJT FABRICATION

The first transistor invented by Bardeen and Brattain in 1947 was the *point contact* transistor. In this device two sharp metal wires, or "cat's whiskers," formed an "emitter" of carriers and a "collector" of carriers. These wires were simply pressed onto a slab of Ge which provided a "base" or mechanical support, through which the injected carriers flowed. This basic invention rapidly led to the BJT, in which charge injection and collection was achieved using two p-n junctions in proximity to each other. The p-n junctions in BJTs can be formed in a variety of ways using thermal diffusion, but modern devices are generally made using ion implantation (Section 5.1.4).

Let us review a simplified version of how to make a double polysilicon, self-aligned n-p-n Si BJT. This is the most commonly used, state-of-the-art technique for making BJTs for use in an IC. Use of n-p-n transistors is more popular than p-n-p devices because of the higher mobility of electrons compared with holes. The process steps are shown in cross-sectional view in Fig. 7–5. A p-type Si substrate is oxidized, windows are defined using photolithography and etched in the oxide. Using the photoresist and oxide as an implant mask, a donor with very small diffusivity in Si, such as As or Sb, is implanted into the open window to form a highly conductive n^+ layer (Fig. 7–5a). Subsequently, the photoresist and the oxide are removed, and a lightly doped n-type epitaxial layer is grown. During this high temperature growth, the implanted n^+ layer diffuses only slightly toward the surface and becomes a conductive *buried collector* (also called a *sub-collector*). The n^+ sub-collector layer guarantees a low collector series resistance when it is connected subsequently to the collector ohmic contact, sometimes through the use of an optional, masked deep n^+ "sinker" implant or diffusion only in the collector contact region (Fig. 7–5c). The lightly doped n-type collector region above the n^+ sub-collector in the part of the BJT where the base and emitter are formed ensures a high base-collector reverse breakdown voltage. (It turns out that wherever the sub-collector is formed, and subsequently the epitaxial layer is grown on top, there is a notch or step in the substrate surface. This notch is not explicitly shown in Fig. 7–5a. This notch is very useful as a marker of the location of the sub-collectors because, subsequently, we have to align the LOCOS isolation mask with respect to the sub-collector.)

For integrated circuits involving not just discrete BJTs, but many interconnected transistors, there are issues involving electrical isolation of adjacent BJTs in order to ensure that there is no electrical cross-talk between them. As described in Section 6.4.1, such an isolation can be achieved by LOCOS to form field or isolation oxides after a B channel stops implant (Fig. 7–5b). Another isolation scheme that is particularly well suited for high-density bipolar circuits involves the formation of shallow trenches by reactive ion etching (RIE), backfilled with oxide and polysilicon (Section 9.3.1). In this process a nitride layer is patterned and used as an etch mask for an anisotropic etch of the silicon to form the trench. Using RIE, a narrow trench about 1 μm deep can be formed with very straight sidewalls. Oxidation inside the trench forms an insulating layer, and the trench is then filled with oxide by low-pressure chemical vapor deposition (LPCVD).

A polysilicon layer is deposited by LPCVD, and doped heavily p^+ with B either during deposition or subsequently by ion implantation. An oxide layer is deposited next by LPCVD. Using photolithography with the base/emitter mask, a window is etched in the polysilicon/oxide stack by RIE (Fig. 7–5c). A heavily doped "extrinsic" p^+ base is formed by diffusion of B from the doped polysilicon layer into the substrate in order to provide a low-resistance, high-speed base ohmic contact. An oxide layer is then deposited by LPCVD, which has the effect of closing up the base window that was etched previously, and B is implanted into this window (Fig. 7–5d). This base implant forms a more lightly p doped "intrinsic" base through which most of the current flows from the emitter to the collector. The more heavily doped extrinsic base forms a collar around the intrinsic base, and serves to reduce the base series resistance. It is critical that the base be enclosed

Bipolar Junction Transistors

Figure 7–5
Process flow
for double
polysilicon, self-
aligned n-p-n BJT:
(a) n^+ buried layer
formation; (b) n
epitaxy followed
by LOCOS
isolation; (c) base-
emitter window
definition and
(optional) masked
"sinker" implant
(P) into collector
contact region;
(d) intrinsic base
implant using
self-aligned oxide
sidewall spacers;
(e) self-aligned
formation of n^+
emitter, as well
as n^+ collector
contact.

well within the collector because otherwise it would be shorted to the p^- substrate. Finally, another LPCVD oxide layer is deposited to close up the base window further, and the oxide is etched all the way to the Si substrate by RIE, leaving oxide *spacers* on the sidewalls. Heavily n^+ doped (typically with As) polysilicon is then deposited on the substrate, patterned and etched, forming *polysilicon emitter (polyemitter)* and collector contacts, as shown in Fig. 7–5e. (The use of two LPCVD polysilicon layers explains why this process is referred to as the double-polysilicon process.) Arsenic from the polysilicon is diffused into the substrate to form the n^+ emitter region nested within the base in a *self-aligned* manner, as well as the n^+ collector contact. Self-alignment refers to the fact that a separate lithography step is not required to form the n^+ emitter region. We cleverly made use of the oxide sidewall spacers to ensure that the n^+ emitter region lies within the intrinsic p-type base. This is critical because otherwise the emitter gets shorted to the collector; we also want a gap between the n^+ emitter and the p^+ extrinsic base, because otherwise the emitter–base junction capacitance becomes too high. In the vertical direction, the difference between the emitter–base junction and the base–collector junction determines the base width. This is made very narrow in high gain, high speed BJTs.

Finally, an oxide layer is deposited by CVD, windows are etched in it corresponding to the emitter (E), base (B), and collector (C) contacts, and a suitable contact metal such as Al is sputter deposited to form the ohmic contacts. The Al is patterned photolithographically using the interconnect mask, and etched using RIE. The many ICs that are made simultaneously on the wafer are then separated into individual dies by sawing, mounted on suitable packages, and the various contacts are wire bonded to the external leads of the package.

In this section we examine the operation of a BJT in more detail. We begin our analysis by applying the techniques of previous chapters to the problem of hole injection into a narrow n-type base region. The mathematics is very similar to that used in the problem of the narrow base diode (Prob. 5.40). Basically, we assume holes are injected into the base at the forward-biased emitter, and these holes diffuse to the collector junction. The first step is to solve for the excess hole distribution in the base, and the second step is to evaluate the emitter and collector currents (I_E, I_C) from the gradient of the hole distribution on each side of the base. Then the base current (I_B) can be found from a current summation or from a charge control analysis of recombination in the base.

We shall at first simplify the calculations by making several assumptions:

1. Holes diffuse from the emitter to collector; drift is negligible in the base region.

2. The emitter current is made up entirely of holes; the emitter injection efficiency is $\gamma = 1$.

7.4 MINORITY CARRIER DISTRIBUTIONS AND TERMINAL CURRENTS

3. The collector saturation current is negligible.

4. The active part of the base and the two junctions are of uniform cross-sectional area A; current flow in the base is essentially one-dimensional from the emitter to collector.

5. All currents and voltages are steady state.

In later sections we shall consider the implications of imperfect injection efficiency, drift due to nonuniform doping in the base, structural effects such as different areas for the emitter and collector junctions, and capacitance and transit time effects in a-c operation.

7.4.1 Solution of the Diffusion Equation in the Base Region

Since the injected holes are assumed to flow from the emitter to collector by diffusion, we can evaluate the currents crossing the two junctions by techniques used in Chapter 5. Neglecting recombination in the two depletion regions, the hole current entering the base at the emitter junction is the current I_E, and the hole current leaving the base at the collector is I_C. If we can solve for the distribution of excess holes in the base region, it is simple to evaluate the gradient of the distribution at the two ends of the base to find the currents. We shall consider the simplified geometry of Fig. 7–6a, in which the base width is W_b between the two depletion regions, and the uniform cross-sectional area is A. In equilibrium, the Fermi level is flat, and the band diagram corresponds to that for two back-to-back p-n junctions. But, for a forward-biased emitter and a reverse-biased collector (normal active mode), the Fermi level splits up into quasi-Fermi levels, as shown in Fig. 7–6b. The barrier at the emitter–base junction is reduced by the forward bias, and that at the collector–base junction is increased by the reverse bias. The excess hole concentration at the edge of the emitter depletion region Δp_E and the corresponding concentration on the collector side of the base Δp_C are found from Eq. (5–29):

$$\Delta p_E = p_n(e^{qV_{EB}/kT} - 1) \tag{7–8a}$$

$$\Delta p_C = p_n(e^{qV_{CB}/kT} - 1) \tag{7–8b}$$

If the emitter junction is strongly forward biased ($V_{EB} \gg kT/q$) and the collector junction is strongly reverse biased ($V_{CB} \ll 0$), these excess concentrations simplify to

$$\Delta p_E \simeq p_n e^{qV_{EB}/kT} \tag{7–9a}$$

$$\Delta p_C \simeq -p_n \tag{7–9b}$$

We can solve for the excess hole concentration as a function of distance in the base $\delta p(x_n)$ using the proper boundary conditions in the diffusion equation, Eq. (4–34b):

$$\frac{d^2\delta p(x_n)}{dx_n^2} = \frac{\delta p(x_n)}{L_p^2} \tag{7–10}$$

Figure 7–6
(a) Simplified
p-n-p transistor
geometry used in
the calculations;
(b) a p-n-p
transistor at
equilibrium (flat
Fermi level) and
with normal active
bias. The quasi-
Fermi levels are
separated by the
applied voltage
times q.

The solution of this equation is

$$\delta p(x_n) = C_1 e^{x_n/L_p} + C_2 e^{-x_n/L_p} \qquad (7\text{--}11)$$

where L_p is the diffusion length of holes in the base region. Unlike the simple problem of injection into a long n region, we cannot eliminate one of the constants by assuming the excess holes disappear for large x_n. In fact, since $W_b \ll L_p$ in a properly designed transistor, most of the injected holes reach the collector at W_b. The solution is very similar to that of the narrow base diode problem. In this case the appropriate boundary conditions are

$$\delta p(x_n = 0) = C_1 + C_2 = \Delta p_E \qquad (7\text{–}12a)$$

$$\delta p(x_n = W_b) = C_1 e^{W_b/L_p} + C_2 e^{-W_b/L_p} = \Delta p_C \qquad (7\text{–}12b)$$

Solving for the parameters C_1 and C_2 we obtain

$$C_1 = \frac{\Delta p_C - \Delta p_E e^{-W_b/L_p}}{e^{W_b/L_p} - e^{-W_b/L_p}} \qquad (7\text{–}13a)$$

$$C_2 = \frac{\Delta p_E e^{W_b/L_p} - \Delta p_C}{e^{W_b/L_p} - e^{-W_b/L_p}} \qquad (7\text{–}13b)$$

These parameters applied to Eq. (7–11) give the full expression for the excess hole distribution in the base region. For example, if we assume that the collector junction is strongly reverse biased [Eq. (7–9b)] and the equilibrium hole concentration p_n is negligible compared with the injected concentration Δp_E, the excess hole distribution simplifies to

$$\delta p(x_n) = \Delta p_E \frac{e^{W_b/L_p} e^{-x_n/L_p} - e^{-W_b/L_p} e^{x_n/L_p}}{e^{W_b/L_p} - e^{-W_b/L_p}} \quad \text{(for } \Delta p_C \simeq 0) \qquad (7\text{–}14)$$

The various terms in Eq. (7–14) are sketched in Fig. 7–7a, and the corresponding excess hole distribution in the base region is demonstrated for a moderate value of W_b/L_p. Note that $\delta p(x_n)$ varies almost linearly between the emitter and collector junction depletion regions. As we shall see, the slight deviation from linearity of the distribution indicates the small value of I_B caused by recombination in the base region.

The minority carrier electron concentrations in the emitter and collector corresponding to a forward-biased emitter and reverse-biased collector are shown in Fig. 7–7b. Here, the excess electron concentration in the p$^+$ emitter is shown to decay exponentially to zero, corresponding to a *long* diode. This is because, at high emitter doping levels, the minority carrier electron diffusion length is often shorter than the thin emitter region. Otherwise, the narrow diode expressions must be used in the emitter region. For polyemitter structures, the carrier concentration profile is more complicated, as discussed later. The exact form of i_{En} and the emitter injection efficiency will therefore depend on these details.

7.4.2 Evaluation of the Terminal Currents

Having solved for the excess hole distribution in the base region, we can evaluate the emitter and collector currents from the gradient of the hole concentration at each depletion region edge. From Eq. (4–22b) we have

$$I_p(x_n) = -qAD_p \frac{d\delta p(x_n)}{dx_n} \qquad (7\text{–}15)$$

$$\delta p(x_n) = M_1 \Delta p_E e^{-x_n/L_p} - M_2 \Delta p_E e^{x_n/L_p}$$

where

$$M_1 = \frac{e^{W_b/L_p}}{e^{W_b/L_p} - e^{-W_b/L_p}}$$

$$M_2 = \frac{e^{-W_b/L_p}}{e^{W_b/L_p} - e^{-W_b/L_p}}$$

Figure 7-7
(a) Sketch of the terms in Eq. (7-14), illustrating the linearity of the hole distribution in the base region. In this example, $W_b/L_p = 1/2$. (b) Electron distributions in the emitter and collector.

This expression evaluated at $x_n = 0$ gives the hole component of the emitter current,

$$I_{Ep} = I_p(x_n = 0) = qA\frac{D_p}{L_p}(C_2 - C_1) \tag{7-16}$$

Similarly, if we neglect the electrons crossing from the collector to base in the collector reverse saturation current, I_C is made up entirely of holes entering the collector depletion region from the base. Evaluating Eq. (7–15) at $x_n = W_b$ we have the collector current

$$I_C = I_p(x_n = W_b) = qA\frac{D_p}{L_p}(C_2 e^{-W_b/L_p} - C_1 e^{W_b/L_p}) \qquad (7\text{–}17)$$

When the parameters C_1 and C_2 are substituted from Eqs. (7–13), the emitter and collector currents take a form that is most easily written in terms of hyperbolic functions:

$$I_{Ep} = qA\frac{D_p}{L_p}\left[\frac{\Delta p_E(e^{W_b/L_p} + e^{-W_b/L_p}) - 2\Delta p_C}{e^{W_b/L_p} - e^{-W_b/L_p}}\right]$$

$$I_{Ep} = qA\frac{D_p}{L_p}\left(\Delta p_E \operatorname{ctnh}\frac{W_b}{L_p} - \Delta p_C \operatorname{csch}\frac{W_b}{L_p}\right) \qquad (7\text{–}18a)$$

$$I_C = qA\frac{D_p}{L_p}\left(\Delta p_E \operatorname{csch}\frac{W_b}{L_p} - \Delta p_C \operatorname{ctnh}\frac{W_b}{L_p}\right) \qquad (7\text{–}18b)$$

Now we can obtain the value of I_B by a current summation, noting that the sum of the base and collector currents leaving the device must equal the emitter current entering. If $I_E \simeq I_{Ep}$ for $\gamma \simeq 1$,

$$I_B = I_E - I_C = qA\frac{D_p}{L_p}\left[(\Delta p_E + \Delta p_C)\left(\operatorname{ctnh}\frac{W_b}{L_p} - \operatorname{csch}\frac{W_b}{L_p}\right)\right]$$

$$I_B = qA\frac{D_p}{L_p}\left[(\Delta p_E + \Delta p_C)\tanh\frac{W_b}{2L_p}\right] \qquad (7\text{–}19)$$

By using the techniques of Chapter 5 we have evaluated the three terminal currents of the transistor in terms of the material parameters, the base width, and the excess concentrations Δp_E and Δp_C. Furthermore, since these excess concentrations are related in a straightforward way to the emitter and collector junction bias voltages by Eq. (7–8), it should be simple to evaluate the transistor performance under various biasing conditions. It is important to note here that Eqs. (7–18) and (7–19) are not restricted to the case of the usual transistor biasing. For example, Δp_c may be $-p_n$ for a strongly reverse-biased collector, or it may be a significant positive number if the collector is positively biased. The generality of these equations will be used in Section 7.5 in considering the application of transistors to switching circuits.

EXAMPLE 7–2 (a) Find the expression for the current I for the transistor connection shown if $\gamma = 1$.

(b) How does the current I divide between the base lead and the collector lead?

(a) Since $V_{CB} = 0$, Eq. (7–8b) gives $\Delta p_C = 0$. Thus from Eq. (7–18a),   **SOLUTION**

$$I_E = I = \frac{qAD_p}{L_p} \Delta p_E \, \text{ctnh} \, \frac{W_b}{L_p}$$

(b) $$I_C = \frac{qAD_p}{L_p} \Delta p_E \, \text{csch} \, \frac{W_b}{L_p}$$

$$I_B = \frac{qAD_p}{L_p} \Delta p_E \, \text{tanh} \, \frac{W_b}{2L_p}$$

where I_C and I_B are the components in the collector lead and base lead, respectively. Note that these results are analogous to those of Probs. 5.40 and 5.41 for the narrow base diode.

7.4.3 Approximations of the Terminal Currents

The general equations of the previous section can be simplified for the case of normal transistor biasing, and such a simplification allows us to gain insight into the current flow. For example, if the collector is reverse biased, $\Delta p_C = -p_n$ from Eq. (7–9b). Furthermore, if the equilibrium hole concentration p_n is small (Fig. 7–8a), we can neglect the terms involving Δp_C. For $\gamma \simeq 1$, the terminal currents reduce to those of Example 7–2:

$$I_E \simeq qA \frac{D_p}{L_p} \Delta p_E \, \text{ctnh} \, \frac{W_b}{L_p} \qquad (7\text{–}20a)$$

Figure 7–8
Approximate excess hole distributions in the base: (a) forward-biased emitter, reverse-biased collector; (b) triangular distribution for $V_{CB} = 0$ or for negligible p_n.

$$I_C \simeq qA\frac{D_p}{L_p}\Delta p_E \operatorname{csch}\frac{W_b}{L_p} \tag{7-20b}$$

$$I_B \simeq qA\frac{D_p}{L_p}\Delta p_E \tanh\frac{W_b}{2L_p} \tag{7-20c}$$

Series expansions of the hyperbolic functions are given in Table 7–1. For small values of W_b/L_p, we can neglect the terms above the first order of the argument. It is clear from this table and Eq. (7–20) that I_C is only slightly smaller than I_E, as expected. The first-order approximation of tanh y is simply y, so that the base current is

$$I_B \simeq qA\frac{D_p}{L_p}\Delta p_E \frac{W_b}{2L_p} = \frac{qAW_b\Delta p_E}{2\tau_p} \tag{7-21}$$

The same approximate expression for the base current is found from the difference in the first-order approximations to I_E and I_C:

$$I_B = I_E - I_C$$

$$\simeq qA\frac{D_p}{L_p}\Delta p_E\left[\left(\frac{1}{W_b/L_p}+\frac{W_b/L_p}{3}\right)-\left(\frac{1}{W_b/L_p}-\frac{W_b/L_p}{6}\right)\right] \tag{7-22}$$

$$\simeq \frac{qAD_pW_b\Delta p_E}{2L_p^2} = \frac{qAW_b\Delta p_E}{2\tau_p}$$

This expression for I_B accounts for recombination in the base region. We must include injection into the emitter in many BJT devices, as discussed in Section 7.4.4.

If recombination in the base dominates the base current, I_B can be obtained from the charge control model, assuming an essentially straight-line hole distribution in the base (Fig. 7–8b). Since the hole distribution diagram appears as a triangle in this approximation, we have

$$Q_p \simeq \tfrac{1}{2}qA\,\Delta p_E W_b \tag{7-23}$$

Table 7-1 Expansions of several pertinent hyperbolic functions.

$$\operatorname{sech} y = 1 - \frac{y^2}{2} + \frac{5y^4}{24} - \cdots$$

$$\operatorname{ctnh} y = \frac{1}{y} + \frac{y}{3} - \frac{y^3}{45} + \cdots$$

$$\operatorname{csch} y = \frac{1}{y} - \frac{y}{6} + \frac{7y^3}{360} - \cdots$$

$$\tanh y = y - \frac{y^3}{3} + \cdots$$

If we consider that this stored charge must be replaced every τ_p seconds and relate the recombination rate to the rate at which electrons are supplied by the base current, I_B becomes

$$I_B \simeq \frac{Q_p}{\tau_p} = \frac{qAW_b\Delta p_E}{2\tau_p} \qquad (7\text{-}24)$$

which is the same as that found in Eqs. (7–21) and (7–22).

Since we have neglected the collector saturation current and have assumed $\gamma = 1$ in these approximations, the difference between I_E and I_C is accounted for by the requirements of recombination in the base. In Eq. (7–24) we have a clear demonstration that the base current is reduced for small W_b and large τ_p. We can increase τ_p by using light doping in the base region, which of course also improves the emitter injection efficiency.

The straight-line approximation of the excess hole distribution (Fig. 7–8) is fairly accurate in calculating the base current. On the other hand, it does not give a valid picture of I_E and I_C. If the distribution were perfectly straight, the slope would be the same at each end of the base region. This would imply zero base current, which is not the case. There must be some "droop" to the distribution, as in the more accurate curve of Fig. 7–7. This slight deviation from linearity gives a steeper slope at $x_n = 0$ than at $x_n = W_b$, and the value of I_E is larger than I_C by the amount I_B. The reason we can use the straight-line approximation in the charge control calculation of base current is that the area under the hole distribution curve is essentially the same in the two cases.

7.4.4 Current Transfer Ratio

The value of I_E calculated thus far in this section is more properly designated I_{Ep}, since we have assumed that $\gamma = 1$ (the emitter current due entirely to hole injection). Actually, there is always some electron injection across the forward-biased emitter junction in a real transistor, and this effect is important in calculating the current transfer ratio. As shown in Example 7–3, the emitter injection efficiency of a p-n-p transistor can be written in terms of the emitter and base properties:

$$\gamma = \left[1 + \frac{L_p^n n_n \mu_n^p}{L_n^p p_p \mu_p^n} \tanh \frac{W_b}{L_p^n}\right]^{-1} \simeq \left[1 + \frac{W_b n_n \mu_n^p}{L_n^p p_p \mu_p^n}\right]^{-1} \qquad (7\text{-}25)$$

In this equation we use superscripts to indicate which side of the emitter–base junction is referred to. For example, L_p^n is the hole diffusion length in the n-type base region and μ_n^p is the electron mobility in the p-type emitter region. In an n-p-n the superscripts and subscripts would be changed along with the majority carrier symbols. Using Eq. (7–20a) for I_{Ep}, and Eq. (7–20b) for I_C, the base transport factor B is

$$B = \frac{I_C}{I_{Ep}} = \frac{\text{csch } W_b/L_p}{\text{ctnh } W_b/L_p} = \text{sech } \frac{W_b}{L_p} \qquad (7\text{-}26)$$

and the current transfer ratio α is the product of B and γ as in Eq. (7–3).

EXAMPLE 7-3   Extend Eq. (7–20a) to include the effects of nonunity emitter injection efficiency ($\gamma < 1$). Derive Eq. (7–25) for γ. Assume that the emitter region is long compared with an electron diffusion length.

SOLUTION   Equation (7–20a) is actually I_{Ep}.

$$I_{En} = \frac{qAD_n^p}{L_n^p} n_p e^{qV_{EB}/kT} \text{ for } V_{EB} \gg kT/q$$

Thus, the total emitter current is

$$I_E = I_{Ep} + I_{En} = qA\left[\frac{D_p^n}{L_p^n}p_n \text{ ctnh } \frac{W_b}{L_p^n} + \frac{D_n^n}{L_p^n}n_p\right]e^{qV_{EB}/kT}$$

$$\gamma = \frac{I_{Ep}}{I_E} = \left[1 + \frac{I_{En}}{I_{Ep}}\right]^{-1} = \left[1 + \frac{\frac{D_n^p}{L_n^p}n_p}{\frac{D_p^n}{L_p^n}p_n} \tanh \frac{W_b}{L_p^n}\right]^{-1}$$

Using $\dfrac{n_p}{p_n} = \dfrac{n_n}{p_p}$, $\dfrac{D_n^p}{D_p^n} = \dfrac{\mu_n^p}{\mu_p^n}$, and $\dfrac{D}{\mu} = \dfrac{kT}{q}$ yields

$$\gamma = \left[1 + \frac{L_p^n n_n \mu_n^p}{L_n^p p_p \mu_p^n} \tanh \frac{W_b}{L_p^n}\right]^{-1}$$

Since we have assumed that the emitter is long compared with the electron diffusion length in the emitter, the long-diode expression applies to I_{En}. On the other hand, for a very narrow emitter width W_e, L_n^p would be replaced by W_e, corresponding to the narrow-diode expression.

**7.5
GENERALIZED
BIASING**

The expressions derived in Section 7.4 describe the terminal currents of the transistor, if the device geometry and other factors are consistent with the assumptions. Real transistors may deviate from these approximations, as we shall see in Section 7.7. The collector and emitter junctions may differ in area, saturation current, and other parameters, so that the proper description of the terminal currents may be more complicated than Eqs. (7–18) and (7–19) suggest. For example, if the roles of the emitter and collector are reversed, these equations predict that the behavior of the transistor is symmetrical. Real transistors, on the other hand, are generally not symmetrical between emitter and collector. This is a particularly important consideration when the transistor is not biased in the usual way. We have discussed normal biasing (sometimes called the *normal active* mode), in which the emitter junction is forward biased and the collector is reverse biased. In some applications, particularly in switching, this normal biasing rule is violated. In these cases it is important to account for the differences in injection and collection properties of the two junctions. In this section we shall develop a generalized approach which accounts for transistor operation in terms of a coupled-diode model, valid for all combinations of emitter and collector bias. This model involves four measurable parameters that can be related to the geometry and material properties of the device. Using this model in conjunction with the charge control approach, we can describe the physical operation of a transistor in switching circuits and in other applications.

7.5.1 The Coupled-Diode Model

If the collector junction of a transistor is forward biased, we cannot neglect Δp_C; instead, we must use a more general hole distribution in the base region. Fig. 7–9a illustrates a situation in which the emitter and collector junctions are both forward biased, so that Δp_E and Δp_C are positive numbers. We can handle this situation with Eqs. (7–18) and (7–19) for the symmetrical transistor. It is interesting to note that these equations can be considered as linear superpositions of the effects of injection by each junction. For example, the straight line hole distribution of Fig. 7–9a can be broken into the two components of Figs. 7–9b and c. One component (Fig. 7–9b) accounts for the holes injected by the emitter and collected by the collector. We can call the resulting currents (I_{EN} and I_{CN}) the *normal mode* components, since they are due to injection from emitter to collector. The component of the hole distribution illustrated by Fig. 7–9c results in currents I_{EI} and I_{CI}, which describe injection in the *inverted mode* of injection from collector to emitter.[3] Of course, these inverted components will be negative, since they account for hole flow opposite to our original definitions of I_E and I_C.

    For the symmetrical transistor, these various components are described by Eqs. (7–18). Defining $a \equiv (qAD_p/L_p)\,\mathrm{ctnh}\,(W_b/L_p)$ and $b \equiv (qAD_p/L_p)\,\mathrm{csch}\,(W_b/L_p)$, we have

$$I_{EN} = a\Delta p_E \quad \text{and} \quad I_{CN} = b\Delta p_E \quad \text{with } \Delta p_C = 0 \qquad (7\text{–}27a)$$

$$I_{EI} = -b\Delta p_C \quad \text{and} \quad I_{CI} = -a\Delta p_C \quad \text{with } \Delta p_E = 0 \qquad (7\text{–}27b)$$

(a)   (b)   (c)

Figure 7–9
Evaluation of a hole distribution in terms of components due to normal and inverted modes: (a) approximate hole distribution in the base with emitter and collector junctions forward biased; (b) component due to injection and collection in the normal mode; (c) component due to the inverted mode.

---

[3]Here the words *emitter* and *collector* refer to physical regions of the device rather than to the functions of injection and collection of holes.

The four components are combined by linear superposition in Eq. (7–18):

$$I_E = I_{EN} + I_{EI} = a\Delta p_E - b\Delta p_C \tag{7–28a}$$
$$= A(e^{qV_{EB}/kT} - 1) - B(e^{qV_{CB}/kT} - 1)$$

$$I_C = I_{CN} + I_{CI} = b\Delta p_E - a\Delta p_C \tag{7–28b}$$
$$= B(e^{qV_{EB}/kT} - 1) - A(e^{qV_{CB}/kT} - 1)$$

where $A \equiv ap_n$ and $B \equiv bp_n$.

We can see from these equations that a linear superposition of the normal and inverted components does give the result we derived previously for the symmetrical transistor. To be more general, however, we must relate the four components of current by factors which allow for asymmetry in the two junctions. For example, the emitter current in the normal mode can be written

$$I_{EN} = I_{ES}(e^{qV_{EB}/kT} - 1), \quad \Delta p_C = 0 \tag{7–29}$$

where I_{ES} is the magnitude of the emitter saturation current in the normal mode. Since we specify $\Delta p_C = 0$ in this mode, we imply that $V_{CB} = 0$ in Eq. (7–8b). Thus we shall consider I_{ES} to be the magnitude of the emitter saturation current with the collector junction short circuited. Similarly, the collector current in the inverted mode is

$$I_{CI} = -I_{CS}(e^{qV_{CB}/kT} - 1), \quad \Delta p_E = 0 \tag{7–30}$$

where I_{CS} is the magnitude of the collector saturation current with $V_{EB} = 0$. As before, the minus sign associated with I_{CI} simply means that in the inverted mode holes are injected opposite to the defined direction of I_C.

The corresponding collected currents for each mode of operation can be written by defining a new α for each case:

$$I_{CN} = \alpha_N I_{EN} = \alpha_N I_{ES}(e^{qV_{EB}/kT} - 1) \tag{7–31a}$$
$$I_{EI} = \alpha_I I_{CI} = -\alpha_I I_{CS}(e^{qV_{CB}/kT} - 1) \tag{7–31b}$$

where α_N and α_I are the ratios of collected current to injected current in each mode. We notice that in the inverted mode the injected current is I_{CI} and the collected current is I_{EI}.

The total current can again be obtained by superposition of the components:

$$I_E = I_{EN} + I_{EI} = I_{ES}(e^{qV_{EB}/kT} - 1) - \alpha_I I_{CS}(e^{qV_{CB}/kT} - 1) \tag{7–32a}$$
$$I_C = I_{CN} + I_{CI} = \alpha_N I_{ES}(e^{qV_{EB}/kT} - 1) - I_{CS}(e^{qV_{CB}/kT} - 1) \tag{7–32b}$$

These relations were derived by J. J. Ebers and J. L. Moll and are referred to as the *Ebers–Moll equations*.[4] While the general form is the same

---

[4] J. J. Ebers and J. L. Moll, "Large-Signal Behavior of Junction Transistors," *Proceedings of the IRE*, 42, pp. 1761–72 (December 1954). In the original paper and in many texts, the terminal currents are all defined as flowing *into* the transistor. This introduces minus signs into the expressions for I_C and I_B as we have developed them here.

as Eqs. (7–28) for the symmetrical transistor, these equations allow for variations in I_{ES}, I_{CS}, α_I, and α_N due to asymmetry between the junctions. Although we shall not prove it here, it is possible to show by reciprocity arguments that

$$\alpha_N I_{ES} = \alpha_I I_{CS} \qquad (7–33)$$

even for nonsymmetrical transistors.

An interesting feature of the Ebers–Moll equations is that I_E and I_C are described by terms resembling diode relations (I_{EN} and I_{CI}), plus terms that provide coupling between the properties of the emitter and collector (I_{EI} and I_{CN}). This *coupled-diode* property is illustrated by the equivalent circuit of Fig. 7–10. In this figure we take advantage of Eq. (7–8) to write the Ebers–Moll equations in the form

$$I_E = I_{ES}\frac{\Delta p_E}{p_n} - \alpha_I I_{CS}\frac{\Delta p_C}{p_n} = \frac{I_{ES}}{p_n}(\Delta p_E - \alpha_N \Delta p_C) \qquad (7–34a)$$

$$I_C = \alpha_N I_{ES}\frac{\Delta p_E}{p_n} - I_{CS}\frac{\Delta p_C}{p_n} = \frac{I_{CS}}{p_n}(\alpha_I \Delta p_E - \Delta p_C) \qquad (7–34b)$$

It is often useful to relate the terminal currents to each other as well as to the saturation currents. We can eliminate the saturation current from the coupling term in each part of Eqs. (7–32). For example, by multiplying Eq. (7–32a) by α_N and subtracting the resulting expression from Eq. (7–32b), we have

$$I_C = \alpha_N I_E - (1 - \alpha_N \alpha_I)I_{CS}(e^{qV_{CB}/kT} - 1) \qquad (7–35)$$

Similarly, the emitter current can be written in terms of the collector current:

$$I_E = \alpha_I I_C + (1 - \alpha_N \alpha_I)I_{ES}(e^{qV_{EB}/kT} - 1) \qquad (7–36)$$

The terms $(1 - \alpha_N \alpha_I)I_{CS}$ and $(1 - \alpha_N \alpha_I)I_{ES}$ can be abbreviated as I_{CO} and I_{EO}, respectively, where I_{CO} is the magnitude of the collector saturation current with the emitter junction *open* ($I_E = 0$) and I_{EO} is the magnitude of the

$$I_B = (1 - \alpha_N)I_{ES}\frac{\Delta p_E}{p_n} + (1 - \alpha_I)I_{CS}\frac{\Delta p_C}{p_n}$$

Figure 7–10
An equivalent circuit synthesizing the Ebers–Moll equations.

Figure 7–11
Equivalent circuits
of the transistor
in terms of the
terminal currents
and the open-
circuit saturation
currents:
(a) synthesis of
Eqs. (7–37);
(b) equivalent
circuit with
normal biasing;
(c) collector
characteristics
with normal
biasing.

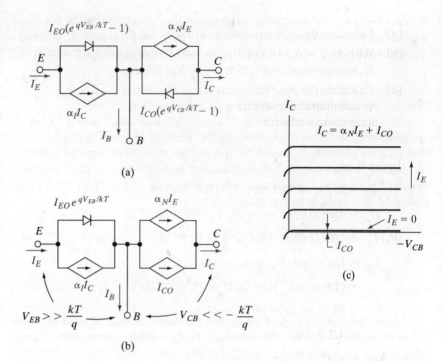

Figure 7–11
Equivalent circuits
of the transistor
in terms of the
terminal currents
and the open-
circuit saturation
currents:
(a) synthesis of
Eqs. (7–37);
(b) equivalent
circuit with
normal biasing;
(c) collector
characteristics
with normal
biasing.

emitter saturation current with the collector junction open. The Ebers–Moll equations then become

$$I_E = \alpha_I I_C + I_{EO}(e^{qV_{EB}/kT} - 1) \tag{7-37a}$$

$$I_C = \alpha_N I_E - I_{CO}(e^{qV_{CB}/kT} - 1) \tag{7-37b}$$

and the equivalent circuit is shown in Fig. 7–11a. In this form the equations describe both the emitter and collector currents in terms of a simple diode characteristic plus a current generator proportional to the other current. For example, under normal biasing the equivalent circuit reduces to the form shown in Fig. 7–11b. The collector current is α_N times the emitter current plus the collector saturation current, as expected. The resulting collector characteristics of the transistor appear as a series of reverse-biased diode curves, displaced by increments proportional to the emitter current (Fig. 7–11c).

EXAMPLE 7–4   A symmetrical p^+-n-p^+ bipolar transistor has the following properties:

	Emitter	Base
$A = 10^{-4}\,cm^2$	$N_a = 10^{17}$	$N_d = 10^{15}\,cm^{-3}$
$W_b = 1\,\mu m$	$\tau_n = 0.1\,\mu s$	$\tau_p = 10\,\mu s$
	$\mu_p = 200$	$\mu_n = 1300\,cm^2/V\text{-}s$
	$\mu_n = 700$	$\mu_p = 450\,cm^2/V\text{-}s$

(a) Calculate the saturation current $I_{ES} = I_{CS}$.

(b) With $V_{EB} = 0.3$ V and $V_{CB} = -40$ V, calculate the base current I_B, assuming perfect emitter injection efficiency.

(c) Calculate the base transport factor B, emitter injection efficiency γ, and amplification factor β, assuming that the emitter region is long compared with L_n.

In the base, **SOLUTION**

$$p_n = n_i^2/n_n = (1.5 \times 10^{10})^2/10^{15} = 2.25 \times 10^5$$

$$D_p = 450(0.0259) = 11.66, L_p = (11.66 \times 10^{-5})^{1/2} = 1.08 \times 10^{-2}$$

$$W_b/L_p = 10^{-4}/1.08 \times 10^{-2} = 9.26 \times 10^{-3}$$

$$\begin{aligned} I_{ES} = I_{CS} &= qA(D_p/L_p)p_n \, \text{ctnh}(W_b/L_p) \\ &= (1.6 \times 10^{-19})(10^{-4})(11.66/1.08 \times 10^{-2}) \\ &\quad (2.25 \times 10^5) \, \text{ctnh} \, 9.26 \times 10^{-3} \\ &= 4.2 \times 10^{-13} \text{ A} \end{aligned}$$

$$\Delta p_E = p_n e^{qV_{EB}/kT}, \Delta p_C \approx 0$$

$$\Delta p_E = 2.25 \times 10^5 \times e^{(0.3/0.0259)} = 2.4 \times 10^{10}$$

$$I_B = qA(D_p/L_p)\Delta p_E \tanh(W_b/2L_p)$$

or

$$I_B = \frac{Q_b}{\tau_p} = qAW_b\Delta p_E/2\tau_p = \mathbf{1.9 \times 10^{-12} \text{ A}}$$

In the emitter,

$$D_n = 700(0.0259) = 18.13$$

$$L_n = (18.13 \times 10^{-7})^{1/2} = 1.35 \times 10^{-3}$$

$$I_{En} = \frac{qAD_n^E}{L_n^E}n_p^E e^{qV_{EB}/kT}$$

$$I_{Ep} = \frac{qAD_p^B}{L_p^B}p_n^B \, \text{ctnh}\frac{W_b}{L_p^B}e^{qV_{EB}/kT}$$

$$\gamma = \frac{I_{Ep}}{I_{En} + I_{Ep}} = \left[1 + \frac{I_{En}}{I_{Ep}}\right]^{-1}$$

$$\gamma = \left[1 + \frac{D_n^E/L_n^E \, n_p^E}{D_p^B/L_p^B \, n_n^B} \tanh \frac{W_b}{L_p}\right]^{-1} \qquad \left(\text{use } \frac{n_p^E}{p_n^B} = \frac{n_n^B}{p_p^E}\right)$$

$$= \left[1 + \frac{18.13 \times 1.08 \times 10^{-2} \times 10^{15}}{11.66 \times 1.35 \times 10^{-3} \times 10^{17}} \tanh 9.26 \times 10^{-3}\right]^{-1} = \mathbf{0.99885}$$

$$B = \text{sech}\frac{W_b}{L_p} = \text{sech } 9.26 \times 10^{-3} = \mathbf{0.99996}$$

$$\alpha = B\gamma = (0.99885)(0.99996) = \mathbf{0.9988}$$

$$\beta = \frac{\alpha}{1 - \alpha} = \frac{0.9988}{0.0012} = \mathbf{832}$$

7.5.2 Charge Control Analysis

The charge control approach is useful in analyzing the transistor terminal currents, particularly in a-c applications. Considerations of transit time effects and charge storage are revealed easily by this method. Following the techniques of the previous section, we can separate an arbitrary excess hole distribution in the base into the normal and inverted distributions of Fig. 7–9. The charge stored in the normal distribution will be called Q_N and the charge under the inverted distribution will be called Q_I. Then we can evaluate the currents for the normal and inverted modes in terms of these stored charges. For example, the collected current in the normal mode I_{CN} is simply the charge Q_N divided by the mean time required for this charge to be collected. This time is the transit time for the normal mode τ_{tN}. On the other hand, the emitter current must support not only the rate of charge collection by the collector but also the recombination rate in the base Q_N/τ_{pN}. Here we use a subscript N with the transit time and lifetime in the normal mode in contrast to the inverted mode, to allow for possible asymmetries due to imbalance in the transistor structure. With these definitions, the normal components of current become

$$I_{CN} = \frac{Q_N}{\tau_{tN}}, \quad I_{EN} = \frac{Q_N}{\tau_{tN}} + \frac{Q_N}{\tau_{pN}} \qquad (7\text{--}38a)$$

Similarly, the inverted components are

$$I_{EI} = -\frac{Q_I}{\tau_{tI}}, \quad I_{CI} = -\frac{Q_I}{\tau_{tI}} - \frac{Q_I}{\tau_{pI}} \qquad (7\text{--}38b)$$

where the I subscripts on the stored charge and on the transit and recombination times designate the inverted mode. Combining these equations as in Eqs. (7–32) we have the terminal currents for general biasing:

$$I_E = Q_N\left(\frac{1}{\tau_{tN}} + \frac{1}{\tau_{pN}}\right) - \frac{Q_I}{\tau_{tI}} \tag{7-39a}$$

$$I_C = \frac{Q_N}{\tau_{tN}} - Q_I\left(\frac{1}{\tau_{tI}} + \frac{1}{\tau_{pI}}\right) \tag{7-39b}$$

It is not difficult to show that these equations correspond to the Ebers–Moll relations [Eq. (7–34)], where

$$\alpha_N = \frac{\tau_{pN}}{\tau_{tN} + \tau_{pN}}, \qquad \alpha_I = \frac{\tau_{pI}}{\tau_{tI} + \tau_{pI}}$$

$$I_{ES} = q_N\left(\frac{1}{\tau_{tN}} + \frac{1}{\tau_{pN}}\right), \quad I_{CS} = q_I\left(\frac{1}{\tau_{tI}} + \frac{1}{\tau_{pI}}\right) \tag{7-40}$$

$$Q_N = q_N\frac{\Delta p_E}{p_n}, \qquad Q_I = q_I\frac{\Delta p_C}{p_n}$$

The base current in the normal mode supports recombination, and the base-to-collector current amplification factor β_N takes the form predicted by Eq. (7–7):

$$I_{BN} = \frac{Q_N}{\tau_{pN}}, \quad \beta_N = \frac{I_{CN}}{I_{BN}} = \frac{\tau_{pN}}{\tau_{tN}} \tag{7-41}$$

This expression for β_N is also obtained from $\alpha_N/(1 - \alpha_N)$. Similarly, I_{BI} is Q_I/τ_{pI}, and the total base current is

$$I_B = I_{BN} + I_{BI} = \frac{Q_N}{\tau_{pN}} + \frac{Q_I}{\tau_{pI}} \tag{7-42}$$

This expression for the base current is substantiated by $I_E - I_C$ from Eq. (7–39).

The effects of time dependence of stored charge can be included in these equations by the methods introduced in Section 5.5.1. We can include the proper dependencies by adding a rate of change of stored charge to each of the injection currents I_{EN} and I_{CI}:

$$i_E = Q_N\left(\frac{1}{\tau_{tN}} + \frac{1}{\tau_{pN}}\right) - \frac{Q_I}{\tau_{tI}} + \frac{dQ_N}{dt} \tag{7-43a}$$

$$i_C = \frac{Q_N}{\tau_{tN}} - Q_I\left(\frac{1}{\tau_{tI}} + \frac{1}{\tau_{pI}}\right) - \frac{dQ_I}{dt} \tag{7-43b}$$

$$i_B = \frac{Q_N}{\tau_{pN}} + \frac{Q_I}{\tau_{pI}} + \frac{dQ_N}{dt} + \frac{dQ_I}{dt} \tag{7-43c}$$

We shall return to these equations in Section 7.8, when we discuss the use of transistors at high frequencies.

In a switching operation a transistor is usually controlled in two conduction states, which can be referred to loosely as the "on" state and the "off" state. Ideally, a switch should appear as a short circuit when turned on and an open circuit when turned off. Furthermore, it is desirable to switch the device from one state to the other with no lost time in between. Transistors do not fit this ideal description of a switch, but they can serve as a useful approximation in practical electronic circuits. The two states of a transistor in switching can be seen in the simple common-emitter example of Fig. 7–12. In this figure the collector current i_C is controlled by the base current i_B over most of the family of characteristic curves. The load line specifies the locus of allowable $(i_C, -v_{CE})$ points for the circuit, in analogy with Fig. 6–2. If i_B is such that the operating point lies somewhere between the two end points of the load line

(a)   (b)

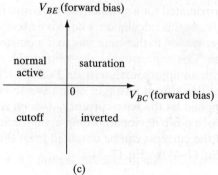

(c)

Figure 7–12
Simple switching circuit for a transistor in the common-emitter configuration: (a) biasing circuit; (b) collector characteristics and load line for the circuit, with cutoff and saturation indicated; (c) operating regimes of a BJT.

(Fig. 7–12b), the transistor operates in the normal active mode. That is, the emitter junction is forward biased and the collector is reverse biased, with a reasonable value of i_B flowing out of the base. On the other hand, if the base current is zero or negative, the point C is reached at the bottom end of the load line, and the collector current is negligible. This is the "off" state of the transistor, and the device is said to be operating in the *cutoff* regime. If the base current is positive and sufficiently large, the device is driven to the *saturation* regime, marked S. This is the "on" state of the transistor, in which a large value of i_C flows with only a very small voltage drop v_{CE}. As we shall see below, the beginning of the saturation regime corresponds to the loss of reverse bias across the collector junction. In a typical switching operation the base current swings from positive to negative, thereby driving the device from saturation to cutoff, and vice versa. In this section we shall explore the nature of conduction in the cutoff and saturation regimes; also we shall investigate the factors affecting the speed with which the transistor can be switched between the two states.

The various regions of operation of a BJT are illustrated in Fig. 7–12c. If the emitter junction is forward biased and the collector reverse biased, we have the normal active mode; the opposite gives us the inverted mode of operation. If both junctions are reverse biased, we get cutoff, leading to a very high impedance state of the BJT; if both junctions are forward biased, we have saturation and a low impedance state.

7.6.1 Cutoff

If the emitter junction is reverse biased in the cutoff regime (negative i_B), we can approximate the excess hole concentrations at the edges of the reverse-biased emitter and collector junctions as

$$\frac{\Delta p_E}{p_n} \simeq \frac{\Delta p_C}{p_n} \simeq -1 \tag{7–44}$$

which implies $p(x_n) = 0$. The excess hole distribution in the base is approximately constant at $-p_n$, with some slope to the distribution at each edge to account for the reverse saturation current in the junctions. The base current i_B can be approximated for a symmetrical transistor on a charge storage basis as $-qAp_nW_b/\tau_p$. In this calculation, a negative excess hole concentration corresponds to *generation* in the same way that a positive distribution indicates recombination. This expression is also obtained by applying Eq. (7–44) to Eq. (7–19) with an approximation from Table 7–1. Physically, a small saturation current flows from n to p in each reverse-biased junction, and this current is supplied by the base current i_B (which is negative when flowing into the base of a p-n-p device according to our definitions). A more general evaluation of the currents can be obtained from the Ebers–Moll equations by applying Eq. (7–44) to Eq. (7–34):

Figure 7–13
The cutoff regime
of a p-n-p transis-
tor: (a) excess
hole distribution
in the base region
with emitter and
collector junctions
reverse biased;
(b) equivalent cir-
cuit corresponding
to Eq. (7–45).

(a)   (b)

$$i_E = -I_{ES} + \alpha_I I_{CS} = -(1 - \alpha_N)I_{ES} \qquad (7\text{–}45a)$$

$$i_C = -\alpha_N I_{ES} + I_{CS} = (1 - \alpha_I)I_{CS} \qquad (7\text{–}45b)$$

$$i_B = i_E - i_C = -(1 - \alpha_N)I_{ES} - (1 - \alpha_I)I_{CS} \qquad (7\text{–}45c)$$

If the short-circuit saturation currents I_{ES} and I_{CS} are small and α_N and α_I are both near unity, these currents will be negligible and the cutoff regime will closely approximate the "off" condition of an ideal switch. The equivalent circuit corresponding to Eq. (7–45) is illustrated in Fig. 7–13b.

7.6.2 Saturation

The saturation regime begins when the reverse bias across the collector junction is reduced to zero, and it continues as the collector becomes forward biased. The excess hole distribution in this case is illustrated in Fig. 7–14.

Figure 7–14
Excess hole
distribution in
the base of
a saturated
transistor:
(a) the beginning
of saturation;
(b) oversaturation.

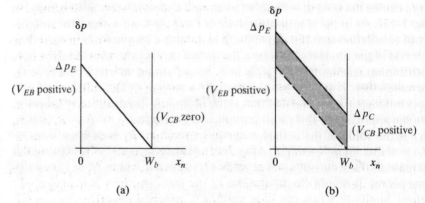

(a)   (b)

The device is saturated when $\Delta p_C = 0$, and forward bias of the collector junction (Fig. 7–14b) leads to a positive Δp_C, driving the device further into saturation. With the load line fixed by the battery and the 5-kΩ resistor in Fig. 7–12, saturation is reached by increasing the base current i_B. We can see how a large value of i_B leads to saturation by applying the reasoning of charge control to Fig. 7–14. Since a certain amount of stored charge is required to accommodate a given i_B (and vice versa), an increase in i_B calls for an increase in the area under the $\Delta p(x_n)$ distribution.

In Fig. 7–14a the device has just reached saturation, and the collector junction is no longer reverse biased. The implication of this condition for the circuit of Fig. 7–12 is easy to state. Since the emitter junction is forward biased and the collector junction has zero bias, very little voltage drop appears across the device from the collector to emitter. The magnitude of $-v_{CE}$ is only a fraction of a volt. Therefore, almost all of the battery voltage appears across the resistor, and the collector current is approximately $40\,\text{V}/5\,\text{k}\Omega = 8\,\text{mA}$. As the device is driven deeper into saturation (Fig. 7–14b), the collector current stays essentially constant while the base current increases. In this saturation condition the transistor approximates the "on" state of an ideal switch.

Although the degree of "oversaturation" (indicated by the shaded area in Fig. 7–14b) does not affect the value of i_C significantly, it is important in determining the time required to switch the device from one state to the other. For example, from previous experience we expect the turn-off time (from saturation to cutoff) to be longer for larger values of stored charge in the base. We can calculate the various charging and delay times from Eq. (7–43). Detailed calculations are somewhat involved, but we can simplify the problem greatly with approximations of the type used in Chapter 5 for transient effects in p-n junctions.

7.6.3 The Switching Cycle

The various mechanisms of a switching cycle are illustrated in Fig. 7–15. If the device is originally in the cutoff condition, a step increase of base current to I_B causes the hole distribution to increase approximately as illustrated in Fig. 7–15b. As in the transient analysis of Chapter 5, we assume for simplicity of calculation that the distribution maintains a simple form in each time interval of the transient. At time t_s the device enters saturation, and the hole distribution reaches its final state at t_2. As the stored charge in the base Q_b increases, there is an increase in the collector current i_C. The collector current does not increase beyond its value at the beginning of saturation t_s, however. We can approximate this saturated collector current as $I_C \simeq E_{CC}/R_L$, where E_{CC} is the value of the collector circuit battery and R_L is the load resistor ($I_C \simeq 8\,\text{mA}$ for the example of Fig. 7–12). There is an essentially exponential increase in the collector current while Q_b rises to its value Q_s at t_s; this rise time serves as one of the limitations of the transistor in a switching application. Similarly, when the base current is switched negative (e.g., to the

Figure 7–15
Switching effects
in a common-
emitter transistor
circuit: (a) circuit
diagram;
(b) approximate
hole distributions
in the base
during switching
from cutoff
to saturation;
(c) base current,
stored charge,
and collector
current during
a turn-on and a
turn-off transient.

(a)

(b)

(c)

t_0 — Cutoff
t_1 — Normal active region
t_s — Beginning of saturation
t_2 — Final saturated state

value $-I_B$), the stored charge must be withdrawn from the base before cutoff is reached. While Q_b is larger than Q_s, the collector current remains at the value I_C, fixed by the battery and resistor. Thus there is a storage delay time t_{sd} after the base current is switched and before i_C begins to fall toward zero. After the stored charge is reduced below Q_s, i_C drops exponentially with the characteristic fall time. Once the stored charge is withdrawn, the base current cannot be maintained any longer at its large negative value and must decay to the small cutoff value described by Eq. (7–45c).

7.6.4 Specifications for Switching Transistors

We can determine t_s and t_{sd} by solving for the time-dependent base current, $i_B(t)$, given by an expression similar to Eq. (5–47). We must also not neglect the charging time of the emitter junction capacitance in going from cutoff to saturation. Since the emitter junction is reverse biased in cutoff, it is necessary for the emitter space charge layer to be charged to the forward-bias condition before collector current can flow. Therefore, we should include a

t_d — Delay time while junction capacitance is charging
t_r — Rise time from $0.1-0.9\,I_C$
t_f — Fall time from $0.9-0.1\,I_C$

Figure 7–16
Collector current during switching transients, including the delay time required for charging the junction capacitance; definitions of the rise time and fall time.

delay time t_d as in Fig. 7–16 to account for this effect. Typical values of t_d are given in the specification information of most switching transistors, along with a *rise time* t_r, defined as the time required for the collector current to rise from 10 to 90% of its final value. A third specification is the *fall time* t_f required for i_C to fall through a similar fraction of its turn-off excursion.

The approach we have taken in analyzing the properties of transistors has involved a number of simplifying assumptions. Some of the assumptions must be modified in dealing with practical devices. In this section we investigate some common deviations from the basic theory and indicate situations in which each effect is important. Since the various effects discussed here involve modifications of the more straightforward theory, they are often labeled "secondary effects." This does not imply that they are unimportant; in fact, the effects described in this section can dominate the conduction in transistors under certain conditions of device geometry and circuit application.

7.7 OTHER IMPORTANT EFFECTS

In this section we shall consider the effects of nonuniform doping in the base region of the transistor. In particular, we shall find that graded doping can lead to a drift component of charge transport across the base, adding to the diffusion of carriers from emitter to collector. We shall discuss the effects of large reverse bias on the collector junction, in terms of widening the space charge region about the junction and avalanche multiplication. We shall see that transistor parameters are affected at high current levels by the degree of injection and by heating effects. We shall consider several structural effects that are important in practical devices, such as asymmetry in the areas of the emitter and collector junctions, series resistance between the base contact and the active part of the base region, and nonuniformity of injection at the emitter junction. All these effects are important in understanding the operation of transistors, and proper consideration of their interactions can contribute greatly to the usefulness of practical transistor circuits.

7.7.1 Drift in the Base Region

The assumption of uniform doping in the base breaks down for implanted junction transistors that usually involve an appreciable amount of impurity grading; for example, the implanted transistor of Fig. 7–5 has a doping profile similar to that sketched in Fig. 7–17. In this example there is a fairly sharp discontinuity in the doping profile, when the donor concentration in the base region becomes smaller than the constant p-type background doping in the collector. Similarly, the emitter is assumed to be a heavily doped (p^+) shallow region, providing a second rather sharp boundary for the base. Within the base region itself, however, the net doping concentration ($N_d - N_a \equiv N$) varies along a profile that decreases from the emitter edge to the collector edge. The most likely doping distribution in the base is a portion of a gaussian (see Section 5.1.4); however, we can clearly see the effect of an impurity gradient by assuming for simplicity that $N(x_n)$ varies exponentially within the base region (Fig. 7–17b).

One important result of a graded base region is that a built-in electric field exists from emitter to collector (for a p-n-p), thereby adding a drift component to the transport of holes across the base. We can demonstrate this effect very simply by considering the required balance of drift and diffusion in the base at equilibrium. If the net donor doping of the base is large enough to allow the usual approximation $n(x_n) \simeq N(x_n)$, the balance of electron drift and diffusion currents at equilibrium requires

$$I_n(x_n) = qA\mu_n N(x_n)\mathcal{E}(x_n) + qAD_n \frac{dN(x_n)}{dx_n} = 0 \qquad (7\text{-}46)$$

Therefore, the built-in electric field is

$$\mathcal{E}(x_n) = -\frac{D_n}{\mu_n}\frac{1}{N(x_n)}\frac{dN(x_n)}{dx_n} = -\frac{kT}{q}\frac{1}{N(x_n)}\frac{dN(x_n)}{dx_n} \qquad (7\text{-}47)$$

For a doping profile $N(x_n)$ that decreases in the positive x_n-direction, this field is positive, directed from emitter to collector.

Figure 7–17
Graded doping in the base region of a p-n-p transistor: (a) typical doping profile on a semilog plot; (b) approximate exponential distribution of the net donor concentration in the base region on a linear plot.

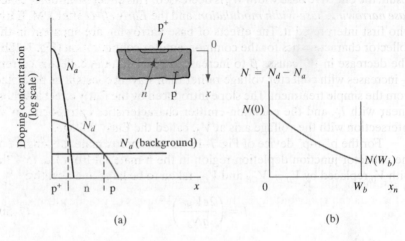

For the example of an exponential doping profile, the electric field $\mathcal{E}(x_n)$ turns out to be constant with position in the base. We can represent an exponential distribution as

$$N(x_n) = N(0)e^{-ax_n/W_b} \quad \text{where } a \equiv \ln\frac{N(0)}{N(W_b)} \qquad (7\text{--}48)$$

Taking the derivative of this distribution and substituting in Eq. (7–47), we obtain the constant field

$$\mathcal{E}(x_n) = \frac{kT}{q}\frac{a}{W_b} \qquad (7\text{--}49)$$

Since this field aids the transport of holes across the base region from emitter to collector, the transit time τ_t is reduced below that of a comparable uniform base transistor. Similarly, electron transport in an n-p-n is aided by the built-in field in the base. This shortening of the transit time can be very important in high-frequency devices (Section 7.8.2). Another approach for obtaining a built-in field is to vary the alloy composition x (and therefore E_g) in a base made of an alloy such as $Si_{1-x}Ge_x$ or $In_xGa_{1-x}As$. We will discuss this further in Section 7.9.

7.7.2 Base Narrowing

In the discussion of transistors thus far, we have assumed that the effective base width W_b is essentially independent of the bias voltages applied to the collector and emitter junctions. This assumption is not always valid; for example, the p^+-n-p^+ transistor of Fig. 7–18 is affected by the reverse bias applied to the collector. If the base region is lightly doped, the depletion region at the reverse-biased collector junction can extend significantly into the n-type base region. As the collector voltage is increased, the space charge layer takes up more of the metallurgical width of the base L_b, and as a result, the effective base width W_b is decreased. This effect is variously called *base narrowing, base-width modulation*, and the *Early effect* after J. M. Early, who first interpreted it. The effects of base narrowing are apparent in the collector characteristics for the common-emitter configuration (Fig. 7–18b). The decrease in W_b causes β to increase. As a result, the collector current I_C increases with collector voltage rather than staying constant as predicted from the simple treatment. The slope introduced by the Early effect is almost linear with I_C, and the common-emitter characteristics extrapolate to an intersection with the voltage axis at V_A, called the Early voltage.

For the p^+-n-p^+ device of Fig. 7–18 we can approximate the length l of the collector junction depletion region in the n material from Eq. (5–23b) with V_0 replaced by $V_0 - V_{CB}$ and V_{CB} taken to be large and negative:

$$l = \left(\frac{2\epsilon V_{BC}}{qN_d}\right)^{1/2} \qquad (7\text{--}50)$$

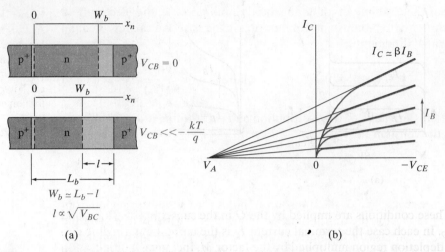

Figure 7–18
The effects of base narrowing on the characteristics of a p^+-n-p^+ transistor: (a) decrease in the effective base width as the reverse bias on the collector junction is increased; (b) common-emitter characteristics showing the increase in I_C with increased collector voltage. The black lines in (b) indicate the extrapolation of the curves to the Early voltage V_A.

If the reverse bias on the collector junction is increased far enough, it is possible to decrease W_b to the extent that the collector depletion region essentially fills the entire base. In this punch-through condition holes are swept directly from the emitter region to the collector, and transistor action is lost. Punch-through is a breakdown effect that is generally avoided in circuit design. In most cases, however, avalanche breakdown of the collector junction occurs before punch-through is reached. We shall discuss the effects of avalanche multiplication in the following section.

In devices with graded base doping, base narrowing is of less importance. For example, if the donor concentration in the base region of a p-n-p increases with position from the collector to the emitter, the intrusion of the collector space charge region into the base becomes less important with increased bias as more donors are available to accommodate the space charge.

7.7.3 Avalanche Breakdown

Before punch-through occurs in most transistors, avalanche multiplication at the collector junction becomes important (see Section 5.4.2). As Fig. 7–19 indicates, the collector current increases sharply at a well-defined breakdown voltage BV_{CBO} for the common-base configuration. For the common-emitter case, however, there is a strong influence of carrier multiplication over a fairly broad range of collector voltage. Furthermore, the breakdown voltage in the common-emitter case BV_{CEO} is significantly smaller than BV_{CBO}. We can understand these effects by considering breakdown for the condition $I_E = 0$ in the common-base case and for $I_B = 0$ in the common-emitter

Figure 7–19
Avalanche
breakdown in
a transistor:
(a) common-base
configuration;
(b) common-
emitter
configuration.

case. These conditions are implied by the O in the subscripts of BV_{CEO} and BV_{CBO}. In each case the terminal current I_C is the current entering the collector depletion region multiplied by the factor M. Including multiplication due to impact ionization, Eq. (7–37b) becomes

$$I_C = (\alpha_N I_E + I_{CO})M = (\alpha_N I_E + I_{CO})\frac{1}{1 - (V_{BC}/BV_{CBO})^n} \quad (7\text{–}51)$$

where for M we have used the empirical expression given in Eq. (5–44).

For the limiting common-base case of $I_E = 0$ (the lowest curve in Fig. 7–19a), I_C is simply MI_{CO}, and the breakdown voltage is well defined, as in an isolated junction. The term BV_{CBO} signifies the collector junction breakdown voltage in common-base with the emitter open. In the common-emitter case the situation is somewhat more complicated. Setting $I_B = 0$, and therefore, $I_C = I_E$ in Eq. (7–51), we have

$$I_C = \frac{MI_{CO}}{1 - M\alpha_N} \quad (7\text{–}52)$$

We notice that in this case the collector current increases indefinitely when $M\alpha_N$ approaches unity. By contrast, M must approach infinity in the common-base case before BV_{CBO} is reached. Since α_N is close to unity in most transistors, M need be only slightly larger than unity for Eq. (7–52) to approach breakdown. Avalanche multiplication thus dominates the current in a common-emitter transistor well below the breakdown voltage of the isolated collector junction. The sustaining voltage for avalanching in the common-emitter case BV_{CEO} is therefore smaller than BV_{CBO}.

We can understand physically why multiplication is so important in the common-emitter case by considering the effect of M on the base current. When an ionizing collision occurs in the collector junction depletion region, a secondary hole and electron are created. The primary and secondary holes are swept into the collector in a p-n-p, but the electron is swept into the base by the junction field. Therefore, the supply of electrons to the base is increased, and from our charge control analysis we conclude that hole injection at the emitter must increase to maintain space charge neutrality. This is a regenerative process, in which an increased injection of holes from the emitter causes an increased multiplication current at the collector junction; this in turn increases the rate at which secondary electrons are swept into the base, calling for more hole injection. Because of this regenerative effect, it is easy to understand why the multiplication factor M need be only slightly greater than unity to start the avalanching process.

7.7.4   Injection Level; Thermal Effects

In discussions of transistor characteristics we have assumed that α and β are independent of carrier injection level. Actually, the parameters of a practical transistor may vary considerably with injection level, which is determined by the magnitude of I_E or I_C. For very low injection, the assumption of negligible recombination in the junction depletion regions is invalid (see Section 5.6.2). This is particularly important in the case of recombination in the emitter junction, where any recombination tends to degrade the emitter injection efficiency γ. Thus we expect that α and β should decrease for low values of I_C, causing the curves of the collector characteristics to be spaced more closely for low currents than for higher currents.

As I_C is increased beyond the low injection level range, α and β increase but fall off again at very high injection. The primary cause of this fall-off is the increase of majority carriers at high injection levels (see Section 5.6.1). For example, as the concentration of excess holes injected into the base becomes large, the matching excess electron concentration can become greater than the background n_n. This base conductivity modulation effect results in a decrease in γ as more electrons are injected across the emitter junction into the emitter region.

Large values of I_C may be accompanied by significant power dissipation in the transistor and therefore heating of the device. In particular, the product of I_C and the collector voltage V_{BC} is a measure of the power dissipated at the collector junction. This dissipation is due to the fact that carriers swept through the collector junction depletion region are given increased kinetic energy, which in turn is given up to the lattice in scattering collisions. It is very important that the transistor be operated in a range such that $I_C V_{BC}$ does not exceed the maximum power rating of the device. In devices designed for high power capability, the transistor is mounted on an efficient heat sink, so that thermal energy can be transferred away from the junction.

If the temperature of the device is allowed to increase due to power dissipation or thermal environment, the transistor parameters change. The most important parameters dependent on temperature are the carrier lifetimes and diffusion coefficients. In Si or Ge devices the lifetime τ_p increases with temperature for most cases, due to thermal reexcitation from recombination centers. This increase in τ_p tends to increase β for the transistor. On the other hand, the mobility decreases with increasing temperature in the lattice-scattering range, varying approximately as $T^{-3/2}$ (see Fig. 3–22). Thus from the Einstein relation, we expect D_p to decrease as the temperature increases, thereby causing a drop in β due to an increasing transit time τ_t. Of these competing processes, the effect of increasing lifetime with temperature usually dominates, and β becomes larger as the device is heated. It is clear from this effect that *thermal runaway* can occur if the circuit is not designed to prevent it. For example, a large power dissipation in the device can cause an increase in T; this results in a large β and therefore a large I_C for a given base current; the large I_C causes more collector dissipation and the cycle continues. This type of runaway of the collector current can result in overheating and destruction of the device.

7.7.5 Base Resistance and Emitter Crowding

A number of structural effects are important in determining the operation of a transistor. For example, the emitter and collector areas are considerably different in the implanted transistor of Fig. 7–20a. This and most other structural effects can be accounted for by differences in α_N, α_I, and other parameters in the Ebers–Moll model. Several effects caused by the structural arrangement of real transistors deserve special attention, however. One of the most important of these effects is the fact that base current must pass from the active part of the base region to the base contacts B. Thus, to be accurate,

Figure 7–20
Effects of a base resistance: (a) cross section of an implanted transistor; (b) and (c) top view, showing emitter and base areas and metallized contacts; (d) illustration of base resistance; (e) expanded view of distributed resistance in the active part of the base region.

we should include a resistance r_b in equivalent models for the transistor to account for voltage drops that may occur between B and the active part of the base. Because of r_b, it is common to contact the base with the metallization pattern on both sides of the emitter, as in Fig. 7–20c.

If the transistor is designed so that the n-type regions leading from the base to the contacts are large in cross-sectional area, the base resistance r_b may be negligible. On the other hand, the distributed resistance r'_b along the thin base region is almost always important.[5] Since the width of the base between the emitter and collector is very narrow, this distributed resistance is usually quite high. Therefore, as base current flows from points within the base region toward each end, a voltage drop occurs along r'_b. In this case the forward bias across the emitter–base junction is not uniform, but instead varies with position according to the voltage drop in the distributed base resistance. In particular, the forward bias of the emitter junction is largest at the corner of the emitter region near the base contact. We can see that this is the case by considering the simplified example of Fig. 7–20e. Neglecting variations in the base current along the path from point A to the contact B, the forward bias of the emitter junction above point A is approximately

$$V_{EA} = V_{EB} - I_B(R_{AD} + R_{DB}) \qquad (7\text{--}53)$$

Actually, the base current is not uniform along the active part of the base region, and the distributed resistance of the base is more complicated than we have indicated. But this example does illustrate the point of nonuniform injection. Whereas the forward bias at A is approximately described by Eq. (7–53), the emitter bias voltage at point D is

$$V_{ED} = V_{EB} - I_B R_{DB} \qquad (7\text{--}54)$$

which can be significantly closer to the applied voltage V_{EB}.

Since the forward bias is largest at the edge of the emitter, it follows that the injection of holes is also greatest there. This effect is called *emitter crowding*, and it can strongly affect the behavior of the device. The most important result of emitter crowding is that high-injection effects described in the previous section can become dominant locally at the corners of the emitter before the overall emitter current is very large. In transistors designed to handle appreciable current, this is a problem which must be dealt with by proper structural design. The most effective approach to the problem of emitter crowding is to distribute the emitter current along a relatively large emitter edge, thereby reducing the current density at any one point. Clearly, what is needed is an emitter region with a large perimeter compared with its area. A likely geometry to accomplish this is a long thin stripe for the emitter, with base contacts on each side (Fig. 7–20b and c). With this geometry the total emitter current I_E is spread out along a rather long edge on each side of the stripe. An even better geometry is several emitter stripes, connected

---

[5]The distributed resistance r'_b is often called the *base spreading resistance*.

Figure 7–21
An interdigitated
geometry to com-
pensate for the
effects of emitter
crowding in a
power transistor:
(a) cross section;
(b) top view
of implanted
regions; (c) top
view with meta-
llized contacts.
The metal
interconnections
are isolated from
the device by
an oxide layer
except where
they contact
the appropriate
base and emitter
regions at
"windows" in the
oxide.

Base contact
metallization

Emitter contact
metallization

Collector contact

(a)   (b)   (c)

electrically by the metallization and separated by interspersing base contacts
(Fig. 7–21). Many such thin emitter and base contact "fingers" can be inter-
laced to provide for handling large current in a power transistor. This is often
called very descriptively an *interdigitated* geometry.

7.7.6 Gummel–Poon Model

The Ebers–Moll model runs into problems if a high degree of accuracy is
required for very small BJTs, or where second-order effects become important. The Gummel–Poon model, which is a charge control model, incorporates much more physics. We present a simplified version of the model here.

As discussed in Section 7.7.1, for typical graded doping profiles in the
base, there is a built-in electric field that causes drift of minority carriers
in the same direction they are diffusing from the emitter to collector. This
forms the starting point for the derivation of the Gummel–Poon model. As
mentioned in Section 7.7.1, this electric field aids the motion of the minority
carriers in the base, so the current can be written as

$$I_{Ep} = qA\mu_p p(x_n)\mathscr{E} - qAD_p \frac{dp(x_n)}{dx_n} \tag{7–55}$$

We can replace the electric field in the base in Eq. (7–55) by the expression
in Eq. (7–47), assuming $n(x_n) = N_d(x_n)$

$$I_{Ep} = qA\mu_p p\left(\frac{-kT}{q}\frac{1}{n}\frac{dn}{dx_n}\right) - qAD_p\frac{dp}{dx_n}$$

$$= -\frac{qAD_p}{n}\left(p\frac{dn}{dx_n} + n\frac{dp}{dx_n}\right) \tag{7–56}$$

where the Einstein relation is used. We recognize the expression in paren-
thesis as the derivative of the *pn* product.

$$I_{Ep} = \frac{-qAD_p}{n} \frac{d(pn)}{dx_n} \qquad (7\text{-}57a)$$

$$\frac{-I_{Ep}n}{qAD_p} = \frac{d(pn)}{dx_n} \qquad (7\text{-}57b)$$

We integrate both sides of Eq. (7–57b) from the emitter–base junction (0) to the base–collector junction (W_b), keeping in mind that the current I_{Ep}, flowing from the emitter to the collector, is more or less constant in the narrow base (so that it can be pulled out of the integral).

$$-I_{Ep} \int_0^{W_b} \frac{ndx_n}{qAD_p} = \int_0^{W_b} \frac{d(pn)}{dx_n} dx_n = p(W_b)n(W_b) - p(0)n(0) \qquad (7\text{-}58)$$

Now, as described in Sections 5.2.2 and 5.3.2, the pn product changes from the equilibrium value

$$pn = n_i^2 \qquad (7\text{-}59a)$$

to the nonequilibrium expression

$$pn = n_i^2 e^{\frac{F_n - F_p}{kT}} = n_i^2 e^{\frac{qV}{kT}} \qquad (7\text{-}59b)$$

where the separation of the Fermi levels is determined by the applied bias across the junction. Applying this to Eq. (7–58), we get

$$p(W_b)n(W_b) = n_i^2 e^{\frac{qV_{CB}}{kT}} \qquad (7\text{-}60a)$$

$$p(0)n(0) = n_i^2 e^{\frac{qV_{EB}}{kT}} \qquad (7\text{-}60b)$$

$$I_{Ep} = \frac{-qAD_p n_i^2 \left(e^{\frac{qV_{CB}}{kT}} - e^{\frac{qV_{EB}}{kT}} \right)}{\int_0^{W_b} ndx_n} \qquad (7\text{-}61)$$

We have assumed a constant hole diffusivity in the base, D_p. The integral in the denominator corresponds to the integrated majority carrier charge in the base, and is known as the *base Gummel number*, Q_B. In the normal active mode of operation, where the collector–base junction is reverse biased (V_{CB} is negative), and the emitter–base junction is forward biased, the emitter hole current flowing to the collector (which is the dominant current) becomes

$$I_{Ep} = \frac{qAD_p n_i^2 e^{\frac{qV_{EB}}{kT}}}{Q_B} \qquad (7\text{-}62a)$$

We can similarly write the base electron current flowing back into the emitter as

$$I_{En} = \frac{qAD_n n_i^2 e^{\frac{qV_{EB}}{kT}}}{Q_E} \qquad (7\text{--}62b)$$

where Q_E is the integrated majority carrier charge in the emitter, known as the *emitter Gummel number*. The crux of the Gummel–Poon model is that the currents are expressed in terms of the net integrated charges in the base and emitter regions, and can easily handle nonuniform doping. Also, since we have obtained expressions for I_{Ep} and I_{En} in terms of Q_B and Q_E, we can write down BJT parameters such as the emitter injection efficiency γ [see Eq. (7–2)], in terms of the Gummel numbers.

We can also modify the Gummel–Poon model to handle several second-order effects such as the Early effect and high-level injection in the base, simply by writing the expression for the base Gummel number, Q_B, more precisely as follows:

$$Q_B = \int_{0(V_{EB})}^{W_b(V_{CB})} n(x_n)dx_n \qquad (7\text{--}63)$$

where we explicitly account for the fact that the integration limits, the base–emitter junction ($x_n = 0$) and the base–collector junction (W_b) are bias dependent. This is, of course, the Early effect (Section 7.7.2).

Furthermore, we see that under high-level injection (Sections 5.6.1 and 7.7.4), the integrated majority carrier charge becomes greater than the integrated base dopant charge:

$$\int_0^{W_b} n(x_n)dx_n > \int_0^{W_b} N_D(x_n)dx_n \qquad (7\text{--}64)$$

Clearly, from Eq. (7–61), this will cause the current from the emitter-to-collector, I_{Ep}, to increase less rapidly with emitter-base voltage at high biases. Based on what we learned in Section 5.6.1 about high-level injection in a diode, the emitter-to-collector current for high-level injection in the base increases as

$$I_C \propto I_{Ep} \propto e^{\frac{qV_{EB}}{2kT}} \qquad (7\text{--}65a)$$

On the other hand, because the emitter doping is typically higher than the base doping, one does not see high-level injection effects in the emitter, and the base current injected into the emitter scales as

$$I_B \propto I_{En} \propto e^{\frac{qV_{EB}}{kT}} \qquad (7\text{--}65b)$$

Hence, for high V_{EB},

$$\beta = \frac{I_C}{I_B} \propto \frac{e^{\frac{qV_{EB}}{2kT}}}{e^{\frac{qV_{EB}}{kT}}} \propto e^{\frac{-qV_{EB}}{2kT}} \propto I_C^{-1}$$

This result shows that the common-emitter gain decreases at high injection levels due to excess majority carriers in the base.

The Gummel–Poon model also accounts for generation–recombination effects in the base-emitter depletion region at low current levels. As discussed in Section 5.6.2, such effects are accounted for by the diode ideality factor, **n**. Hence the base current injected into the emitter can be written as

$$I_B \propto I_{En} \propto e^{\frac{qV_{EB}}{\mathbf{n}kT}} \qquad (7\text{–}66a)$$

On the other hand, the generally large emitter current injected into the base is not likely to be affected by the generation–recombination effects. Therefore,

$$I_{Ep} \propto e^{\frac{qV_{EB}}{kT}} \qquad (7\text{–}66b)$$

Thus, for low V_{EB} or low I_C, the current gain

$$\beta = \frac{I_C}{I_B} \propto \frac{e^{\frac{qV_{EB}}{kT}}}{e^{\frac{qV_{EB}}{\mathbf{n}kT}}} \propto e^{\frac{qV_{EB}}{kT}\left(1-\frac{1}{\mathbf{n}}\right)} \propto I_C^{\left[1-\frac{1}{\mathbf{n}}\right]} \qquad (7\text{–}67)$$

The transistor collector current I_C and the base current I_B are plotted on a semilog scale as a function of V_{EB} in Fig. 7–22a. This is referred to as a *Gummel* plot. The current gain β is shown as a function of I_C in Fig. 7–22b. We see the dependence of β on I_C in the different bias regions, as described by the Gummel–Poon model. At low injection levels β is degraded by poor emitter injection efficiency [Eq. (7–67)], and at high currents β decreases due to excess majority charge in the base, which degrades γ. It can be shown that if one neglects the Early effect (i.e., we assume an infinite Early voltage) and the drop of β at high current levels, the Gummel–Poon model simplifies to the Ebers–Moll model.

7.7.7 Kirk Effect

The current gain drops at high collector currents due to yet another mechanism known as the *Kirk effect*. This involves an effective widening of the neutral base due to modification of the depletion space charge distribution at the reverse-biased base-collector junction. This is caused by the buildup

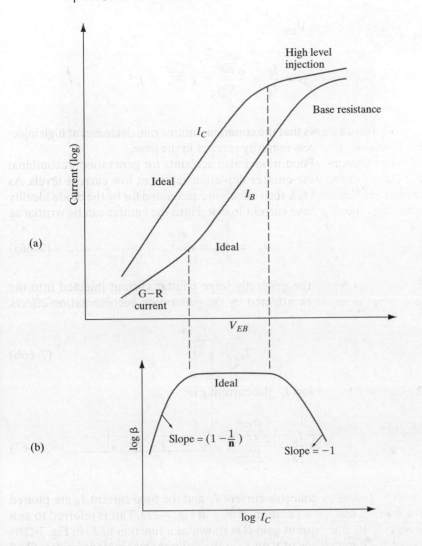

Figure 7–22
Current–voltage
characteristics
of BJTs: (a) the
Gummel plot of
log of collector
and base currents
as a function
of emitter-base
forward bias;
(b) d-c common-
emitter current
gain ($=I_C/I_B$) as a
function of I_C. For
the intermediate
range, we have
ideal behavior
where both I_C
and I_B increase
exponentially with
forward bias with
ideality factor
n = 1, leading
to a current-
independent gain.
For very low
forward biases,
the generation–
recombination
(G–R) current
increases I_B and
the gain drops.
For high forward
biases, high-level
injection effects
cause the I_C to
increase more
slowly (**n** = 2)
than I_B, and the
gain drops as
I_C^{-1}.

of mobile carriers due to increased current flow from the emitter to the collector. This is illustrated in Fig. 7–23 for a p-n-p BJT. Notice that the polarity of these mobile charges adds to the fixed donor charges on the base side of the base-collector depletion region, but subtracts from the fixed acceptor charges on the collector side of the junction (Fig. 7–23c). Therefore, fewer uncompensated donors (and thus a smaller depletion width) are needed to maintain the reverse voltage V_{CB} across this junction. As a result, the neutral base width increases from W_b in Fig. 7–23b to W_b' in Fig. 7–23c. Also, the depletion region extends more into the collector side. This is tantamount to moving the base-collector junction deeper into the collector. This leads to an effective widening of the neutral base region (the Kirk effect) and to a drop of the current gain and an increase of the base transit time.

Figure 7–23
Kirk effect:
(a) cross section
of p-n-p BJT;
(b) space-charge
distribution in the
base-collector
reverse-biased
junction for very
low currents;
(c) space-charge
distribution at the
base-collector
junction for higher
current levels.
We see that the
injected mobile
holes (shown
in color) add to
the space charge
of the immobile
donors on the
base side of
the depletion
region, but
subtract from the
space charge
of the immobile
acceptors on the
collector side.
This leads to a
widening of the
neutral base width
from W_b to W_b'.

The electric field profile in the collector depletion region in the presence of uncompensated dopant charges and mobile carriers (due to the current flow) is given by Poisson's equation.

$$\frac{d\mathcal{E}}{dx} = \frac{1}{\epsilon}\left[q(N_d^+ - N_a^-) + \frac{I_c}{Av_d}\right] \qquad (7\text{–}68)$$

where the mobile carrier charge concentration is given by the last term, and v_d is the drift velocity of the carriers.

The voltage across the reverse-biased collector-base junction, V_{CB}, is related to the electric field profile by:

$$V_{CB} = -\int_{W_b}^{W_c} \mathcal{E}dx \qquad (7\text{–}69)$$

Assuming that V_{CB} is fixed, and I_C increases, the last term in Eq. (7–68) becomes more important with respect to the ionized dopant charges. In Poisson's equation [Eq. (7–68)], the extra holes injected into the depletion region have the same effect as if the doping level on the base side were increased and that on the collector side decreased. Since the integral of this field with respect to distance is fixed at V_{CB} [Eq. (7–69)], this implies that the depletion region on the base side collapses.

Although we have chosen to illustrate the Kirk effect for a p-n-p BJT, similar results are obtained for the n-p-n transistor. Obviously, the treatment is identical except for the polarity of the various charges. From a more detailed analysis, for n-p-n devices with an n^+ sub-collector, it can be shown that the base widening can extend at even higher current levels all the way through the lightly doped collector region to the heavily doped buried sub-collector.

In this section we discuss the properties of bipolar transistors under high-frequency operation. Some of the frequency limitations are junction capacitance, charging times required when excess carrier distributions are altered, and transit time of carriers across the base region. Our aim here is not to attempt a complete analysis of high-frequency operation, but rather to consider the physical basis of the most important effects. Therefore, we shall include the dominant capacitances and charging times and discuss the effects of the transit time on high-frequency devices.

**7.8
FREQUENCY
LIMITATIONS OF
TRANSISTORS**

7.8.1 Capacitance and Charging Times

The most obvious frequency limitation of transistors is the presence of junction capacitance at the emitter and collector junctions. We have considered this type of capacitance in Chapter 5, and we can include junction capacitors C_{je} and C_{jc} in circuit models for the transistor (Fig. 7–24a). If there is some equivalent resistance r_b between the base contact and the active part of the base region, we can also include it in the model, along with r_c to account for a series collector resistance.[6] Clearly, the combinations of r_b with C_{je} and r_c with C_{jc} can introduce important time constants into a-c circuit applications of the device.

From Section 5.5.4 we recall that capacitive effects can arise from the requirements of altering the carrier distributions during time-varying injection. In a-c circuits the transistor is usually biased to a certain steady state operating point characterized by the d-c quantities V_{BE}, V_{CE}, I_C, I_B, and I_E,

---

[6]Since elements such as r_b and r_c in Fig. 7–24 are added to the basic transistor model we have previously analyzed, it is most convenient to refer here to the terminal voltages and currents as v'_{be}, i'_c, and so on. In this way we can use previously derived expressions involving the internal quantities [i_b and v_{eb} in Eq. (7–74), for example]. In most circuits texts the primes are instead used for the internal quantities, just the opposite method from that used here.

Figure 7–24
Models for a-c
operation:
(a) inclusion of
base and collector
resistances
and junction
capacitances;
(b) hybrid-pi
model synthesiz-
ing Eqs. (7–74)
and (7–75).

and then a-c signals are superimposed upon these steady state values. We shall call the a-c terms v_{be}, v_{ce}, i_c, i_b, and i_e. Total (a-c + d-c) quantities will be lowercase with capitalized subscripts.

If a small a-c signal is applied to the emitter p-n junction along with a d-c level, we can show that

$$\Delta p_E(t) \simeq \Delta p_E(\text{d-c})\left(1 + \frac{qv_{eb}}{kT}\right) \qquad (7\text{–}70)$$

We can relate this time-varying excess hole concentration to the stored charge in the base region, and then use Eq. (7–43) to determine the resulting currents. For simplicity we shall assume the device is biased in the normal active mode and use only $Q_N(t)$. Assuming an essentially triangular excess hole distribution in the base, Eq. (7–23) gives

$$Q_N(t) = \tfrac{1}{2}qAW_b\Delta p_E(t) = \tfrac{1}{2}qAW_b\Delta p_E(\text{d-c})\left[1 + \frac{qv_{eb}}{kT}\right] \qquad (7\text{–}71)$$

The terms outside the brackets constitute the d-c stored charge $I_{B}\tau_p$:

$$Q_n(t) = I_B\tau_p\left(1 + \frac{qv_{eb}}{kT}\right) \qquad (7\text{–}72)$$

Now that we have a simple relation for the time-dependent stored charge, we can use Eq. (7–43c) to write the total base current as

$$i_B(t) = \frac{Q_N(t)}{\tau_p} + \frac{dQ_N(t)}{dt} \qquad (7\text{–}73\text{a})$$

As discussed in Section 5.5.4, we must be careful about boundary conditions in determining where the stored charges are extracted or "reclaimed" in a diode. For the emitter-base diode in a BJT, we have a "short" diode where Eq. (5–64) is applicable. The result is that only two-thirds of the stored charge is reclaimed. Hence, we obtain

$$i_B(t) = I_B + \frac{q}{kT}I_B v_{eb} + \frac{2}{3}\frac{q}{kT}I_B \tau_p \frac{dv_{eb}}{dt} \qquad (7\text{–}73\text{b})$$

The a-c component of the base current is

$$i_b = G_{se}v_{eb} + C_{se}\frac{dv_{eb}(t)}{dt} \qquad (7\text{–}74)$$

where

$$G_{se} \equiv \frac{q}{kT}I_B \quad \text{and} \quad C_{se} \equiv \frac{2}{3}\frac{q}{kT}I_B\tau_p = \frac{2}{3}G_{se}\tau_p$$

Thus, as in the case of the simple diode, an a-c conductance and capacitance are associated with the emitter-base junction due to charge storage effects. From Eq. (7–43b) we have

$$i_C(t) = \frac{Q_N(t)}{\tau_t} = \beta I_B + \frac{q}{kT}\beta I_B v_{eb}$$

$$i_c = g_m v_{eb} \quad \text{where } g_m \equiv \frac{q}{kT}\beta I_B = \frac{3}{2}\frac{C_{se}}{\tau_t} \qquad (7\text{–}75)$$

The quantity g_m is an a-c *transconductance*, which is evaluated at the steady state value of collector current $I_C = \beta I_B$. We can synthesize Eqs. (7–74) and (7–75) in an equivalent a-c circuit as in Fig. 7–24b. In this equivalent circuit the voltage v_{be} used in the calculations appears "inside" the device, so that a new applied voltage v'_{be} must be used external to r_b to refer to the voltage applied between the contacts, and similarly for v'_{ce}. This equivalent model is discussed in detail in most electronic circuits texts; it is often called a *hybrid-pi* model.

From Fig. 7–24b it is clear that several charging times are important in the a-c operation of a transistor; the most important are the time required to charge the emitter and collector depletion regions and the delay time in altering the charge distribution in the base region. Other delay times included in a complete analysis of high-frequency transistors are the transit time through the collector depletion region and the charge storage time in the collector region. If all of these are included in a single delay time τ_d, we can estimate the upper frequency limit of the device. This is usually defined as the *cutoff frequency* for the transistor $f_T \equiv (2\pi t_d)^{-1}$. It is possible to show that f_T represents the frequency at which the a-c amplification for the device $[\beta(a\text{-}c) \equiv h_{fe} \equiv \partial i_c'/\partial i_b']$ drops to unity.

7.8.2 Transit Time Effects

In high-frequency transistors the ultimate limitation is often the transit time across the base. For example, in a p-n-p device the time τ_t required for holes to diffuse from emitter to collector can determine the maximum frequency of operation for the device. We can calculate τ_t for a transistor with normal biasing and $\gamma = 1$ from Eq. (7–20) and the relation $\beta \approx \tau_p/\tau_t$:

$$\beta \approx \frac{\operatorname{csch} W_b/L_p}{\tanh W_b/2L_p} = \frac{2L_p^2}{W_b^2} = \frac{2D_p\tau_p}{W_b^2} = \frac{\tau_p}{\tau_t}$$

$$\tau_t = \frac{W_b^2}{2D_p} \tag{7–76}$$

Another instructive way of calculating τ_t is to consider that the diffusing holes *seem* to have an average velocity $\langle v(x_n) \rangle$ (actually the individual hole motion is completely random, as discussed in Section 4.4.1). The hole current $i_p(x_n)$ is then given by

$$i_p(x_n) = qAp(x_n)\langle v(x_n) \rangle \tag{7–77}$$

The transit time is

$$\tau_t = \int_0^{W_b} \frac{dx_n}{\langle v(x_n) \rangle} = \int_0^{W_b} \frac{qAp(x_n)}{i_p(x_n)} dx_n \tag{7–78}$$

For a triangular distribution as in Fig. 7–8b, the diffusion current is almost constant at $i_p = qAD_p\Delta p_E/W_b$, and τ_t becomes

$$\tau_t = \frac{qA\,\Delta p_E W_b/2}{qAD_p\Delta p_E/W_b} = \frac{W_b^2}{2D_p} \tag{7–79}$$

as before. The average velocity concept should not be pushed too far in the case of diffusion, but it does serve to illustrate the point that a delay time exists between the injection and collection of holes.

We can estimate the transit time for a typical device by choosing a value of W_b, say 0.1 μm (10^{-5}cm). For Si, a typical number for D_p is about 10 cm^2/s; then for this transistor $\tau_t = 0.5 \times 10^{-11}$ s. Approximating the upper frequency limit as $(2\pi\tau_t)^{-1}$, we can use the transistor to about 30 GHz. Actually, this estimate is too optimistic because of other delay times.

The transit time can be reduced by making use of field-driven currents in the base. For the implanted transistor of Fig. 7–17, the holes drift in the built-in field from emitter to collector over most of the base region. By increasing the doping gradient in the base, we can reduce the transit time and thereby increase the maximum frequency of the transistor.

7.8.3 Webster Effect

While the transit time expression [Eq. (7–79)] is valid for low-level injection, τ_t is reduced by up to a factor of 2 under high-level injection. This occurs because the majority carrier concentration increases significantly above its equilibrium value in the base, to match the injected minority carrier concentration. Since the minority carrier concentration decreases from the base-emitter junction to the base-collector junction (see Fig. 7–8), so does the majority carrier concentration. This tends to create a diffusion of the majority carriers from emitter to base. Such a majority carrier diffusion would upset the drift–diffusion balance required to maintain a quasi-equilibrium distribution in the base. Therefore, a built-in electric field develops in the base to create an opposing majority carrier drift current. The direction of this induced field then *aids* the minority carrier transport from the emitter to the collector, reducing the transit time τ_t in Eq. (7–79).

This is known as the Webster effect. It is interesting to note that this effect is similar to the drift field effects in the base region due to nonuniform base doping (Section 7.7.1). For the Webster effect, the induced field is not due to nonuniform doping but rather the nonuniform majority carrier concentration induced by carrier injection.

7.8.4 High-Frequency Transistors

The most obvious generality we can make about the fabrication of high-frequency transistors is that the physical size of the device must be kept small. The base width must be narrow to reduce the transit time, and the emitter and collector areas must be small to reduce junction capacitance. Unfortunately, the requirement of small size generally works against the requirements of power rating for the device. Since we usually require a trade-off between frequency and power, the dimensions and other design features of the transistor must be tailored to the specific circuit requirements. On the other hand, many of the fabrication techniques useful for power devices can be adapted to increase the frequency range. For example, the method of interdigitation (Fig. 7–21) provides a means of increasing the useful emitter edge length while keeping the overall emitter area to a minimum. Therefore, some form of interdigitation is generally used in transistors designed for high frequency and reasonable power requirements.

Another set of parameters that must be considered in the design of a high-frequency device is the effective resistance associated with each region of the transistor. Since the emitter, base, and collector resistances affect the various RC charging times, it is important to keep them to a minimum.

Therefore, the metallization patterns contacting the emitter and base regions must not present significant series resistance. Furthermore, the semiconductor regions themselves must be designed to reduce resistance. For example, the series base resistance r_b of an n-p-n device can be reduced greatly by performing a p$^+$ diffusion between the contact area on the surface and the active part of the base region. Further reduction of base resistance by heavy doping of the base requires the use of a heterojunction (Section 7.9) to maintain γ at an acceptable value.

In Si, n-p-n transistors are usually preferred, since the electron mobility and diffusion coefficient are higher than for holes. It is common to fabricate n-p-n transistors in n-type epitaxial material grown on an n$^+$ substrate. The heavily doped substrate provides a low-resistance contact to the collector region, while maintaining low doping in the epitaxial collector material to ensure a high breakdown voltage of the collector junction (see Section 7.3). It is important, however, to keep the collector depletion region as small as possible to reduce the transit time of carriers drifting through the collector junction. This can be accomplished by making the lightly doped collector region narrow so that the depletion region under bias extends to the n$^+$ substrate.

As described in Section 7.3, an n$^+$ polysilicon layer is generally deposited on the top of the single-crystal n$^+$ emitter. The reason for this can be understood from Fig. 7–25. If an ohmic contact were formed directly on top of the narrow n$^+$ emitter, the excess minority carrier hole concentration profile would have a steep gradient because the excess minority carrier concentrations are zero at the ohmic contacts. This leads to a large back-injected base current I_{Ep} into the emitter and a degraded emitter injection efficiency. The use of a polysilicon emitter causes the hole concentration profile to have a gentler slope near the base-emitter junction, thereby leading to an improved γ. The steeper slope of the hole concentration profile in the polysilicon emitter simply reflects the fact that the grain boundary defects in polysilicon lead to a shorter diffusion length.

Figure 7–25
Excess minority hole concentration profile in the emitter region of an n-p-n transistor with and without the use of polyemitters. The carrier profile if an ohmic contact is formed directly on the single-crystal Si emitter is shown by the dashed line.

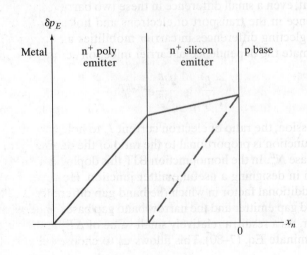

In addition to the various parameters of the device itself, the transistor must be packaged properly to avoid parasitic resistance, inductance, or capacitance at high frequencies. We shall not attempt to describe the many techniques for mounting and packaging transistors here, since methods vary greatly among manufacturers.

In Section 7.4.4 we saw that the emitter injection efficiency of a bipolar transistor is limited by the fact that carriers can flow from the base into the emitter region, over the emitter junction barrier, which is reduced by the forward bias. According to Eq. (7–25) it is necessary to use lightly doped material for the base region and heavily doped material for the emitter to maintain a high value of γ and, therefore, α and β. Unfortunately, the requirement of light base doping results in undesirably high base resistance. This resistance is particularly noticeable in transistors with very narrow base regions. Furthermore, degenerate doping can led to a slight shrinkage of E_g in the emitter as the donor states merge with the conduction band. This can decrease the emitter injection efficiency. Therefore, a more suitable BJT for high frequency would have a heavily doped base and a lightly doped emitter. This is just the opposite of the traditional BJT discussed thus far in this chapter. To accomplish such a radically different transistor design, we need some other mechanism instead of doping to control the relative amount of injection of electrons and holes across the emitter junction.

If transistors are made in materials that allow heterojunctions to be used, the emitter injection efficiency can be increased without strict requirements on doping. In Fig. (7–26) an n-p-n transistor made in a single material (*homojunction*) is contrasted with a *heterojunction bipolar transistor (HBT)*, in which the emitter is a wider band gap semiconductor. It is possible in such a structure for the barrier for electron injection (qV_n) to be smaller than the hole barrier (qV_p). Since carrier injection varies exponentially with the barrier height, even a small difference in these two barriers can make a very large difference in the transport of electrons and holes across the emitter junction. Neglecting differences in carrier mobilities and other effects, we can approximate the dependence of carrier injection across the emitter as

$$\frac{I_n}{I_p} \propto \frac{N_d^E}{N_a^B} e^{\Delta E_g/kT} \tag{7–80}$$

In this expression, the ratio of electron current I_n to hole current I_p crossing the emitter junction is proportional to the ratio of the doping in the emitter N_d^E and the base N_a^B. In the homojunction BJT this doping ratio is all we have to work with in designing a useful emitter junction. However, in the HBT there is an additional factor in which the band gap difference ΔE_g between the wide band gap emitter and the narrow band gap base appears in an exponential factor. As a result, a relatively small value of ΔE_g in the exponential term can dominate Eq. (7–80). This allows us to choose the doping terms

7.9 HETEROJUNCTION BIPOLAR TRANSISTORS

Figure 7–26
Contrast of carrier
injection at the
emitter of (a) a
homojunction
BJT and (b) a
heterojunction
bipolar transistor
(HBT). In the
forward-biased
homojunction
emitter, the
electron barrier
qV_n and the
hole barrier qV_p
are the same.
In the HBT with
a wide band
gap emitter, the
electron barrier
is smaller than
the hole barrier,
resulting in the
preferential
injection of
electrons across
the emitter
junction.

Figure 7–26
Contrast of carrier injection at the emitter of (a) a homojunction BJT and (b) a heterojunction bipolar transistor (HBT). In the forward-biased homojunction emitter, the electron barrier qV_n and the hole barrier qV_p are the same. In the HBT with a wide band gap emitter, the electron barrier is smaller than the hole barrier, resulting in the preferential injection of electrons across the emitter junction.

for lower base resistance and emitter junction capacitance. In particular, we can choose a heavily doped base to reduce the base resistance and a lightly doped emitter to reduce junction capacitance.

    The heterojunction shown in Fig. 7–26 has a smooth barrier, without the spike and notch commonly observed for heterojunctions (see Fig. 5–46). It is possible to smooth out such discontinuities in the bands by grading the composition of the ternary or quaternary alloy between the two materials (Fig. 7–27). Clearly, grading out the conduction band spike improves the electron injection by reducing the barrier that electrons must overcome. There are some HBT designs, however, that make use of the spike as a "launching ramp" to inject hot electrons into the base.

Figure 7–27
SiGe graded base in a Si n-p-n transistor. The built-in drift field in the conduction band in the base aids electron transport.

Materials commonly used in HBTs obviously include the AlGaAs/GaAs system because of its wide range of lattice-matched composition. In addition, the InGaAsP system (including $In_{0.53}Ga_{0.47}As$) grown on InP has become popular in HBT design. It is also possible to make HBTs using elemental semiconductor heterostructures such as $Si/Si_{1-x}Ge_x$. In this material system, the band gap difference ΔE_g between the Si emitter and the narrower band gap $Si_{1-x}Ge_x$ base occurs primarily in the valence band. As a result, a rather small addition of Ge to the base results in higher electron injection efficiency than is possible in homojunction silicon bipolar transistors.

If the SiGe alloy composition in the base of an n-p-n is varied such that E_g decreases slightly from the emitter side to the collector side of the base, a built-in electric field accelerates electrons through the base region (Fig. 7–27). The resulting field-aided base transport is a major advantage of the HBT. Such graded Ge profiles make the structure more manufacturable, because one does not have to worry about a mismatch between the p-n junction and the heterojunction.

SUMMARY

7.1 A BJT consists of an emitter-base (EB) diode connected *back to back* to a collector-base (CB) diode. In the *normal active* mode of operation, the EB junction is forward biased such that carriers injected from the emitter can diffuse across the *narrow* base and be collected by the reverse-biased CB junction.

7.2 The terminal currents can be determined by solving the drift–diffusion and continuity equations for a narrow-base diode with suitable boundary conditions. The fraction of the total emitter current that is due to injected carriers from emitter to base is the *emitter injection efficiency* and is made close to unity by doping the emitter much higher than the base. Another elegant way to increase emitter injection efficiency is to use a larger band gap emitter than in the base, as in heterojunction bipolar transistors (*HBT*).

7.3 The fraction of the carriers that survives diffusion across the narrow base is the *base transport factor*, which is made close to unity by making the base width narrow compared with the diffusion length. The product of emitter injection efficiency and base transport factor gives the current transfer ratio (I_C/I_E), from which one can determine the common-emitter current gain (I_C/I_B). *Active devices such as BJTs provide power gain.*

7.4 Equivalent-circuit models such as *Ebers–Moll* treat the BJT as *two coupled back-to-back diodes*, in parallel with controlled current sources. These diodes can be forward or reverse biased for switching applications. If they are both forward biased, the BJT is in a low impedance state (saturation); if they are both reverse biased, it is in a high impedance state (cutoff).

7.5 A *charge control analysis* of BJTs is possible (as for other devices) in terms of the integrated carrier concentration in the base. I_C is given by the base charge divided by the base transit time, while I_B is the base charge divided by the carrier lifetime (for unity emitter injection efficiency).

7.6 The *Gummel–Poon* charge control model gives the current components in terms of the integrated base and emitter dopant charges (Gummel numbers). It is more accurate and can handle some second-order effects better than Ebers–Moll.

7.7 Second-order effects include I_C increase due to neutral base narrowing for increasing CB reverse bias (*Early* effect), current gain drop at high I_C (*Kirk* effect), I_E crowding at the emitter edges due to series resistance effects, and BJT breakdown at high biases.

PROBLEMS

7.1 Given the data of Prob. 5.2, plot the doping profiles $N_a(x)$ and $N_d(x)$ for the following double-diffused transistor: The starting wafer is n-type Si with $N_d = 10^{16}\,\text{cm}^{-3}$; $N_s = 5 \times 10^{13}\,\text{cm}^{-2}$ boron atoms are deposited on the surface, and these atoms are diffused into the wafer at 1100°C for 1 hr ($D = 3 \times 10^{-13}\,\text{cm}^2/\text{s}$ for B in Si at 1100°C); then the wafer is placed in a phosphorus diffusion furnace at 1000°C for 15 min ($D = 3 \times 10^{-14}\,\text{cm}^2/\text{s}$ for P in Si at 1000°C). During the emitter diffusion, the surface concentration is held constant at $5 \times 10^{20}\,\text{cm}^{-3}$. You may assume that the base doping profile does not change appreciably during the emitter diffusion, which takes place at a lower temperature and for a shorter time. Find the width of the base region from plots of $N_a(x)$ and $N_d(x)$. *Hint:* Use five-cycle semilog paper and let x vary from zero to about 1.5 μm in steps that are chosen to be simple multiples of $2\sqrt{Dt}$.

7.2 Sketch the ideal collector characteristics ($i_C, -v_{CE}$) for the transistor of Fig. 7–4; let i_B vary from zero to 0.2 mA in increments of 0.02 mA, and let $-v_{CE}$ vary from 0 to 10 V. Draw a load line on the resulting characteristics for the circuit of Fig. 7–4, and find the steady state value of $-V_{CE}$ graphically for $I_B = 0.1$ mA.

7.3 Calculate the minority excess hole distribution $\delta p(x)/\Delta p_E$ in the base of a p-n-p bipolar junction transistor (BJT), assuming $W_B/L_P = 0.2$ and 0.5. The calculations have to be carried out for the base distance of L_P and $2L_P$.

7.4 Show the bias polarities and depletion regions of an *npn* BJT in the *normal active, saturation, and cutoff* modes of operation. Draw the three sketches one below the other to (qualitatively) reflect the depletion widths for these biases, and the relative emitter, base, and collector doping.

Consider a BJT with a base transport factor of 1.0 and an emitter injection efficiency of 0.5.

Calculate roughly by what factor would doubling the base width of a BJT would increase, decrease, or leave unchanged the emitter injection efficiency and base transport factor? Repeat for the case of emitter doping increased $5 \times =$. Explain with key equations, and assume other BJT parameters remain unchanged!

7.5 An npn BJT has emitter, base, and collector doping levels of 10^{19} cm^{-3}, 5×10^{18} cm^{-3}, and 10^{17} cm^{-3}, respectively. It is biased in the normal active mode, with an emitter-base voltage of 1V. If the neutral base width is 100 nm, the emitter is 200 nm wide, and we have *negligible* base recombination, calculate the emitter current, emitter injection efficiency, and base transport factor. You can assume electron and hole mobility of 500 and 100 cm^2/V-s, respectively, in the emitter, and 800 and 250 cm^2/V-s in the base. The device gets heated up to 400 K during operation such that $n_i = 10^{12}$ cm^{-3}, and $\epsilon_r = 15$. Qualitatively sketch the device structure, the carrier concentrations, and the band diagram under bias below it. Assume that the carrier lifetimes are 0.1 μs everywhere.

7.6 Redraw Fig. 7–3 for an n$^+$-p-n BJT, and explain the various components of current flow and current directions for the normal active mode of operation. Draw the energy band diagram for equilibrium and this bias condition.

7.7 In a p-n-p transistor emitter, doping is 5×10^{18}/cm^3, base doping is 10^{17}/cm^3, base width is 0.985 μm, diffusion lengths for electrons and holes are the same at 10μm. Assume $\tau_p = \tau_n = 10^{-7}$ sec, find the emitter injection efficiency, the base transport factor, and the transistor gains if electron and hole mobility are 1250 and 450 cm^2/V-sec, respectively.

7.8 (a) In a BJT, we increase the base doping by a factor of 10 and halve the base width. *Calculate approximately* by what factor the collector current changes in the normal active mode, assuming that everything else stays the same. (b) In a certain BJT, the emitter doping is 100 times greater than the base doping, the emitter width is 0.1 times the base width, and we can assume both base and emitter widths to be much shorter than the carrier diffusion lengths L_n and L_p. What is the emitter injection efficiency? What is the base transport factor? (c) Suppose $L_n = L_p$. Now assuming that both emitter and base are much wider than the diffusion lengths, what is the emitter injection efficiency and base transport factor?

7.9 The symmetrical p$^+$-n-p$^+$ transistor of Fig. P7–7 is connected as a diode in the four configurations shown. Assume that $V \gg kT/q$. Sketch $\Delta p(x_n)$ in the base region for each case. Which connection seems most appropriate for use as a diode? Why?

Figure P7–7

7.10 Derive the expression for the excess minority hole concentration by solving the diffusion equation in a uniformly doped p-n-p bipolar transistor in forward active region having base width W_B.

7.11 (a) Find the expression for the current I for the transistor connection of Fig. P7–7b; compare the result with the narrow-base diode problem (Prob. 5.40).

   (b) How does the current I divide between the base lead and the collector lead?

7.12 For a p-n-p BJT with $N_E > N_B > N_C$, show the dominant current components, with proper arrows, for directions in the normal active mode. If $I_{Ep} = 10$ mA, $I_{En} = 100\ \mu A, I_{Cp} = 9.8$ mA, and $I_{Cn} = 1\ \mu A$, calculate the base transport factor, emitter injection efficiency, common-base current gain, common-emitter current gain, and I_{CBO}. If the minority stored base charge is 4.9×10^{-11} C, calculate the base transit time and lifetime.

7.13 A Si p-n-p BJT at $T = 300$ K has uniform dopings of $N_E = 10^{18}/cm^3, N_B = 10^{16}/cm^3$, and $N_C = 10^{15}/cm^3$. The metallurgical base width is 1.2 μm.

   (a) Calculate the peak electric field at the CB junction and the CB depletion capacitance/unit area for normal biasing, with a CB bias of 30 V.

   (b) Estimate the neutral base width narrowing at this voltage, ignoring the EB depletion region.

7.14 It is obvious from Eqs. (7–35) and (7–36) that I_{EO} and I_{CO} are the saturation currents of the emitter and collector junctions, respectively, with the opposite junction open circuited.

   (a) Show that this is true from Eqs. (7–32).

   (b) Find expressions for the following excess concentrations: Δp_C with the emitter junction forward biased and the collector open; Δp_E with the collector junction forward biased and the emitter open.

   (c) Sketch $\Delta p(x_n)$ in the base for the two cases of part (b).

7.15 A symmetrical p^+np bipolar junction transistor made of Si has the following specifications:

Emitter	Base
$N_a = 10^{18}/cm^3$	$N_d = 10^{16}/cm^3$
$\tau_n = 10^{-6}$ sec	$\tau_n = 10^{-6}$ sec
$\mu_P = 200$ cm^2/V-sec	$\mu_p = 400$ cm^2/V-sec
$\mu_n = 800$ cm^2/V-sec	$\mu_n = 1250$ cm^2/V-sec

Base width is 0.8 μm and device area is 10^{-4} cm^2. Compute the saturation currents and the electron and hole components of emitter current under 0.2 V of emitter-base applied bias.

7.16 (a) How is it possible that the average time an injected hole spends in transit across the base τ_t is shorter than the hole lifetime in the base τ_p?

(b) Explain why the turn-on transient of a BJT is faster when the device is driven into oversaturation.

7.17 Use Example 5–7 to design an n-p-n heterojunction bipolar transistor with reasonable γ and base resistance.

7.18 The current amplification factor β of a BJT is very sensitive to the base width as well as to the ratio of the base doping to the emitter doping. Calculate and plot β for a p-n-p BJT with $L_p^n = L_n^p$, for:

(a) $n_n = p_p$, $W_b/L_p^n = 0.01$ to 1;

(b) $W_b = L_p^n$, $n_n/p_p = 0.01$ to 1.

Neglect mobility variations ($\mu_n^p = \mu_p^n$).

7.19 (a) How much charge (in coulombs) due to excess holes is stored in the base of the transistor shown in Fig. 7–4 at the d-c bias given?

(b) Why is the base transport factor B different in the normal and inverted modes for the transistor shown in Fig. 7–5?

7.20 A Si p-n-p transistor has the following properties at room temperature:

$\tau_n = \tau_p = 0.1$ μs

$D_n = D_p = 10$ cm^2/s

$N_E = 10^{19}$ cm^{-3} = emitter concentration

$N_B = 10^{16}$ cm^{-3} = base concentration

$N_C = 10^{16}$ cm^{-3} = collector concentration

W_E = emitter width = 3 μm

W = metallurgical base width = 1.5 μm = distance between base-emitter junction and base-collector junction

A = cross-sectional area = 10^{-5} cm^2

Calculate the neutral base width W_b for $V_{CB} = 0$ and $V_{EB} = 0.2$ V. Repeat for 0.6 V.

7.21 For the BJT in Prob. 7.20, calculate the base transport factor and the emitter injection efficiency for $V_{EB} = 0.2$ and 0.6 V.

7.22 For the BJT in Prob. 7.20, calculate α, β, I_E, I_B, and I_C for the two values of V_{EB}. What is the base Gummel number in each case?

7.23 A Si p-n-p BJT has the following parameters at room temperature.

Emitter	Base	Collector
$N_a = 5 \times 10^{18}\,\text{cm}^{-3}$	$N_d = 10^{16}$	$N_a = 10^{15}$
$\tau_n = 100$ ps	$\tau_p = 2500$ ps	$\tau_n = 2\,\mu\text{s}$
$\mu_n = 150\,\text{cm}^2/V\text{-}s$	$\mu_n = 1500$	$\mu_n = 1500$
$\mu_p = 100\,\text{cm}^2/V\text{-}s$	$\mu_p = 400$	$\mu_p = 450$
Base width $W_b = 0.2\,\mu\text{m}$		
Area $= 10^{-4}\,\text{cm}^2$		

Calculate the β of the transistor from B and γ, and using the charge control model. Comment on the results.

7.24 For the BJT in Prob. 7.23, calculate the charge stored in the base when $V_{CB} = 0$ and $V_{EB} = 0.7$ V. If the base transit time is the dominant delay component for this BJT, what is the f_T?

7.25 Consider a Si n-p-n transistor at $T = 300$ K with these specifications: emitter current $(I_E) = 1$ mA, base width $(W_B) = 100$ nm, collector-base depletion width $(x_{dc}) = 50$ nm, $C_\mu = 0.1$ pF, $C_{je} = 1$ pF, diffusion coefficent for electrons $(D_n) = 25$ cm²/sec, collector resistance $(r_C) = 20\,\Omega$, collector capacitance $(C_S) = 0.1$ pF, and electron saturation velocity $(v_s) = 2.3 \times 10^7$ cm/sec. Calculate the base transit time for the transistor. Calculate the cut off frequency for the transistor.

7.26 A n-p-n BJT at room temperature has these data available: emitter diffusion coefficient $(D_E) = 10$ cm²/sec, base diffusion coefficient $(D_B) = 25$ cm²/sec, base width $(W_B) = 0.70\,\mu\text{m}$, emitter width $(W_E) = 0.50\,\mu\text{m}$, emitter doping $(N_E) = 10^{18}/\text{cm}^3$, base doping $(N_B) = 10^{16}/\text{cm}^3$, emitter and base recombination lifetimes are $\tau_{E0} = 10^{-7}$ sec and $\tau_{B0} = 5 \times 10^{-7}$ sec, recombination current density $(J_{r0}) = 5 \times 10^{-8}$ A/cm², and the applied B-E bias is 0.5 V. Calculate

(a) emitter injection efficiency (γ),

(b) base transport factor (B),

(c) recombination factor,

(d) CE current gain (β),

(e) CB current gain (α).

READING LIST   Very useful applets for understanding BJT operation are available at https://nanohub.org/resources/animations

Bardeen, J., and W. H. Brattain. "The Transistor, a Semiconductor Triode." *Phys. Rev.* 74 (1948), 230.

Hu, C. "Modern Semiconductor Devices for Integrated Circuits," Freely available online.

Muller, R. S., and T. I. Kamins. *Device Electronics for Integrated Circuits.* New York: Wiley, 1986.

Neamen, D. A. *Semiconductor Physics and Devices: Basic Principles.* Homewood, IL: Irwin, 2003.

Neudeck, G. W. *Modular Series on Solid State Devices: Vol. III. The Bipolar Junction Transistor.* Reading, MA: Addison-Wesley, 1983.

Shockley, W. "The Path to the Conception of the Junction Transistor." *IEEE Trans. Elec. Dev.* ED-23 (1976), 597.

Sze, S. M. *Physics of Semiconductor Devices.* New York: Wiley, 1981.

Taur, Y., and T. H. Ning. *Fundamentals of Modern VLSI Devices.* Cambridge: Cambridge University Press, 1998.

Question 1   SELF QUIZ

Consider the following BJT circuit and somewhat idealized transistor characteristics where, in particular, the voltage drop across the forward-biased base-emitter junction is assumed to be constant and equal to 1 V, for simplicity.

(a) What is the (common-emitter) gain β?

(b) Draw the load line on the transistor characteristics.

(c) What is the collector-emitter voltage drop in this circuit within half a volt?

(d) If voltage V_1 could be changed, what value of V_1 would drive the BJT in this circuit to the edge of saturation?

(e) For the given base current of 0.1 mA, consistent with your answer to part (b), what is the collector-emitter voltage drop, V_{CE}, in this circuit within half a volt?

(f) What minimum value of I_B (assuming V_1 to be variable) would drive the BJT transistor into saturation?

Question 2

The following is a band diagram within an n-p-n BJT at equilibrium. Sketch in the Fermi level as a function of position. Qualitative accuracy is sufficient.

Question 3

Would decreasing the base width of a BJT *increase, decrease*, or leave *unchanged* the following, assuming that the device remained unchanged otherwise? (Circle your choice for each.)

(a)   The emitter injection efficiency γ? increase/unchanged/decrease

(b)   The base transport factor B? increase/unchanged/decrease

(c)   The (common-emitter) gain β? increase/unchanged/decrease

(d)   The *magnitude* of the Early voltage V_A? increase/unchanged/decrease

Question 4

Sketch the cross section of an n-p-n BJT and point out the dominant current components on it showing the correct directions of the various current vectors. If we increase the base doping, qualitatively explain how the various components change.

Question 5

Would decreasing the base doping of the BJT *increase, decrease*, or leave essentially *unchanged* (circle the correct answers):

(a)   Emitter injection efficiency γ? increase/decrease/unchanged

(b)   Base transport factor B? increase/decrease/unchanged

(c)   Magnitude of the Early voltage V_A? increase/decrease/unchanged

Question 6

A pnp Bipolar transistor has the following properties. $A = 10^{(-4)}cm^2$, $Wb = 1$ um. Emitter parameters are $Na = 10^{18}$, $Tn = 0.2$ us, $Up = 200$, $Un = 700$. Base parameters are $Nd = 10^{14}$, $Tp = 9$ ms, $Un = 1300$, $Up = 450$. Calculate the transistor current. Assuming the emitter region is large.

Question 7

When a transistor is connected in common base its gain factor is 0.97. If it is connected in common emitter and also in common collector calculate the gains respectively.

Question 8

The common base DC current gain of a transistor must be 0.967 and the emitter current is 5 mA. Find the necessary value of the base current and the collector current.

Question 9

The common collector gain of a transistor is 51. Calculate the base current if the collector current is 1.5 mA.

Chapter 8
Optoelectronic Devices

OBJECTIVES

1. Understand solar cells
2. Study photodetectors such as APDs
3. Study incoherent light sources (LEDs) and coherent light sources (lasers)

So far we have primarily concentrated on electronic devices. There is also a wide variety of very interesting and useful device functions involving the interaction of photons with semiconductors. These devices provide the optical sources and detectors that allow broadband telecommunications and data transmission over optical fibers. This important area of device applications is called *optoelectronics*. In this chapter we will discuss devices that detect photons and those that emit photons. Devices that convert optical energy into electrical energy include photodiodes and solar cells. Emitters of photons include incoherent sources such as light-emitting diodes (LEDs) and coherent sources in the form of lasers.

8.1
PHOTODIODES

In Section 4.3.4 we saw that bulk semiconductor samples can be used as photoconductors by providing a change in conductivity proportional to an optical generation rate. Often, junction devices can be used to improve the speed of response and the sensitivity of detectors of optical or high-energy radiation. Two-terminal devices designed to respond to photon absorption are called *photodiodes*. Some photodiodes have extremely high sensitivity and response speed. Since modern electronics often involves optical as well as electrical signals, photodiodes serve important functions as electronic devices. In this section, we shall investigate the response of p-n junctions to optical generation of electron–hole pairs (EHPs) and discuss a few typical *photodiode detector* structures. We shall also consider the very important use of junctions as *solar cells,* which convert absorbed optical energy into useful electrical power.

8.1.1 Current and Voltage in an Illuminated Junction

In Chapter 5 we identified the current due to drift of minority carriers across a junction as a generation current. In particular, carriers generated within the depletion region W are separated by the junction field, electrons being collected in the n region and holes in the p region. Also, minority carriers generated thermally within a diffusion length of each side of the junction diffuse to the depletion region and are swept to the other side by the electric field. If the junction is uniformly illuminated by photons with $h\nu > E_g$, an added generation rate g_{op} (EHP/cm³-s) participates in this current (Fig. 8–1). The number of holes created per second within a diffusion length of the transition region on the n side is $AL_p g_{op}$. Similarly $AL_n g_{op}$ electrons are generated per second within L_n of x_{p0} and $AW g_{op}$ carriers are generated within W. The resulting current due to the collection of these optically generated carriers by the junction is

$$\boxed{I_{op} = qA g_{op}(L_p + L_n + W)} \qquad (8–1)$$

If we call the thermally generated current described in Eq. (5–37b) I_{th}, we can add the optical generation of Eq. (8–1) to find the total reverse current with illumination. Since this current is directed from n to p, the diode equation [Eq. (5–36)] becomes

$$I = I_{th}(e^{qV/kT} - 1) - I_{op}$$

$$I = qA\left(\frac{L_p}{\tau_p}p_n + \frac{L_n}{\tau_n}n_p\right)(e^{qV/kT} - 1) - qA g_{op}(L_p + L_n + W) \qquad (8–2)$$

Thus the I–V curve is lowered by an amount proportional to the generation rate (Fig. 8–1c). This equation can be considered in two parts—the current described by the usual diode equation and the current due to optical generation.

When the device is short circuited ($V = 0$), the terms from the diode equation cancel in Eq. (8–2), as expected. However, there is a short-circuit

$hv > E_g$

$\delta p_{op} = g_{op}\tau_p$

$I_{op} = qAL_p g_{op}$

$g_{op} = 0$

g_1
g_2
g_3

$g_3 > g_2 > g_1$

(a)   (b)   (c)

Figure 8–1
Optical generation of carriers in a p-n junction: (a) absorption of light by the device; (b) current I_{op} resulting from EHP generation within a diffusion length of the junction on the n side; (c) I–V characteristics of an illuminated junction.

current from n to p equal to I_{op}. Thus the I–V characteristics of Fig. 8–1c cross the I-axis at negative values proportional to g_{op}. When there is an open circuit across the device, $I = 0$ and the voltage $V = V_{oc}$ is

$$V_{oc} = \frac{kT}{q}\ln[I_{op}/I_{th} + 1]$$

$$= \frac{kT}{q}\ln\left[\frac{L_p + L_n + W}{(L_p/\tau_p)p_n + (L_n/\tau_n)n_p}g_{op} + 1\right] \qquad (8\text{–}3a)$$

For the special case of a symmetrical junction, $p_n = n_p$ and $\tau_p = \tau_n$, we can rewrite Eq. (8–3a) in terms of the thermal generation rate $p_n/\tau_n = g_{th}$ and the optical generation rate g_{op}. Neglecting generation within W:

$$V_{oc} \simeq \frac{kT}{q}\ln\frac{g_{op}}{g_{th}} \quad \text{for } g_{op} \gg g_{th} \qquad (8\text{–}3b)$$

Actually, the term $g_{th} = p_n/\tau_n$ represents the *equilibrium* thermal generation–recombination rate. As the minority carrier concentration is increased by optical generation of EHPs, the lifetime τ_n becomes shorter, and p_n/τ_n becomes larger (p_n is fixed, for a given N_d and T). Therefore, V_{oc} cannot increase indefinitely with increased generation rate; in fact, the limit on V_{oc} is the equilibrium contact potential V_0 (Fig. 8–2). This result is to be expected, since the contact potential is the maximum forward bias that can appear across a junction. The appearance of a forward voltage across an illuminated junction is known as the *photovoltaic effect*.

Depending on the intended application, the photodiode of Fig. 8–1 can be operated in either the third or fourth quarters of its I–V characteristic. As Fig. 8–3 illustrates, power is delivered to the device from the external circuit when the current and junction voltage are both positive or both negative (first or third quadrants). In the fourth quadrant, however, the junction voltage is positive and the current is negative. In this case power is delivered from the junction to the external circuit (notice that in the fourth quadrant the current flows from the negative side of V to the positive side, as in a battery).

Figure 8–2
Effects of illumination on the open-circuit voltage of a junction: (a) junction at equilibrium; (b) appearance of a voltage V_{oc} with illumination.

(a)   (b)

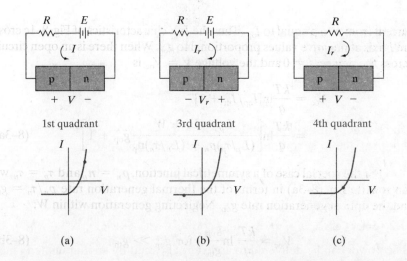

Figure 8–3
Operation of an illuminated junction in the various quadrants of its I–V characteristic; in (a) and (b), power is delivered to the device by the external circuit; in (c) the device delivers power to the load.

1st quadrant   3rd quadrant   4th quadrant

(a)   (b)   (c)

If power is to be extracted from the device, the fourth quadrant is used; on the other hand, in applications as a photodetector we usually reverse bias the junction and operate it in the third quadrant. We shall investigate these applications more closely in the discussion to follow.

EXAMPLE 8–1

For steady state optical excitation, we can write the hole diffusion equation as

$$D_p \frac{d^2 \delta p}{dx^2} = \frac{\delta p}{\tau_p} - g_{op}$$

Assume that a long p^+-n diode is uniformly illuminated by an optical signal, resulting in g_{op} EHP/cm^3-s. Calculate the hole diffusion current $I_p(x_n)$ and evaluate it at $x_n = 0$. Compare the result with Eq. (8–2) evaluated for a p^+-n junction.

SOLUTION

$$\frac{d^2 \delta p}{dx_n^2} = \frac{\delta p}{L_p^2} - \frac{g_{op}}{D_p}$$

$$\delta p(x_n) = B e^{-x_n/L_p} + \frac{g_{op} L_p^2}{D_p}$$

At $x_n = 0$, $\delta p(0) = \Delta p_n$. Thus, $B = \Delta p_n - \dfrac{g_{op} L_p^2}{D_p}$

(a) $\delta p(x_n) = [p_n(e^{qV/kT} - 1) - g_{op} L_p^2/D_p] e^{-x_n/L_p} + g_{op} L_p^2/D_p$

$$\frac{d\delta p}{dx_n} = -\frac{1}{L_p} [\Delta p_n - g_{op} L_p^2/D_p] e^{-x_n/L_p}$$

(b) $\quad I_p(x_n) = -qAD_p\dfrac{d\delta p}{dx_n} = \dfrac{qAD_p}{L_p}[\Delta p_n - g_{op}L_p^2/D_p]e^{-x_n/L_p}$

$$I_p(x_n = 0) = \dfrac{qAD_p}{L_p}p_n(e^{qV/kT} - 1) - qAL_p g_{op}$$

The last equation corresponds to Eq. (8–2) for $n_p \ll p_n$, except that the component due to generation on the p side is not included.

8.1.2 Solar Cells

Since power can be delivered to an external circuit by an illuminated junction, it is possible to convert solar energy into electrical energy. If we consider the fourth quadrant of Fig. 8–3c, it appears doubtful that much power can be delivered by an individual device. The voltage is restricted to values less than the contact potential, which in turn is generally less than the band gap voltage E_g/q. For Si the voltage V_{oc} is less than about 1 V. The current generated depends on the illuminated area, but typically I_{op} is in the range 10–100 mA for a junction with an area of about 1 cm^2. However, if many such devices are used, the resulting power can be significant. In fact, arrays of p-n junction solar cells are currently used to supply electrical power for many space satellites. Solar cells can supply power for the electronic equipment aboard a satellite over a long period, which is a distinct advantage over batteries. The array of junctions can be distributed over the surface of the satellite or can be contained in solar cell "paddles" attached to the main body of the satellite (Fig. 8–4a). A 72MW solar cell plant in Italy is shown in Fig. 8–4b.

To utilize a maximum amount of available optical energy, it is necessary to design a solar cell with a large area junction located near the surface of the device (Fig. 8–5). The planar junction is formed by diffusion or ion implantation, and the surface is coated with appropriate materials to reduce reflection and to decrease surface recombination. Many compromises must be made in solar cell design. In the device shown in Fig. 8–5, for example, the junction depth d must be less than L_p in the n material to allow holes generated near the surface to diffuse to the junction before they recombine; similarly, the thickness of the p region must be such that electrons generated in this region can diffuse to the junction before recombination takes place. This requirement implies a proper match between the electron diffusion length L_n, the thickness of the p region, and the mean optical penetration depth $1/\alpha$ [see Eq. (4–2)]. It is desirable to have a large contact potential V_0 to obtain a large photovoltage, and therefore heavy doping is indicated; on the other hand, long lifetimes are desirable and these are reduced by doping too

(a)   (b)

Figure 8–4
(a) Solar cell arrays attached to the International Space Station. The solar array wings measure 74 m tip to tip. Each wing contains 32,800 solar cells and can produce 62 kW of power for the station. (Courtesy of NASA.) (b) 72MW terrestrial solar plant in Italy. (Courtesy of MEMC/Sun Edison.)

(a)   (b)

Figure 8–5
Configuration of a solar cell: (a) enlarged view of the planar junction; (b) top view, showing metal contact "fingers."

heavily. It is important that the series resistance of the device be very small so that power is not lost to heat due to ohmic losses in the device itself. A series resistance of only a few ohms can seriously reduce the output power of a solar cell (Prob. 8.7). Since the area is large, the resistance of the p-type body of the device can be made small. However, contacts to the thin n region require special design. If this region is contacted at the edge, current must flow along the thin n region to the contact, resulting in a large series resistance. To prevent this effect, the contact can be distributed over the n surface by providing small contact fingers as in Fig. 8–5b. These narrow contacts serve to reduce the series resistance without interfering appreciably with the incoming light.

Figure 8–6
I–V characteristics
of an illuminated
solar cell. The
maximum power
rectangle is
shaded.

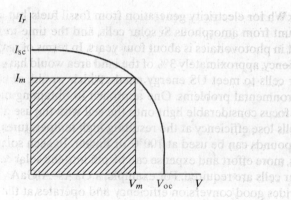

Figure 8–6 shows the fourth-quadrant portion of a solar cell characteristic, with I_r plotted upward for the convenience of illustration. The open-circuit voltage V_{oc} and the short-circuit current I_{sc} are determined for a given light level by the cell properties. The maximum power delivered to a load by this solar cell occurs when the product VI_r is a maximum. Calling these values of voltage and current V_m and I_m, we can see that the maximum delivered power illustrated by the shaded rectangle in Fig. 8–6 is less than the $I_{sc}V_{oc}$ product. The ratio $I_mV_m/I_{sc}V_{oc}$ is called the *fill factor*, and is a figure of merit for solar cell design.

Applications of solar cells are not restricted to outer space. It is possible to obtain useful power from the sun in terrestrial applications using solar cells, even though the solar intensity is reduced by the atmosphere. Current worldwide total power generation capability is ~15 TW and corresponds to an annual energy usage of ~500 quads (1 quad = 10^{15}, or a quadrillion, BTU), with an annual increase of 1–2%. Of this, ~80% comes from fossil fuels (oil, natural gas, and coal), which will be exhausted in several hundred years. In addition, CO_2 emissions and global warming have spurred a renewed interest in "green" sources of energy such as photovoltaics, of which the current installed capacity worldwide is about 100 GW. About 1 kW/m^2 is available in a particularly sunny location (translating to about 600 TW potentially available worldwide), but not all of this solar power can be converted to electricity. Much of the photon flux is at energies less than the cell band gap and is not absorbed. High-energy photons are strongly absorbed, and the resulting EHPs may recombine at the surface. A well-made single-crystal Si cell can have about 25% efficiency for solar energy conversion, providing ~250 W/m^2 of electrical power under full illumination. This is a modest amount of power per unit solar cell area, considering the cost and effort involved in fabricating a large area of Si cells. Amorphous Si thin-film solar cells can be made more cheaply, but have lower efficiencies (~10%) because of the defects in the material.

The cost and scalability of photovoltaic technology are of paramount importance for terrestrial applications. Currently, it costs only about 3 cents per kWh for electricity generation from fossil fuels, but about 10 times that amount from amorphous Si solar cells, and the time to recover the investment in photovoltaics is about four years. In terms of scalability, at 10% cell efficiency, approximately 3% of the land area would have to be covered with solar cells to meet US energy needs, which would, of course, create other environmental problems. One approach to obtaining more power per cell is to focus considerable light onto the cell with the use of mirrors. Although Si cells lose efficiency at the resulting high temperatures, GaAs and related compounds can be used at 100°C or higher. In such solar concentrator systems, more effort and expense can be put into the solar cell fabrication, since fewer cells are required. For example, a GaAs–AlGaAs heterojunction cell provides good conversion efficiency and operates at the elevated temperatures that are common in solar concentrator systems. In such systems, the area required is shifted from the cell to the concentrator.

A Si solar cell has a short-circuit current of 100 mA and an open-circuit voltage of 0.8 V under full solar illumination. The fill factor is 0.7. What is the maximum power delivered to a load by this cell?

EXAMPLE 8–2

$$P_{max} = (f.f.)\, I_{sc} V_{oc} = (0.8)(100)(0.7) = \mathbf{56\ mW}$$

SOLUTION

8.1.3 Photodetectors

When the photodiode is operated in the third quadrant of its I–V characteristic (Fig. 8–3b), the current is essentially independent of voltage but is proportional to the optical generation rate. Such a device provides a useful means of measuring illumination levels or of converting time-varying optical signals into electrical signals.

In most optical detection applications the detector's speed of response, or bandwidth, is critical. For example, if the photodiode is to respond to a series of light pulses 1 ns apart, the photogenerated minority carriers must diffuse to the junction and be swept across to the other side in a time much less than 1 ns. The carrier diffusion step in this process is time consuming and should be eliminated if possible. Therefore, it is desirable that the width of the depletion region W be large enough so that most of the photons are absorbed within W rather than in the neutral p and n regions. When an EHP is created in the depletion region, the electric field sweeps the electron to the n side and the hole to the p side. Since this carrier drift occurs in a very short time, the response of the photodiode can be quite fast. When the carriers are generated primarily within the depletion layer W, the detector is called a *depletion layer photodiode*. Obviously, it is desirable to dope at least

Figure 8-7
Schematic
representation
of a p-i-n
photodiode.

one side of the junction lightly so that W can be made large. The appropriate width for W is chosen as a compromise between sensitivity and speed of response. If W is wide, most of the incident photons will be absorbed in the depletion region, leading to a high sensitivity. Also, a wide W results in a small junction capacitance [see Eq. (5–62)], thereby reducing the RC time constant of the detector circuit. On the other hand, W must not be so wide that the time required for drift of photogenerated carriers out of the depletion region is excessive, leading to low bandwidth.

One convenient method of controlling the width of the depletion region is to build a *p-i-n photodetector* (Fig. 8–7). The "i" region need not be truly intrinsic, as long as the resistivity is high. It can be grown epitaxially on the n-type substrate, and the p region can be obtained by implantation. When this device is reverse biased, the applied voltage appears almost entirely across the i region. If the carrier lifetime within the i region is long compared with the drift time, most of the photogenerated carriers will be collected by the n and p regions. An important figure of merit for a photodetector is the external quantum efficiency η_Q, defined as the number of carriers that are collected for every photon impinging on the detector. For a photocurrent density J_{op}, we collect J_{op}/q carriers per unit area per second. For an incident optical power density of P_{op}, the number of photons shining on the detector per unit area per second is $P_{op}/h\nu$. Therefore,

$$\eta_Q = (J_{op}/q)/(P_{op}/h\nu) \qquad (8-4)$$

For a photodiode that has no current gain, the maximum η_Q is unity. If low-level optical signals are to be detected, it is often desirable to operate the photodiode in the avalanche region of its characteristic. In this mode, each photogenerated carrier results in a significant change in the current because of avalanche multiplication, leading to *gain* and external quantum efficiencies of greater than 100%. *Avalanche photodiodes* (APDs) are useful as detectors in fiber-optic systems (Section 8.2.2).

The type of photodiode described here is sensitive to photons with energies near the band gap energy (*intrinsic* detectors). If $h\nu$ is less than E_g, the photons will not be absorbed; on the other hand, if the photons are much more energetic than E_g, they will be absorbed very near the surface, where the recombination rate is high. Therefore, it is necessary to choose a photodiode material with a band gap corresponding to a particular region of the spectrum. Detectors sensitive to longer wavelengths can be designed such that photons can excite electrons into or out of impurity levels (*extrinsic detectors*). However, the sensitivity of such extrinsic detectors is much less than intrinsic detectors, where EHPs are generated by excitation across the band gap.

By using lattice-matched multilayers of compound semiconductors, the band gap of the absorbing region can be tailored to match the wavelength of light being detected. Wider band gap material can then be used as a window through which the light is transmitted to the absorbing region (Fig. 8–8). For example, we saw in Fig. 1–13 that InGaAs with an In mole fraction of 53% can be grown epitaxially on InP with excellent lattice-matching. This composition of InGaAs has a band gap of about 0.75 eV, which is sensitive to a useful wavelength for fiber-optic systems (1.55 μm), as we shall see in Section 8.2.2. In making a photodiode using InGaAs as the active material, it is possible to bring the light through the wider band gap $In_{0.52}Al_{0.48}As$ (also lattice-matched to InP), thus greatly reducing surface recombination effects. In the case of APDs requiring narrow-band-gap material, it is often advantageous to absorb the light in the narrow-gap semiconductor (e.g., InGaAs) and transport the resulting carriers to a junction made in wider band gap material (e.g., InAlAs), where the avalanche multiplication takes place at high fields. Such a separation of the absorption and multiplication APDs avoids the excessive leakage currents typical of reverse-biased junctions in narrow-gap materials. In this particular structure, there is also a doped InAlAs *charge* layer, leading to a SACM APD, which helps optimize (decrease) the electric field further between the multiplication and absorption regions. In certain APDs, one can grade the alloy composition between the high-band-gap multiplication regions and the lower-band-gap absorption region to avoid any band-edge discontinuities, which can trap photogenerated carriers. The photocurrent and dark current both increase with bias because of avalanche multiplication (Fig. 8–8b). One obviously wants to maximize the difference ΔI between the photocurrent I_p and the dark current I_d. The ratio of ΔI at different voltages to that at a low reference voltage is defined as the *gain* of the APD.

8.1.4 Gain, Bandwidth, and Signal-to-Noise Ratio of Photodetectors

In optical communication systems, the sensitivity (which depends on gain) of the photodetector and its response time (bandwidth) are of critical importance. Typical gain–bandwidth characteristics of such a SACM APD are shown in Fig. 8–8c and are limited by the transit time of carriers through the structure. Unfortunately, designs that increase gain tend to decrease bandwidth and vice versa. It is common to express the *gain–bandwidth product* as a figure of merit for detectors. In a p-i-n diode, there is no gain mechanism, since at most one EHP is collected by the junction for each photon absorbed. Thus, the gain is essentially unity, and the gain–bandwidth

Figure 8–8

Use of multilayer heterojunctions to enhance the photodiode operation: (a) an APD in which light near 1.55 μm is absorbed in a narrow-band-gap material (InGaAs, $E_g = 0.75$ eV) after passing through a wider-gap material (InP and InAlAs); electrons are swept to an InAlAs junction, where avalanche multiplication takes place. The i regions are lightly doped; (b) photocurrent, dark current, and gain increasing as a function of bias because of avalanche multiplication; (c) typical gain–bandwidth characteristics of such a SACM APD. [After X. Zheng, J. Hsu, J. Hurst, X. Li, S. Wang, X. Sun, A. Holmes, J. Campbell, A. Huntington, and L. Coldren, *IEEE J. Quant. Elec.*, 40(8), pp. 1068–1073, Aug. 2004.]

product is determined by the bandwidth, or frequency response. In a p-i-n, the response time is dependent on the width of the depletion region.

Another important property of detectors is the *signal-to-noise (S/N) ratio*, which is the amount of usable information compared with the background noise in the detector. In the case of photoconductors, the major source of noise is random thermal motion of the carriers, leading to fluctuations in the dark current (called *Johnson noise*). The noise current increases with temperature ($\sim kT$) and with the conductance of the material in the dark. Therefore, the photoconductor noise at a given temperature can be reduced by increasing the dark resistance. Yet another source of noise at low frequencies is $1/f$ or flicker noise, due to carrier trapping and detrapping at defects.

In a p-i-n diode, the dark current is smaller and the dark resistance much higher than in a photoconductor, and the main source of noise is random thermal generation–recombination of EHPs within this region (called *shot noise*). The shot noise is ultimately due to the quantization of the charge of electrons and holes. The noise in a p-i-n device is considerably lower than that in a photoconductor, as well as in APDs, for reasons described next.

Avalanche photodiodes have the advantage of providing gain through the avalanche multiplication effect. The disadvantage is increased noise relative to the p-i-n, due to random fluctuations in the avalanche process. This noise is reduced if the impact ionization in the high-field region is due to only one type of carrier, since more fluctuations in the ionization process occur when both electrons and holes participate. In Si, the ability of electrons to create EHPs in an impact ionization event is much higher than for holes. Therefore, Si APDs can be operated with high gain and relatively low noise. Unfortunately, Si APDs cannot be used for most fiber-optic transmission because Si is transparent at the wavelengths of low loss and low dispersion ($\lambda = 1.55$ and $1.3 \ \mu m$) for optical fibers. For these longer wavelengths, $In_{0.53}Ga_{0.47}As$ has become the material of choice. However, the ionization rates of electrons and holes in most compound semiconductors are comparable, which degrades their noise and frequency response relative to Si APDs.

The various sources of noise determine the S/N ratio in a photodetector. One quantifies it as a noise-equivalent power (NEP), which is the minimum detectable signal that would produce the same rms output as the noise. The detectivity of the photodetector is then defined as $D = 1/NEP$.

The NEP depends on the area of the photodetector as well as the bandwidth. The specific detectivity, D^*, is then defined as that for a detector of unit area and a bandwidth of 1 Hz. Clearly, once the bandwidth requirements are met, it is desirable to choose a photodetector with the highest D^*.

Another approach that has demonstrated excellent performance in terms of both high sensitivity and bandwidth utilizes a waveguide structure (Fig. 8–9). Here, unlike the situation with the p-i-n photodiode (Fig. 8–7) or the APD (Fig. 8–8), the light strikes the photodiode perpendicular to the current transport. The advantage is that now the absorption region can be made quite long, along the photon path, leading to high sensitivity, while at the same time the photogenerated carriers have to traverse a short distance in the perpendicular direction, leading to short transit times and high bandwidth.

Figure 8–9

Schematic of a waveguide photodiode. The photons are strongly absorbed in the narrow-band-gap InGaAs region A, and carriers are multiplied by the avalanche process in region M. The charge region C helps optimize the electric field profile between A and M.

8.2 LIGHT-EMITTING DIODES

When carriers are injected across a forward-biased junction, the current is usually accounted for by recombination in the transition region and in the neutral regions near the junction. In a semiconductor with an indirect band gap, such as Si or Ge, the recombination releases heat to the lattice. On the other hand, in a material characterized by direct recombination, considerable light may be given off from the junction under forward bias. This effect, called *injection electroluminescence* (Section 4.2.2), provides an important application of diodes as generators of light. The use of LEDs in digital displays is well known. There are also other important applications, in traffic and automotive signals and in illumination. Another important device making use of radiative recombination in a forward-biased p-n junction is the *semiconductor laser*. As we shall see in Section 8.4, lasers emit coherent light in much narrower wavelength bands than LEDs, with more collimation (directionality), and are very useful for fiber-optic communication systems, as described in Section 8.2.2.

For LEDs, the frequency (color) of the photon is governed by the band gap of the semiconductor as given by the Planck relation, $h\nu = E_g$, which, in appropriate units, can be expressed as $E_g (\text{eV}) = 1.24/\lambda$ (μm). A very important metric of an LED is the external quantum efficiency η_{ext}, which is defined as the light output divided by the electrical input power:

$$\eta_{\text{ext}} = (\text{Internal radiative efficiency}) \times (\text{Extraction efficiency}) \quad (8\text{–}5)$$

The internal efficiency is a function of the quality of the material and the structure and composition of the layer. Defects in the material will clearly lead to nonradiative recombination. However, even if the internal efficiency is high, not all emitted photons are extracted from the LED. The emitted photons from an LED have a wide angular distribution, unlike those in a laser. For example, if an LED had a planar surface, the photons incident on the semiconductor–air interface at angles greater than a critical angle would undergo total internal reflection and ultimately be lost via absorption within the semiconductor. Hence, typically, LEDs are made with a dome-type encapsulation, which acts as a lens so that more of the photons can be extracted.

8.2.1 Light-Emitting Materials

The band gaps of various binary compound semiconductors are illustrated in Fig. 4–4 relative to the spectrum. There is a wide variation in band gaps and, therefore, in available photon energies, extending from the ultraviolet (GaN, 3.4 eV) into the infrared (InSb, 0.18 eV). In fact, by utilizing ternary and quaternary compounds the number of available energies can be increased significantly (see Figs. 1–13 and 3–6). A good example of the variation in photon energy obtainable from the compound semiconductors is the ternary alloy gallium arsenide–phosphide, which is illustrated in Fig. 8–10. When the percentage of As is reduced and P is increased in this material, the resulting band gap varies from the direct 1.43-eV gap of GaAs (infrared) to the indirect 2.26-eV gap of GaP (green). The band gap of $GaAs_{1-x}P_x$ varies almost linearly with x until the 0.45 composition is reached, and electron–hole recombination is direct over this range. The most common alloy composition used in red LED displays is $x \simeq 0.4$. For this composition the band gap is direct, since the Γ minimum (at $\mathbf{k} = 0$) is the lowest part of the conduction band. This results in efficient radiative recombination, and the emitted photons (~ 1.9 eV) are in the red portion of the spectrum.

For $GaAs_{1-x}P_x$ with P concentrations above 45 percent, the band gap is due to the indirect X minimum. Radiative recombination in such indirect materials is generally unlikely, because electrons in the conduction band have different momentum from holes in the valence band (see Fig. 3–5). Interestingly, however, indirect $GaAs_{1-x}P_x$ (including GaP, $x = 1$) doped with nitrogen can be used in LEDs with light output in the yellow to green portions of the spectrum. This is possible because the nitrogen impurity binds an electron very tightly. This confinement in real space (Δx) means that the electron momentum is spread out in momentum space Δp by the Heisenberg uncertainty principle [see Eq. (2–18)]. As a result, the momentum conservation rules, which generally prevent radiative recombination in indirect materials, are circumvented. Thus nitrogen doping of $GaAs_{1-x}P_x$ is not only useful technologically, but also provides an interesting and practical illustration of the uncertainty principle.

In many applications light from a laser or an LED need not be visible to the eye. Infrared emitters such as GaAs, InP, and mixed alloys of these compounds are particularly well suited to fiber-optical communication systems or TV remote controls. For example, a laser or LED can be used in

Figure 8–10
Conduction band
energies as a
function of alloy
composition for
$GaAs_{1-x}P_x$.

conjunction with a photodiode or other photosensitive device to transmit
information optically between locations. By varying the current through the
diode, the light output can be modulated such that analog or digital information appears in the optical signal directed at the detector. Alternatively,
the information may be introduced between the source and detector. For
example, a semiconductor laser-photodetector arrangement can be used in
a compact disc or DVD system for reading digital information from the
spinning disc. A light emitter and a photodiode form an *optoelectronic pair*,
which provides complete electrical isolation between input and output, since
the only link between the two devices is optical. In an *optoelectronic isolator*,
both devices may be mounted on a ceramic substrate and packaged together
to form a unit that passes information while maintaining isolation.

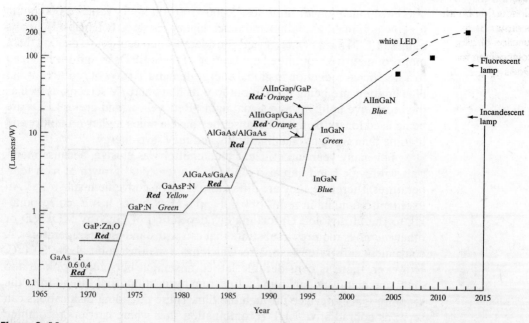

Figure 8–11

Improvement of luminous intensity of LEDs over time. From *Solid State Electronics*, Sixth Edition, by Ben G. Streetman and Sanjay Kumar Banerjee. © 2006 Pearson Education, Inc., Upper Saddle River, NJ. All Rights Reserved.

In view of the broad range of applications requiring semiconductor lasers and LEDs with visible and infrared wavelengths, the wide variety of available III–V materials is extremely useful. In addition to the AlGaAs and GaAsP systems shown in Fig. 3–6 and Fig. 8–10, the InAlGaP system is useful for red, yellow, and orange wavelengths, and AlGaInN is a strong emitter in the blue and green. Why is there so much interest in short wavelength emitters such as blue-green LEDs? As shown in Fig. 8–11, moderate efficiency (~10 lumens/watt) red, green, and yellow-green LEDs have existed for a long time in the GaAsP system, based on concepts such as N isoelectronic doping. More recently, in the mid-1990s, much higher brightness and efficiency (~30 lumens/watt) red-orange-yellow LEDs based on the InAlGaP system have been developed. The higher-band-gap InAlGaN system has direct band gaps over the entire alloy composition range and hence offers highly efficient light emission in the blue and green part of the spectrum. A major goal of the optoelectronics community has been the achievement of high-efficiency red, green, and blue emitters, because those colors are the three primary colors of the spectrum. By combining these color LEDs (or in conjunction with suitable phosphors), one can form intense white light sources (~500 lumens) with luminous efficiencies ~2 times greater than those of conventional incandescent lightbulbs. Since general-purpose illumination typically requires kilolumens of light, it may be practical to combine a few of these high-brightness LEDs for that purpose. They also have much longer lifetimes (5,000–100,000 hours versus 2,000 hours for conventional lightbulbs) and much higher energy efficiencies. The costs of these LEDs have been reduced considerably in recent years, making them more competitive. Continued application of these LEDs in lighting can lead to a significant reduction in global energy demand. Arrays of red, green, and blue emitters are being used in outdoor displays and TV screens, as well as in automotive taillights and signal lights. Red, yellow, and green LEDs are being used for traffic lights because they have a much higher reliability and lifetime than conventional lightbulbs, and they save energy.

For many years an efficient blue emitter was elusive, because materials with wide band gap also tend to require crystal growth at high temperatures. Therefore, they are difficult to grow on convenient substrates. An excellent candidate in terms of band gap is GaN, which has E_g corresponding to the ultraviolet. Unfortunately, deposition of GaN by MOCVD or other methods requires a substrate that can withstand high temperatures. A convenient substrate is sapphire, which has a melting point above 2000°C. However, there is considerable lattice mismatch between sapphire and GaN, and epitaxial GaN films suffer from dislocations that thread from the sapphire-GaN interface through the film. These threading dislocations can serve as nonradiative EHP recombination sites where carriers recombine with their energy given up as heat rather than light. This is not good news for an LED material, and for many years GaN films were inefficient light emitters. As sometimes happens (too bad it's not more often), nature provides a way around a problem that seems insurmountable. In this case it turns out that addition of In during the growth of the GaN film provides a way to avoid catastrophic loss of carriers at dislocations. Since In is not completely miscible in GaN, In-rich clusters form in InGaN which have a smaller band gap than the rest of the film. Therefore, carriers diffusing through the InGaN can fall into the potential well of the lower band gap cluster and recombine radiatively. If the density of such low-bandgap clusters significantly outnumbers the density of threading dislocations, many of the electron-hole pairs can survive to recombine giving off light. This discovery revolutionized the search for wide-bandgap materials to allow light emission in the blue and violet spectra. White light can be obtained by combining red, green, and blue emitters or by coating a blue or violet emitter with phosphors that can reemit various wavelengths to achieve white light. In recent years these white LED have been engineered to be extremely efficient, allowing the application of such high brightness LEDs in lighting applications.

One problem that is faced with LEDs is that many of the photons that are generated cannot be extracted from the device if it is a planar structure. The reason is that the semiconductor has a higher refractive index than the surrounding (air) medium, and for a light ray impinging on the surface at greater than the critical angle, it undergoes total internal reflection, and is re-absorbed. Hence, it is important to texture the surface of the LEDs to create micro-lenses such that a larger fraction of the light rays can be extracted. There are also important packaging challenges to dissipate heat from the devices by creating proper heat sinks. Therefore, considerable device engineering has been applied to the design of these devices in recent years, and the results have been impressive in terms of lumens out for a given power into the LED. Finally, after many years of work by crystal growers, device designers and packaging engineers, LEDs have become widespread in lighting as well as in displays.

8.2.2 Fiber-Optic Communications

The transmission of optical signals from source to detector can be greatly enhanced if an *optical fiber* is placed between the light source and the detector. An optical fiber is essentially a "light pipe" or waveguide for optical frequencies. The fiber is typically drawn from a boule of glass to a diameter of ~ 25 μm. The fine glass fiber is relatively flexible and can be used to guide optical signals over distances of kilometers without the necessity of perfect alignment between source and detector. This significantly increases the applications of optical communication in areas such as telephone and data transmission.

One type of optical fiber has an outer layer of very pure fused silica (SiO_2), with a core of germanium doped glass having a higher index of refraction (Fig. 8–12a).[1] Such a *step-index* fiber maintains the light beam primarily in the central core with little loss at the surface. The light is transmitted along the length of the fiber by internal reflection at the step in the refractive index.

Figure 8–12
Two examples of multimode fibers: (a) *a step index* having a core with a slightly larger refractive index **n**; (b) *a graded index* having, in this case, a parabolic grading of **n** in the core. The figure illustrates the cross section (left) of the fiber, its index-of-refraction profile (center), and typical mode patterns (right).

[1]The *index of refraction* (or *refractive index*) **n** compares the velocity of light v in the material with its velocity c in a vacuum: $n = c/v$. Thus, if $n_1 > n_2$ in Fig. 8–12a, the velocity of light is greater in material 2 than in 1. The value of **n** varies somewhat with the wavelength of light.

Losses in the fiber at a given wavelength can be described by an attenuation coefficient α [similar to the absorption coefficient of Eq. (4–3)]. The intensity of the signal at a distance x along the fiber is then related to the starting intensity by the usual expression.

$$\mathbf{I}(x) = \mathbf{I}_0 e^{-\alpha x} \qquad (8\text{–}6)$$

The attenuation is not the same for all wavelengths, however, and it is therefore important to choose a signal wavelength carefully. A plot of α vs. λ for a typical silica glass fiber is shown in Fig. 8–13. It is clear that dips in α near 1.3 and 1.55 μm provide "windows" in the attenuation, which can be exploited to reduce the degradation of signals. The overall decrease in attenuation with increasing wavelength is due to the reduced scattering from small random inhomogeneities which result in fluctuations of the refractive index on a scale comparable to the wavelength. This type of attenuation, called *Rayleigh scattering,* decreases with the fourth power of wavelength. This effect is observed at sunrise and sunset, when attenuation of short wavelength blue and green light results in red and orange sunlight. Obviously, Rayleigh scattering encourages operation at long wavelengths in fiber-optic systems. However, a competing process of infrared absorption dominates for wavelengths longer than about 1.7 μm, due to vibrational excitation of the atoms making up the glass. Therefore, a useful minimum in absorption for silica fibers occurs at about 1.55 μm, where epitaxial layers in the (In, Ga) (As, P) system can be grown lattice-matched to InP substrates (see Fig. 1–13).

Another consideration in choice of operating wavelength is the *pulse dispersion,* or spreading of data pulses as they propagate down the fiber. This

Figure 8–13
Typical plot of attenuation coefficient α vs. wavelength λ for a fused silica optical fiber. Peaks are due primarily to OH$^-$ impurities.

effect can be caused by the wavelength dependence of the refractive index, causing different optical frequencies to travel down the fiber with slightly different velocities. This effect, called *chromatic dispersion,* is much less pronounced at the 1.3 μm window in Fig. 8–13. Another cause of dispersion is the fact that different modes propagate with different path lengths (Fig. 8–12a). This type of dispersion can be reduced by grading the refractive index of the core (Fig. 8–12b) such that various modes are continually refocused, reducing the differences in path lengths.

The light source in a fiber-optic system today is a laser, because the light is made up of essentially a single frequency and allows a very large information bandwidth. (Semiconductor lasers suitable for fiber-optic communications will be discussed in Section 8.4.) In early optoelectronic systems for fiber optics, it was most convenient to use the well-established GaAs–AlGaAs system for making lasers and LEDs. These light sources are highly efficient, and good detectors can be made using Si p-i-n or APDs. However, these sources operate in the wavelength range near 0.9 μm, where the attenuation is greater than that for longer wavelengths. Modern systems, therefore, operate near the 1.3- and 1.55 μm minima shown in Fig. 8–13. At these wavelengths, lasers can be made by using InGaAs or InGaAsP grown on InP, and detectors can be made of the same materials (see Fig. 8–8).

Multimode fibers are larger (~25 μm in diameter) than *single-mode* fibers (~5 μm) and transmit a coherent laser beam. By forming numerous optical fibers into a bundle, with an appropriate jacket for mechanical strength, an enormous amount of information can be transmitted over long distances.[2] Depending upon the losses in the fibers, repeater stations may be required periodically along the path. Thus, many photodetectors and laser sources are required in a fiber-optic system. Semiconductor device development, including appropriate binary, ternary, and quaternary compounds for both emitters and detectors, is therefore crucial to the successful implementation of such optical communications systems. A schematic of a fiber-optic transmission system is shown in Fig. 8–14.

What composition x of $Al_xGa_{1-x}As$ would emit red light at 680 nm? What composition of $GaAs_{1-x}P_x$?

EXAMPLE 8–3

The band gap E_g (eV) $= 1.24/\lambda$ (μm) $= 1.24/0.68 = 1.82$ eV.
From Fig. 3–6, we get $Al_{0.32}Ga_{0.68}As$.
From Fig. 8–10, we get $GaAs_{0.68}P_{0.32}$.

SOLUTION

---

[2]Transmission rates of 40 Gbit/s are becoming standard, but even higher rates of 400 Gbit/s have been achieved using ultradense-wavelength-division multiplexing (UDWDM). This approach uses slightly different wavelengths or colors to carry different channels of information along the same fiber. As a convenient calibration of the 40 Gbit/s rate, it is worth noting that the human eye is able to transmit about 1 Gbit/s to the brain.

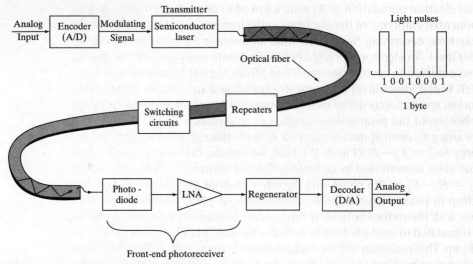

Figure 8–14
Schematic of a fiber-optic communication system illustrating the transmission of analog signals, such as those in telephony or TV. After the signal is converted to a digital electrical signal, it is used to modulate the laser light output as light pulses that are transmitted down the fiber, with periodic amplification of the signal with repeaters to compensate for fiber loss. Switching circuits route signals appropriately. After the optical signal is transformed to an electrical output by a photodetector and a low-noise preamplifier (LNA), it is converted to an analog signal, once distortions of the digital signals due to propagation through the fiber have been corrected with the use of a "regenerator."

**8.3
LASERS**

The word LASER is an acronym for *light amplification by stimulated emission of radiation*, which sums up the operation of an important optical and electronic device. The laser is a source of highly directional, monochromatic, coherent light, and as such it has revolutionized some longstanding optical problems and has created some new fields of basic and applied optics. The light from a laser, depending on the type, can be a continuous beam of low or medium power, or it can be a short burst of intense light delivering millions of watts. Light has always been a primary communications link between humans and the environment, but until the invention of the laser, the light sources available for transmitting information and performing experiments were generally neither monochromatic nor coherent, and were of relatively low intensity. Thus the laser is of great interest in optics; but it is equally important in optoelectronics, particularly in fiber-optic communications. The last three letters in the word *laser* are intended to imply how the device operates: by the *stimulated emission* of *radiation*. In Chapter 2 we discussed the emission of radiation when excited electrons fall to lower energy states; but generally, these processes occur randomly and can therefore be classed as *spontaneous emission*. This means that the rate at which electrons fall from an upper level of energy E_2 to a lower level E_1 is at every instant proportional to the number of electrons remaining in E_2 (the *population* of E_2). Thus if an initial electron population in E_2 were allowed to decay, we would expect an exponential emptying of the electrons to the lower energy level, with a mean decay time describing how much time an average electron spends in the upper level. An electron in a higher or excited state need not wait for spontaneous emission to occur, however; if conditions are right, it can be *stimulated* to fall to the lower level and emit its photon in a time much shorter than its mean spontaneous decay time. The stimulus is provided by the presence of photons of the proper wavelength. Let us visualize an electron in state E_2 waiting to drop spontaneously to E_1 with the emission of a photon of energy $h\nu_{12} = E_2 - E_1$ (Fig. 8–15). Now we assume that this electron in the upper state is immersed in an intense field of photons, each having energy $h\nu_{12} = E_2 - E_1$, and in phase with the other photons. The electron is induced to drop in energy from E_2 to E_1, contributing a photon whose wave is *in phase* with the radiation field. If this process continues and other electrons are stimulated to emit photons in the same fashion, a large radiation field can build up. This radiation will be *monochromatic* since each photon will have an energy of precisely $h\nu_{12} = E_2 - E_1$ and will be *coherent*, because all the photons released will be in phase and reinforcing. This process of stimulated emission can be described quantum mechanically to relate the probability of emission to the intensity of the radiation field. Without quantum mechanics we can make a few observations here about the relative rates at which the absorption and emission processes occur. Let us assume the instantaneous populations of E_1 and E_2 to be n_1 and n_2, respectively. We know from earlier discussions of distributions and the Boltzmann factor that at *thermal equilibrium* the relative population will be

$$\frac{n_2}{n_1} = e^{-(E_2 - E_1)/kT} = e^{-h\nu_{12}/kT} \qquad (8\text{–}7)$$

if the two levels contain an equal number of available states.

The negative exponent in this equation indicates that $n_2 \ll n_1$ at equilibrium; that is, most electrons are in the lower energy level as expected. If the atoms exist in a radiation field of photons with energy $h\nu_{12}$, such that the energy density of the field is $\rho(\nu_{12})$,[3] then stimulated emission can occur along

Figure 8–15
Stimulated transition of an electron from an upper state to a lower state, with accompanying photon emission.

---

[3]The energy density $\rho(\nu_{12})$ indicates the total energy in the radiation field per unit volume and per unit frequency, due to photons with $h\nu_{12} = E_2 - E_1$.

Figure 8–16
Balance of
absorption and
emission in
steady state:
(a) stimulated
emission;
(b) absorption;
(c) spontaneous
emission.

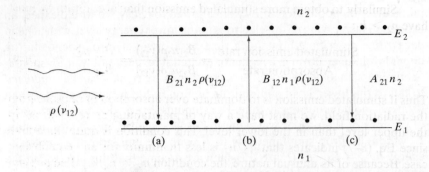

with absorption and spontaneous emission. The rate of stimulated emission is proportional to the instantaneous number of electrons in the upper level n_2 and to the energy density of the stimulating field $\rho(\nu_{12})$. Thus we can write the stimulated emission rate as $B_{21}n_2\rho(\nu_{12})$, where B_{21} is a proportionality factor. The rate at which the electrons in E_1 absorb photons should also be proportional to $\rho(\nu_{12})$, and to the electron population in E_1. Therefore, the absorption rate is $B_{12}n_1\rho(\nu_{12})$, where B_{12} is a proportionality factor for absorption. Finally, the rate of spontaneous emission is proportional only to the population of the upper level. Introducing still another coefficient, we can write the rate of spontaneous emission as $A_{21}n_2$. For steady state the two emission rates must balance the rate of absorption to maintain constant populations n_1 and n_2 (Fig. 8–16).

$$
\begin{array}{ccc}
B_{12}n_1\rho(\nu_{12}) & = & A_{21}n_2 & + & B_{21}n_2\rho(\nu_{12}) \\
\text{Absorption} & = & \text{spontaneous} & + & \text{stimulated} \\
& & \text{emission} & & \text{emission}
\end{array}
\tag{8–8a}
$$

This relation was described by Einstein, and the coefficients B_{12}, A_{21}, B_{21} are called the *Einstein coefficients*. We notice from Eq. (8–8a) that no energy density ρ is required to cause a transition from an upper to a lower state; spontaneous emission occurs without an energy density to drive it. The reverse is not true, however; exciting an electron to a higher state (absorption) requires the application of energy, as we would expect thermodynamically.

At equilibrium, the ratio of the stimulated to spontaneous emission rates is generally very small, and the contribution of stimulated emission is negligible. With a photon field present,

$$
\frac{\text{Stimulated emission rate}}{\text{Spontaneous emission rate}} = \frac{B_{21}n_2\rho(\nu_{12})}{A_{21}n_2} = \frac{B_{21}}{A_{21}}\rho(\nu_{12})
\tag{8–8b}
$$

As Eq. (8–8b) indicates, the way to enhance the stimulated emission over spontaneous emission is to have a very large photon field energy density $\rho(\nu_{12})$. In the laser, this is encouraged by providing an *optical resonant cavity* in which the photon density can build up to a large value through multiple internal reflections at certain frequencies (ν).

Similarly, to obtain more stimulated emission than absorption we must have $n_2 > n_1$:

$$\frac{\text{Stimulated emission rate}}{\text{Absorption rate}} = \frac{B_{21}n_2\rho(v_{12})}{B_{12}n_1\rho(v_{12})} = \frac{B_{21}}{B_{12}}\frac{n_2}{n_1} \qquad (8\text{--}9)$$

Thus if stimulated emission is to dominate over absorption of photons from the radiation field, we must have a way of maintaining more electrons in the upper level than in the lower level. This condition is quite unnatural, since Eq. (8–7) indicates that n_2/n_1 is less than unity for any equilibrium case. Because of its unusual nature, the condition $n_2 > n_1$ is called *population inversion*. It is also referred to as a condition of *negative temperature*. This rather startling terminology emphasizes the nonequilibrium nature of population inversion, and refers to the fact that the ratio n_2/n_1 in Eq. (8–7) could be larger than unity only if the temperature were negative. Of course, this manner of speaking does not imply anything about temperature in the usual sense of that word. The fact is that Eq. (8–7) is a thermal equilibrium equation and cannot be applied to the situation of population inversion without invoking the concept of negative temperature.

In summary, Eqs. (8–8b) and (8–9) indicate that if the photon density is to build up through a predominance of stimulated emission over both spontaneous emission and absorption, two requirements must be met. We must provide (1) an optical resonant cavity to encourage the photon field to build up and (2) a means of obtaining population inversion.

An optical resonant cavity can be obtained using reflecting mirrors to reflect the photons back and forth, allowing the photon energy density to build up. One or both of the end mirrors are constructed to be partially transmitting so that a fraction of the light will "leak out" of the resonant system. This transmitted light is the output of the laser. Of course, in designing such a laser one must choose the amount of transmission to be a small perturbation on the resonant system. The gain in photons per pass between the end plates must be larger than the transmission at the ends, scattering from impurities, absorption, and other losses. The arrangement of parallel plates providing multiple internal reflections is similar to that used in the Fabry–Perot interferometer;[4] thus the reflecting ends of the laser cavity are often referred to as Fabry–Perot faces. As Fig. 8–17 indicates, light of a particular frequency can be reflected back and forth within the resonant cavity in a reinforcing (coherent) manner if an integral number of half-wavelengths fit between the end mirrors. Thus the length of the cavity for stimulated emission must be

$$L = \frac{m\lambda}{2} \qquad (8\text{--}10)$$

---

[4]Interferometers are discussed in many sophomore physics texts.

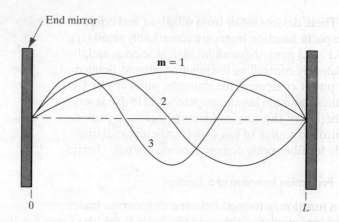

where **m** is an integer. In this equation λ is the photon wavelength within the laser material. If we wish to use the wavelength λ_0 of the output light in the atmosphere (often taken as the vacuum value), the index of refraction **n** of the laser material must be considered

$$\lambda_0 = \lambda \mathbf{n} \qquad (8\text{--}11)$$

In practice, $L \gg \lambda$, and Eq. (8–10) is automatically satisfied over some portion of the mirror. An important exception occurs in the vertical cavity surface-emitting lasers discussed in Section 8.4.4, for which the cavity length is comparable to the wavelength.

There are ways of obtaining population inversion in the atomic levels of many solids, liquids, and gases, and in the energy bands of semiconductors. Thus the possibilities for laser systems with various materials are quite extensive. An early laser system used a ruby rod. In gas lasers, electrons are excited to metastable levels in molecules to achieve population inversion. These are interesting and useful laser systems, but in view of our emphasis on semiconductor devices in this book, we will move to the description of semiconductor lasers.

**8.4
SEMICONDUCTOR
LASERS**

The laser became an important part of semiconductor device technology in 1962 when the first p-n junction lasers were built in GaAs (infrared)[5] and GaAsP (visible).[6] We have already discussed the incoherent light emission from p-n junctions (LEDs), generated by the spontaneous recombination of electrons and holes injected across the junction. In this section we shall concentrate on the requirements for population inversion due to these injected carriers and the nature of the coherent light from p-n junction

---

[5]R. N. Hall et al., *Physical Review Letters* 9, pp. 366–368 (November 1, 1962); M. I. Nathan et al., *Applied Physics Letters* 1, pp. 62–64 (November 1, 1962); T. M. Quist et al., *Applied Physics Letters* 1, pp. 91–92 (December 1, 1962).
[6]N. Holonyak, Jr., and S. F. Bevacqua, *Applied Physics Letters* 1, pp. 82–83 (December 1, 1962).

lasers. These devices differ from solid, gas, and liquid lasers in several important respects. Junction lasers are remarkably small (typically on the order of $0.1 \times 0.1 \times 0.3$ mm), they exhibit high efficiency, and the laser output is easily modulated by controlling the junction current. Semiconductor lasers operate at low power compared, for example, with ruby or CO_2 lasers; on the other hand, these junction lasers compete with He–Ne lasers in power output. Thus the function of the semiconductor laser is to provide a portable and easily controlled source of low-power coherent radiation. They are particularly suitable for fiber-optic communication systems (Section 8.2.2).

8.4.1 Population Inversion at a Junction

If a p-n junction is formed between degenerate materials, the bands under forward bias appear as shown in Fig. 8–18. If the bias (and thus the current) is large enough, electrons and holes are injected into and across the transition region in considerable concentrations. As a result, the region about the junction is far from being depleted of carriers. This region contains a large concentration of electrons within the conduction band and a large concentration of holes within the valence band. If these population densities are high enough, a condition of population inversion results, and the region about the junction over which it occurs is called an *inversion region*.[7]

Population inversion at a junction is best described by the use of the concept of *quasi-Fermi levels* (Section 4.3.3). Since the forward-biased condition of Fig. 8–18 is a distinctly nonequilibrium state, the equilibrium equations defining the Fermi level are not applicable. In particular, the concentration of electrons in the inversion region (and for several diffusion lengths into the p material) is larger than equilibrium statistics would imply; the same is also true for the injected holes in the n material. We can use Eq. (4–15) to describe the carrier concentrations in terms of the quasi-Fermi levels for electrons and holes in steady state. Thus

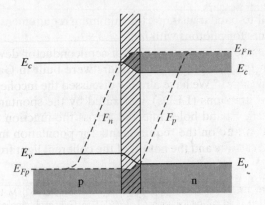

Figure 8–18
Band diagram of a p-n junction laser under forward bias. The crosshatched region indicates the inversion region at the junction.

[7]This is a different meaning of the term from that used in reference to MOS transistors.

$$n = N_c e^{-(E_c - F_n)/kT} = n_i e^{(F_n - E_i)/kT} \qquad (8\text{--}12a)$$

$$p = N_v e^{-(F_p - E_v)/kT} = n_i e^{(E_i - F_p)/kT} \qquad (8\text{--}12b)$$

Using Eqs. (8–12a) and (b), we can draw F_n and F_p on any band diagram for which we know the electron and hole distributions. For example, in Fig. 8–18, F_n in the neutral n region is essentially the same as the equilibrium Fermi level E_{Fn}. This is true to the extent that the electron concentration on the n side is equal to its equilibrium value. However, since large numbers of electrons are injected across the junction, the electron concentration begins at a high value near the junction and decays exponentially to its equilibrium value n_p deep in the p material. Therefore, F_n drops from E_{Fn} as shown in Fig. 8–18. We notice that, deep in the neutral regions, the quasi-Fermi levels are essentially equal. The separation of F_n and F_p at any point is a measure of the departure from equilibrium at that point. Obviously, this departure is considerable in the inversion region, since F_n and F_p are separated by an energy greater than the band gap (Fig. 8–19).

Unlike the case of the two-level system discussed in Section 8.3, the condition for population inversion in semiconductors must take into account the distribution of energies available for transitions between the bands. The basic definition of population inversion holds—for dominance of stimulated emission between two energy levels separated by energy $h\nu$, the electron population of the upper level must be greater than that of the lower level. The unusual aspect of a semiconductor is that bands of levels are available for such transitions. Population inversion obviously exists for transitions between the bottom of the conduction band E_c and the top of the valence band E_v in Fig. 8–19. In fact, transitions between levels in the conduction band up to F_n and levels in the valence band down to F_p take place under conditions of population inversion. For any given transition energy $h\nu$ in a semiconductor, population inversion exists when

$$(F_n - F_p) > h\nu \qquad (8\text{--}13a)$$

For band-to-band transitions, the minimum requirement for population inversion occurs for photons with $h\nu = E_c - E_v = E_g$

$$(F_n - F_p) > E_g \qquad (8\text{--}13b)$$

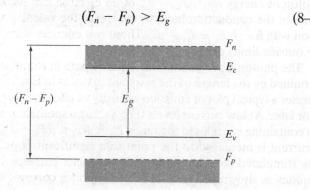

Figure 8–19
Expanded view of the inversion region.

(a)   (b)

Figure 8–20
Variation of the inversion-region width with forward bias: $V(a) < V(b)$.

When F_n and F_p lie within their respective bands (as in Fig. 8–19), stimulated emission can dominate over a range of transitions, from $h\nu = (F_n - F_p)$ to $h\nu = E_g$. As we shall see below, the dominant transitions for laser action are determined largely by the resonant cavity and the strong recombination radiation occurring near $h\nu = E_g$.

In choosing a material for junction laser fabrication, it is necessary that electron–hole recombination occur directly, rather than through trapping processes such as are dominant in Si or Ge. Gallium arsenide is an example of such a "direct" semiconductor. Furthermore, we must be able to dope the material n-type or p-type to form a junction. If an appropriate resonant cavity can be constructed in the junction region, a laser results in which population inversion is accomplished by the bias current applied to the junction (Fig. 8–20).

8.4.2 Emission Spectra for p-n Junction Lasers

Under forward bias, an inversion layer can be obtained along the plane of the junction, where a large population of electrons exists at the same location as a large hole population. A second look at Fig. 8–19 indicates that spontaneous emission of photons can occur due to direct recombination of electrons and holes, releasing energies ranging from approximately $F_n - F_p$ to E_g. That is, an electron can recombine over an energy from F_n to F_p, yielding a photon of energy $h\nu = F_n - F_p$, or an electron can recombine from the bottom of the conduction band to the top of the valence band, releasing a photon with $h\nu = E_c - E_v = E_g$. These two energies serve as the approximate outside limits of the laser spectra.

The photon wavelengths which participate in stimulated emission are determined by the length of the resonant cavity as in Eq. (8–10). Figure 8–21 illustrates a typical plot of emission intensity vs. photon energy for a semiconductor laser. At low current levels (Fig. 8–21a), a spontaneous emission spectrum containing energies in the range $E_g < h\nu < (F_n - F_p)$ is obtained. As the current is increased to the point that significant population inversion exists, stimulated emission occurs at frequencies corresponding to the cavity modes as shown in Fig. 8–21b. These modes correspond to successive numbers of integral half-wavelengths fitted within the cavity, as described by Eq. (8–10). Finally, at a still higher current level, a most preferred mode or

Figure 8–21
Light intensity
vs. photon
energy $h\nu$ for a
junction laser:
(a) incoherent
emission below
threshold;
(b) laser modes
at threshold;
(c) dominant laser
mode above
threshold. The
intensity scales
are greatly
compressed from
(a) to (b) to (c).

set of modes will dominate the spectral output (Fig. 8–21c). This very intense mode represents the main laser output of the device; the output light will be composed of almost monochromatic radiation superimposed on a relatively weak radiation background, due primarily to spontaneous emission.

The separation of the modes in Fig. 8–21b is complicated by the fact that the index of refraction **n** for GaAs depends on wavelength λ. From Eq. (8–10) we have

$$\mathbf{m} = \frac{2L\mathbf{n}}{\lambda_0} \tag{8–14}$$

If **m** (the number of half-wavelengths in L) is large, we can use the derivative to find its rate of change with λ_0:

$$\frac{d\mathbf{m}}{d\lambda_0} = -\frac{2L\mathbf{n}}{\lambda_0^2} + \frac{2L}{\lambda_0}\frac{d\mathbf{n}}{d\lambda_0} \tag{8–15}$$

Now reverting to discrete changes in **m** and λ_0, we can write

$$-\Delta\lambda_0 = \frac{\lambda_0^2}{2L\mathbf{n}}\left(1 - \frac{\lambda_0}{\mathbf{n}}\frac{d\mathbf{n}}{d\lambda_0}\right)^{-1}\Delta\mathbf{m} \tag{8–16}$$

If we let $\Delta\mathbf{m} = -1$, we can calculate the change in wavelength $\Delta\lambda_0$ between adjacent modes (i.e., between modes **m** and **m** − 1).

8.4.3 The Basic Semiconductor Laser

To build a p-n junction laser, we need to form a junction in a highly doped, direct semiconductor (GaAs, for example), construct a resonant cavity in the proper geometrical relationship to the junction, and make contact to the junction in a mounting which allows for efficient heat transfer. The first lasers were built as shown in Fig. 8–22. Beginning with a degenerate n-type sample, a p region is formed on one side, for example by diffusing Zn into the n-type GaAs. Since Zn is in column II of the periodic table and is introduced substitutionally on Ga sites, it serves as an acceptor in GaAs; therefore, the heavily doped Zn diffused layer forms a p⁺ region (Fig. 8–22b). At this point we have a large-area planar p-n junction. Next, grooves are cut or etched

Figure 8–22
Fabrication
of a simple
junction laser:
(a) degenerate
n-type sample;
(b) diffused p
layer; (c) isolation
of junctions by
cutting or etching;
(d) individual
junction to be
cut or cleaved
into devices;
(e) mounted laser
structure.

along the length of the sample as in Fig. 8–22c, leaving a series of long p regions isolated from each other. These p-n junctions can be cut or broken apart (Fig. 8–22d) and then cleaved into devices of the desired length.

At this point in the fabrication process, the very important requirements of a resonant cavity must be considered. It is necessary that the front and back faces (Fig. 8–22e) be flat and parallel. This can be accomplished by cleaving. If the sample has been oriented so that the long junctions of Fig. 8–22d are perpendicular to a crystal plane of the material, it is possible to cleave the sample along this plane into laser devices, letting the crystal structure itself provide the parallel faces. The device is then mounted on a suitable header, and contact is made to the p region. Various techniques are used to provide adequate heat sinking of the device for large forward current levels.

8.4.4 Heterojunction Lasers

The device described above was the first type used in the early development of semiconductor lasers. Since the device contains only one junction in a single type of material, it is referred to as a *homojunction* laser. To obtain more efficient lasers, and particularly to build lasers that operate at room temperature, it is necessary to use multiple layers in the laser structure. Such devices, called *heterojunction lasers*, can be made to operate continuously at room temperature to satisfy the requirements of optical communications. An example of a heterojunction laser is shown in Fig. 8–23. In this structure the injected carriers are confined to a narrow region so that population inversion can be built up at lower current levels. The result is a lowering of the *threshold current* at which laser action begins. Carrier confinement is obtained in this single-heterojunction laser by the layer of AlGaAs grown epitaxially on the GaAs.

In GaAs the laser action occurs primarily on the p side of the junction due to a higher efficiency for electron injection than for hole injection. In a normal p-n junction the injected electrons diffuse into the p material such

Figure 8–23
Use of a single
heterojunction
for carrier
confinement in
laser diodes:
(a) AlGaAs
heterojunction
grown on the
thin p-type GaAs
layer; (b) band
diagrams for
the structure of
(a), showing the
confinement of
electrons to the
thin p region
under bias.

that population inversion occurs for only part of the electron distribution near the junction. However, if the p material is narrow and terminated in a barrier, the injected electrons can be confined near the junction. In Fig. 8–23a, an epitaxial layer of p-type AlGaAs ($E_g \simeq 2\,\text{eV}$) is grown on top of the thin p-type GaAs region. The wider band gap of AlGaAs effectively terminates the p-type GaAs layer, since injected electrons do not surmount the barrier at the GaAs–AlGaAs heterojunction (Fig. 8–23b). As a result of the confinement of injected electrons, laser action begins at a substantially lower current than for simple p-n junctions. In addition to the effects of carrier confinement, the change of refractive index at the heterojunction provides a waveguide effect for optical confinement of the photons.

A further improvement can be obtained by sandwiching the active GaAs layer between two AlGaAs layers (Fig. 8–24). This *double-heterojunction* structure further confines injected carriers to the active region, and the change in refractive index at the GaAs–AlGaAs boundaries helps to confine the generated light waves. In the double-heterojunction laser shown in Fig. 8–24b the injected current is restricted to a narrow stripe along the lasing direction, to reduce the total current required to drive the device. This type of laser was a major step forward in the development of lasers for fiber-optic communications.

Separate Confinement and Graded Index Channels.   One of the disadvantages of the double-heterostructure laser shown in Fig. 8–24 is the fact that the carrier confinement and the optical waveguiding both depend on the same heterojunctions. It is much better to optimize these two functions by using a narrow confinement region for keeping the carriers in a region of high recombination, and a somewhat wider optical waveguide region. In Fig. 8–25a we show a *separate confinement* laser in which the width of the optical

Figure 8–24
A double-heterojunction laser structure: (a) multiple layers used to confine injected carriers and provide waveguiding for the light; (b) a stripe geometry designed to restrict the current injection to a narrow stripe along the lasing direction. One of many methods for obtaining the stripe geometry, this example is obtained by proton bombardment of the unshaded regions in (b), which converts the GaAs and AlGaAs to a semi-insulating form.

waveguiding region (w) is optimized by using the refractive index step at a separate heterojunction from that used to confine the carriers. For example, in the GaAs–Al$_x$Ga$_{1-x}$As system the optical confinement (waveguiding) occurs at a boundary with much larger composition x (and therefore smaller refractive index) than is the case for the carrier confinement barrier. By grading the composition of the AlGaAs it is possible to obtain even better waveguiding. For example, in Fig. 8–25b a parabolic grading

Figure 8–25
Separate confinement of carriers and waveguiding: (a) use of separate changes in AlGaAs alloy composition to confine carriers in the region (d) of the smallest band gap and to obtain waveguiding (w) at the larger step in the refractive index; (b) grading the alloy composition, and therefore the refractive index, for better waveguiding and carrier confinement.

of the refractive index leads to a waveguide within the laser analogous to that shown in Fig. 8–12 for a fiber. This *graded index separate confinement heterostructure (GRINSCH)* laser also provides built-in fields for better electron confinement.

Vertical Cavity Surface-Emitting Lasers (VCSELs).   There are advantages to laser structures in which light is emitted normal to the surface, including ease of device testing on the wafer before packaging. An interesting approach is the VCSEL, in which the cavity mirrors are replaced by DBRs, which use many partial reflectors spaced to reflect light constructively. DBRs can be grown by MBE or OMVPE. In Fig. 8–26 the bottom DBR mirror of a VCSEL is composed of many alternating layers of AlAs and GaAs with thickness one-quarter of a wavelength in each material. The top mirror is composed of deposited dielectric layers (alternating ZnSe and MgF). Current is funneled into the active region from the top contact by using an oxide layer achieved by laterally oxidizing an AlGaAs layer to form an aluminum oxide. The active region of the laser employs InGaAs–GaAs quantum wells, and the GaAs cavity between the two DBRs is one wavelength long. The VCSEL can be made with much shorter cavity length than other structures, and as a result of Eq. (8–16) the laser modes are widely separated in wavelength. Thus single-mode laser operation is more easily achieved with the VCSEL. Lasing can be achieved at very low current (< 50 μA) with this device.

8.4.5 Materials for Semiconductor Lasers

We have discussed the properties of the junction laser largely in terms of GaAs and AlGaAs. However, as discussed in Section 8.2.2, the InGaAsP/InP system is particularly well suited for the type of lasers used in fiber-optic communication systems. Lattice-matching (Section 1.4.1) is important in creating heterostructures by epitaxial growth. The fact that the AlGaAs band

Figure 8–26
Schematic cross section of oxide-confined vertical cavity surface-emitting laser diode. [D. G. Deppe et al., *IEEE J. Selected Topics in Quantum Elec.*, 3(3) (June 1997): 893–904.]

gap can be varied by choice of composition on the column III sublattice allows the formation of barriers and confining layers such as those shown in Section 8.4.4. The quaternary alloy InGaAsP is particularly versatile in the fabrication of laser diodes, allowing considerable choice of wavelength and flexibility in lattice-matching. By choice of composition, lasers can be made in the infrared range 1.3–1.55 μm required for fiber optics. Since four components can be varied in choosing an alloy composition, InGaAsP allows simultaneous choice of energy gap (and therefore emission wavelength) and lattice constant (for lattice-matched growth on convenient substrates). In many applications, however, other wavelength ranges are required for laser output. For example, the use of lasers in pollution diagnostics requires wavelengths farther in the infrared than are available from InGaAsP and AlGaAs. In this application the ternary alloy PbSnTe provides laser output wavelengths from about 7 μm to more than 30 μm at low temperatures, depending on the material composition. For intermediate wavelengths, the InGaSb system can be used.

Materials chosen for the fabrication of semiconductor lasers must be efficient light emitters and also be amenable to the formation of p-n junctions and in most cases the formation of heterojunction barriers. These requirements eliminate some materials from practical use in laser diodes. For example, semiconductors with indirect band gaps are not sufficiently efficient light emitters for practical laser fabrication. The II–VI compounds, on the other hand, are generally very efficient at emitting light but junctions are difficult to form. By modern crystal growth techniques such as MBE and MOVPE it is possible to grow junctions in ZnS, ZnSe, ZnTe, and alloys of these materials, using N as the acceptor. Lasers can be made in these materials which emit in the green and blue-green regions of the spectrum.

In recent years much progress has been made in the growth of large band gap semiconductors using GaN, and its alloys with InN and AlN. The InAlGaN system has direct band gaps over the entire alloy composition range, and hence offers very efficient light emission. Band gaps range from about 2 eV for InN to 3.4 eV for GaN and 5 eV for AlN. This covers the wavelength range from about 620 nm to about 248 nm, which is from blue to UV. The resurgence of interest in this field was triggered by the work of Nakamura at Nichia Corporation in Japan who demonstrated very high-efficiency blue light emitting diodes (LEDs) in GaN.

Two of the problems that had stymied progress in this field since pioneering work by Pankove in the 1970s was the absence of a suitable substrate having sufficient lattice match with GaN, and the inability to achieve p-type doping in this semiconductor. GaN bulk crystals cannot be grown easily because of the high vapor pressure of the nitrogen-bearing precursor (generally ammonia). This requires growth at high temperature and pressure. This precludes using bulk GaN wafers as substrates for epitaxial growth. However, epitaxial layers can be grown on other substrates with reasonable success, in spite of the lattice mismatch.

GaN exists in the cubic zinc blende form (which is the preferred structure) as well as the hexagonal wurtzite form. It was demonstrated recently that cubic GaN could be grown heteroepitaxially on sapphire, even though it is not lattice-matched to GaN. In fact, sapphire does not even have a cubic crystal structure—it is hexagonal. The lattice constant of GaN is about 4.5 Å, while that of sapphire is 4.8 Å, which is a huge lattice mismatch. Contrary to what would normally be expected, however, high-quality epitaxial GaN films can be grown on sapphire by MOCVD using ammonia and tri-methyl gallium as the precursors. One possible reason for the high quality of the films, as evidenced by blue LEDs and short wavelength lasers fabricated in these nitrides, is that these large-band-gap semiconductors have very high chemical bond strengths. As discussed in Section 8.2.1, the addition of In to GaN results in lower bandgap In-rich regions which provide sites for radiative recombination, minimizing the loss of carriers at dislocations. Another breakthrough required in the nitrides was the ability to achieve high p-type doping so that p-n junctions could be formed. It has been demonstrated that Mg (which is a column II element) doping of MOCVD films, followed by high temperature annealing can be used to achieve high acceptor concentrations in these systems.

Short wavelength emitters such as UV/blue semiconductor lasers are important for storage applications such as digital versatile discs (DVDs), which are higher density versions of compact discs (CDs). The storage density on these discs is inversely proportional to the square of the laser wavelength that is used to read the information. Thus reducing the laser wavelength by a factor of two leads to a four-fold increase of storage density. Such an increased storage capacity opens up entirely new applications for DVDs that were not possible previously with conventional CDs, for example, the storage of full-length movies. A recent example of success in this rapidly progressing field is a 417-nm semiconductor laser made with InGaN multi–quantum-well heterostructures.

8.4.6 Quantum Cascade Lasers

The lasers described above are bipolar devices involving interband transitions. Electrons in the conduction band recombine with holes in the valence band, and photons are emitted at an energy determined by the bandgap. This limits laser operation to direct bandgap materials for reasons discussed in Chapter 4.

The quantum cascade laser (QCL), on the other hand, involves unipolar operation based on inter-subband transitions in a series of coupled quantum wells, separated by superlattices (Fig. 8–27). As discussed in Chapter 1 and 3, quantum wells and superlattices are made of semiconductor heterostructures with layer thicknesses comparable to or smaller than the deBroglie wavelengths of the electrons.

In quantum wells, one gets confinement in one direction, but plane wave states in the other two directions. This leads to sub-band levels shown

Figure 8–27
Quantum cascade laser based on three-level system in conduction band. Photons are emitted each time there is a transition from level 3 to 2 in this "staircase" of stages. Carriers are injected from level 1 of one stage to level 3 of the next stage through a superlattice (SL) miniband.

in Fig. 8–27. By carefully designing the quantum well structure in a QCL, one can design a three-state system (Fig. 8–27). By biasing the QCL, carriers are injected from the left into state 3, creating a population inversion between states 3 and 2. There is a relatively thick tunnel barrier between states 3 and 2 in order to allow the population inversion. However, the barrier must be narrow enough to allow overlap of the wavefunctions in states 3 and 2, and allow transitions between these levels and allow lasing. Photons in the QCL are emitted upon transition to state 2. Carriers in state 2 are closely coupled by a thin tunnel barrier to state 1, and are immediately removed to this state, so that the population inversion between states 3 and 2 can be maintained. Carriers in state 1 are subsequently injected to state 3 in the next stage of the QCL through the digitally graded superlattice (SL), and the whole process is repeated, until the current is extracted on the right-hand side of the QCL. It is clear that the number of photons emitted per electron injected depends on the number of these energy staircases, 1, 2, 3.

Since the QCL involves electronic transitions entirely within conduction inter-subband quantum well states, it does not require a direct bandgap semiconductor, and the photon energy is not related to the bandgaps of the semiconductors used in the superlattice. Instead, the photon energies are much lower, and are determined by the quantum well design and the sub-band energies. This enables one to generate THz radiation in a very important portion of the electromagnetic spectrum between micro/sub-mm waves and far infrared (300 GHz – 3 THz) where there is a paucity of good sources, leading to the so-called THz gap. This frequency range is very useful, for example, for biomolecule and chemical species detection because many molecular transitions are in this frequency range.

SUMMARY	**8.1** The *emission and absorption of light by semiconductors* gives rise to useful *optoelectronic* devices. Emission typically occurs in *direct* band gap materials. Indirect semiconductors are less optically efficient because they require the involvement of both photons (which carry energy, but little momentum) and phonons (which carry momentum, but little energy).

8.2 In some optoelectronic devices, *electron–hole pairs* (EHPs) are *generated* by the *absorption* of *light*. These carriers can be collected as electrical energy in solar cells or photodetectors. Generated EHPs add to the thermally generated reverse current in diodes (Eq. 8–2), from which one can obtain the open-circuit voltage or short-circuit current in solar cells, a potential renewable source of energy.

8.3 In photodetectors, there is a trade-off between *speed* (which requires a short absorption region for a short transit time) and *sensitivity* (which requires long absorption regions). Clever structures to get *both* include *waveguide* photodetectors. One can achieve *gain* by using APDs, in which impact ionization can increase the number of EHPs generated for a certain number of absorbed photons. However, this can be at the expense of increased impact ionization *noise* in photodiodes.

8.4 Photodiodes, in conjunction with light emitters, are used with optical fibers for fiber-optic communication, which is the backbone of the Internet and worldwide communication today. Optical fibers are waveguides that work on the basis of the total internal reflection of light from a low-refractive-index outer layer to a high-refractive-index medium (glass).

8.5 Semiconductors can be used not only to *detect* photons, but also to *emit* photons by the *recombination* of EHPs in *direct* band gap semiconductors. Light emitters can be noncoherent, such as LEDs, or coherent, such as lasers. The color of light depends on the semiconductor, because the photon frequency is proportional to the band gap (Planck relationship).

8.6 Lasers are more difficult to make than LEDs, because they require not just EHPs, but *population inversion* (i.e., more carriers in the higher energy levels than in the lower ones). This enables *stimulated* emission of *phase-coherent* radiation (governed by the Einstein *B* coefficient) to dominate over *phase-incoherent spontaneous* radiation (determined by the Einstein *A* coefficient). Lasers also require an optical cavity to allow the photon field to build up. Light can come out from the side of the cavity, as in edge-emitting lasers, or from the top surface, as in vertical cavity surface-emitting lasers (VCSELs). Double-heterostructure lasers are useful because they allow both carrier and photon confinement.

PROBLEMS	**8.1** For the p-i-n photodiode of Fig. 8–7, (a) explain why this detector does not have gain; (b) explain how making the device more sensitive to low light levels degrades its speed; (c) if this device is to be used to detect light with $\lambda = 0.6 \ \mu m$, what material would you use and what substrate would you grow it on?

8.2 We make a quantum well by sandwiching a 60 Å layer of GaAs ($E_g = 1.43$ eV) between AlAs with a bandgap of 2.18 eV. We can assume two-thirds of the bandgap difference appear as conduction band discontinuity, and the rest in the valence band. The electron and hole effective masses in GaAs are $0.067\,m_0$ and $0.5\,m_0$, respectively. If we make an LED out of this heterostructure, what is the lowest energy photon that can be emitted from this GaAs layer? If we make a photodetector out of this, what is the longest wavelength that can be detected? You can assume the infinite potential well approximation for this calculation. How many confined states can you have in the conduction and valence bands in the GaAs layer? Qualitatively sketch the electron and hole probability density functions for these states. How far from the heterointerfaces is the hole most likely to be in the second excited state?

8.3 For a Si solar cell, the dark saturation current is $2\,\mu$A and the short circuit current is 150 mA. When it is optically illuminated, the optically generated current is 0.1 mA. Find the corresponding voltage at current of 100 mA.

8.4 For a Si photoconductor of length 5 μm, doped n-type at 10^{15} cm^{-3}, calculate the *change* in current density when we shine light on the photoconductor under the following circumstances: We create 10^{20} electron-hole pairs/cm^3-s and carrier–recombination lifetimes, $\tau = 0.1$ μs. The applied voltage is 2.5 V across the photoconductor's length. How about if we increase the voltage to 2500 V? The electron and hole mobilities are 1500 cm^2/V-s and 500 cm^2/V-s, respectively, in the ohmic region for electric fields below 10^4 V/cm. For higher fields, electrons and holes have a saturation velocity of 10^7 cm/s.

8.5 A Si solar cell with a dark saturation current I_{th} of 5 nA is illuminated such that the short-circuit current is 200 mA. Plot the I–V curve for the cell as in Fig. 8–6. (Remember that I is negative, but is plotted positive as I_r.)

8.6 What is the main limiting factor in increasing the efficiency of a solar cell?

8.7 A major problem with solar cells is internal resistance, generally in the thin region at the surface, which must be only partially contacted, as in Fig. 8–5. Assume that the cell of Prob. 8.5 has a series resistance of 1 Ω, so that the cell voltage is reduced by the IR drop. Replot the I–V curve for this case and compare with the cell of Prob. 8.5.

8.8 (a) Why must a solar cell be operated in the fourth quadrant of the junction I–V characteristic?

    (b) What is the advantage of a quaternary alloy in fabricating LEDs for fiber optics?

    (c) Why is a reverse-biased GaAs p-n junction not a good photodetector for light of $\lambda = 1$ μm?

8.9 A Si solar cell 2 cm × 2 cm with $I_{th} = 32$ nA has an optical generation rate of 10^{18} EHP/cm^3-s within $L_p = L_n = 2$ μm of the junction. If the depletion width is 1 μm, calculate the short-circuit current and the open-circuit voltage for this cell.

8.10 The maximum power delivered by a solar cell can be found by maximizing the I–V product.

(a) Show that maximizing the power leads to the expression

$$\left(1 + \frac{q}{kT}V_{mp}\right)e^{qV_{mp}/kT} = 1 + \frac{I_{sc}}{I_{th}}$$

where V_{mp} is the voltage for maximum power, I_{sc} is the magnitude of the short-circuit current, and I_{th} is the thermally induced reverse saturation current.

(b) Write this equation in the form $\ln x = C - x$ for the case $I_{sc} \gg I_{th}$, and $V_{mp} \gg kT/q$.

(c) Assume a Si solar cell with a dark saturation current I_{th} of 1.5 nA is illuminated such that the short-circuit current is $I_{sc} = 100$ mA. Use a graphical solution to obtain the voltage V_{mp} at maximum delivered power.

(d) What is the maximum power output of the cell at this illumination?

8.11 For a solar cell, Eq. (8–2) can be rewritten

$$V = \frac{kT}{q}\ln\left(1 + \frac{I_{sc} + I}{I_{th}}\right)$$

Given the cell parameters of Prob. 8.10, plot the I–V curve as in Fig. 8–6 and draw the maximum power rectangle. Remember that I is a negative number but is plotted positive as I_r in the figure. I_{th} and I_{sc} are positive magnitudes in the equation.

8.12 Solar cells are severely degraded by unwanted series resistance. For the cell described in Prob. 8.7, include a series resistance R, which reduces the cell voltage by the amount IR. Calculate and plot the fill factor for a series resistance R from 0 to 5Ω, and comment on the effect of R on cell efficiency.

8.13 During the absorption spectra measurement of an unknown semiconductor material, the peak of the spectra appears around 364 nm. What is the band gap of the device and what material is this? If the majority carrier in that material will be able to move with 5×10^5 cm/sec velocity, what will be the carrier mass for that material?

8.14 A semiconductor material of band gap 1.2 eV is used to make a device. At what wavelength it will emit radiation? Is the emitted radiation in the optical range? From these, can you predict the band gap nature of the semiconductor material under observation?

8.15 The degenerate occupation of bands shown in Fig. 8–19 helps maintain the laser requirement that emission must overcome absorption. Explain how the degeneracy prevents band-to-band absorption at the emission wavelength.

8.16 Assume that the system described by Eq. (8–7) is in thermal equilibrium at an extremely high temperature such that the energy density $\rho(v_{12})$ is essentially infinite. Show that $B_{12} = B_{21}$.

8.17 The system described by Eq. (8–7) interacts with a blackbody radiation field whose energy density per unit frequency at ν_{12} is

$$\rho(\nu_{12}) = \frac{8\pi h \nu_{12}^3}{c^3}[e^{h\nu_{12}/kT} - 1]^{-1}$$

from Planck's radiation law. Given the result of Prob. 8.16, find the value of the ratio A_{21}/B_{12}.

8.18 In a compound $Al_xGa_{1-x}As$ material, calculate the energy band gap for the AL concentration of 0.40 using linear interpolation method at 300 K temperature. Calculate the minimum carrier concentration n = p for population inversion in AlGaAs at 300 K if the intrinsic carrier concentration is $2.1 \times 10^3/cm^3$.

8.19 In a Si base long p^+n diode, the excess hole distribution due to optical excitation becomes

$$\delta p(x_n) = \left[p_n \cdot (e^{qV/KT} - 1) - g_{op} \cdot \frac{L_p^2}{D_p} \right] \cdot e^{-x_n/L_p} + g_{op} \cdot \frac{L_p^2}{D_p}$$

Suppose for such a device acceptor concentration is $10^{18}/cm^3$, diffusion coefficient for holes is 10.36 cm^2/sec, mobility for holes is 400 cm^2/V-sec, carrier lifetime = 10 ns, and applied bias is 0.7 V. Due to uniform illumination, $10^{20}/cm^3$ EHP is generated. Now calculate the excess hole distribution for this long diode at a distance of twice the diffusion length from the junction at the n side.

READING LIST

Bhattacharya, P. *Semiconductor Optoelectronic Devices.* Englewood Cliffs, NJ: Prentice Hall, 1994.

Campbell, J. C., A. G. Dentai, W. S. Holden, and B. L. Kasper. "High Performance Avalanche Photodiode with Separate Absorption, Grading and Multiplication Regions." *Electronics Letters,* 19 (1983): 818+.

Casey, Jr., H. C., and M. B. Panish. *Heterostructure Lasers: Part A. Fundamental Principles.* New York: Academic Press, 1978.

Cheo, P. K. *Fiber Optics and Optoelectronics,* 2d ed. Englewood Cliffs, NJ: Prentice Hall, 1990.

Denbaars, S. P. "Gallium Nitride Based Materials for Blue to Ultraviolet Optoelectronic Devices." *Proc. IEEE,* 85 (11) (November 1997): 1740–1749.

Dupuis, R. D. "AlGaAs-GaAs Lasers Grown by MOCVD–A Review." *Journal of Crystal Growth* 55 (October 1981): 213–222.

Faist, J., Capasso, F., Sivco, D., Sirtori C., Hutchinson A., and Cho A.Y. *Quantum Cascade Laser, Science* 264 (5158) (April 1994): 553–556.

Jewell, J. L., and G. R. Olbright. "Surface-Emitting Lasers Emerge from the Laboratory." *Laser Focus World* 28 (May 1992): 217–223.

Palais, J. C. *Fiber Optic Communication,* 3d ed. Englewood Cliffs, NJ: Prentice Hall, 1992.

Pankove, J. I. *Optical Processes in Semiconductors.* Englewood Cliffs, NJ: Prentice Hall, 1971.

Singh, J. *Optoelectronics: An Introduction to Materials and Devices.* New York: McGraw-Hill, 1996.

Verdeyen, J. T. *Laser Electronics*, 3d ed. Englewood Cliffs, NJ: Prentice Hall, 1994.

Yamamoto, Y., and R. E. Slusher. "Optical Processes in Microcavities." *Physics Today* 46 (June 1993): 66–73.

SELF QUIZ   **Question 1**

Consider the following band diagram of a simple LED. Assume essentially all recombination is direct and results in light emission. The forward-bias current consists of holes injected from a contact on the left and electrons injected from a contact on the right.

(a) In which region would you expect the optical recombination rate to be the greatest? Circle one.

Region(s) A / Region(s) B / Region C

(b) What is the approximate energy of the emitted photons in eV?

(c) For a steady state current $I = 10$ mA, assuming all photons escape, what is the optical output power consistent with your answer to part (b)? _____ W

(hint) Watts $=$ Amps $\cdot$ eV/q $=$ Amps $\cdot$ Volts

(d) If the voltage drop across the depletion region is 0.4 V, what is the separation of the quasi-Fermi levels in Region C? How can this be less than the total forward bias of 1.4 V?

(e) What is the electrical power consumed? _____ W

(f) In terms of the ratio of optical power out (c) to electrical power in (e), how efficient is this LED? _____ %

Question 2

A solar cell has a short-circuit current of 50 mA and an open-circuit voltage of 0.7 V under full illumination. What is the maximum power delivered by this cell if the fill factor is 0.8?

Question 3

If one makes an LED in a semiconductor with a direct band gap of 2.5 eV, what wavelength light will it emit? Can you use it to detect photons of wavelength 0.9 μm? 0.1 μm?

Question 4

What is most attractive about solar cells as a global energy source? Why haven't they been adopted more widely so far?

Question 5

A solar cell has short circuit current of 50 mA and an open circuit voltage of 0.9 V under full solar illumination. Calculate the maximum power delivered to the load if the fill factor is 0.6 V.

Question 6

A silicon solar cell with a dark saturation current of 5 nA and a short circuit current when illuminated is 200 mA. Calculate the open circuit voltage if the fill factor is 0.5 and the maximum power delivered is 60 mV.

Question 7

A band gap of a semiconductor is 2 eV calculate the frequency and momentum of the photon that is emitted.

Question 8

In an LED a band gap is 3 eV calculate the wavelength of light that emits.

Chapter 9

Integrated Circuits

OBJECTIVES

1. Understand IC scaling issues
2. Describe CMOS process integration
3. Understand the basics of logic gates and CCDs
4. Study the operation of different memory cells—SRAMs, DRAMs, flash
5. Understand IC packaging

Just as the transistor revolutionized electronics by offering more flexibility, convenience, and reliability than the vacuum tube, the integrated circuit enables new applications for electronics that were not possible with discrete devices. Integration allows complex circuits consisting of millions of transistors, diodes, resistors, and capacitors to be included in a chip of semiconductor. This means that sophisticated circuitry can be miniaturized for use in space vehicles, in large-scale computers, and in other applications where a large collection of discrete components would be impractical. In addition to offering the advantages of miniaturization, the simultaneous fabrication of many ICs on a single Si wafer greatly reduces the cost and increases the reliability of each of the finished circuits. Certainly discrete components have played an important role in the development of electronic circuits; however, most circuits are now fabricated on the Si chip rather than with a collection of individual components. Therefore, the traditional distinctions between the roles of circuit and system designers do not apply to IC development.

In this chapter we shall discuss various types of ICs and the fabrication steps used in their production. We shall investigate techniques for building large numbers of transistors, capacitors, and resistors on a single chip of Si, as well as the interconnection, contacting, and packaging of these circuits in usable form. All the processing techniques discussed here are very basic and general. There would be no purpose in attempting a comprehensive review of all the subtleties of device fabrication in a book of this type. In fact, the only way to keep up with such an expanding field is to study the current literature. Many good reviews are suggested in the reading list at the end of this chapter; more important, current issues of those periodicals cited can be consulted for up-to-date information regarding IC technology. Having the background of this chapter, one should be able to read the current literature and thereby keep abreast of the present trends in this very important field of electronics.

In this section we provide an overview of the nature of integrated circuits and the motivation for using them. It is important to realize the reasons, both technical and economic, for the dramatic rise of ICs to their present role in electronics. We shall discuss several main types of ICs and point out some of the applications of each. More specific fabrication techniques will be presented in later sections.

**9.1
BACKGROUND**

9.1.1 Advantages of Integration

It might appear that building complicated circuits, involving many interconnected components on a single Si substrate, would be risky both technically and economically. In fact, however, modern techniques allow this to be done reliably and relatively inexpensively; in most cases an entire circuit on a Si chip can be produced much more inexpensively and with greater reliability than a similar circuit built up from individual components. The basic reason is that many identical circuits can be built simultaneously on a single Si wafer (Fig. 9–1); this process is called *batch fabrication*. Although the processing steps for the wafer are complex and expensive, the large number of resulting integrated circuits makes the ultimate cost of each fairly low. Furthermore, the processing steps are essentially the same for a circuit containing millions of transistors as for a simpler circuit. This drives the IC industry to build increasingly complex circuits and systems on each chip, and use larger Si wafers (e.g., 12-inch diameter). As a result, the number of components in each circuit increases without a proportional increase in the ultimate cost of the system. The implications of this principle are tremendous for circuit designers; it greatly increases the flexibility of design criteria. Unlike circuits with individual transistors and other components wired together or placed on a circuit board, ICs allow many "extra" components to be included without greatly raising the cost of the final product. Reliability is also improved since all devices and interconnections are made on a single rigid substrate, greatly minimizing failures due to the soldered interconnections of discrete component circuits.

　　The advantages of ICs in terms of miniaturization are obvious. Since many circuit functions can be packed into a small space, complex electronic equipment can be employed in many applications where weight and space are critical, such as in aircraft or space vehicles. In large-scale computers it is now possible not only to reduce the size of the overall unit but also to facilitate maintenance by allowing for the replacement of entire circuits quickly and easily. Applications of ICs are pervasive in such consumer products as watches, calculators, automobiles, telephones, television, and

Figure 9–1
A 300-mm-diameter (about 12-inch) wafer of integrated circuits. The circuits are tested on the wafer and then sawed apart into individual chips for mounting into packages. (Photograph courtesy of Texas Instruments.)

appliances. Miniaturization and the cost reduction provided by ICs mean that we all have increasingly more sophisticated electronics at our disposal.

Some of the most important advantages of miniaturization pertain to response time and the speed of signal transfer between circuits. For example, in high-frequency circuits it is necessary to keep the separation of various components small to reduce time delay of signals. Similarly, in very high-speed computers it is important that the various logic and information storage circuits be placed close together. Since electrical signals are ultimately limited by the speed of light (about 1 ft/ns), physical separation of the circuits can be an important limitation. As we shall see in Section 9.5, *large-scale integration* (LSI) of many circuits on a Si chip has led to major reductions in computer size, thereby tremendously increasing speed and function density. In addition to decreasing the signal transfer time, integration can reduce parasitic capacitance and inductance between circuits. Reduction of these parasitics can provide significant improvement in the operating speed of the system.

We have discussed several advantages of reducing the size of each unit in the batch fabrication process, such as miniaturization, high-frequency and switching speed improvements, and cost reduction due to the large number of circuits fabricated on a single wafer. Another important advantage has to do with the percentage of usable devices (often called the *yield*) which results from batch fabrication. Faulty devices usually occur because of some defect in the Si wafer or in the fabrication steps. Defects in the Si can occur because of lattice imperfections and strains introduced in the crystal growth, cutting, and handling of the wafers. Usually such defects are extremely small, but their presence can ruin devices built on or around them. Reducing the size of each device greatly increases the chance for a given device to be free of such defects. The same is true for fabrication defects, such as the presence of a dust particle on a photolithographic mask. For example, a lattice defect or dust particle $\frac{1}{2}$ μm in diameter can easily ruin a circuit which includes the damaged area. If a fairly large circuit is built around the defect it will be faulty; however, if the device size is reduced so that four circuits occupy the same area on the wafer, chances are good that only the one containing the defect will be faulty and the other three will be good. Therefore, the percentage yield of usable circuits increases over a certain range of decreasing chip area. There is an optimum area for each circuit, above which defects are needlessly included and below which the elements are spaced too closely for reliable fabrication.

9.1.2 Types of Integrated Circuits

There are several ways of categorizing ICs as to their use and method of fabrication. The most common categories are *linear* or *digital,* according to application, and *monolithic* or *hybrid,* according to fabrication.

A linear IC is an IC that performs amplification or other essentially linear operations on signals. Examples of linear circuits are simple amplifiers, operational amplifiers, and analog communications circuits. Digital circuits involve logic and memory, for applications in computers, calculators, microprocessors, and the like. By far the greatest volume of ICs has been in the digital field, since large numbers of such circuits are required. Because digital circuits generally require only the "on–off" operation of transistors, the design requirements for integrated digital circuits are often less stringent than for linear circuits. Although transistors can be fabricated as easily in an integrated form as in a discrete form, passive elements (resistors and capacitors) are usually more difficult to produce to close tolerances in ICs.

Integrated circuits that are included entirely on a single chip of semiconductor (usually Si) are called *monolithic* circuits (Fig. 9–1). The word *monolithic* literally means "one stone" and implies that the entire circuit is contained in a single piece of semiconductor. Any additions to the semiconductor sample, such as insulating layers and metallization patterns, are intimately bonded to the surface of the chip. A *hybrid* circuit may contain one or more monolithic circuits or individual transistors bonded to an insulating substrate with resistors, capacitors, or other circuit elements, together with appropriate interconnections. Monolithic circuits have the advantage that all of their components are contained in a single rigid structure that can be batch fabricated; that is, hundreds of identical circuits can be built simultaneously on a Si wafer. On the other hand, hybrid circuits offer excellent isolation between components and allow the use of more precise resistors and capacitors. Furthermore, hybrid circuits are often less expensive to build in small numbers.

9.2 EVOLUTION OF INTEGRATED CIRCUITS

The IC was invented in February 1959 by Jack Kilby of Texas Instruments. The planar version of the IC was developed independently by Robert Noyce at Fairchild in July 1959. Since then, the evolution of this technology has been extremely fast paced. One way to gauge the progress of the field is to look at the complexity of ICs as a function of time. Fig. 9–2 shows the number of transistors used in MOS *microprocessor* IC chips as a function of time. It is amazing that on this semilog plot, where we have plotted the log of the component count as a function of time, we get a straight line over four decades, indicating that there has been an exponential growth in the complexity of chips. The component count has roughly doubled every 18 months, as was noted early on by Gordon Moore of Intel corporation. This regular doubling has become known as *Moore's law*.

The history of ICs can be described in terms of different eras, depending on the component count. Small-scale integration refers to the integration of $1-10^2$ devices, medium-scale integration to the integration of 10^2-10^3 devices, LSI to the integration of 10^3-10^5 devices, very large-scale integration to the integration of 10^5-10^6 devices, and now ultra large-scale integration (ULSI) to the integration of 10^6-10^9 devices. Of course, these boundaries are somewhat fuzzy. The next generation has been dubbed *gigascale integration*. Wags have suggested that after that we will have RLSI, or "ridiculously large-scale integration."

The main factor that has enabled this increase in complexity is the ability to shrink or scale devices. Typical dimensions or feature sizes of state-of-the-art *dynamic random-access memories (DRAMs)* at different times are also shown as a semilog plot in Fig. 9–3. Once again, we see a straight line, reflecting an exponential decrease in the typical feature sizes with time over four decades. Clearly, one can pack a larger number of components with greater functionality on an IC if they are smaller. As discussed in Section 6.5.9, scaling also has other advantages in terms of faster ICs which consume less power.

While scaling represents an opportunity, it also presents tremendous technological challenges. The most notable among these challenges lie in lithography and etching, as discussed in Section 5.1. However, since scaling of horizontal dimensions also requires scaling of vertical geometries, as discussed in Section 6.5.9, there are also tremendous challenges in terms of doping, gate dielectrics, and metallization. In addition, small features and large chips require device fabrication in extremely clean environments. Particles that may not have caused yield problems in a 1-μm IC technology can have catastrophic effects for a 22 nm process, which requires purer chemicals,

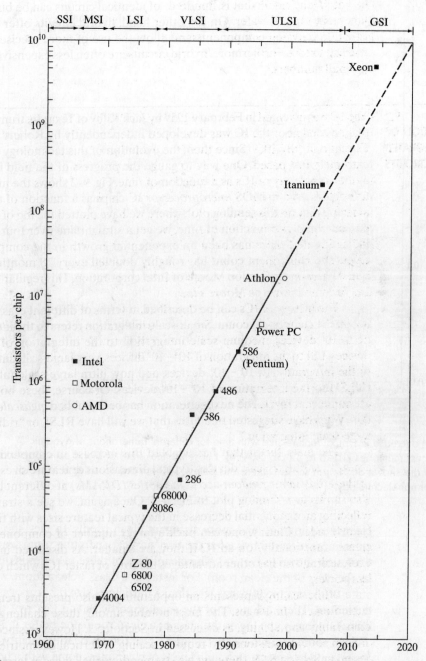

Figure 9–2

Moore's law for integrated circuits: Exponential increase in transistor count as a function of time for different generations of microprocessors. The dashed line indicates projections based on the International Technology Roadmap for Semiconductors (ITRS). Notice that the transistor count in the future may not increase at the same rate as in the past, due to practical constraints such as economics and power dissipation.

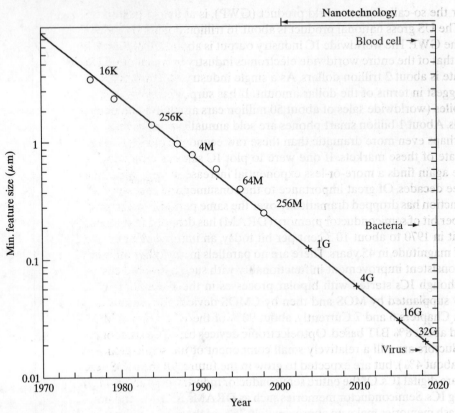

Figure 9–3
Exponential decrease in typical feature size with time for different generations of dynamic
random-access memories (16-kb to 32-Gb DRAMs). For reference, sizes of blood cells, bacteria,
and viruses are shown on the μm scale. Dimensions below 100 nm are considered to be in
the realm of nanotechnology.

cleaner equipment, and more stringent clean rooms. In fact, the levels of
cleanliness required bypassed the best surgical operating rooms early in the
evolution shown in Fig. 9–3. The cleanliness of these facilities is designated
by the *class* of the clean room. For instance, a Class 1 clean room, which was
state-of-the-art in 2000, has less than 1 particle of size 0.2 μm or larger per
cubic foot. There are more of the smaller particles and fewer of the larger
ones. Obviously, the lower the class of a clean room, the better it is. A Class
1 clean room is much cleaner than a Class 100 fabrication facility, or "fab."
As one might expect, such high levels of cleanliness come with a hefty price
tag: A state-of-the-art fab in 2014 comes equipped with a price tag of about
5–10 billion dollars.

In spite of the costs, the economic payoff for ULSI is tremendous. Just
for calibration, let us examine some economic statistics at the dawn of the
third millennium. The total annual economic output of all the countries in the

world, or the so-called gross world product (GWP), is about 85 trillion US dollars. The US gross national product is about 16 trillion dollars, or about a fifth of the GWP. The worldwide IC industry output is about 350 billion dollars, and that of the entire worldwide electronics industry in which these ICs participate is about 2 trillion dollars. As a single industry, electronics is one of the biggest in terms of the dollar amount. It has surpassed, for example, automobiles (worldwide sales of about 50 million cars annually) and petrochemicals. About 1 billion smart phones are sold annually worldwide.

Perhaps even more dramatic than these raw economic numbers is the growth rate of these markets. If one were to plot IC sales as a function of time, one again finds a more-or-less exponential increase in sales with time over three decades. Of great importance to the consumer, the cost per electronic function has dropped dramatically over the same period. For example, the cost per bit of semiconductor memory (DRAM) has dropped from about 1 cent/bit in 1970 to about 10^{-5} cent per bit today, an improvement of five orders of magnitude in 45 years. There are no parallels in any other industry for this consistent improvement in functionality with such a lowered cost.

Although ICs started with bipolar processes in the 1960s, they were gradually supplanted by MOS and then by CMOS devices, for reasons discussed in Chapters 6 and 7. Currently, about 90% of the IC market is MOS based and about 8% BJT based. Optoelectronic devices based on compound semiconductors are still a relatively small component of the semiconductor market (about 4%), but are expected to grow in the future. Of the MOS ICs, the bulk are digital ICs. Of the entire semiconductor industry, only about 14% are analog ICs. Semiconductor memories such as DRAMs, SRAMs, and non-volatile flash memories make up approximately 25% of the market, microprocessors about 25%, and other application-specific ICs (ASICs) about 20%.

Now we shall consider the various elements that make up an integrated circuit, and some of the steps in their fabrication. The basic elements are fairly easy to name—transistors, resistors, capacitors, and some form of interconnection. There are some elements in integrated circuits, however, which do not have simple counterparts in discrete devices. We shall consider one of these, charge transfer devices, in Section 9.4. Discussion of fabrication technology is difficult in a book of this type, since device fabrication engineers seem to make changes faster than typesetters do! Since this important and fascinating field is changing so rapidly, the reader should obtain a basic understanding of device design and processing from this discussion and then search out new innovations in the current literature.

**9.3
MONOLITHIC
DEVICE ELEMENTS**

9.3.1 CMOS Process Integration

A particularly useful device for digital applications is a combination of n-channel and p-channel MOS transistors on adjacent regions of the chip. This *complementary MOS* (commonly called *CMOS*) combination is illustrated in the basic inverter circuit of Fig. 9–4a. In this circuit the drains of the two transistors are connected together and form the output, while the input terminal is the common connection to the transistor gates. The p-channel device has a negative threshold voltage, and the n-channel transistor has a positive threshold voltage. Therefore, a zero voltage input ($V_{in} = 0$) gives zero gate voltage for the n-channel device, but the voltage between the gate and source of the p-channel device is $-V_{DD}$. Thus the p-channel device is on, the n-channel device is off, and the full voltage V_{DD} is measured at V_{out} (i.e., V_{DD} appears across the nonconducting n-channel transistor). Alternatively, a positive value of V_{in} turns the n-channel transistor on, and the p-channel off. The output voltage measured across the "on" n-channel device is essentially zero. Thus, the circuit operates as an inverter—with a binary "1" at the input, the output is in the "0" state, whereas a "0" input produces a "1" output. The beauty of this circuit is that one of the devices is turned off for either condition. Since the devices are connected in series, no drain current flows, except for a small charging current during the switching process from one state to the other. Since the CMOS inverter uses ultra little power, it is particularly useful in applications such as electronic watch circuits that depend on very low power consumption. CMOS is also advantageous in ultra large-scale integrated circuits (Section 9.5), since even small power

Figure 9–4
Complementary MOS structure: (a) CMOS inverter; (b) formation of p-channel and n-channel devices together.

dissipation in each transistor becomes a problem when millions of them are integrated on a chip.

The device technology for achieving CMOS circuits consists mainly in arranging for both n- and p-channel devices with similar threshold voltages on the same chip. To achieve this goal, a diffusion or implantation must be performed in certain areas to obtain n and p regions for the fabrication of each type of device. These regions are called *tubs, tanks,* or *wells* (Fig. 9–5). The critical parameter of the tub is its net doping concentration, which must be closely controlled by ion implantation. With the tub in place, source and drain implants are performed to make the n-channel and p-channel transistors. Matching of the two transistors is achieved by control of the surface doping in the tub and by threshold adjustment of both transistors by ion implantation.

Including bipolar transistors in the basic CMOS technology allows flexibility in circuit design, particularly for providing drive currents. The combination of bipolar and CMOS (called BiCMOS) provides circuits with increased speed.

Attention must be paid in CMOS designs to the fact that combining n-channel and p-channel devices in proximity can lead to inadvertent (*parasitic*) bipolar structures. In fact, a p-n-p-n structure can be found in Fig. 9–4b, which can serve as an inefficient but troublesome *thyristor* (see Chapter 10). Under certain biasing conditions the p-n-p part of the structure can supply base current to the n-p-n structure, causing a large current to flow. This process, called *latchup,* can be a serious problem in CMOS circuits. Several methods have been used to eliminate the latchup problem, including using both n-type and p-type tubs, separated by trench isolation (Fig. 9–6). The use of two separate tubs (wells) also allows independent control of threshold voltages in both types of transistor.

We can illustrate most of the common fabrication steps for MOS integrated circuits by studying the flow of a twin-well Self-Aligned siLICIDE (SALICIDE) CMOS process. This process is particularly important because most high-performance digital ICs, including microprocessors, memories and application-specific ICs (ASICs) are made basically in this way. In order to make enhancement-mode n-channel devices, we need a p-type substrate, and vice versa. Since CMOS requires both, we must start either with an n-type or a p-type wafer and then make selected regions of the substrate have opposite doping by forming wells. For example, Fig. 9–5a shows a lightly doped p-epitaxial layer on a p^+-substrate. We can make n-channel devices in this layer. By implanting n-wells wherever needed, we can make p-channel devices also. This is an n-well CMOS process. Alternatively, if we start with an n-substrate and make p-wells in certain regions, we have a p-well CMOS process. For optimal device performance, however, it is usually desirable to separately implant both the n- and the p-well regions, which is called *twin-well* CMOS. The rationale for this can be appreciated if we keep in mind that for a state-of-the-art IC, typical doping levels are $\sim 10^{18}\,\mathrm{cm}^{-3}$ and junction

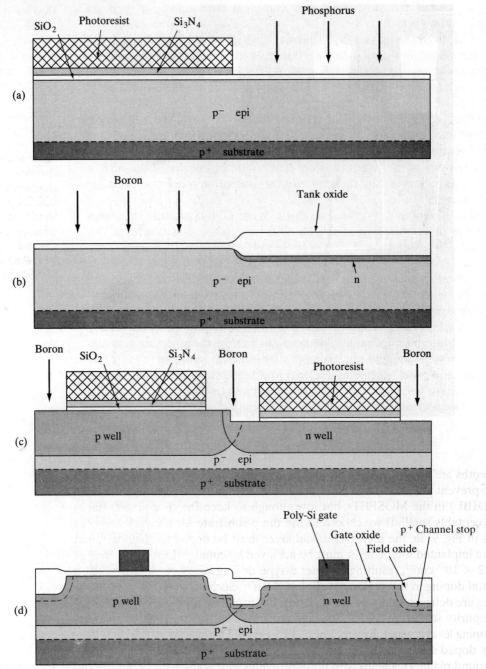

Figure 9–5
Self-aligned twin well process: (a) an n-well formation using P donor implant and a photoresist mask; (b) p-well formation using B acceptor implant. A thick (~200 nm) "tank" oxide layer is grown wherever the silicon nitride–oxide stack is etched off, and the tank oxide is used to block the B implant in the n-wells in a self-aligned manner; (c) an isolation pattern for field transistors showing a B channel stop implant using a photoresist mask; (d) local oxidation of silicon wherever the nitride mask is removed, leading to thick LOCOS field oxide.

Figure 9–6
Trench isolation:
A trench or
groove is etched
in the substrate
with the use of
RIE and is refilled
with oxide and
polysilicon. Trench
isolation provides
superior electrical
isolation
compared with
LOCOS, and uses
less Si real estate.
(Photograph
Courtesy by Tom
Way IMD/BTV
©1998 IBM.)

depths are ~1 μm in these wells. The doping levels have to be high enough to prevent punch-through breakdown due to drain-induced barrier lowering (DIBL) in the MOSFETs, but low enough to keep the threshold voltages acceptably small. If we choose to use the p-substrate for n-channel devices as in Fig. 9–5a, the p-type epitaxial layer must be doped to 10^{18} cm^{-3}, and the implanted n-type layer must be achieved by counter-doping at a level of ~2×10^{18} cm^{-3}, resulting in a net n-type doping of ~1×10^{18} cm^{-3}, but a total doping in this region of ~3×10^{18} cm^{-3}. Such high levels of total doping are detrimental to carrier transport because they cause excessive ionized impurity scattering. Hence, for high performance ICs, the starting epitaxial doping level is generally very low (~10^{16} cm^{-3}). This layer is grown on a heavily doped substrate (~10^{19} cm^{-3}), to provide a highly conducting electrical ground plane. This helps with noise problems in ICs and helps minimize the problem of *latchup* by bypassing majority carriers (in this case holes) to the p$^+$ substrate.

To form the twin wells in a self-aligned fashion, we first grow thermally a "pad" oxide (~20 nm) on the Si substrate, followed by low-pressure chemical vapor deposition (LPCVD) of silicon nitride (~20 nm). As shown in Fig. 9–5a, this oxide–nitride stack is covered by photoresist, and a window is opened for the n-well. Reactive ion etching (RIE) is then used to etch the oxide–nitride stack. Using the photoresist as an implant mask, we then do an n-type implant using phosphorus. Phosphorus is preferred to As for this purpose because P is lighter and has a higher projected range; also, P diffuses faster. This fast diffusion is needed to drive the dopants fairly deep into the substrate to form the n-well. After the implant, the photoresist is removed, and the patterned wafer is subjected to wet oxidation to grow a "tank" oxide (~200 nm). Note in Fig. 9–5b that the tank oxidation process consumes Si from the substrate, and the resulting oxide swells up. In fact, for every micron of thermally grown oxide, the oxidation consumes 0.44 μm of Si, resulting in a 2.2-fold volume expansion. The oxide does not grow in the regions that are protected by silicon nitride, because nitride blocks the diffusion of oxygen and water molecules (and thereby prevents oxidation of the Si substrate). The pad oxide that is used under the nitride has two roles: It minimizes the thermal-expansion mismatch and concomitant stress between silicon nitride and the substrate; it also prevents chemical bonding of the silicon nitride to the silicon substrate.

Using the tank oxide as a *self-aligned* implant mask (i.e., without actually having to do a separate photolithographic step), one does a p-type well implant using boron (B; Fig. 9–5b). The tank oxide must thus be much thicker than the projected range of the B. The concept of self-alignment is very important and is a recurring theme in IC processing. It is simpler and cheaper to use self-alignment than a separate lithographic step. It also allows a tighter packing density of the twin wells, because it is not required to account for lithographic misalignment during layout. The P and the B are then diffused into the substrate to a well depth of typically a micron by a drive-in diffusion at very high temperatures (~1000°C) for several hours. After this diffusion, the silicon nitride–oxide stack and the tank oxide are etched away. Since the tank oxidation consumes Si from the substrate, etching it off leads to a step in the Si substrate delineating the n-well and p-well regions. The step is important in terms of the alignment of subsequent reticles and is shown in an exaggerated fashion in Fig. 9–5c. The step, however, is disadvantageous from the depth-of-focus point of view during lithography. So, instead of a self-aligned twin-well process as just described, one often uses two separate lithography steps for the two well implants. This approach leads to a more planar structure, but a slightly larger well geometry because the wells are not self-aligned. There are many other variations of CMOS processes used, depending on the application.

Next, we form the isolation regions or the field transistors that guarantee that there will be no electrical cross talk between adjacent transistors, unless they are intentionally interconnected (Fig. 9–5c). This is achieved by ensuring that the threshold voltage of any parasitic transistor that may form in the isolation regions is much higher than the power supply voltage on the chip, so that the parasitic channel can never turn on under operating conditions. From the threshold voltage expression [Eq. (6–38)], we notice that V_T can be raised by increasing substrate doping and increasing gate oxide thickness. However, a problem with that approach is the subthreshold slope S [Eq. (6–66)], which degrades with increasing substrate doping and gate oxide thickness. One needs to optimize both V_T and S such that the off-state leakage current in the field between transistors is sufficiently low at zero gate bias.

A stack of silicon dioxide–silicon nitride is photolithographically patterned as in Fig. 9–5c and subjected to RIE. A boron *"channel stop"* implant between the twin wells increases the acceptor doping and thus increases the threshold voltage in the p-well between the n-channel transistors (the *field threshold*). However, B will compensate the donor doping on the n-well side, and thus reduce the threshold in the n-well between p-channel devices. The B channel stop dose must thus be optimized to have acceptably high field thresholds in both types of wells.

After the channel stop implant, the photoresist is removed and the wafer with the patterned nitride–oxide stack shown in Fig. 9–5c (without photoresist) is subjected to wet oxidation to selectively grow a field oxide ~ 300 nm thick. The nitride layer blocks oxidation of the Si substrate in the regions where we plan to make the transistors. This procedure, where Si is oxidized to form SiO_2 in regions not protected by nitride, is called LOCal Oxidation of Silicon (LOCOS) (Section 6.4.1). In this case, LOCOS provides electrical isolation between the two transistors, as shown in Fig. 9–5d.

The volume expansion of $2.2\times$ upon oxidation is an important issue because the selective oxidation occurs in narrow, confined regions. The compressive stress, if excessive, can cause dislocation defects in the substrate. Another issue is the lateral oxidation near the nitride mask edges, which causes the nitride mask to lift up near the edges, forming what is known as a *bird's beak* and causing a *lateral moat encroachment* of ~ 0.2 μm into each active region, thereby wasting precious Si real estate. There have been various modified LOCOS and other isolation schemes proposed to minimize this lateral encroachment. A notable example is *Shallow Trench Isolation* (STI) which involves using RIE to etch a shallow (~ 1 μm) trench or groove in the Si substrate after the isolation pattern, filling it up completely by deposition of a dielectric layer of SiO_2 and polysilicon by LPCVD, and then using chemical mechanical polishing (CMP) to planarize the structure (Fig. 9–6). This consumes less Si real estate compared with LOCOS, but gives superior isolation because the sharp corners at the bottom of the trench give rise to potential barriers that block leakage currents (the *corner effect*).

The pad oxide between the nitride and the Si surface minimizes the stress due to the nitride, and prevents bonding of the nitride to the Si, as mentioned above. Any residual nitride on the Si would retard subsequent gate oxide formation, leading to weak spots in the gate region of the MOSFETs. This problem is known as the *white ribbon* effect or the *Kooi* effect, after the Dutch scientist who first identified it. The pad oxide mitigates this problem, but does not solve it completely. Therefore, very often a "sacrificial" or "dummy" oxide is grown to consume a layer of Si containing any residual nitride, and this oxide is wet etched prior to the growth of the actual gate oxide.

In many modern CMOS processes, LOCOS has been supplanted by STI. Here, we use RIE to etch shallow grooves or trenches (~0.2 μm deep) in the isolation regions. After growing a thin thermal oxide to passivate the surface, we fill up the trench with LPCVD oxide and grind the surface flat with CMP. STI has no moat encroachment, unlike LOCOS, and is capable of superior electrical isolation using less Si real estate.

Next, an ultra-thin (0.3 nm) gate oxide is grown on the substrate. Since the electrical quality of this oxide and its interface with the Si substrate is of paramount importance to the operation of the MOSFETs, dry oxidation is used for this step. This is followed by deposition of a high-k gate dielectric. It is immediately covered with LPCVD polysilicon or a metal gate electrode in order to minimize contamination of the gate oxide. The polysilicon gate layer is doped very heavily (typically n^+ using a phosphorus dopant source, $POCl_3$ in a diffusion furnace) all the way to the polysilicon–oxide interface in order to make it behave electrically like a metal electrode. Alternatively, the LPCVD polysilicon film may also be *in situ* doped during the deposition itself by flowing in an appropriate dopant gas such as phosphine or diborane. Heavy doping of the gate material is very important, because otherwise a depletion layer can be formed in the polysilicon gate (the *poly depletion* effect). This could result in a depletion capacitance in series with the gate oxide capacitance, thereby reducing the overall gate capacitance and, therefore, the drive current [see Eq. (6–53)]. The high doping (~10^{20} cm^{-3}) in the polysilicon gate is also important for reducing the resistance of the gate and its RC time constant. The uniformly high doping in the polysilicon layer is facilitated by the presence of the grain boundary defects in the film, because diffusivity of dopants along grain boundaries is many orders of magnitude higher than in single-crystal Si. If metal gate electrodes such as TiN are used, these problems go away. Sometimes, a polysilicon gate may be deposited on a thin metal gate electrode to make a composite structure.

The doped polysilicon layer or metal gate is then patterned to form the gates, and etched anisotropically by RIE to achieve vertical sidewalls. That is extremely important because this etched gate is used as a self-aligned implant mask for the source/drain implants. As mentioned above, self-aligned processes are always desirable in terms of process simplicity and packing density. It is particularly useful in this case because we thereby guarantee that there will be *some* overlap of the gate with the source/drain but minimal overlap. The overlap is determined by the lateral scattering of the ions and by the lateral diffusion of the dopants during subsequent thermal processing (such as source/drain implant anneals). If there were no overlap, the channel would have to be turned on in this region by the gate fringing fields. The resulting potential barrier in the channel would degrade the device current. On the other hand, if there is too much overlap, it leads to an overlap capacitance between the source or drain and the gate. This is particularly bothersome near the drain end because it leads to the Miller overlap capacitance which causes undesired capacitive feedback between the output drain terminal and the input gate terminal (see Section 6.5.8).

Fabrication steps for the n-channel MOSFETs in the p-well are shown in Fig. 9–7. After the polysilicon gate is etched, we first do a self-aligned n-type source–drain implant, during which the tank masking level is used to protect the PMOS devices with a layer of photoresist. The NMOS source and drain implants are done in two stages. The first implant is a lightly doped drain (LDD) implant (Fig. 9–7a). This is typically a dose of $\sim 10^{13}$–10^{14} cm^{-2}, corresponding to a concentration of 10^{18}–10^{19} cm^{-3}, and an ultra-shallow junction depth of 50–100 nm. When a MOSFET is operated in the saturation region, the drain-channel junction is reverse biased, resulting in a very high electric field in the pinch-off region. As we saw in Section 5.4 for reverse-biased p-n junctions, reducing the doping level increases the depletion width and makes the peak electric field at the junction smaller. As discussed in Section 6.5.9, electrons traveling from the source to the drain in the channel can gain kinetic energy and thereby become hot electrons, which create damage. The low doping in the LDD helps reduce hot carrier effects at the drain end. The shallow junction depths in the LDD are also important for reducing short channel effects such as DIBL and charge sharing (Sections 6.5.10 and 6.5.11). The penalty that we pay with the use of an LDD region is that the source-to-drain series resistance goes up, which degrades the drive current.

As the technology is evolving toward lower power supply voltages, hot carrier effects are becoming less important. This, along with the need to reduce series resistance, has driven the trend toward increasing doping in the LDD to levels above 10^{19} cm^{-3}. In fact, the use of the term LDD then becomes a bit of a misnomer, and is often replaced by the term *source/drain extension* or *tip*.

After the LDD regions are formed alongside the polysilicon gate, we implant deeper (~ 200 nm) and more heavily doped (10^{20} cm^{-3}) source and drain junctions farther away from the gate edges (Fig. 9–7d). This more conductive region allows ohmic contacts to the source and drain to be formed more easily than they could be directly to the LDD regions, and reduces the source/drain series resistance. This implant is done using a self-aligned scheme by the formation of *sidewall oxide spacers*. After removing the photoresist covering the PMOS devices, we deposit *conformal* LPCVD oxide (~ 100–200 nm thick) using an organic precursor called tetra-ethyl-ortho-silicate (TEOS) over the entire wafer at fairly high temperatures ($\sim 700°C$) (Fig. 9–7b). The term conformal means that the deposited film has the same thickness everywhere, and follows the topography on the wafer. This oxide layer is then subjected to RIE, which is anisotropic (i.e., it etches predominantly in the vertical direction) (Section 5.1.7). If the RIE step is timed to just etch off the deposited oxide on the flat surfaces, it leaves oxide sidewall spacers on the edges of the polysilicon gate, as shown in Fig. 9–7c. This sidewall spacer is used as a self-aligned mask to protect the LDD regions very near the gate during the heavier, deeper n^+ source and drain implants (Fig. 9–7d).

Figure 9–7
Fabrication of
the LDD structure,
using sidewall
spacers. The
polysilicon gate
covers the thin
gate oxide and
masks the first
low-dose implant
(a). A thick layer
is deposited by
CVD (b) and is
anisotropically
etched away
to leave only
the sidewall
spacers (c). These
spacers serve as
a mask for the
second, high-dose
implant. After a
drive-in diffusion,
the LDD structure
results (d).

Next, the NMOS devices are masked by photoresist, and a p^+ source and drain implant is done for the PMOSFETs (Fig. 9–8a). It may be noted that an LDD was not used for the PMOS. This is due to the fact that hot hole effects are less problematic than hot electron degradation, partly due to the lower hole mobility and partly due to the higher $Si–SiO_2$ barrier in the valence band (5 eV) than in the conduction band (3.1 eV). After the source–drain implants are done, the dopants are activated and the ion implant damage is healed by a furnace anneal, or more frequently using a rapid thermal anneal. In this anneal we use the minimum acceptable temperature and time combination (the thermal budget) because it is critically important to keep the dopant profiles as compact as possible in ultra-small MOSFETs.

We can now appreciate why most CMOS logic devices are made on p-type substrates, rather than n-type. The n-channel MOSFETs generate a lot more substrate current due to hot carrier effects than PMOSFETs. The holes, thus generated, can more easily flow to ground in a p-type substrate, than in an n-substrate. Also, it is easier to dope substrates p-type with B during Czochralski crystal growth than n-type with Sb. Antimony is the preferred donor, rather than As or P for bulk doping of the Si melt, because Sb evaporates less than the other species.

The use of n^+ polysilicon gates for both NMOS and PMOS devices raises some interesting device issues. Since the Fermi level in the n^+ gate is very close to the Si conduction band, its work function is well suited to achieving a low V_T for NMOS ($\Phi_{ms} \sim -1$ V), but not for PMOS ($\Phi_{ms} \sim 0$ V). From the V_T expression [Eq. (6–38)], we notice that the second and third terms approach zero as thin-oxide technology evolves because C_i is getting larger. For high drive current we want V_T to be in the neighborhood of ~ 0.3 to ~ 0.7 V for NMOS (-0.3 to -0.7 V for PMOS). We find from Eq. (6–38) that the p-well doping can be optimized to achieve the correct V_T for the NMOS transistor, while at the same time being high enough to prevent punch-through breakdown between source and drain. For the PMOS transistor, on the other hand, an n-well doping of the order of 10^{18} cm^{-3} prevents punch-through, but the Fermi potential, ϕ_F, is so large and negative that the V_T is too negative. That forces us to do a separate acceptor implant to adjust V_T for the PMOS devices (Fig. 9–8b). The acceptor dose is low enough that the p-layer is fully depleted at zero gate bias, leading to enhancement-mode, rather than depletion-mode, transistors. In CMOS we try to make the negative V_T of the PMOS device about the same value as the positive V_T of the NMOS.

Close examination of the band diagram in the channel of the PMOSFET along the vertical direction (perpendicular to the gate oxide) shows that the energy minimum for the holes in the inversion layer is slightly below (~ 100 nm) the oxide–silicon interface, leading to what is known as *buried channel operation* for PMOS (Fig. 9–8c). On the other hand, for NMOS, the electron energy minimum in the inversion layer occurs right at the oxide–silicon interface, leading to surface channel

Figure 9–8

Buried channel PMOS: (a) self-aligned p^+ source–drain implant with no LDD using photoresist to protect NMOSFETs. A p-type V_T adjust implant is shown in color in the channel; (b) doping profile as a function of depth in the middle of the channel, showing the p-type V_T adjust implant near the surface; (c) electron potential energy as a function of depth in the middle of the channel, showing holes collecting in the "buried" channel. For higher gate bias, the PMOS operation changes to a surface channel, as indicated by the dashed line.

operation.[1] There are good and bad aspects of this buried channel behavior for PMOS. Since the holes in the inversion layer of the PMOSFET travel slightly away from the oxide–silicon interface, they do not suffer as much channel mobility degradation as the electrons in the NMOSFET due to surface roughness scattering. That is good, because hole mobilities in Si are generally lower than electron mobilities, which forces us to make PMOS devices wider than the NMOSFETs to get similar drive currents. However, buried channel devices have a greater propensity toward DIBL and punch-through breakdown. Hence, as the size of MOSFETs is reduced, the DIBL problem becomes worse, and there is a desire to have surface channel operation for both NMOS and PMOS. Thus, there is interest in so-called dual gate CMOS, where n^+ polysilicon gates are used for NMOSFETs and p^+ gates are used for PMOSFETs. Such dual work function gates can be achieved by depositing the polysilicon undoped and then using the source and drain implants themselves to also dope the gates appropriately. This approach exploits the high polysilicon grain boundary diffusivities to degenerately dope the gates, at the same time having ultra-shallow source and drain junctions to minimize DIBL.

As a historical footnote, it may be added that MOSFETs initially used Al gates which could not withstand high temperature processing. Hence, the source and drain regions had to be formed first, either by diffusion or by implant, and then the Al gate was deposited and patterned. Such nonself-aligned processes suffered from the Miller capacitance mentioned previously. What made self-aligned source and drain regions viable was the use of polysilicon, which has a sufficiently high melting point to withstand subsequent processing. Recent research on MOSFET technology is going back full circle to metal gates, but this time using refractory metals such as tungsten (W). These metals have better conductivity than heavily doped polysilicon, and a work function that is better suited for CMOS. The Fermi level of W is near the middle of the Si band gap, which makes the flat band voltage and the threshold voltage more symmetric and better matched between NMOS and PMOS, and avoids the buried channel effect.

The next step is to form a metal–silicon alloy or silicide in the source/drain and gate regions of the MOSFETs in order to reduce the series resistance (and thereby the RC time constants), and increase the drive current. This involves depositing a thin layer of a refractory metal such as Ti over the entire wafer by sputtering, and reacting the Ti with Si wherever they come in *direct* contact, by doing a two-step heat treatment in an N ambient (Fig. 9–9a). A 600°C anneal results in the formation of Ti_2Si (the C49 phase according to metallurgists, which has fairly high resistivity),

---

[1]We can qualitatively understand why the acceptor implant in the channel leads to such a buried channel behavior. Assume for a moment that the acceptor dose was high enough that the p-layer was not depleted at zero bias. In such a depletion-mode device, a positive gate bias to turn off the device would first deplete the surface region of holes, still leading to hole conduction deeper in the substrate away from the oxide–Si interface.

Figure 9–9
The formation of silicided source–drain and gate regions for low-resistance contacts: (a) a layer of refractory metal is deposited and reacted in regions of exposed Si to form a conducting silicide layer; (b) the unreacted metal is removed and a CVD glass is deposited and patterned for contact metallization; (c) cross-sectional micrograph of LDD MOSFET with gate length of 52 nm. (Photograph courtesy of Texas Instruments.)

followed by an 800°C anneal which converts the Ti_2Si to the C54 phase, $TiSi_2$, which has an extremely low resistivity of ~17 $\mu\Omega$-cm, much lower than that of the most heavily doped Si. On the other hand, the Ti on top of the sidewall oxide spacers does not form a silicide and stays as unreacted

Ti or forms TiN because the process is done in an N ambient. The Ti and TiN can be etched off selectively by using a wet hydrogen peroxide-based etch, which does not attack the titanium disilicide, thereby electrically isolating the gates from the source/drains. Note that this process results in a SALICIDE without a separate masking level only on the source/drains and the polysilicon gate, where the silicide is often termed a *polycide*. This results in very high-performance MOSFETs.

Finally, the MOSFETs have to be properly interconnected according to the circuit layout, using the metallization level. This involves LPCVD of an oxide dielectric layer doped with B and P, which is known as *boro-phospho-silicate glass* (BPSG) on the entire wafer, patterning it by means of the contact-level reticle and using RIE to open up the contact holes to the substrate (Fig. 9–9b). The B and P allow the oxide layer to soften and reflow more readily upon annealing, thereby helping planarize or smooth out the topography on the wafer. This shaping of the millions of very small contact holes is critical on a ULSI chip, because otherwise metal deposited on the surface into the contact holes may not reach completely into the holes, leading to a catastrophic open circuit. In fact, sometimes a CVD tungsten layer is selectively deposited in the contact holes to form a contact *plug* before one proceeds to the next step. Then a suitable metal layer such as Al (alloyed with ~1 percent Si and ~4 percent Cu) is sputter deposited over the wafer, patterned using the metal interconnect level, and subjected to metal RIE. The Si is added to the Al to solve the junction *spiking* problem, whereby pure Al can incorporate the solid solubility limit of Si from the shallow source/drain regions. This would allow the Al to "spike," or short, through the p-n junction. The Cu is added to enlarge the grain size in the Al interconnect films, which are polycrystalline, making it harder for the electrons moving during current flow to nudge the Al atoms along, thereby opening voids (producing open circuits) in the interconnect. This is an example of an *electromigration* phenomenon. A cross-sectional picture of an LDD MOSFET with SALICIDE is shown in Fig. 9–9c.

In a modern ULSI chip, the complexity of the device layout generally demands that multiple levels of metallization be used for interconnecting the devices (Fig. 9–10). Hence, after the first metal is deposited, an intermetal dielectric isolation layer such as SiO_2 is deposited by low-temperature CVD. Low temperatures are very important in this *back-end* part of the processing because by now all the active devices are in place and one cannot allow the dopants to diffuse significantly. Also, the metallization cannot withstand temperatures higher than ~500°C. The dielectric isolation layer must be suitably planarized prior to the deposition of the next layer of metal, and this is generally done by CMP. Planarization is important because if metal is deposited on a surface with rough topography and subjected to RIE, there can be residual metal sidewall filaments or "stringers" at the steps for the same reason one gets sidewall oxide spacers on either side of the MOSFET gate in Fig. 9–7. These metal stringers can cause short circuits between adjacent metal lines. Planarization is also important in

Integrated Circuits

Figure 9–10
Multilevel interconnect: Cross section of IC showing levels of Cu interconnections with suitably planarized intermetal dielectrics. The transistors are at the very bottom and correspond to 22 nm CMOS. (Photograph courtesy of Intel.)

maintaining good depth of focus during photolithography. After planarization of the isolation layer, one uses photolithography to open up a new set of contact holes called *vias,* followed by deposition, patterning and RIE of the next layer of metal, and so on for multi-level metallization. As mentioned previously, W metal plugs are sometimes selectively deposited to fill up the via holes prior to the metal deposition, and reduce the likelihood of an open circuit.

Finally, a protective overcoat is deposited on the IC to prevent contamination and failure of the devices due to the ambient (Fig. 9–10). This generally involves plasma CVD of silicon nitride, which has the nice attribute that it blocks the diffusion of water vapor and Na through it. Sodium, as mentioned in Section 6.4.3, causes a mobile ion problem in the gate dielectric of MOS devices. Sometimes, the protective overcoat is a BPSG layer. After the overcoat is deposited, openings are etched for the metal bond pads. After the chips are tested in an automated tester, the *known good dies* are packaged and wire bonded, as discussed in Section 9.6.

9.3.2 Integration of Other Circuit Elements

One of the most revolutionary developments of integrated circuit technology is the fact that integrated transistors are cheaper to make than are more mundane elements such as resistors and capacitors. There are, however, numerous applications calling for diodes, resistors, capacitors, and inductors in integrated form. In this section we discuss briefly how these circuit elements can be implemented on the chip. We will also discuss a very important circuit element—the interconnection pattern that ties all of the integrated devices together in a working system.

Diodes.   It is simple to build p-n junction diodes in a monolithic circuit. It is also common practice to use transistors to perform diode functions. Since many transistors are included in a monolithic circuit, no special diffusion step is required to fabricate the diode element. There are a number of ways in which a transistor can be connected as a diode. Perhaps the most common method is to use the emitter junction as the diode, with the collector and base shorted. This configuration is essentially the narrow base diode structure, which has high switching speed with little charge storage (Prob. 5.40). Since all the transistors can be made simultaneously, the proper connections can be included in the metallization pattern to convert some of the transistors into diodes.

Resistors.   Diffused or implanted resistors can be obtained in monolithic circuits by using the shallow junctions used in forming the transistor regions (Fig. 9–11a). For example, during the base implant, a resistor can be implanted which is made up of a thin p-type layer within one of the n-type islands. Alternatively a p region can be made during the base implant, and an n-type resistor channel can be included within the resulting p region during the emitter implant step. In either case, the resistance channel can be isolated from the rest of the circuit by proper biasing of the surrounding material. For example, if the resistor is a p-type channel obtained during the base implant, the surrounding n material can be connected to the most positive potential in the circuit to provide reverse-bias junction isolation. The resistance of the channel depends on its length, width, depth of the implant, and resistivity of the implanted material. Since the depth and resistivity are determined by the requirements of the base or emitter implant, the variable parameters are the length and width. Two typical resistor geometries are shown in Fig. 9–11b. In each case the resistor is long compared with its width, and a provision is made on each end for making contact to the metallization pattern.

Design of diffused resistors begins with a quantity called the *sheet resistance* of the diffused layer. If the average resistivity of a diffused region is ρ, the resistance of a given length L is $R = \rho L/wt$, where w is the width and t is the thickness of the layer. Now if we consider one square of the material,

(a)

(b)

Figure 9–11
Monolithic resistors: (a) cross section showing use of base and emitter diffusions for resistors; (b) top view of two resistor patterns.

such that $L = w$, we have the sheet resistance $R_s \sim \rho/t$ in units of ohms per square. We notice that R_s measured for a given layer is numerically the same for any size square. This quantity is simple to measure for a thin diffused layer by a four-point probe technique.[2] Therefore, for a given diffusion, the sheet resistance is generally known with good accuracy. The resistance then can be calculated from the known value of R_s and the ratio L/w (the *aspect ratio*) for the resistor. We can make the width w as small as possible within the requirements of heat dissipation and photolithographic limitations and then calculate the required length from w and R_s. Design criteria for diffused resistors include geometrical factors, such as the presence of high current density at the inside corner of a sharp turn. In some cases it is necessary to round corners slightly in a folded or zigzag resistor (Fig. 9–12b) to reduce this problem.

To reduce the amount of space used for resistors or to obtain larger resistance values, it is often necessary to obtain surface layers having larger sheet resistance than is available during the standard base or emitter implants. We can use a different implant, such as the V_T adjust implant, to form shallow regions having very high sheet resistance ($\sim 10^5 \ \Omega$/square). This procedure can provide a considerable saving of space on the chip. In integrated FET circuits it is common to replace load resistors with depletion-mode transistors, as mentioned in Section 6.5.5.

Capacitors.   One of the most important elements of an integrated circuit is the capacitor. This is particularly true in the case of memory circuits, where charge is stored in a capacitor for each bit of information. Figure 9–12

Figure 9–12 Integrated capacitor for DRAM cells. A one-transistor memory cell in which the transistor stores and accesses charge in an adjacent planar MOS capacitor.

---

[2]This is a very useful method in which current is introduced into a wafer at one probe and is collected at another probe, and the voltage is measured by two probes in between. Special formulas are required to calculate resistivity or sheet resistance from these measurements.

illustrates a one-transistor DRAM cell, in which the n-channel MOS transistor provides access to the adjacent MOS capacitor. The top plate of the capacitor is polysilicon, and the bottom plate is an inversion charge contacted by an n^+ region of the transistor. The terms *bit line* and *word line* refer to the row and column organization of the memory (Section 9.5.2). One can also make use of the capacitance associated with p-n junctions, as discussed in Section 5.5.5.

Inductors. Inductors have not been incorporated into ICs in the past, because it is much harder to integrate inductors than the other circuit elements. Also, there has not been a great need for integrating inductors. Recently, that has changed because of the growing need for rf analog ICs for portable communication electronics. Inductors are very important for such applications, and can be made with reasonable Q factors using spiral wound thin metal films on an IC. Such spiral patterns can be defined by photolithography and etching techniques compatible with IC processing, or they can be incorporated in a hybrid IC.

Contacts and Interconnections. During the metallization step, the various regions of each circuit element are contacted and proper interconnection of the circuit elements is made. Aluminum is commonly used for the top metallization, since it adheres well to Si and to SiO_2 if the temperature is raised briefly to about 550°C after deposition. Gold is used on GaAs devices, but the adhesion properties of Au to Si and SiO_2 are poor. Gold also creates deep traps in Si.

As mentioned throughout this chapter, silicide contacts and doped polysilicon conductors are commonly used in integrated circuits. By opening windows through the oxide layers to these conductors, Al metallization can be used to contact them and connect them to other parts of the circuit. In cases where Al is used to contact the Si surface, it is usually necessary to use Al containing about 1% Si to prevent the metal from incorporating Si from the layer being contacted, thereby causing "spikes" in the surface. Thin diffusion barriers are also used between the Al and Si layers, to prevent migration between the two. The refractory silicides mentioned in Section 9.3.1 serve this purpose.

Increased complexity and packing density in integrated circuits inevitably leads to a need for multilayer metallization. Multiple levels of Cu metallization can be incorporated with interspersing dielectrics. In general, the metals may all be Al, Cu or they may be different conductors such as polysilicon or refractory metals (depending on the heat each is subjected to in subsequent processing). Also, the dielectrics may be deposited oxides, borophospho-silicate glass for reflow planarization, nitrides, and so on. The planarization of the surface is extremely important to prevent breaks in the metallization, which can occur in traversing a step on the surface. Various approaches using reflow glass, polyimide, and other materials to achieve pla-narization have been used, along with CMP.

The most important challenge in designing interconnects is the RC time constant, which affects the speed and active power dissipation of the chip. A very simplistic model of two layers of interconnects with an inter-metal dielectric (Figs. 9–13 and 9–14) shows that it can be regarded as a parallel plate capacitor. Regarding the interconnect as a rectangular resistor, its resistance is given by

$$R = \frac{\rho L}{tw} = R_s \frac{L}{w} \qquad (9\text{–}1a)$$

where R_s is the sheet resistance, and the other symbols are defined in Fig. 9–14. The capacitance is given by

$$C = \frac{\epsilon L w}{d} \qquad (9\text{–}1b)$$

The RC time constant is then

$$\left(\frac{\rho L}{wt}\right)\left(\frac{\epsilon L w}{d}\right) = \frac{\rho \epsilon L^2}{td} = \frac{R_s \epsilon L^2}{d} \qquad (9\text{–}2)$$

Interestingly, for this simple one-dimensional model, the width of the inter-connect w cancels out. Therefore, it does not make sense to use wider con-ductors for high-speed operation. It is also impractical to do so in terms of packing density. Of course, in reality we must account for the fringing electric fields, and therefore account for width dependence. From Eq. (9–2), it is clear we need as thick a metal layer (within practical limits of deposition times and etching times) and as low a resistivity as possible. Low resistivities are also

Figure 9–13
Multilevel interconnects: Micrograph of multilevel interconnects in an IC. The inter-level dielectrics have been etched off to reveal the copper interconnect lines. (Photograph Courtesy of IBM)

Figure 9–14
Equivalent circuit illustrating the various parasitic capacitive elements associated with a multilevel interconnect. On the top right hand corner of the figure, we focus on the parallel plate capacitor model referred to in Eqs. (9–1) and (9–2).

important in minimizing ohmic voltage drops in metal bus lines that carry power from one end of a chip to the other. Aluminum is very good in this regard, and thus was a mainstay for Si technology for many years. Aluminum also has other nice attributes such as good ohmic contacts to both n and p-type Si, and good adhesion to oxides.

Copper has even lower resistivity (1.7 $\mu\Omega$-cm) than Al (3 $\mu\Omega$-cm) and is about two orders of magnitude less susceptible to electromigration. Hence, it is an excellent alternative to Al for very high speed ICs (Fig. 9–13). The process breakthroughs that have made Cu viable for metallization include new electrodeposition and electroplating techniques because CVD or sputter deposition is not very practical for Cu. It is also very difficult to use RIE for Cu because the etch byproducts for Cu are not very volatile. Hence, instead of RIE, Cu patterning is based on the so-called Damascene process where grooves are first etched in a dielectric layer, Cu is deposited on it, and the metal layer is chemically-mechanically polished down, leaving inlaid metal lines in the oxide grooves. In this method, the metal does not have to be etched directly using RIE, which is always a difficult process. The name "damascene" is derived from a metallurgical technique in ancient Turkey where metal artwork was inlaid into swords and other artifacts using this type of process. Copper can create traps deep in the band gap of Si; hence, a suitable barrier layer such as Ti is needed between the Cu layer and the Si substrate.

Other parameters in Eq. (9–2) that can minimize the RC time constant are clearly the use of a thick inter-metal dielectric layer (once again within the limits of practicality in terms of deposition times), and as low a dielectric constant material as possible. Silicon dioxide has a relative dielectric constant of 3.9. There is active research in low dielectric constant materials (sometimes referred to as low-k materials). These include organic materials such as polyimides, or xerogels/aerogels which have air pockets or porosity purposely built in to minimize the dielectric constant.

In designing the layout of elements for a monolithic circuit, topological problems must be solved to provide efficient interconnection without *crossovers*—points at which one conductor crosses another conductor. If crossovers must be made on the Si surface, they can be accomplished easily at a resistor. Since the implanted or diffused resistor is covered by SiO_2, a conductor can be deposited crossing the insulated resistor. In cases requiring crossovers where no resistor is available, a low-value implanted resistor can be inserted in one of the conductor paths. For example, a short n^+ region can be implanted during the source/drain step and contacted at each end by one of the conductors. The other conductor can then cross over the oxide layer above the n^+ region. Usually, this can be accomplished without appreciable increase in resistance, since the n^+ region is heavily doped and its length can be made small.

During the metallization step, appropriate points in the circuit are connected to relatively large *pads* to provide for external contacts. These metal pads are visible in photographs of monolithic circuits as rectangular areas spaced around the periphery of the device. In the mounting and packaging process, these pads are contacted by small Au or Al wires or by special techniques such as those discussed in Section 9.6.

9.4 CHARGE TRANSFER DEVICES

One of the most interesting and broadly useful integrated devices is the *charge-coupled device (CCD)*. The CCD is part of a broader class of structures known generally as *charge transfer devices*. These are dynamic devices that move charge along a predetermined path under the control of clock pulses. These devices find applications in signal processing and imaging. In this section we lay the groundwork for understanding these devices, but their present forms and variety of applications must be found in the current literature.

9.4.1 Dynamic Effects in MOS Capacitors

The basis of the CCD is the dynamic storage and withdrawal of charge in a series of MOS capacitors. Thus we must begin by extending the MOS discussion of Chapter 6 to include the basics of dynamic effects. Figure 9–15 shows an MOS capacitor on a p-type substrate with a large positive gate pulse applied. A depletion region exists under the gate, and the surface potential increases considerably under the gate electrode. In effect, the surface potential forms a *potential well,* which can be exploited for the storage of charge.

If the positive gate bias has been applied for a sufficiently long time, electrons accumulate at the surface and the steady state inversion condition is established. The source of these carriers is the thermal generation of electrons at or near the surface. In effect, the inversion charge tells us the capacity of the well for storage charge. The time required to fill the well thermally is called the *thermal relaxation time,* and it depends on the quality of the semiconductor material and its interface with the insulator. For good materials the thermal relaxation time can be much longer than the charge storage times involved in CCD operation.

If instead of a steady state bias we apply a large positive pulse to the MOS gate electrode, a deep potential well is first created. Before inversion has occurred by thermal generation, the depletion width is greater than it would be at equilibrium $(W > W_m)$. This transient condition is sometimes called *deep depletion.* If we can inject electrons into this potential well electrically or optically, they will be stored there.[3] The storage is temporary,

(a)

(b) ϕ_s

Signal charge

Figure 9–15
An MOS capacitor with a positive gate pulse: (a) depletion region and surface charge; (b) potential well at the interface, partially filled with electrons corresponding to the surface charge shown in (a).

[3]The potential well should not be confused with the depletion region, which extends into the bulk of the semiconductor. The "depth" of the well is measured in electrostatic potential, not distance. Electrons stored in the potential well are in fact located very near the semiconductor surface.

however, because we must move the electrons out to another storage location before thermal generation becomes appreciable.

What is needed is a simple method for allowing charge to flow from one potential well to an adjacent one quickly and without losing much charge in the process. If this is accomplished, we can inject, move, and collect packets of charge dynamically to do a variety of electronic functions.

9.4.2 The Basic CCD

The original CCD structure proposed in 1969 by Boyle and Smith of Bell Laboratories consisted of a series of metal electrodes forming an array of MOS capacitors as shown in Fig. 9–16. Voltage pulses are supplied in three lines (L_1, L_2, L_3), each connected to every third electrode in the row (G_1, G_2, G_3). These voltages are clocked to provide potential wells, which vary with time as in Fig. 9–16. At time t_1 a potential well exists under each G_1 electrode, and we assume this well contains a packet of electrons from a previous operation. At time t_2 a potential is applied also to the adjacent electrode G_2, and the charge equalizes across the common G_1–G_2 well. It is easy to visualize this process by thinking of the mobile charge in analogy

Figure 9–16
The basic CCD, composed of a linear array of MOS capacitors. At time t_1, the G_1 electrodes are positive, and the charge packet is stored in the G_1 potential well. At t_2 both G_1 and G_2 are positive, and the charge is distributed between the two wells. At t_3 the potential on G_1 is reduced, and the charge flows to the second well. At t_4 the transfer of charge to the G_2 well is completed.

with a fluid, which flows to equalize its level in the expanding container. This fluid model continues at t_3 when V_1 is reduced, thus decreasing the potential well under G_1. Now the charge flows into the G_2 well, and this process is completed at t_4 when V_1 is zero. By this process the packet of charge has been moved from under G_1 to G_2. As the procedure is continued, the charge is next passed to the G_3 position, and continues down the line as time proceeds. In this way charge can be injected using an input diode, transported down the line, and detected at the other end.

9.4.3 Improvements on the Basic Structure

Several problems arise in the implementation of the CCD structure of Fig. 9–16. For example, the separation between electrodes must be very small to allow coupling between the wells. An improvement can be made by using an over-lapping gate structure such as that shown in Fig. 9–17. This can be done, for example, with poly-Si electrodes separated by SiO_2 or with alternating poly-Si and metal electrodes.

One of the problems inherent to the charge transfer process is that some charge is inevitably lost during the many transfers along the CCD. If the charges are stored at the Si–SiO₂ interface, surface states trap a certain amount of charge. Thus if the "0" logic condition is an empty well, the leading edge of a train of pulses is degraded by the loss of charge required in filling the traps which were empty in the "0" condition. One way of improving this situation is to provide enough bias in the "0" state to accommodate the interface and bulk traps. This procedure is colorfully referred to as using a *fat zero*. Even with the use of fat zeros, the signal is degraded after a number of transfers, by inherent inefficiencies in the transfer process.

Transfer efficiency can be improved by moving the charge transfer layer below the semiconductor–insulator interface. This can be accomplished by using ion implantation or epitaxial growth to create a layer of opposite type than the substrate. This shifts the maximum potential under each electrode into the semiconductor bulk, thus avoiding the semiconductor–insulator interface. This type of device is referred to as a *buried channel* CCD.

The three-phase CCD shown in Fig. 9–16 is only one example of a variety of CCD structures. Figure 9–18 illustrates one method for achieving a two-phase system, in which voltages are sequentially applied to alternating

Figure 9–17
An overlapping gate CCD structure. One set of electrodes is polycrystalline Si, and the overlapping gates are Al in this case. SiO₂ separates the adjacent electrodes.

Figure 9–18
A two-phase CCD with an extra potential well built in under the right half of each electrode by donor implantation.

gate electrodes from two lines. A two-level poly-Si gate structure is used, in which the gate electrodes overlap, and a donor implant near the Si surface creates a built-in well under half of each electrode. When both gates are turned off (b), potential wells exist only under the implanted regions, and charge can be stored in any of these wells. With electrode G_2 pulsed positively, the charge packet shown in (b) is transferred to the deepest well under G_2, which is its implanted region as (c) indicates. Then with both gates off, the wells appear as in (b) again, except that the charge is now under the G_2 electrode. The next step in the transfer process is obviously to pulse G_1 positively, so that the charge moves to the implanted region under the G_1 electrode to the right.

Other improvements to the basic structure are important in various applications. These include channel stops or other methods for achieving lateral confinement for the stored charge. Regeneration points must be included in the array to refresh the signal after it has been degraded.

9.4.4 Applications of CCDs

CCDs are used in a number of ways, including signal processing functions such as delay, filtering, and multiplexing several signals. Another interesting application of CCDs is in imaging for astronomy or in solid state cameras, in which an array of photosensors is used to form charge packets proportional to light intensity, and these packets are shifted to a detector point for readout. There are numerous ways of accomplishing this in CCDs, including the linear array line scanner, in which the second dimension is obtained by moving the scanner relative to the image. Alternatively, an area image sensor

Figure 9–19
A charge-coupled device image sensor shown as large white rectangular areas, with peripheral signal processing circuitry. (Photograph courtesy of Texas Instruments.)

can be made which scans the image electronically in both dimensions. The latter device can be used as an alternative to the electron beam-addressed television imaging tube (Fig. 9–19).

In the early development of integrated circuits it was felt that the inevitable defects that occur in processing would prevent the fabrication of devices containing more than a few dozen logic gates. One approach to integration on a larger scale tried in the late 1960s involved fabricating many identical logic gates on a wafer, testing them, and interconnecting the good ones (a process called *discretionary wiring*). While this approach was being developed, however, radical improvements were made in device processing which increased the yield of good chips on a wafer dramatically. By the early 1970s it was possible to build circuits with many hundreds of components per chip, with reasonable yield. These improvements made discretionary wiring obsolete almost as soon as it was developed. By reducing the number of processing defects, improving the packing density of components, and increasing the wafer size, it is now possible to place millions of device elements on a single chip of silicon and to obtain many perfect chips per wafer.

A major factor in the development of integrated circuits has been the continual reduction in size of the individual elements (transistors, capacitors) within each circuit. Through improved design and better lithography, there has been a dramatic shrinking of the minimum feature size (e.g., a transistor gate) used in these devices. The results of shrinking the elements in a 256-Mb-DRAM are shown in Fig. 9–20. By reducing the minimum feature

9.5 ULTRA LARGE-SCALE INTEGRATION (ULSI)

size in successive steps from 0.13 to 0.11 μm, the die area was reduced from about 135 mm^2 in the first-generation design to less than 42 mm^2 in the fifth-generation device. Obviously, more of the smaller chips can be made by batch fabrication on the wafer, and the effort in shrinking the design is rewarded in a more profitable device.

Successive designs using reduced feature sizes have made dramatically increased circuit complexity possible. DRAM design has set the pace over the past two decades, in which successive 1-Mb, 4-Mb, and 16-Mb memories led to similar powers of two increase to the Gb range. Figure 9–21 illustrates the size comparison of a 128-Mb memory with an equivalent amount of memory in the form of two 64-Mb and eight 16-Mb chips. These are examples of ULSI.

Although the achievement of many powers of two in memory is impressive and important, other ULSI chips are important for the integration of many different system functions. A *microprocessor* includes functions

(a)   (b)   (c)

for a computer central processing unit (CPU), along with memory, control, timing, and interface circuits required to perform very complex computing functions. The complexity of such devices is shown in Fig. 9–22, which illustrates a microprocessor chip.

Before leaving this section it might be useful to provide some calibration regarding the dimensions we have been discussing. Figure 9–23 compares the size of 64-Mb DRAM circuit interconnect elements with a human hair, on the same scale. We can see that the densely packed 0.18 μm lines on this ULSI memory chip are dwarfed by the scanning electron micrograph of a human hair which has the diameter of about 50 microns. Current generation DRAMs have feature sizes of ~25 nm (0.025 μm).

Although the focus of this book is devices and not circuits, it is important to look at some typical applications of MOS capacitors and FETs in semiconductor logic and memory ULSI, which constitute about 90% of all ICs. This should give the reader a better feel for why we have studied the physics of MOS devices in Chapter 6. This is clearly not a comprehensive discussion, because the design and analysis of circuits is a large subject covered in other books and courses. We will first look at some digital logic applications, followed by some typical memory devices.

9.5.1 Logic Devices

A very simple and basic circuit element is the inverter, which serves to flip the logic state. When its input voltage is high (corresponding to logic "1"), its output voltage is low (logic "0"), and vice versa. Let us start the analysis with

Figure 9–22
An example of ULSI, the Intel 22nm quad core processor with 1.4 billion transistors. (Photograph courtesy of Intel.)

(a)

(b)

a resistor-loaded n-channel MOSFET inverter to illustrate the principles in
the simplest possible manner (Fig. 9–24a). Then, we will extend the treatment
to the slightly more complicated CMOS inverters which are much more useful and more common today.

A key concept for inverters is the *voltage transfer characteristic* (VTC),
which is a plot of the output voltage as a function of the input bias (Fig. 9–24c).
The VTC gives us information, for example, about how much noise the digital
circuit can handle, and the speed of switching of the logic gates. There are five

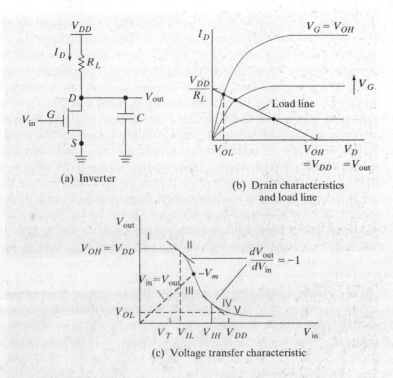

(a) Inverter

(b) Drain characteristics and load line

(c) Voltage transfer characteristic

Figure 9–24
Resistor load inverter voltage transfer character-istics (VTC): (a) NMOSFET with load resistor R_L and load parasitic capacitance C; (b) determination of VTC by superimposing the load line (linear I–V ohmic characteristics of the resistor) on NMOSFET output characteristics; (c) VTC showing output voltage as a function of input voltage. The five key points on the VTC are logic high (V_{OH}), logic low (V_{OL}), unity gain points (V_{IL} and V_{IH}), and logic threshold where input equals output (V_m).

key operating points (marked I through V) on the VTC. They include V_{OH}, corresponding to the logic high or "1", V_{OL}, corresponding to the logic low or "0", and V_m, corresponding to the intersection of a line with unity slope (where $V_{out} = V_{in}$) with the VTC. V_m, known as the logic threshold (not to be confused with the V_T of the MOSFETs), is important when two invert-ers are cross-coupled in a flip-flop circuit because the output of one is fed to the input of the other, and vice versa. Two other key points are the unity gain points, V_{IL} and V_{IH}. The significance of these points is that if the input voltage is between them, the change of the input is amplified and we get a larger change of the output voltage. Outside of this operating range, the change of the input voltage is attenuated. Clearly, any noise voltage which puts the input voltage between V_{IL} and V_{IH} would be amplified, and lead to a potential problem with the circuit operation.

Let us see how to go about determining the VTC. From the cir-cuit in Fig. 9–24a, we see that in the output loop from the power supply to ground, the current through the resistor load is the same as the drain cur-rent of the MOSFET. The power supply voltage is equal to the voltage drop across the resistor plus the drain-to-source voltage. To determine the VTC, we superimpose the load line of the load element (in this case a straight line for an ohmic resistor) on the output characteristics of the MOSFET (Fig. 9–24b). This is similar to our load line discussion in Section 6.1.1. The load line goes through V_{DD} on the voltage axis because when the current in the output loop is zero, there is no voltage drop across the resistor and all the voltage appears across the MOSFET. On the current axis, the load line goes through V_{DD}/R_L because when the voltage across the MOSFET is zero, the voltage across the resistor must be V_{DD}. As we change the input bias, V_{in}, we change the gate bias on the MOSFET, and thus in Fig. 9–24b, we go from one constant V_G curve to the next. At each input bias (and a corresponding constant V_G curve) the intersection of the load line with that curve tells us what the drain bias V_D is, which is the same as the output voltage. This is because at the point of intersection, we satisfy the condition that for the d-c case where the capacitor does not play any role, the current through the resistor is the same as the MOSFET current. (Later on, we shall see that in the a-c case when the logic gates are switched, we need to worry about the displacement current through the capacitor when it is charged or discharged.) It can be clearly seen from Fig. 9–24c that as the input voltage (or V_G) changes from low to high, the output voltage decreases from a high of V_{DD} to a low of V_{OL}. We can solve for any point on this VTC curve analytically simply by recognizing whether the MOSFET is in the linear region or in saturation, using the corresponding drain current expression [Eq. (6–49) or (6–53)] and setting it equal to the resistor current. As an illustration, suppose we want to determine the logic "0" level, V_{OL}. This occurs when the input V_G is high and the output V_D is low, putting the transistor in the linear region. Using Eq. (6–49), we can write

$$I_D = k\left[V_G - V_T - \frac{V_D}{2}\right]V_D = k\left[V_{DD} - V_T - \frac{V_{OL}}{2}\right]V_{OL} \quad (9\text{–}3a)$$

Since in the d-c case the current through the MOSFET is the same as that through the resistor,

$$I_D = I_L = \frac{V_{DD} - V_{OL}}{R_L} \quad (9\text{–}3b)$$

We can solve for V_{OL} if we know R_L and the MOSFET parameters. Alternatively, we can design the value of R_L to achieve a certain V_{OL}. What might dictate the choice of R_L? We shall see later in this section that for many applications we use two of these inverters in a cross-coupled manner to form a bistable flip-flop. The output of one inverter is fed back to the input of the other, and vice versa. Clearly, the V_{OL} must be designed to be significantly less than the V_T of the MOSFET. Otherwise, neither MOSFET will be fully turned off, and the flip-flop will not function properly. Similarly, all the other points on the VTC can be determined analytically by using the appropriate MOSFET drain current expression, and setting it equal to the current through the resistor.

We can make some general observations from this analysis. We want the transition region of the VTC (between V_{IL} and V_{IH}) to be as steep (i.e., high gain) as possible, and the transition should be around $V_{DD}/2$. High gain guarantees a high-speed transition from one logic state to the other.

It is necessary to increase the load resistance to increase this gain in the transition region.

The transition around $V_{DD}/2$ guarantees high *noise immunity* or *margin* for both logic "1" and logic "0" levels. To appreciate the importance of noise immunity, we must recognize that in combinatorial or sequential digital circuits, the output of one inverter or logic gate is often fed into the input of the next stage. Noise immunity is a measure of how much noise voltage the circuit can tolerate at the input, and still have the digital outputs be at the correct logic level in the subsequent stages. For example in Fig. 9–24c, if the input is nominally at zero, the output should be high (logic "1"). If this is fed into another inverter stage, its output should be low, and so on. If a noise spike causes the input of the first stage to go above V_m, the output voltage decreases sufficiently to potentially create errors in the digital levels in subsequent stages. Having a symmetric transition of the VTC around $V_{DD}/2$ ensures that the noise margin is high for both logic levels.

One problem with the resistor load inverter is that the V_{OL} is low, but not zero. This, coupled with the fact that the load element is a passive resistor that cannot be turned off, causes high standby power dissipation in this circuit. These problems are addressed by the CMOS structure described next.

We can determine the VTC for the CMOS case exactly as for the resistor load, although the math is somewhat more messy (Fig. 9–25). As mentioned previously, for an input voltage V_{in}, the V_G of the NMOSFET is V_{in}, but that of the PMOSFET is $V_{in} - V_{DD}$. Similarly, if the output voltage is V_{out}, the V_D of the NMOSFET is V_{out}, but that of the PMOS is $V_{out} - V_{DD}$. The load element now is not a simple resistor with a linear current–voltage relationship, but instead is the PMOSFET device whose "load line" is a set of $I_D - V_D$ output characteristics (Fig. 9–25b). The V_{out} can be determined as a function of the V_{in} by recognizing whether the NMOSFET and the PMOSFET are in the linear or saturation region of their characteristics, and using the appropriate current expressions. At each point, we would set the NMOSFET I_D equal to the PMOSFET I_D.

As in the case of the resistive load, there are five key points on the VTC (Fig. 9–25c). They are logic "1" equal to V_{DD}, logic "0" equal to 0, logic threshold V_m where $V_{in} = V_{out}$, and the two unity gain points, V_{IH} and V_{IL}. In region I in Fig. 9–25c, the NMOSFET is OFF, and $V_{out} = V_{DD}$. Similarly, in region V, the PMOSFET is OFF, and $V_{out} = 0$. We can illustrate the calculation in region II, where the NMOSFET is in saturation and the PMOSFET is in the linear region. In this case, we must use Eq. (6–53) for the saturation drain current of the NMOSFET. We are considering the long channel case.

$$I_{DN} = \frac{k_N}{2} (V_{in} - V_{TN})^2 \tag{9–4a}$$

On the other hand, we must use Eq. (6–49) for the PMOSFET in the linear region.

$$I_{DP} = k_P \left[(V_{DD} - V_{in}) + V_{TP} - \frac{(V_{DD} - V_{out})}{2} \right] (V_{DD} - V_{out}) \tag{9–4b}$$

(a)   (b)

(c)

(d)

Figure 9–25

CMOS inverter voltage transfer characteristics: (a) NMOSFET with PMOSFET load and load parasitic capacitance, C; (b) determination of VTC by superimposing load line (output characterisitics of PMOSFET shown as dotted line) on NMOSFET output characteristics; (c) VTC showing output voltage as a function of input voltage. The five key points on the VTC are logic high (V_{OH}), logic low (V_{OL}), unity gain points (V_{IL} and V_{IH}), and logic threshold where input equals output (V_m); (d) switching current from V_{DD} to ground when the input voltage is in a range where both the NMOSFET and the PMOSFET are on.

Here V_{TN} and V_{TP} are the n- and p-channel threshold voltages. In the d-c case, since the output load capacitor does not play a role, the drain current through the PMOSFET device must be equal in magnitude to that through the NMOSFET. (However, for the a-c case, we need to consider the displacement current through the capacitor.)

$$I_{DN} = I_{DP} \tag{9–5a}$$

Using Eq. (6–53) for the NMOSFET in saturation, and Eq. (6–49) for the PMOSFET in the linear region.

$$\frac{k_N}{2k_P}(V_{in} - V_{TN})^2 = \left[V_{DD} - V_{in} + V_{TP} - \frac{V_{DD} - V_{out}}{2} \right](V_{DD} - V_{out})$$

$$= \left[\frac{V_{DD}}{2} - V_{in} + V_{TP} + \frac{V_{out}}{2} \right](V_{DD} - V_{out}) \tag{9–5b}$$

From Eq. (9–5b), we can get an analytical relation between the input and output voltages valid in region II. We can get similar relationships in the other regions of the VTC.

Region IV is very similar to region II in Fig. 9–25c, except that now the NMOS is in the linear regime, while the PMOSFET is in saturation. In region III, both the NMOSFET and the PMOSFET are in saturation. Since the output impedance of a MOSFET is very high, this is tantamount to a semi-infinite load resistor, thereby resulting in a very steep transition region. That is why a CMOS inverter switches faster than the resistor load case. The CMOS inverter is also preferable because in either logic state (regions I or V), either the NMOSFET or the PMOSFET is OFF, and the standby power dissipation is very low. In fact, the current in either logic state corresponds to the (very low) source/drain diode leakage.

We want the transition region (region III) to be at $V_{DD}/2$ from the point of view of symmetry and noise immunity. Once again, by setting the NMOSFET I_D equal to that of the PMOSFET, it can be shown that the transition occurs at

$$V_{in} = (V_{DD} + \chi V_{TN} + V_{TP})/(1 + \chi) \tag{9–6a}$$

where

$$\chi = \left(\frac{k_N}{k_P} \right)^{\frac{1}{2}} = \frac{\left[\bar{\mu}_n C_i \left(\frac{Z}{L} \right)_N \right]^{\frac{1}{2}}}{\left[\bar{\mu}_p C_i \left(\frac{Z}{L} \right)_P \right]^{\frac{1}{2}}} \tag{9–6b}$$

We can design V_{in} to be at $V_{DD}/2$ by choosing $V_{TN} = -V_{TP}$ and $\chi = 1$. Since the effective electron mobility in the channel of a Si MOSFET is roughly twice that of the hole mobility, we must design CMOS circuits to have a $(Z/L)_P = 2(Z/L)_N$ to achieve the condition $\chi = 1$.

We can combine such CMOS inverters to form other logic gates for combinatorial circuits such as NOR gates and NAND gates (Fig. 9–26). The truth tables for these gates are shown in Fig. 9–27. By applying combinations of logic "high" or logic "low" to inputs A and B, we get the output states corresponding to the truth tables. The synthesis of logic circuits corresponding to these truth tables can be done using Boolean algebra and De Morgan's laws. The upshot of these laws is that any logic circuit can be made using inverters in conjunction with either NAND gates or NOR gates. Which would be preferable from a device physics point of view? We see from Fig. 9–26, that in the NOR gate the PMOSFET devices T_3 and T_4 are in series, while for the NAND it is the NMOSFETs (T_1 and T_2). Since the electron channel mobilities are twice hole mobilities, we would obviously prefer NMOSFETs. Therefore, the preferred choice is NAND, along with inverters.

Figure 9–26
Logic gates and CMOS implementation of (a) NOR gate (b) NAND gate.

We can also estimate the power dissipation in the inverter circuit. We already know that the standby power dissipation is very small, being governed by the OFF state leakage current of either the NMOSFET or the PMOSFET, depending on the logic state. This leakage current depends on the source and drain diode leakage currents, or if the V_T is low, on the subthreshold leakage of the MOSFET that is turned OFF (see Section 6.5.7).

While the inverter is switching, there is also a transient current from the power supply to ground when both the transistors are ON (see Fig. 9–25d). This is known as the *switching current* or the *commutator current*. The magnitude of this current will clearly depend on the values of V_{TN} and V_{TP}. The higher the magnitudes of the thresholds, the less is the input voltage swing for which both the PMOSFET and the NMOSFET will be ON while the input voltage is being changed. The commutator current is then less during switching, which is desirable from a reduced power dissipation point of view. However, this reduction of power dissipation by increasing threshold voltages is obtained at the expense of reduced drive current and, therefore, overall speed of the circuit.

Input		Output Y	
A	B	AND	NAND
0	0	0	1
0	1	0	1
1	0	0	1
1	1	1	0

(a)

Input		Output Y	
A	B	OR	NOR
0	0	0	1
0	1	1	0
1	0	1	0
1	1	1	0

(b)

Input		Output Y
A	B	XOR
0	0	0
0	1	1
1	0	1
1	1	0

(c)

Figure 9–27
(a) AND/NAND logic symbols and truth table;
(b) OR/NOR logic symbols and truth table;
(c) XOR logic symbol and truth table.

The speed penalty due to reduction of drive current is because in a digital circuit, while switching between logic states, the MOSFET drive currents must charge and discharge the parasitic capacitors that are inevitably associated with the output node (Fig. 9–25a). There is also some power dissipation involved in charging and discharging load capacitors attached to the output of the inverter. This load capacitance depends mostly on the input gate oxide capacitance of the MOSFETs of the next inverter stage (or logic gate) that this inverter (or logic gate) may be driving, along with some small parasitic capacitances. The input load capacitance of a single inverter is given by gate oxide capacitance per unit area C_i times the device areas.

$$C_{inv} = C_i\{(ZL)_N + (ZL)_P\} \tag{9–7}$$

The total load capacitance is then multiplied by a factor that depends on the *fan-out* of the circuit, which is the number of gates that are being driven in parallel by the inverter (or logic gate). It is necessary to add up the load capacitances for all the inverters or logic gates that are being driven by this inverter stage. The energy expended in charging up the equivalent load capacitor, C, is the integral of the product of the time-dependent voltage times the time-dependent displacement current through the capacitor during the charging cycle.

$$E_C = \int i_p(t)[V_{DD} - v(t)]dt \tag{9–8a}$$

$$= V_{DD} \int i_p(t)dt - \int i_p(t)v(t)dt$$

The energy stored in C is then obtained by considering the displacement current ($i_p(t) = C\,dv/dt$) through the capacitor:

$$E_c = V_{DD}\int C\frac{dv}{dt}dt - \int Cv\frac{dv}{dt}dt$$

$$= CV_{DD}\int_0^{V_{DD}} dv - C\int_0^{V_{DD}} v\,dv = CV_{DD}^2 - \frac{1}{2}CV_{DD}^2 \tag{9–8b}$$

Similarly, during one discharging cycle we get

$$E_d = \int i_n(t)v(t)dt = -\int_{V_{DD}}^0 Cv\,dv = \frac{1}{2}CV_{DD}^2 \tag{9–9}$$

If the inverter (or gate) is being charged and discharged at a frequency f, we get an active power dissipation

$$P = CV_{DD}^2 f \tag{9–10}$$

In addition to power dissipation, we are also concerned with the speed of logic circuits. The speed of a gate, such as the one shown in Fig. 9–25, is determined by the *propagation delay* time t_P. We define the time required for the output to go from the logic high V_{OH} to $V_{OH}/2$ as t_{PHL}. The converse (to go from logic low $V_{OL}(=0)$ to $V_{OH}/2$) is defined as t_{PLH}. We can write down approximate estimates for these times by recognizing that for the output to go from high to low (or logic "1" to "0"), the NMOSFET has to discharge the output node toward ground. During this period, the NMOSFET will be in saturation. Assuming a constant saturation current as an approximation, we obtain from Eq. (6–53)

$$t_{PHL} = \frac{\frac{1}{2} C V_{DD}}{I_{DN}} = \frac{\frac{1}{2} C V_{DD}}{\frac{k_N}{2}(V_{DD} - V_{TN})^2} \tag{9–11a}$$

This is the decrease of charge on the capacitor divided by the discharging current. Conversely,

$$t_{PLH} = \frac{\frac{1}{2} C V_{DD}}{I_{DP}} = \frac{\frac{1}{2} C V_{DD}}{\frac{k_P}{2}(V_{DD} + V_{TP})^2} \tag{9–11b}$$

Knowing these times helps us considerably in designing circuits that meet the speed requirements of a design. Of course, for accurate numerical estimates of these propagation time delays or of the power dissipation we need to use computers. A very popular program to do so is the Simulation Program with Integrated Circuit Emphasis (SPICE). This discussion illustrates that the device physics plays an important role in the design and analysis of such circuits.

9.5.2 Semiconductor Memories

In addition to logic devices such as microprocessors, integrated circuits depend on semiconductor memories. We can illustrate many key MOS device physics issues by looking at three of the most important types of semiconductor memory cells: the *static random-access memory (SRAM)*, the *dynamic random-access memory (DRAM)*, and the non-volatile *flash memory cell*. SRAMs and DRAMs are volatile in the sense that the information is lost if the power supply is removed. For flash memories, however, information is stored indefinitely. For SRAMs, the information is static, meaning that as long as the power supply is on, the information is retained. On the other hand, the information stored in the cells of a DRAM must periodically be refreshed because stored charge representing one of the logic states leaks away rapidly. The refresh time must be short compared with the time needed for stored charge to degrade.

The overall organization of all these types of memories is rather similar, and is shown in Fig. 9–28. We will not describe the memory organization in

Figure 9–28
Organization of a random access memory (RAM): The memory array consists of memory cells arranged in an orthogonal array. There is one memory cell at the intersection of one row (wordline) and one column (bitline). To address a particular memory cell, the N row addresses are latched in from the N address pins, and decoded by the 2^N row decoders. All the memory cells on the selected row are read by the 2^N sense amplifiers. Of those, a cell (one bit) or group of cells (byte or word) is selected for transfer to the data output buffers depending on the column addresses that are decoded by the 2^N column decoders. Generally, to save pin count on the package, the N column addresses are provided in a multiplexed fashion to the same N address pins as the row addresses, *after* the row addresses have already been latched in.

great detail here, but will instead focus on the device physics. We need to know the type of cell that is used at the intersection of the rows or word-lines, and the columns or bitlines. These memories are all random access in the sense that the cells can be addressed for write or read operations in any order, depending on the row and column addresses provided to the address pins, unlike memories such as hard disks or floppy disks on a computer which can only be addressed sequentially. Generally, the same set of pins is used for both the row and the column addresses, in order to save pin count. This forces us to use what is known as address multiplexing. First, the row addresses are provided at the address pin, and decoded using row decoders. For N row addresses, we can have 2^N rows or wordlines. The row decoders then cause the selected wordline to go high, so that all the 2^N cells (corresponding to N column addresses) on this wordline are accessed for either read or write, through sense amplifiers at the end of the 2^N columns or bitlines. After the appropriate row has been decoded, the appropriate column addresses are provided to the same address pins, and the column decoders are used to select the bit or group of bits (known as *byte* or *word*) out of all the 2^N bits on the selected wordline. We can either write into or read from the selected bit (or group of bits) using the sense amplifiers, which are basically flip-flops or differential amplifiers.

SRAMs. A group of four 6-transistor CMOS SRAM cells is shown in Fig. 9–29. Each cell is found in this case at the intersection of a row or wordline, and a column or bitline (along with its logical complement known as bitline-bar). The cell is a flip-flop, consisting of two cross-coupled CMOS inverters. Clearly, it is bistable: if the output of one inverter is high (corresponding to the NMOSFET being OFF, and the PMOSFET ON), that high voltage is fed to the input of the other cross-coupled inverter, and the output of the other inverter will be low. This is one logic state (say "1") of the SRAM. Conversely, the other stable state of the flip-flop can be considered to be the other logic state (say "0"). Many of the device issues

Figure 9–29
An array of 4 CMOS SRAM cells. The bitline and bitline (bitline-bar) are logical complements of each other.

Wordline 0

Wordline m'

Bitline 0   Bitline 0   Bitline m   Bitline m

are identical to those described in Section 9.5.1 in connection with the VTC of inverters. We aim for a symmetric transition from V_{OH} to V_{OL} at $V_{DD}/2$ with a high gain in the transition region, to improve noise immunity and speed of convergence of the SRAM cell. The speed of convergence determines how fast the SRAM flip-flop latches into one stable logic state or the other. The cells are accessed through two access transistors whose gates are controlled by the wordline. That is why this is called a 6-transistor cell. Other SRAM cells use load resistors in the inverters, rather than PMOSFETs, leading to a 4-transistor, 2-resistor cell. As discussed in Section 9.5.1, the CMOS cell has superior performance, but at the expense of occupying more area.

Unless the row decoders cause a particular wordline to go high, the SRAM cells on that wordline are electrically isolated. By selecting a particular wordline, the access transistors on that row are turned ON and act as logic transmission gates between the output nodes of the SRAM cell and the bitline and its complement, the bitline-bar. During a read operation, the bitline and its complement are both precharged to the same voltage. Once the access transistors are turned ON, a small voltage differential develops between bitline and bitline-bar because the output nodes of the SRAM are at different voltages (0 and V_{DD}). The voltage differential that is established is due to a charge redistribution that occurs between the parasitic capacitance associated with the output nodes of the SRAM and the bitline capacitance. This voltage difference is amplified by the sense amplifiers. As mentioned previously, the sense amplifiers are differential amplifiers, very similar in configuration to the SRAM flip-flop cell itself. The bitline and bitline-bar (complement of the bitline) are fed to the two inputs of the sense amplifier, and the voltage differential is amplified until the voltage separation is V_{DD}.

DRAMs. The DRAM cell structure is shown in Fig. 9–30. The information is stored as charge on an MOS capacitor, which is connected to the bitline through a switch which is an MOS *pass transistor,* the gate of which is controlled by the wordline. There is one such cell at each intersection of the orthogonal array of wordlines and bitlines, exactly as for SRAMs. When the wordline voltage becomes higher than the V_T of the pass transistor (MOSFET between the bitline and the storage capacitor), the channel is turned ON, and connects the bitline to the MOS storage capacitor. The gate of this capacitor (or capacitor plate) is permanently connected to the power supply voltage V_{DD}, thereby creating a potential well under it which tends to be full of inversion electrons for a p-type substrate (Fig. 9–31a). We apply either 0 V to the bitline (generally corresponding to logic "0"), or V_{DD} (corresponding to logic "1"), and the appropriate voltage appears as the substrate potential of the MOS capacitor. For a stored "0" in the cell, the potential well that is created under the MOS capacitor by the plate voltage is full of inversion charge (Fig. 9–31b,c). When the wordline

Figure 9–30
One transistor,
one capacitor
DRAM cell
equivalent circuit:
the storage MOS
capacitor is
connected to the
bitline through
the pass transistor
(MOSFET switch)
whose gate is
controlled by the
wordline.

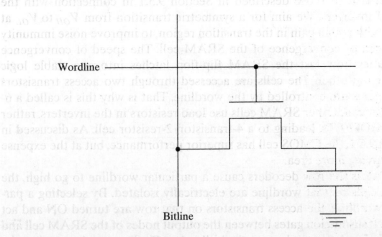

Wordline

Bitline

voltage is turned low such that the MOS pass transistor is turned off, the inversion charge under the storage capacitor stays the same; this is the stable state of the capacitor. On the other hand, if a positive voltage (V_{DD}) is applied to the bitline, it draws out the inversion electrons through the pass transistor (Fig. 9–31d,e). When the pass transistor is cut off, we end up with an empty potential well under the MOS capacitor plate. Over a period of time, the potential well tends to be filled up by minority carrier electrons that are constantly created by thermal generation–recombination in the substrate and are collected under the charged MOS capacitor plate. Hence, the logic "1" degrades towards the logic "0". That is why a DRAM is considered to be "dynamic" unlike an SRAM. It is necessary to periodically restore the logic levels or "refresh" the stored information.

There are interesting device physics issues regarding the pass transistor. This is like the access transistor in the SRAM, or a logic transmission gate. We see that in this MOSFET, neither the source nor the drain is permanently grounded. In fact, which side acts as the source and which as the drain depends on the circuit operation. When we are writing a logic "1" into the cell, the bitline voltage is held high ($=V_{DD}$). As this voltage is written into the cell, it is as if the source of the pass transistor gets charged up to V_{DD}. Another way of looking at this is that with respect to the source, the substrate bias of the pass transistor is $-V_{DD}$. The body effect of the MOSFET (Section 6.5.6) causes its V_T to increase. This is very important because for the pass transistor to operate as a transmission gate it is necessary that it be in the linear regime throughout, and not get into saturation (with a concomitant voltage drop across the pinch-off region). Hence, the gate or the wordline voltage must be held at V_{DD} (which is the final voltage of the source/drains) *plus* the V_T of the MOSFET, taking body effect into account. It is also important to make sure that the leakage of the pass transistor is low enough to

Figure 9–31
DRAM cell structure and cell operation: (a) cell structure corresponding to equivalent circuit of Fig. 9–30; (b)–(e) potentials under bitline, pass transistor channel and storage capacitor during write "0", store "0", write "1" and store "1" operations. It shows that the logic state "0" corresponds to a filled potential well (stable state), while the logic state "1" corresponds to an empty potential well (unstable state) that is filled up over time by minority carriers generated in the substrate and leakage through the pass transistor.

satisfy refresh requirements of the DRAM. Not only must the source/drain diodes be low leakage, but the V_T and the subthreshold slope must be optimized such that subthreshold leakage for the grounded wordline case is low enough.

The stored charge difference between the two logic states can be determined by looking at the capacitance–voltage (C–V) characteristics of the MOS capacitor (Fig. 9–32). For a stored "1", essentially there is a substrate bias applied to the MOS capacitor, which raises its V_T due to the body effect (Section 6.5.6). Hence, the C–V characteristics shift to the right for a stored "1". Since the MOS capacitance is not a fixed capacitance, but is voltage dependent, we saw earlier that it must be defined in a differential form [Eq. (6–34a)]. Alternatively, we can write down the stored charge under the capacitor as

$$Q = \int C(V)\,dV \qquad (9\text{–}12)$$

This is simply the area under the C–V curve. The charge differential that distinguishes the logic "1" and the logic "0" is the difference of areas under the capacitance–voltage curves in the two cases (Fig. 9–32).

When reading the cell, the pass transistor is turned on, and the MOS storage capacitor charge is dumped on the bitline capacitance C_B, precharged to V_B (typically $= V_{DD}$). The swing of the bitline voltage will clearly depend on the voltage V_C stored in the storage cell capacitance C_C. As in the case of the SRAM, the change of the bitline voltage depends

Figure 9–32
C–V characteristics of DRAM MOS capacitor in stored "0" and stored "1" states. The difference of area under the C–V curves shown by hatch-marked pattern reflects the charge differential between the two states.

Figure 9–33
Equivalent circuit showing charge redistribution between cell capacitance (C_C) and bitline capacitance (C_B) on one side, versus dummy cell (C_D) and bitline capacitance (C_B) on other.

on the capacitance ratio between the bitline and the cell. To do differential sensing in the case of DRAMs, we do not use two bitlines per cell as for SRAMs. Instead, we compare the bitline voltage for the selected cell with a reference bitline voltage to which is connected a dummy cell whose MOS capacitance, C_D, is roughly half that of the actual cell capacitance, C_C. Typical values of C_B, C_C, and C_D in a DRAM are 800 fF, 50 fF, and 20 fF, respectively. The voltage differential that is applied to the sense amplifier then becomes (Fig. 9–33)

$$\Delta V = \frac{C_C V_C + C_B V_B}{C_B + C_C} - \frac{C_C V_D + C_B V_B}{C_B + C_D}$$

$$= \frac{(V_B - V_D)C_B C_D - (V_B - V_C)C_B C_C - (V_C - V_D)C_C C_D}{(C_B + C_C)(C_B + C_D)}$$

(9–13a)

If V_D is set to zero, the expression simplifies to:

$$\Delta V = \frac{(V_B C_B - V_C C_C)C_D - (V_B - V_C)C_B C_C}{(C_B + C_C)(C_B + C_D)}$$

(9–13b)

Putting the cell voltage V_C equal to 0 V or 5 V, and typical, acceptable bitline-to-cell capacitance ratios $C_B/C_C (= 15-20)$ in Eq. (9–13b), we get different polarities of the differential voltage of the order of ± 100 mV for logic "1" and logic "0", respectively, which can be detected by sense amplifiers. From Eq. (9–13b), it can be seen that for much higher bitline-to-cell capacitance ratios, the swing of the bitline voltage will be negligible, regardless of the cell voltage. The minimum required cell capacitance C_C is about 50 fF, governed by so-called soft errors. DRAMs, like everything else on Earth, are constantly being bombarded by cosmic rays, and high-energy alpha particles can create electron–hole pairs in semiconductors. A typical collected charge due to one of these events is about 100 fC. This spurious charge can be neglected if the cell capacitance is 50 fF and 5 V is applied to the cell, for which the stored charge is roughly 250 fC. The DRAM cell then becomes immune to typical alpha particle hits.

Maintaining a cell capacitance of 50 fF as the cell dimensions are reduced from one generation of DRAM to the next is a tremendous technological challenge. One way to look at this problem is shown in Fig. 9–34. The challenge is to store more charge per unit area on the planar surface (A_s) of the Si substrate. Approximating the MOS capacitance as a fixed, voltage-independent capacitor, we can write the stored charge Q as

$$Q = CV = (\epsilon A_C / d)V \tag{9-14}$$

where ϵ is the permittivity of the dielectric, d is its thickness, and A_C is the capacitor area. As shown in Fig. 9–34, the historical way of achieving

Time	Past	Present	Future
Approaches	Scaled dielectric	Trench/ stacked capacitor	Alternate dielectric
Problems	Tunneling & wearout	Fabrication	Material properties
$\dfrac{Q}{A_s} = \dfrac{CV}{A_s} = \dfrac{V}{d} \times \dfrac{A_c}{A_s} \times \epsilon$			

Figure 9–34
Various approaches (past, present, and future) of achieving higher DRAM cell capacitance and charge storage density without increasing cell size. A_s = Area on wafer taken by capacitor; A_c = Area of capacitor. For a planar capacitor $A_c = A_s$; however, for nonplanar structures $A_c > A_s$. $C = A_c \epsilon / d$ is the capacitance; and $Q = CV$ is the total stored charge in a fixed, voltage-independent capacitor.

the desired capacitance has been to scale the dielectric thickness, d. But that runs into the problems discussed in Section 6.4.7. Another approach, which is being taken currently, is to use fabrication schemes to increase the area devoted to the MOS storage capacitor, A_c, even as we reduce the planar surface area on the wafer, A_s, used for making this storage capacitance. Obviously, this can be done by moving away from a purely planar structure, and exploiting the third dimension. We can go down into the Si by digging "trenches" in the substrate with RIE and forming a trench storage capacitor on the sidewalls of the trench (Fig. 9–35a). Alternatively, we can go up from the substrate by stacking multiple layers of capacitor electrodes to increase the "stacked" capacitor area (Fig. 9–35b). Other tricks that have been tried are to purposely create a rough polysilicon surface on the capacitor plates to increase the surface area. In the future, alternative materials may be used. For example, the ferroelectrics have much higher dielectric constant than SiO_2 and offer larger capacitance without increasing area or reducing thickness. Promising materials include barium strontium titanate and zirconium oxide.

Flash Memories.   Another interesting MOS device is the flash memory, which is the most important type of nonvolatile memory. The memory cell structure is shown in Fig. 9–36. It is very simple and compact, and looks just like a MOSFET, except that it has two gate electrodes, one on top of the other. The top electrode is the one that we have direct electrical access to,

(a)   (b)

Figure 9–35
Increasing cell capacitance by exploiting the vertical dimension: (a) trench capacitors involve etching a trench in the substrate so that the larger area on the sidewalls can be used to increase capacitance; (b) stacked capacitors go "up" rather than "down" as in trenches, and increase capacitor area by using multiple polysilicon capacitor plates or "fins," as well as by exploiting the topography of the cell surface.

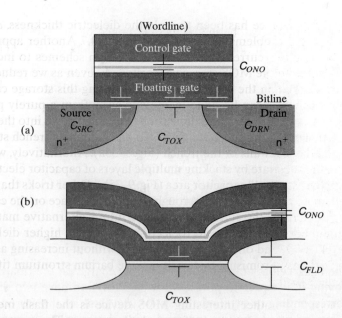

Figure 9–36
Flash memory cell
structure: (a) cell
structure shown
along the channel
length showing
the control gate
(wordline),
floating gate
below it, the
source and the
drain (bitline);
(b) view of cell
along the width of
the MOSFET. The
various coupling
capacitors to the
floating gate are
shown.

and is known as the control gate. Below that we have a so-called "floating" gate that is capacitively coupled to the control gate and the underlying silicon.

The capacitive coupling of the floating gate to the various terminals is illustrated in Fig. 9–36 in terms of the various coupling capacitance components. The floating gate and the control gate are separated by a stacked oxide–nitride–oxide dielectric in typical flash devices. The capacitance between these two gates is called C_{ONO} because of the oxide–nitride–oxide makeup of the dielectric stack. The total capacitance C_{TOT} is the sum of all the parallel components shown in Fig. 9–36.

$$C_{TOT} = C_{ONO} + C_{TOX} + C_{FLD} + C_{SRC} + C_{DRN} \qquad (9\text{–}15)$$

where C_{TOX} is the floating gate-to-channel capacitance through the tunnel oxide, C_{FLD} is the floating gate-to-substrate capacitance in the LOCOS field oxide region, and C_{SRC} and C_{DRN} are the gate-to-source/drain overlap capacitances.

Since it is isolated by the surrounding dielectrics, the charge on the floating gate Q_{FG} is not changed by (moderate) changes of the terminal biases.

$$Q_{FG} = 0 = C_{ONO}(V_{FG} - V_G) + C_{SRC}(V_{FG} - V_S)$$
$$+ C_{DRN}(V_{FG} - V_D) \qquad (9\text{–}16)$$

We assume that the substrate bias is fixed, and hence ignore the contributions from C_{TOX} and C_{FLD}, which couple the floating gate to the substrate. The floating gate voltage can be indirectly determined by the various terminal voltages, in terms of the gate, drain, and source coupling ratios as defined in Eq. (9–17).

$$V_{FG} = V_G \cdot GCR + V_S \cdot SCR + V_D \cdot DCR \qquad (9\text{–}17)$$

where

$$GCR = \frac{C_{ONO}}{C_{TOT}}$$

$$DCR = \frac{C_{DRN}}{C_{TOT}}$$

$$SCR = \frac{C_{SRC}}{C_{TOT}}$$

The basic cell operation involves putting charge on the floating gate or removing it, in order to program the MOSFET to have two different V_T's, corresponding to two logic levels. We can think of the stored charge on the floating gate to be like the fixed oxide charge in the V_T expression [Eq. (6–38)]. If many electrons are stored in the floating gate, the V_T of an NMOSFET is high; the cell is considered to have been "programmed" to exhibit the logic state "0". On the contrary, if electrons have been removed from the floating gate, the cell is considered to have been "erased" into a low V_T state or logic "1".

How do we go about transferring charges into and out of the floating gate? To program the cell, we can use channel hot carrier effects that we discussed in Section 6.5.9. We apply a high field to both the drain (bitline) and floating gate (wordline) such that the MOSFET is in saturation. It was discussed in Section 6.5.9 that the high longitudinal electric field in the pinch-off region accelerates electrons toward the drain and makes them energetic (hot). We maximize such hot carrier effects near the drain pinch-off region in a flash device by making the drain junction somewhat shallower than the source junction (Fig. 9–37a). This can be achieved by a separate higher energy source implant that is masked in the drain region. If the kinetic energy of electrons is high enough, a few can become hot enough to be scattered into the floating gate. They must surmount the 3.1-eV energy barrier that exists between the conduction band of Si and that of SiO$_2$, or hot electrons can tunnel through the oxide (Fig. 9–37b). Once they get into the floating gate, electrons become trapped in the 3.1-eV potential well between the floating polysilicon gate and the oxides on either side. This barrier is extremely high for a trapped (low kinetic energy) electron. Therefore the trapped electrons essentially stay in the floating gate forever, unless the cell is intentionally erased. That is why a flash memory is nonvolatile.

To erase the cell, we use Fowler–Nordheim tunneling between the floating gate and the source in the overlap region (Fig. 9–38a). A high positive voltage (say ~12 V) is applied to the source with the control gate

Figure 9–37
Hot carrier programming of the flash cell: (a) flash memory cell structure with typical biases required for writing into the cell. The channel of the MOSFET is pinched off in saturation; (b) band diagram along a vertical line in the middle of MOSFET channel showing hot electrons in the channel being injected across the gate oxide and getting trapped in the floating gate.

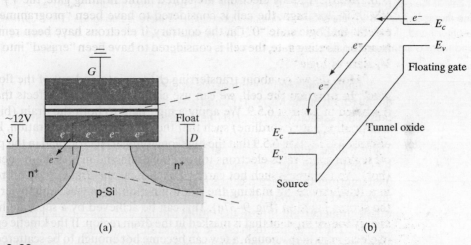

Figure 9–38
Fowler–Nordheim tunneling erasure: (a) flash memory cell structure with typical biases required for erasing the cell; (b) band diagram as a function of depth in the gate/source overlap region of the MOSFET showing quantum mechanical tunneling of carriers from the floating gate into the oxide, and subsequent drift to the source.

grounded. The polarity of the field is such that electrons tunnel from the floating gate into the source region, through the oxide barrier (Section 6.4.7). The band diagram (along a vertical line in this overlap region) during the operation is shown in Fig. 9–38b. Interestingly, in a flash device we make use of two effects that are considered to be "problems" in regular MOS devices: hot carrier effects and Fowler–Nordheim tunneling.

Figure 9–39
Drain (bitline) current versus control gate (wordline) voltage transfer characteristics of the MOSFET in a flash cell: if the cell is programmed to a high V_T (logic "0"), and a read voltage is applied to the wordline that is below this V_T, the MOSFET does not conduct, and there is negligible bitline current. On the other hand, if the cell had been erased to a low V_T state (logic "1") the MOSFET is turned ON, and there is significant bitline current.

During the read operation, we apply a moderate voltage (~ 1 V) to the bitline (drain of the MOSFET), and a wordline (control gate) voltage V_{CG} that causes the capacitively coupled floating gate voltage to be between that of the high V_T and the low V_T state of the programmed flash memory cell (Fig. 9–39). There will be negligible drain current flow in the bit line (drain) for the high V_T case because the gate voltage is less than the threshold voltage. We will then interpret the selected cell as being in state "0." For the low V_T case, since the applied gate voltage is higher than the threshold voltage of the cell, there will be drain current flow in the bitline (drain), and this can be interpreted as state "1." The read operation can be understood by looking at the transfer characteristics of the MOSFET in the programmed and erased states (Fig. 9–39).

9.6
TESTING,
BONDING, AND
PACKAGING

After the preceding discussions of rather dramatic fabrication steps in monolithic circuit technology, the processes of attaching leads and packaging the devices could seem rather mundane. Such an impression would be far from accurate, however, since the techniques discussed in this section are crucial to the overall fabrication process. In fact, the handling and packaging of individual circuits can be the most critical steps of all from the viewpoints of cost and reliability. The individual IC chip must be connected properly to outside leads and packaged in a way that is convenient for use in a larger circuit or system. Since the devices are handled individually once they are separated from the wafer, bonding and packaging are expensive processes. Considerable work has been done to reduce the steps required in bonding. We shall discuss the most straightforward technique first, which involves bonding individual leads from the contact pads on the circuit to terminals in the package. Then we shall consider two important methods for making all bonds simultaneously. Finally, we shall discuss a few typical packaging methods for ICs.

9.6.1 Testing

After the wafer of monolithic circuits has been processed and the final metallization pattern defined, it is placed in a holder under a microscope and is aligned for testing by a multiple-point probe (Fig. 9–40). The probe contacts the various pads on an individual circuit, and a series of tests are made of the electrical properties of the device. The various tests are programmed to be made automatically in a very short time. These tests may take only milliseconds for a simple circuit, to several seconds for a complex ULSI chip. The information from these tests is fed into a computer, which compares the results with information stored in its memory, and a decision is made regarding the acceptability of the circuit. If there is some defect so that the circuit falls below specifications, the computer remembers that chip must be discarded. The probe automatically steps the prescribed distance to the next circuit on the wafer and repeats the process. After all of the circuits have been tested and the substandard ones noted, the wafer is removed from the testing machine, sawed between the circuits, and broken apart (Fig. 9–41). Then each die that passed the test is picked up and placed in the package. In the testing process, information from tests on each die can be stored to facilitate analysis of the rejected circuits or to evaluate the fabrication process for possible changes.

9.6.2 Wire Bonding

The earliest method used for making contacts from the monolithic chip to the package was the bonding of fine Au wires. Later techniques expanded wire bonding to include Al wires and several types of bonding processes. Here we shall outline only a few of the most important aspects of wire bonding.

If the chip is to be wire bonded, it is first mounted solidly on a metal lead frame or on a metallized region in the package. In this process a thin layer of Au (perhaps combined with Ge or other elements to improve the metallurgy of the bond) is placed between the bottom of the chip and the substrate; heat and a slight scrubbing motion are applied, forming an alloyed bond which holds the chip firmly to the substrate. This process is called *die bonding*. Generally, die bonding is done by a robotic arm that picks up each die, orients it, and places it for bonding. Once the chip is mounted, the interconnecting wires are attached from the various contact pads to posts on the package (Fig. 9–42).

In Au wire bonding, a spool of fine Au wire (about 0.007−0.002-inch diameter) is mounted in a *lead bonder* apparatus, and the wire is fed through a glass or tungsten carbide *capillary* (Fig. 9–43a). A hydrogen gas flame jet is swept past the wire to form a ball on the end. In *thermocompression bonding* the chip (or in some cases the capillary) is heated to about 360°C, and the capillary is brought down over the contact pad. When pressure is exerted

Figure 9–40
Automated probing of devices: (a) high-speed testing of ICs is done using probe cards having a rigidly fixed array of probes that corresponds to the bond pad pattern on the IC to be tested. Many electrical signals are provided or measured by the automated tester at the various pins. After one chip is tested, the tester mechanically moves the wafer to the next die location; (b) array of Al bond pads near the chip periphery, some showing probe marks. The space between the arrays of bond pads is the "scribe line" along which the wafer will be sawed into individual chips after testing. (© 2004 Micron Technology, Inc. All rights reserved. Used with permission.)

(a)

(b)

by the capillary on the ball, a bond is formed between the Au ball and the Al pad (Fig. 9–43b). Then the capillary is raised and moved to a post on the package. The capillary is brought down again, and the combination of force and temperature bonds the wire to the post. After raising the capillary again, the hydrogen flame is swept past, forming a new ball (Fig. 9–43c); then the process is repeated for the other pads on the chip.

There are many variations in this basic method. For example, the substrate heating can be eliminated by *ultrasonic bonding*. In this method a tungsten carbide capillary is held by a tool connected to an ultrasonic transducer. When it is in contact with a pad or a post, the wire is vibrated under pressure to form a bond. Other variations include techniques for automatically removing the "tail," which is left on the post in Fig. 9–43c. When the bond to the chip is made by exerting pressure on a ball at the end of the Au wire, it is called a *ball bond* or a *nail-head bond*, because of the shape of the deformed ball after the bond is made (Fig. 9–44a).

Aluminum wire can be used in ultrasonic bonding; it has several advantages over Au, including the absence of possible metallurgical problems in bonds between Au and Al pads. When Al wire is used, the flame-off step is replaced by cutting or breaking the wire at appropriate points in the process. In forming a bond, the wire is bent under the edge of a wedge-shaped bonding tool (Fig. 9–43d). The tool then applies pressure and ultrasonic vibration, forming the bond (Fig. 9–43e and f). The resulting flat bond, formed by the bent wire wedged between the tool and the bonding surface, is called a *wedge bond*. A closeup view of ball and wedge bonds is given in Fig. 9–44.

Figure 9–43
Wire bonding techniques: (a) capillary positioned over one of the contact pads for a ball (nail-head) bond; (b) pressure exerted to bond the wire to the pad; (c) post bond and flame-off; (d) wedge bonding tool; (e) pressure and ultrasonic energy applied; (f) post bond completed and wire broken or cut for next bond.

(a)   (b)

Figure 9–44
Scanning electron micrographs of a ball bond (a) and a wedge bond (b). (© 2004 Micron Technology, Inc. All rights reserved. Used with permission.)

9.6.3 Flip-Chip Techniques

The time consumed in bonding wires individually to each pad on the chip can be overcome by several methods of simultaneous bonding. The *flip-chip* approach is typical of these methods. Relatively thick metal is deposited on the contact pads before the devices are separated from the wafer. After separation, the deposited metal is used to contact a matching metallized pattern on the package substrate.

In the flip-chip method, "bumps" of solder or special metal alloys are deposited on each contact pad. These metal bumps can be distributed over the die (Fig. 9–45). After separation from the wafer, each chip is turned upside down, and the bumps are properly aligned with the metallization pattern on the substrate. At this point, ultrasonic bonding or solder attaches each bump to its corresponding connector on the substrate. An obvious advantage of this method is that all connections are made simultaneously. Disadvantages include the fact that the bonds are made under the chip and therefore cannot be inspected visually. Furthermore, it is necessary to heat and/or exert pressure on the chip.

9.6.4 Packaging

The final step in IC fabrication is packaging the device in a suitable medium that can protect it from the environment of its intended application. In most cases this means the surface of the device must be isolated from moisture and contaminants and the bonds and other elements must be protected from corrosion and mechanical shock. The problems of surface protection are greatly minimized by modern passivation techniques, but it is still necessary to provide some protection in the packaging. In every case, the choice of package type must be made within the requirements of the application and cost considerations. There are many techniques for encapsulating devices, and the various methods are constantly refined and changed. Here we shall consider just a few general methods for the purpose of illustration.

In the early days of IC technology, all devices were packaged in metal headers. In this method the device is alloyed to the surface of the header, wire bonds are made to the header posts, and a metal lid is welded over the device and wiring. Although this method has several drawbacks, it does provide complete sealing of the unit from the outside environment. This is often called a *hermetically sealed* device. After the chip is mounted on the header and bonds are made to the posts, the header cap can be welded shut in a controlled environment (e.g., an inert gas), which maintains the device in a prescribed atmosphere.

Integrated circuits are now mounted in packages with many output leads (Fig. 9–46). In one version the chip is mounted on a stamped metal lead frame and wire bonding is done between the chip and the leads. The package is formed by applying a ceramic or plastic case and trimming away the unwanted parts of the lead frame.

Broadly speaking, packages can be through-hole-mount that involve inserting the package pins through holes on the printed circuit board (PCB) before soldering, or surface-mount type where the leads do not pass through holes in the PCB. Instead, surface-mounted package leads are aligned to electrical contacts on the PCB, and are connected simultaneously by solder reflow. Most packages can be made using ceramic or plastic (which is cheaper). The ICs are hermetically sealed for protection from the environment. The pins can be on one side (single inline or zig-zag pattern of leads), two sides (dual inline package or DIP) or four sides of the package (quad package) (Fig. 9–46). More advanced packages have leads distributed over a

Figure 9–46

Various types of packaging for ICs: Packages can be through-hole-mount or surface-mount type, and be made out of plastic or ceramic. The pins can be on one side (SIP), two sides (DIP), or four sides (quad) of the package, or distributed over the surface of the package (PGAs or BGAs).

Figure 9–47
Ceramic column grid array (CCGA): This advanced ceramic package is a type of pin grid array made up of several hundred metal columns. Several ICs with metallized solder bumps on them as in Fig. 9–45 can be flip-chip bonded on the back of this package, making this a multi-chip module (MCM). (Photograph courtesy of IBM.)

Figure 9–48
Ball grid array: In this package, the IC in the middle is wire bonded to electrical connections on the package. The package itself has an array of solder "balls" on the top, which can be properly aligned and surface-mount connected simultaneously to electrical sockets on a PCB using solder reflow. (Photograph courtesy of IBM.)

large portion of the surface of the package as in through-hole-mounted pin grid arrays (PGAs) (Fig. 9–47) or surface-mounted ball grid arrays (BGAs) (Fig. 9–48). By not restricting the leads to the edges of the package, the pin count can be increased dramatically, which is very attractive for advanced ULSI in which a large number of electrical leads must be accessed.

Since a sizable fraction of the cost of an IC is due to bonding and packaging, there have been a number of innovations for automating the process. These include the use of film reels that contain the metal contact pattern onto which the chips can be bonded. The film can then be fed into packaging equipment, where the position registration capabilities of a film reel can be used for automated handling. This process, called *tape-automated bonding (TAB)*, is particularly useful in mounting several chips on a large ceramic substrate having multilevel interconnection patterns (called a *multichip module*).

SUMMARY

9.1 The progress of ICs can be characterized by an exponential increase in the transistor count and a corresponding decrease in feature size with time (Moore's law). The economics are driven by device scaling and batch processing.

9.2 The dominant IC technology is digital CMOS, which is the basis of logic circuits (microprocessors), memories (DRAMs, SRAMs, and NVM), and application-specific ICs (ASICs).

PROBLEMS

9.1 In a uniform p-type Si sample, As is diffused to have a donor profile of 10^{18}/cm^3, where acceptor concentration becomes negligible in comparison of donor concentration. Find the resulting value of the sheet resistance of the diffused layer up to the junction depth of 5 μm of the device. If the mobility for electrons is $\mu_n = 500$ cm^2/ V-sec, then what will be the value for the conductivity?

9.2 A typical sheet resistance of a base diffusion layer is 200 Ω/square.

(a) What should be the aspect ratio of a 10-kΩ resistor, using this diffusion?

(b) Draw a pattern for this resistor (see Fig. 9–12b) which uses little area for a width $w = 5$ μm.

9.3 A 3-μm n-type epitaxial layer ($N_d = 10^{16}$ cm^{-3}) is grown on a p-type Si substrate. Areas of the n layer are to be junction isolated (see Fig. 9–11a) by a boron diffusion at 1200°C ($D = 2.5 \times 10^{-12}$ cm^2/s). The surface boron concentration is held constant at 10^{20} cm^{-3} (see Prob. 5.2).

(a) What time is required for this isolation diffusion?

(b) How far does an Sb-doped buried layer ($D = 2 \times 10^{-13}$ cm^2/s) diffuse into the epitaxial layer during this time, assuming the concentration at the substrate-epitaxial boundary is constant at 10^{20} cm^{-3}?

9.4 A 500-μm-thick p-type Si wafer with a doping level of 1×10^{15} cm^{-3} has a certain region in which we do a constant source solid-solubility-limited P diffusion, resulting in a junction depth of 0.8 μm and a surface concentration of 6×10^{19} cm^{-3}.

We do sheet resistance measurements on the two parts of the wafer. What is the measured sheet resistance of the p-type part? If we have a sheet resistance of 90 Ω/square in the n-type part, what is the *average* resistivity there?

READING LIST

Information about the evolution of integrated circuit technology is available at http://public.itrs.net/

Campbell, S. A. *The Science and Engineering of Microelectronic Fabrication.* New York: Oxford, 2001.

Chang, C. Y., and S. M. Sze. *ULSI Technology.* New York: McGraw-Hill, 1996.

Chang, C. Y., and S. M. Sze. *ULSI Devices.* New York: John Wiley, 2000.

Howe, R. T., and C. G. Sodini. *Microelectronics: An Integrated Approach.* Upper Saddle River, NJ: Prentice Hall, 1997.

Jaeger, R. C. *Modular Series on Solid State Devices: Vol. V. Introduction to Microelectronic Fabrication.* Reading, MA: Addison-Wesley, 1988.

Rabaey, J. M. *Digital Integrated Circuits.* Upper Saddle River, NJ: Prentice Hall, 1996.

Seraphim, D. P., R. C. Lasky, and C. Y. Li, eds. *Principles of Electronic Packaging.* New York: McGraw-Hill, 1989.

Sharma, A. K. *Semiconductor Memories.* New York: IEEE Press, 1997.

Tummala, R. R. and E. J. Rymaszewski. *Microelectronics Packaging Handbook.* New York: Chapman and Hall, 1997.

Wolf, S., and R. N. Tauber. *Silicon Processing for the VLSI Era.* Sunset Beach, CA: Lattice Press, 2000.

SELF QUIZ   **Question 1**

Study the ITRS roadmap chapters on Process, Integration, Devices and Structures (PIDS) and on Front End Processes (FEP) available at http://public.itrs.net/. This has projections about next-generation CMOS devices.

- Plot some of the projected MOS device parameters from the various tables as a function of time. Do they obey Moore's law?

- Based on what you have learned in Chapters 6 and 9, do the required $I_{D(Sat)}$ numbers for NMOSFETs for various technology nodes make sense? How about some of the other MOSFET requirements in other tables that are color-coded red?

Question 2

Discuss consequences (one good, one bad) of quantum mechanical tunneling in MOSFETs.

Question 3

What is hot electron damage, and is it more or less severe than hot hole damage? Why? How can you minimize hot carrier damage?

Question 4

Why are MOSFETs manufactured with {100} planes parallel to the $Si-SiO_2$ interface?

Question 5

The sheet resistance of a diffusion layer is 100 ohms per square find the aspect ratio if a resistance of 6 kΩ is using the diffusion.

Question 6

A DC source is applied to an AC manufactured of mosfet technology. The drain current is 2 mA. Calculate the load current.

Question 7

A 400 um silicon wafer of p type has a doping level of 10^16 cm if diffusion is used. A junction depth of 0.6 um and a surface concentration of 5×10^18 cm/cube is obtained. calculate the sheet resistance in n type if the sheet resistance of p type is 90 ohms/cm^2.

Chapter 10

High-Frequency, High-Power and Nanoelectronic Devices

The diodes and transistors we have discussed thus far constitute the vast majority of semiconductor devices. However, there are a number of specialty devices that deserve our attention, and novel devices and materials can form the basis of future applications. In this chapter we describe two types of *negative conductance* devices, with applications in high-frequency circuits. Then we will discuss the semiconductor controlled rectifier (SCR), an important switching device which can handle large amounts of power. Finally we will consider new materials and device applications which depend on some very interesting extensions of the physics of materials we used in previous chapters. These new materials and new applications of physics will likely form the basis for the electronics of the future.

10.1	The tunnel diode is a p-n junction device that operates in certain regions

10.1
TUNNEL DIODES

The tunnel diode is a p-n junction device that operates in certain regions of its *I–V* characteristic by the quantum mechanical tunneling of electrons through the potential barrier of the junction (see Sections 2.4.4 and 5.4.1). The tunneling process for reverse current is essentially the Zener effect, although negligible reverse bias is needed to initiate the process in tunnel diodes. As we shall see in this section, the tunnel diode (often called the Esaki diode after L. Esaki, who received the Nobel Prize in 1973 for his work on the effect) exhibits the important feature of *negative resistance* over a portion of its *I–V* characteristic.

10.1.1 Degenerate Semiconductors

Thus far, we have discussed the properties of relatively pure semiconductors; any impurity doping represented a small fraction of the total atomic density of the material. Since the few impurity atoms were so widely spaced throughout the sample, we could be confident that no charge transport could take place within the donor or acceptor levels themselves. At high doping, the impurities are so close together that we can no longer consider the donor level as being composed of discrete, noninteracting energy states. Instead, the donor states form a band, which may overlap the bottom of the conduction band. If the conduction-band electron concentration n exceeds the effective density of states N_c, the Fermi level is no longer within the band gap, but lies within the conduction band. When this occurs, the material is called *degenerate* n-type. The analogous case of degenerate p-type material occurs when the acceptor concentration is very high and the Fermi level lies in the valence band. We recall that the energy states below E_F are mostly filled and states above E_F are empty, except for a small distribution dictated by the Fermi statistics. Thus, in a degenerate n-type sample, the region between E_c and E_F is for the most part filled with electrons, and in a degenerate p-type sample, the region between E_v and E_F is almost completely filled with holes.

A p-n junction between two degenerate semiconductors is illustrated in terms of energy bands in Fig. 10–1a. This is the equilibrium condition, for which the Fermi level is constant throughout the junction. We notice that E_{Fp} lies below the valence-band edge on the p side, and E_{Fn} is above the conduction-band edge on the n side. Thus, the bands must overlap on the energy scale in order for E_F to be constant. This overlapping of bands is very important; it means that, with a small forward or reverse bias, filled states and empty states appear opposite each other, separated by essentially the width of the depletion region. If the metallurgical junction is sharp, the depletion region will be very narrow for such high-doping concentrations, and the electric field at the junction will be quite large. Hence, the conditions for electron tunneling are met: filled and empty states separated by a narrow potential barrier of finite height. In Fig. 10–1, the bands are shown filled to the Fermi level for convenience of illustration, with the understanding that a distribution is implied.

Since the bands overlap under equilibrium conditions, a small reverse bias (Fig. 10–1b) allows electron tunneling from the filled valence-band states below E_{Fp} to the empty conduction-band states above E_{Fn}. This condition is similar to the Zener effect, except that no bias is required to create the condition of overlapping bands. As the reverse bias is increased, E_{Fn} continues to move down the energy scale with respect to E_{Fp}, placing more filled states on the p side opposite empty states on the n side. Thus, the tunneling of electrons from p to n increases with increasing reverse bias. The resulting conventional current is opposite to the electron flow—that is, from n to p. At equilibrium (Fig. 10–1a), there is equal tunneling from n to p and from p to n, giving a zero net current.

When a small forward bias is applied (Fig. 10–1c), E_{Fn} moves up in energy with respect to E_{Fp} by the amount qV. Thus, electrons below E_{Fn}

on the n side are placed opposite empty states above E_{Fp} on the p side. Electron tunneling occurs from n to p as shown, with the resulting conventional current from p to n. This forward-tunneling current continues to increase with increased bias as more filled states are placed opposite empty states. However, as E_{Fn} continues to move up with respect to E_{Fp}, a point is reached at which the bands begin to pass by each other. When this occurs, the number of filled states opposite empty states decreases. The resulting decrease in tunneling current is illustrated in Fig. 10–1d. This region of the *I–V* characteristic is important in that the *decrease* in tunneling current with *increased* bias produces a region of negative slope; that is, the *dynamic resistance dV/dI* is negative. This negative-resistance region is useful in oscillators.

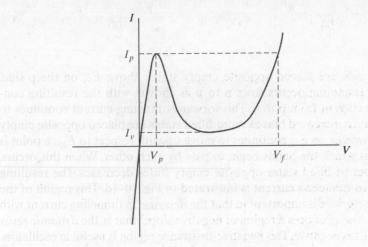

Figure 10–2
Band diagram (a) and I–V characteristic (b) for the tunnel diode beyond the tunnel current region. In (b), the tunneling component of current is shown by the solid curve and the diffusion current component is dashed.

If the forward bias is increased beyond the negative-resistance region, the current begins to increase again (Fig. 10–2). Once the bands have passed each other, the characteristic resembles that of a conventional diode. The forward current is now dominated by the diffusion current—electrons surmounting their potential barrier from n to p and holes surmounting their potential barrier from p to n. Of course, the diffusion current is present in the forward tunneling region, but it is negligible compared with the tunneling current.

The total tunnel diode characteristic (Fig. 10–3) has the general shape of an N (if a little imagination is applied); therefore, it is common to refer to this characteristic as exhibiting a *type-N negative resistance*. It is also called a *voltage-controlled negative resistance*, meaning that the current decreases rapidly at some critical voltage (in this case, the *peak voltage* V_p, taken at the point of maximum forward tunneling).

The values of *peak tunneling current* I_p and *valley current* I_v (Fig. 10–3) determine the magnitude of the negative-resistance slope for a diode of given material. For this reason, their ratio I_p/I_v is often used as a figure of

Figure 10–3
Total tunnel diode characteristic.

merit for the tunnel diode. Similarly, the ratio V_p/V_f is a measure of the voltage spread between the two positive-resistance regions.

The negative resistance of the tunnel diode can be used in a number of ways to achieve oscillation and other circuit functions. The fact that the tunneling process does not present the time delays of drift and diffusion makes the tunnel diode a natural choice for certain high-speed circuits. However, the tunnel diode has not achieved widespread application, because of its relatively low current operation and competition from other devices.

10.2
THE IMPATT
DIODE

In this section, we describe a type of microwave negative-conductance device that operates by a combination of carrier injection and transit-time effects. Diodes with simple p-n junction structure, or with variations on that structure, are biased to achieve tunneling or avalanche breakdown, with an a-c voltage superimposed on the d-c bias. The carriers generated by the injection process are swept through a drift region to the terminals of the device. We shall see that the a-c component of the resulting current can be approximately 180° out of phase with the applied voltage under proper conditions of bias and device configuration, giving rise to negative conductance and oscillation in a resonant circuit. Transit-time devices can convert d-c to microwave a-c signals with high efficiency and are very useful in the generation of microwave power for many applications.

The original suggestion for a microwave device employing transit-time effects was made by W. T. Read and involved an n^+-p-i-p^+ structure such as that shown in Fig. 10–4. This device operates by injecting carriers into the drift region and is called an *impact avalanche transit-time (IMPATT)* diode. Although IMPATT operation can be obtained in simpler structures, the Read diode is best suited for illustration of the basic principles. The device consists essentially of two regions: (1) the n^+-p region, at which avalanche multiplication occurs, and (2) the i (essentially intrinsic) region, through which generated holes must drift in moving to the p^+ contact. Similar devices can be built in the p^+-n-i-n^+ configuration, in which electrons resulting from

Figure 10–4
The Read diode:
(a) basic device
configuration;
(b) electric field
distribution in
the device under
reverse bias.

avalanche multiplication drift through the i region, taking advantage of the higher mobility of electrons compared with holes.

Although detailed calculations of IMPATT operation are complicated and generally require computer solutions, the basic physical mechanism is simple. Essentially, the device operates in a negative-conductance mode when the a-c component of current is negative over a portion of the cycle during which the a-c voltage is positive, and vice versa. The negative conductance occurs because of two processes, causing the current to lag behind the voltage in time: (1) a delay due to the avalanche process and (2) a further delay due to the transit time of the carriers across the drift region. If the sum of these delay times is approximately one-half cycle of the operating frequency, negative conductance occurs and the device can be used for oscillation and amplification.

From another point of view, the a-c conductance is negative if the a-c component of carrier flow drifts opposite to the influence of the a-c electric field. For example, with a d-c reverse bias on the device of Fig. 10–4, holes drift from left to right (in the direction of the field), as expected. Now, if we superimpose an a-c voltage such that $\mathscr{E}$ decreases during the negative half-cycle, we would normally expect the drift of holes to decrease also. However, in IMPATT operation, the drift of holes through the i region actually increases while the a-c field is decreasing. To see how this happens, let us consider the effects of avalanche and drift for various points in the cycle of applied voltage (Fig. 10–5).

To simplify the discussion, we shall assume that the p region is very narrow and that all the avalanche multiplication takes place in a thin region near the n^+-p junction. We shall approximate the field in the narrow p region by a uniform value. If the d-c bias is such that the critical field for avalanche E_a is just met in the n^+-p space charge region (Fig. 10–5a), avalanche multiplication begins at $t = 0$. Electrons generated in the avalanche move to the n^+ region, and holes enter the i drift region. We assume that the device is mounted in a resonant microwave circuit so that an a-c signal can be maintained at a given frequency. As the applied a-c voltage goes positive, more and more holes are generated in the avalanche region. In fact, the pulse of holes (dotted line) generated by the multiplication process continues to grow as long as the electric field is above E_a (Fig. 10–5b). It can be shown that the particle current due to avalanche increases exponentially with time while the field is above the critical value. The important result of this growth is that the hole pulse reaches its peak value, not at $\pi/2$, when the voltage is maximum, but at π (Fig. 10–5c). Therefore, there is a phase delay of $\pi/2$ inherent in the avalanche process itself. A further delay is provided by the drift region. Once the avalanche multiplication stops ($\omega t > \pi$), the pulse of holes simply drifts toward the p^+ contact (Fig. 10–5d). But during this period, the a-c terminal voltage is negative. Therefore, the dynamic conductance is negative, and energy is supplied to the a-c field.

If the length of the drift region is chosen properly, the pulse of holes is collected at the p^+ contact just as the voltage cycle is completed, and the cycle then repeats itself. The pulse will drift through the length L of the i region

Figure 10–5
Time dependence
of the growth
and drift of holes
during a cycle of
applied voltage
for the Read
diode: (a) $\omega t = 0$;
(b) $\omega t = \pi/2$;
(c) $\omega t = \pi$
(d) $\omega t = 3\pi/2$.
The hole pulse
is sketched as a
dotted line on the
field diagram.

during the negative half-cycle if we choose the transit time to be one-half
the oscillation period; that is,

$$\frac{L}{v_d} = \frac{1}{2}\frac{1}{f}, \quad f = \frac{v_d}{2L} \tag{10-1}$$

where f is the operating frequency and v_d is the drift velocity for holes.[1]
Therefore, for a Read diode, the optimum frequency is one-half the inverse
transit time v_d/L of holes across the drift region. In choosing an appropriate resonant circuit for this device, the parameter L is critical. For example,
taking $v_d = 10^7$ cm/s for Si, the optimum operating frequency for a device
with an i region length of 5 μm is $f = 10^7/2(5 \times 10^{-4}) = 10^{10}$ Hz. Negative

---

[1]In general, v_d is a function of the local electric field. However, these devices are normally operated with
fields in the i region sufficiently large that holes drift at their scattering-limited velocity (Fig. 3–24). In this
case, the drift velocity does not vary appreciably with the a-c variations in the field.

resistance is exhibited by an IMPATT diode for frequencies somewhat above and below this optimum frequency for exact 180° phase delay. A careful analysis of the small-signal impedance shows that the minimum frequency for negative conductance varies as the square root of the d-c bias current for frequencies in the neighborhood of that described by Eq. (10–1).

Although the Read diode of Fig. 10–4 displays most directly the operation of IMPATT devices, simpler structures can be used, and in some cases they may be more efficient. Negative conductance can be obtained in simple p-n junctions or in p-i-n devices. In the case of the p-i-n, most of the applied voltage occurs across the i region, which serves as a uniform avalanche region and also as a drift region. Therefore, the two processes of delay due to avalanche and drift, which were separate in the case of the Read diode, are distributed within the i region of the p-i-n. This means that both electrons and holes participate in the avalanche and drift processes.

Microwave devices that operate by the *transferred-electron* mechanism are often called *Gunn diodes*, after J. B. Gunn, who first demonstrated one of the forms of oscillation. In the transferred-electron mechanism, the conduction electrons of some semiconductors are shifted from a state of high mobility to a state of low mobility by the influence of a strong electric field. Negative conductance operation can be achieved in a diode[2] for which this mechanism applies, and the results are varied and useful in microwave circuits.

10.3
THE GUNN DIODE

First, we shall describe the process of electron transfer and the resulting change in mobility. Then we shall consider some of the modes of operation for diodes using this mechanism.

10.3.1 The Transferred-Electron Mechanism

In Section 3.4.4, we discussed the non-linearity of mobility at high electric fields. In most semiconductors, the carriers reach a scattering-limited velocity, and the plot of velocity vs. field saturates at high fields (Fig. 3–24). In some materials, however, the energy of electrons can be raised by an applied field to the point that they transfer from one region of the conduction band to another, higher-energy region. For some band structures, negative conductivity can result from this electron transfer. To visualize the process, let us recall the discussion of energy bands in Section 3.1.

A simplified $E(k)$ band structure for GaAs is shown in Fig. 10–6 for reference; some of the detail has been omitted in this diagram to isolate the essential features of electron transfer between bands. In n-type GaAs, the valence band is filled and the *central valley* (or *minimum*) of the conduction band at $\Gamma(\mathbf{k} = 0)$ normally contains the conduction electrons. There is a set of *subsidiary minima* at L (sometimes called *satellite valleys*) at higher

---

[2]These devices are called diodes, since they are two-terminal devices. No p-n junction is involved, however. Gunn effect and related devices utilize bulk instabilities, which do not require junctions.

Figure 10–6
Simplified band
diagram for
GaAs, illustrating
the lower (Γ) and
upper (L) valleys
in the conduction
band.

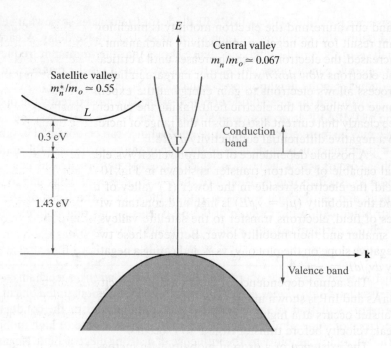

energy,[3] but these minima are many kT above the central valley and are normally unoccupied. Therefore, the direct band gap at Γ and the energy bands centered at $\mathbf{k} = 0$ are generally used to describe the conduction processes in GaAs. This was true, for example, of GaAs lasers, discussed in Section 8.4. The presence of the satellite valleys at L is crucial to the Gunn effect, however. If the material is subjected to an electric field above some critical value (about 3000 V/cm), the electrons in the central Γ valley of Fig. 10–6 gain more energy than the 0.30 eV separating the valleys; therefore, there is considerable scattering of electrons into the higher-energy satellite valley at L.

Once the electrons have gained enough energy from the field to be transferred into the higher-energy valley, they remain there as long as the field is greater than the critical value. The explanation for this involves the fact that the combined effective density of states for the upper valleys is much greater than for the central valley (by a factor of about 24). Although we shall not prove it here, it seems reasonable that the probability of electron scattering between valleys should depend on the density of states available in each case and that scattering from a valley with many states into a valley with few states would be unlikely. As a result, once the field increases above the critical value, most conduction electrons in GaAs reside in the satellite valleys and exhibit properties typical of that region of the conduction band. In particular, the effective mass for electrons in the higher L valleys is almost eight times as great as in the central valley because of the smaller

---

[3]We have shown only one satellite valley for convenience; there are other equivalent valleys for different directions in k-space. The effective mass ratio of 0.55 refers to the combined satellite valleys.

band curvature, and the electron mobility is much lower. This is an important result for the negative conductivity mechanism: As the electric field is increased, the electron velocity increases until a critical field is reached; then the electrons *slow down* with further increase in field. The electron transfer process allows electrons to gain energy at the expense of velocity over a range of values of the electric field. Taking the current density as $qv_d n$, we see clearly that current also drops in this range of increasing field, giving rise to a negative differential conductivity $dJ/d\mathscr{E}$.

A possible dependence of electron velocity vs. electric field for a material capable of electron transfer is shown in Fig. 10–7. For low values of field, the electrons reside in the lower (Γ) valley of the conduction band, and the mobility ($\mu_\Gamma = v_d/E$) is high and constant with field. For high values of field, electrons transfer to the satellite valleys, where their velocity is smaller and their mobility lower. Between these two states is a region of negative slope on the plot of v_d vs. $\mathscr{E}$, indicating a negative differential mobility $dv_d/dE = -\mu^*$.[4]

The actual dependence of electron drift velocity on electric field for GaAs and InP is shown in Fig. 10–8. The negative resistance due to electron transfer occurs at a higher field for InP, and the electrons achieve a higher peak velocity before transfer from Γ to L occurs.

The existence of a drop in mobility with increasing electric field and the resultant possibility of negative conductance were predicted by Ridley and Watkins and by Hilsum several years before Gunn demonstrated the

Figure 10–7

A possible characteristic of electron drift velocity vs. field for a semiconductor exhibiting the transferred-electron mechanism.

μ_Γ = Mobility in central (Γ) valley

μ_L = Mobility in satellite (L) valley

μ^* = Average magnitude of negative differential mobility during transition

---

[4]This is a rather crude approximation, since μ^* is not a constant, but varies considerably with field; the negative dielectric relaxation time therefore changes with time as the domain grows.

Figure 10–8
Electron drift
velocity vs. field
for GaAs and InP.

effect in GaAs. The mechanism of electron transfer is therefore often called the Ridley–Watkins–Hilsum mechanism. This negative conductivity effect depends only on the bulk properties of the semiconductor and not on junction or surface effects. It is therefore called a *bulk negative differential conductivity (BNDC)* effect.

10.3.2 Formation and Drift of Space Charge Domains

If a sample of GaAs is biased such that the field falls in the negative conductivity region, space charge instabilities result, and the device cannot be maintained in a d-c stable condition. To understand the formation of these instabilities, let us consider first the dissipation of space charge in the usual semiconductor. It can be shown from treatment of the continuity equation that a localized space charge dies out exponentially with time in a homogeneous sample with positive resistance (Prob. 10.3). If the initial space charge is Q_0, the instantaneous charge is

$$Q(t) = Q_0 e^{-t/\tau_d} \tag{10-2}$$

where $\tau_d = \epsilon/\sigma$ is called the *dielectric relaxation time*. Because of this process, random fluctuations in carrier concentration are quickly neutralized and space charge neutrality is a good approximation for most semiconductors in the usual range of conductivities. For example, the dielectric relaxation time for a 1.0 Ω-cm Si or GaAs sample is approximately 10^{-12} s.

Equation (10–2) gives a rather remarkable result for cases in which the conductivity is negative. For these cases, τ_d is negative also and *space charge fluctuations build up* exponentially in time rather than dying out. This means that normal random fluctuations in the carrier distribution can grow into large space charge regions in the sample. Let us see how this occurs in a GaAs sample biased in the negative conductivity regime. The velocity–field diagram for n-type GaAs is illustrated in Fig. 10–9a. If we assume a small shift of electron concentration in some region of the device, a dipole layer can form as shown in Fig. 10–9b. Under normal conditions, this dipole would die out quickly. However, under conditions of negative conductivity, the charge within the dipole, and therefore the local electric field, builds up as shown in Fig. 10–9c. Of course, this buildup takes place in a stream of electrons drifting from the cathode to the anode, and the dipole (now called a *domain*) drifts along with the stream as it grows. Eventually, the drifting domain will reach the anode, where it gives up its energy as a pulse of current in the external circuit.

During the initial growth of the domain, an increasing fraction of the applied voltage appears across it, at the expense of electric field in the rest of the bar. As a result, it is unlikely that more than one domain will be present in the bar at a time; after the formation of one domain, the electric field in the rest of the bar quickly drops below the threshold value for negative conductivity. If the bias is d-c, the field outside the moving domain will stabilize at a positive conductivity point such as A in Fig. 10–9a, and the field inside the domain will stabilize at the high-field value B. A small dipole forms from a random noise fluctuation (or, more likely, at a permanent *nucleation site* such as a crystal defect, a doping inhomogeneity, or the cathode itself), and this dipole grows

(a)

(b)

(c)

Figure 10–9
Buildup and drift of a space charge domain in GaAs: (a) velocity–field characteristic for n-type GaAs; (b) formation of a dipole; (c) growth and drift of a dipole for conditions of negative conductivity.

and drifts down the bar as a domain. The formation of stable domains is not the only mode of operation for transferred electron devices. Nor is it the most desirable mode for most applications, since the resulting short pulses of current are inefficient sources of microwave power. Removal of heat is a very serious problem in these devices. The power dissipation may be 10^7 W/cm^3 or greater (Prob. 10.5), giving rise to considerable heating of the sample. If the application does not require continuous operation, peak powers of hundreds of watts can be achieved in pulses of microwave oscillation.

10.4
THE P-N-P-N
DIODE

One of the most common applications of electronic devices is in switching, which requires the device to change from an "off" or *blocking* state to an "on" or *conducting* state. We have discussed the use of transistors in this application, in which base current drives the device from cutoff to saturation. Similarly, diodes and other devices can be used to serve as certain types of switches. There are a number of important switching applications that require a device remain in the blocking state under forward bias until switched to the conducting state by an external signal. Several devices that fulfill this requirement have been developed, including the *semiconductor-controlled rectifier (SCR)*.[5] These devices are typified by a high impedance (the "off" condition) under forward bias until a switching signal is applied; after switching, they exhibit low impedance (the "on" condition). The signal required for switching can be varied externally; therefore, the devices can be used to block or pass currents at predetermined levels.

The SCR is a four-layer (p-n-p-n) structure that effectively blocks current through two terminals until it is turned on by a small signal at a third terminal. We shall begin by investigating the current flow in a two-terminal p-n-p-n device and then extend the discussion to include triggering by a third terminal. We shall see that the p-n-p-n structure can be considered for many purposes as a combination of p-n-p and n-p-n transistors, and the analysis in Chapter 7 can be used as an aid in understanding its behavior.

10.4.1 Basic Structure

First we consider a four-layer diode structure with an *anode* terminal A at the outside p region and with a *cathode* terminal K at the outside n region (Fig. 10–10a). We shall refer to the junction nearest the anode as j_1, the center junction as j_2, and the junction nearest the cathode as j_3. When the anode is biased positively with respect to the cathode (v positive), the device is forward biased. However, as the I–V characteristic of Fig. 10–10b indicates, the forward-biased condition of this diode can be considered in two separate states: the high-impedance, or *forward-blocking*, state and the low-impedance, or *forward-conducting*, state. In the device illustrated here, the forward I–V characteristic switches from the blocking to the conducting state at a critical peak forward voltage V_p.

---

[5]Since Si is the material commonly used for this device, it is often called a silicon-controlled rectifier.

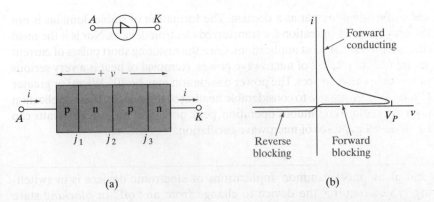

Figure 10–10
A two-terminal
p-n-p-n device:
(a) basic structure
and common
circuit symbol;
(b) I–V
characteristic.

We can anticipate the discussion of conduction mechanisms that follows by noting that an initial positive voltage v places j_1 and j_3 under forward bias and the center junction j_2 under reverse bias. As v is increased, most of the forward voltage in the blocking state must appear across the reverse-biased junction j_2. After switching to the conducting state, the voltage from A to K is very small (less than 1 V), and we conclude that, in this condition, all three junctions must be forward biased. The mechanism by which j_2 switches from reverse bias to forward bias is the subject of much of the discussion that follows.

In the *reverse-blocking* state (v negative), j_1 and j_3 are reverse biased and j_2 is forward biased. Since the supply of electrons and holes to j_2 is restricted by the reverse-biased junctions on either side, the device current is limited to a small saturation current arising from the thermal generation of electron–hole pairs (EHPs) near j_1 and j_3. The current remains small in the reverse-blocking condition until avalanche breakdown occurs at a large reverse bias. In a properly designed device, with guards against surface breakdown, the reverse breakdown voltage can be several thousand volts. We shall now consider the mechanism by which this device, often called a *Shockley diode*, switches from the forward-blocking state to the forward-conducting state.

10.4.2 The Two-Transistor Analogy

The four-layer configuration of Fig. 10–10a suggests that the p-n-p-n diode can be considered as two coupled transistors: j_1 and j_2 form the emitter and collector junctions, respectively, of a p-n-p transistor; similarly, j_2 and j_3 form the collector and emitter junctions of an n-p-n transistor. (Note that the emitter of the n-p-n is on the right, which is the reverse of what we usually draw.) In this analogy, the collector region of the n-p-n is in common with the base of the p-n-p, and the base of the n-p-n serves as the collector region of the p-n-p. The center junction j_2 serves as the collector junction for both transistors.

This two-transistor analogy is illustrated in Fig. 10–11. The collector current i_{C1} of the p-n-p transistor drives the base of the n-p-n, and the base current i_{B1} of the p-n-p is dictated by the collector current i_{C2} of the n-p-n. If we associate an emitter-to-collector current transfer ratio α with each transistor, we can use the analysis in Chapter 7 to solve for the current i.

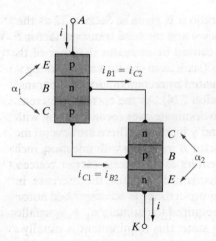

Using Eq. (7–37b) with $\alpha_1 = \alpha_N$ for the p-n-p, $\alpha_2 = \alpha_N$ for the n-p-n, and with I_{C01} and I_{C02} for the respective collector saturation currents, we have

$$i_{C1} = \alpha_1 i + I_{C01} = i_{B2} \qquad (10\text{–}3a)$$

$$i_{C2} = \alpha_2 i + I_{C02} = i_{B1} \qquad (10\text{–}3b)$$

But the sum of i_{C1} and i_{C2} is the total current through the device:

$$i_{C1} + i_{C2} = i \qquad (10\text{–}4)$$

Taking this sum in Eq. (10–3) we have

$$i(\alpha_1 + \alpha_2) + I_{C01} + I_{C02} = i \qquad (10\text{–}5)$$

$$i = \frac{I_{C01} + I_{C02}}{1 - (\alpha_1 + \alpha_2)} \qquad (10\text{–}5)$$

As Eq. (10–5) indicates, the current i through the devices is small (approximately the combined collector saturation currents of the two equivalent transistors) as long as the sum $\alpha_1 + \alpha_2$ is small compared with unity. As the sum of the alphas approaches unity, the current i increases rapidly. The current does not increase without limit as Eq. (10–5) implies, however, because the derivation is no longer valid as $\alpha_1 + \alpha_2$ approaches unity. Since j_2 becomes forward biased in the forward-conducting state, both transistors become saturated after switching. The two transistors remain in saturation in the forward-conducting state.

10.4.3 Variation of α with Injection

Since the two-transistor analogy implies that switching involves an increase in the alphas to the point that $\alpha_1 + \alpha_2$ approaches unity, it may be helpful to review how alpha varies with injection for a transistor. The emitter-to-collector current transfer ratio α is given in Section 7.2 as the product of the emitter injection efficiency γ and the base transport factor B. An increase in α with injection can be caused by increases in either of these factors or both. At very low currents (such as in the forward-blocking state of p-n-p-n diodes), γ is usually dominated by recombination in the transition region of the emitter junction (Section 7.7.4). As the current is increased, injection across the junction begins to dominate over recombination within the transition region (Section 5.6.2), and γ increases. There are several mechanisms by which the base transport factor B increases with injection, including the saturation of recombination centers as the excess carrier concentration becomes large. Whichever mechanism dominates, the increase in $\alpha_1 + \alpha_2$ required for switching of the p-n-p-n diode is accomplished automatically. In general, no special design is required to maintain $\alpha_1 + \alpha_2$ smaller than unity during the forward-blocking state; this requirement is usually met at low currents by the dominance of recombination within the transition regions of j_1 and j_3.

10.4.4 Forward-Blocking State

When the device is biased in the forward-blocking state (Fig. 10–12a), the applied voltage v appears primarily across the reverse-biased junction j_2. Although j_1 and j_3 are forward biased, the current is small. The reason for this becomes clear if we consider the supply of electrons available to n_1 and holes to p_2. Focusing attention first upon j_1, let us assume that a hole is injected from p_1 into n_1. If the hole recombines with an electron in n_1 (or in the j_1 transition region), that electron must be resupplied to the n_1 region to maintain space charge neutrality. The supply of electrons in this case is severely restricted, however, by the fact that n_1 is terminated in j_2, a reverse-biased

Figure 10–12
Three bias states of the p-n-p-n diode: (a) the forward-blocking state; (b) the forward-conducting state; (c) the reverse-blocking state.

junction. In a normal p-n diode, the n region is terminated in an ohmic contact, so that the supply of electrons required to match recombination (and injection into p) is unlimited. In this case, however, the electron supply is restricted essentially to those electrons generated thermally within a diffusion length of j_2. As a result, the current passing through the j_1 junction is approximately the same as the reverse saturation current of j_2. A similar argument holds for the current through j_3; holes required for injection into n_2 and to feed recombination in p_2 must originate in the saturation current of the center junction j_2. The applied voltage v divides appropriately among the three junctions to accommodate this small current throughout the device.

In this discussion, we have tacitly assumed that the current crossing j_2 is strictly the thermally generated saturation current. This implies that electrons injected by the forward-biased junction j_3 do not diffuse across p_2 in any substantial numbers, to be swept across the reverse-biased junction into n_1 by transistor action. This is another way of saying that α_2 (for the "n-p-n transistor") is small. Similarly, the supply of holes to p_2 is primarily thermally generated, since few holes injected at j_1 reach j_2 without recombination (i.e., α_1 is small for the "p-n-p"). Now we can see physically why Eq. (10–5) implies a small current while $\alpha_1 + \alpha_2$ is small: Without the transport of charge provided by transistor action, the thermal generation of carriers is the only significant source of electrons to n_1 and holes to p_2.

10.4.5 Conducting State

The charge transport mechanism changes dramatically when transistor action begins. As $\alpha_1 + \alpha_2$ approaches unity by one of the mechanisms described, many holes injected at j_1 survive to be swept across j_2 into p_2. This helps to feed the recombination in p_2 and to support the injection of holes into n_2. Similarly, the transistor action of electrons injected at j_3 and collected at j_2 supplies electrons for n_1. Obviously, the current through the device can be much larger once this mechanism begins. The transfer of injected carriers across j_2 is regenerative, in that a greater supply of electrons to n_1 allows greater injection of holes at j_1 while maintaining space charge neutrality; this greater injection of holes further feeds p_2 by transistor action, and the process continues to repeat itself.

If $\alpha_1 + \alpha_2$ is large enough, so that many electrons are collected in n_1 and many holes are collected in p_2, the depletion region at j_2 begins to decrease. Finally, the reverse bias disappears across j_2 and is replaced by a forward bias, in analogy with a transistor that is biased deep in saturation. When this occurs, the three small forward-bias voltages appear as shown in Fig. 10–12b. Two of these voltages essentially cancel in the overall v, so that the forward voltage drop of the device from anode to cathode in the conducting state is not much greater than that of a single p-n junction. For Si, this forward drop is less than 1 V, until ohmic losses become important at high current levels.

We have discussed the current transport mechanisms in the forward-blocking and forward-conducting states, but we have not indicated how switching is initiated from one state to the other. Basically, the requirement is that the carrier injection at j_1 and j_2 must somehow be increased so that significant transport of injected carriers across j_2 occurs. Once this transport begins, the regenerative nature of the process takes over and switching is completed.

10.4.6 Triggering Mechanisms

The most common method of triggering a two-terminal p-n-p-n is simply to raise the bias voltage to the peak value V_p. This type of *voltage triggering* results in a breakdown (or significant leakage) of the reverse-biased junction j_2; the accompanying increase in current provides the injection at j_1 and j_3, as well as the transport required for switching to the conducting state. The breakdown mechanism commonly occurs by the combination of *base-width narrowing* and *avalanche multiplication*.

When carrier multiplication occurs in j_2, many electrons are swept into n_1 and holes into p_2. This process provides to these regions the majority carriers needed for increased injection by the emitter junctions. Because of transistor action, the full breakdown voltage of j_2 need not be reached. As we showed in Eq. (7–52), breakdown occurs in the collector junction of a transistor with $i_B = 0$ when $M\alpha = 1$. In the coupled-transistor case of the p-n-p-n diode, breakdown occurs at j_2 when

$$M_p\alpha_1 + M_n\alpha_2 = 1 \qquad (10\text{--}6)$$

where M_p is the hole multiplication factor and M_n is the multiplication factor for electrons.

As the bias v increases in the forward-blocking state, the depletion region about j_2 spreads to accommodate the increased reverse bias on the center junction. This spreading means that the neutral base regions on either side (n_1 and p_2) become thinner. Since α_1 and α_2 increase as these base widths decrease, triggering can occur by the effect of base-width narrowing. A true punch-through of the base regions is seldom required, since moderate narrowing of these regions can increase the alphas enough to cause switching. Furthermore, switching may be the result of a combination of avalanche multiplication and base-width narrowing, along with possible leakage current through j_2 at high voltage. From Eq. (10–6), it is clear that, with avalanche multiplication present, the sum $\alpha_1 + \alpha_2$ need not approach unity to initiate breakdown of j_2. Once breakdown begins, the increased numbers of carriers in n_1 and p_2 drive the device to the forward-conducting state by the regenerative process of coupled transistor action. As switching proceeds, the reverse bias is lost across j_2 and the junction breakdown mechanisms are no longer active. Therefore, base narrowing and avalanche multiplication serve only to start the switching process.

If a forward-bias voltage is applied rapidly to the device, switching can occur by a mechanism commonly called *dv/dt triggering*. Basically, this type of triggering occurs as the depletion region of j_2 adjusts to accommodate the increasing voltage. As the depletion width of j_2 increases, electrons are removed from the n_1 side, and holes are removed from the p_2 side, of the junction. For a slow increase in voltage, the resulting flow of electrons toward j_1 and holes toward j_3 does not constitute a significant current. If dv/dt is large, however, the rate of charge removal from each side of j_2 can cause the current to increase significantly. In terms of the junction capacitance (C_{j2}) of the reverse-biased junction, the transient current is given by

$$i(t) = \frac{dC_{j2}v_{j2}}{dt} = C_{j2}\frac{dv_{j2}}{dt} + v_{j2}\frac{dC_{j2}}{dt} \tag{10-7}$$

where v_{j2} is the instantaneous voltage across j_2. This type of current flow is often called *displacement current*. The rate of change of C_{j2} must be included in calculating current, since the capacitance varies with time as the depletion width changes.

The increase in current due to a rapid rise in voltage can cause switching well below the steady state triggering voltage V_P. Therefore, a dv/dt rating is usually specified along with V_P for p-n-p-n diodes. Obviously, dv/dt triggering can be a disadvantage in circuits subjected to unpredictable voltage transients.

The various triggering mechanisms discussed in this section apply to the two-terminal p-n-p-n diode. As we shall see in the next section, the SCR is triggered by an external signal applied to a third terminal.

**10.5
THE
SEMICONDUCTOR-
CONTROLLED
RECTIFIER**

The semiconductor-controlled rectifier (SCR) is useful in many applications, such as power switching and various control circuits. This device can handle currents from a few milliamperes to hundreds of amperes. Since it can be turned on externally, the SCR can be used to regulate the amount of power delivered to a load simply by passing current only during selected portions of the line cycle. A common example of this application is the light-dimmer switch used in many homes. At a given setting of this switch, an SCR is turned on and off repetitively, such that all or only part of each power cycle is delivered to the lights. As a result, the light intensity can be varied continuously from full to dark. The same control principle can be applied to motors, heaters, and many other systems. We shall discuss this type of application next, after first establishing the fundamentals of device operation.

The most important four-layer device in power circuit applications is the three-terminal SCR[6] (Fig. 10-13). This device is similar to the p-n-p-n diode, except that a third lead (*gate*) is attached to one of the base regions. When the SCR is biased in the forward-blocking state, a small current

---

[6]This device is often called a *thyristor* to indicate its function as a solid state analogue of the gas thyratron, a gas-filled tube that passes current when an arc discharge occurs at a critical firing voltage. In a manner analogous to the gate current control of the SCR, this firing voltage can be varied by a voltage applied to a third electrode.

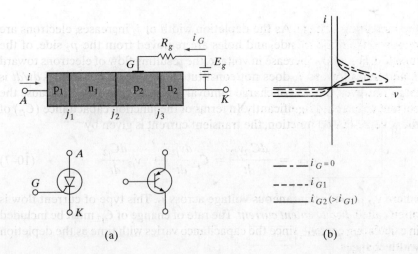

Figure 10–13
A semiconductor-
controlled
rectifier:
(a) four-layer
geometry and
common circuit
symbols; (b) I–V
characteristics.

supplied to the gate can initiate switching to the conducting state. As a result, the anode switching voltage V_P decreases as the current i_G applied to the gate is increased (Fig. 10–13b). This type of turn-on control makes the SCR a useful and versatile device in switching and control circuits (Fig. 10–14).

To visualize the *gate-triggering* mechanism, let us assume that the device is in the forward-blocking state, with a small saturation current flowing from anode to cathode. A positive gate current causes holes to flow from the gate into p_2, the base of the n-p-n transistor. This added supply of holes and the accompanying injection of electrons from n_2 into p_2 initiates transistor action in the n-p-n. After a transit time τ_{t2}, the electrons injected by j_3 arrive at the center junction and are swept into n_1, the base of the p-n-p. This causes an increase in hole injection of j_1, and these holes diffuse across the base n_1 in a transit time τ_{t1}. Thus, after a delay time of approximately $\tau_{t1} + \tau_{t2}$, transistor action is established across the entire p-n-p-n, and the device is driven into the forward-conducting state. In most SCRs, the delay time is less than a few microseconds and the gate current required for turn-on is only a few milliamperes. Therefore, the SCR can be turned on by a very small amount of power in the gate circuit. On the other hand, the device current i can be many amperes, and the power controlled by the device may be very large.

It is not necessary to maintain the gate current once the SCR switches to the conducting state; in fact, the gate essentially loses control of the device after regenerative transistor action is initiated. For most devices, a gate current pulse lasting a few microseconds is sufficient to ensure switching. Ratings of minimum gate pulse height and duration are generally provided for particular SCR devices.

10.5.1 Turning Off the SCR

Turning off the SCR—changing it from the conducting state to the blocking state—can be accomplished by reducing the current i below a critical value

Figure 10–14
Example of the
use of an SCR
to control the
power delivered
to a load:
(a) schematic
diagram of
the circuit;
(b) waveforms
of the delivered
signal and the
phase-variable
trigger pulse.

(called the *holding current*) required to maintain the $\alpha_1 + \alpha_2 = 1$ condition. In some SCR devices, gate turnoff can be used to reduce the alpha sum below unity. For example, if the gate voltage is reversed in Fig. 10–14, holes are extracted from the p_2 base region. If the rate of hole extraction by the gate is sufficient to remove the n-p-n transistor from saturation, the device turns off. However, there are often problems involving the lateral flow of current in p_2 to the gate; nonuniform biasing of j_3 can result from the fact that the bias on this emitter junction varies with position when a lateral current flows. Therefore, SCR devices must be specifically designed for turn-off control; at best, this turn-off capability can be utilized only over a limited range for a given device.

**10.6
INSULATED-
GATE BIPOLAR
TRANSISTOR**

We saw in Section 10.5 that the SCR has difficulty in efficiently turning off the device using the gate. We need to use additional circuitry to reduce the anode-to-cathode current below the holding current to change the SCR from the conducting state to the blocking state. This is, of course, clumsy and expensive.

Hence, the *insulated-gate bipolar transistor (IGBT)* was invented by Baliga in 1979 to address this issue. This variation on the SCR can easily be turned off from the conducting to the blocking state by the action of the gate. This device is also known by several other names, such as conductivity-modulated FET (COMFET), insulated-gate transistor (IGT), insulated-gate rectifier (IGR), gain-enhanced MOSFET (GEMFET), and bipolar FET (BiFET).

Figure 10–15
Structure of an insulated-gate bipolar transistor.

The basic structure is shown for an n-channel device in Fig. 10–15. It combines an SCR with a MOSFET that is able to connect or disconnect the n^+ cathode to the n^- base region, depending on the gate bias of the MOSFET. The MOSFET channel length is determined by the p region, which is formed by diffusion of the acceptors implanted in the same region as the n^+ cathode. In other words, the channel length is determined not by the lithography of the gate, as in a conventional MOSFET but rather by the diffusion of the acceptors. Such a MOSFET structure is known as a *double-diffused MOSFET* (DMOS). The DMOS device is essentially an NMOSFET.

The main part of the IGBT is the n^- region, which acts as the drain of the DMOS device. This is generally a thick (~50 μm) epitaxial region with a low doping (~10^{14} cm^{-3}) grown on a heavily p^+-doped substrate that forms the anode. The n^- region can therefore support a large blocking voltage in the "off" state. In the "on" state, the conductivity of this lightly doped region is modulated (increased) by the electrons injected from the n^+ cathode and the holes injected from the p^+ anode—hence the alternative name *conductivity-modulated FET* (COMFET). The increased conductivity allows the voltage drop across the device to be minimal in the "on" state.

The I–V characteristics are shown in Fig. 10–16. If the DMOS gate voltage is zero (or below the threshold voltage), an n-type inversion region is not formed in the p-type channel region and the n^+ cathode is not shorted to the n^- base. The structure then looks exactly like a conventional SCR that allows minimum current flow in either polarity until breakdown is reached. For positive anode-to-cathode bias V_{AK}, avalanche breakdown occurs at the n^--p junction, while for negative V_{AK} avalanche occurs at the n^--p^+ junction.

When a gate bias is applied to the DMOS gate, we see that, for positive V_{AK}, there is significant current flow (Fig. 10–17). The characteristics look like that of a MOSFET, with one difference: Instead of the current starting to increase from the origin, there is an offset or cut-in voltage of ~0.7 V, as with a diode. The reason for this can be understood by looking at the equivalent circuit in Fig. 10–17a. For small V_{AK} up to the offset voltage, the structure looks like a DMOS in series with a p-i-n diode made up of the p^+ substrate

Figure 10–16
Output *I–V*
characteristics of
an insulated-gate
bipolar transistor
(n channel).

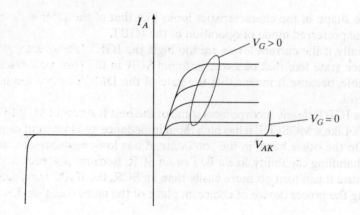

(the anode), the n^- blocking region (the base), which is essentially like an intrinsic region, and the n^+ cathode. In this regime, there is negligible voltage drop across the DMOS device, and the p-i-n device is in forward bias. The injected carriers from the anode and the cathode recombine in the n^- region. As we saw in Chapter 5, for a diode dominated by recombination in the depletion region, the *I–V* characteristics show an exponential behavior, with a diode ideality factor of $n = 2$. Therefore, in this region, we get

$$I_A \propto \exp(qV_{AK}/2kT) \tag{10–8}$$

On the other hand, when V_{AK} is larger than the offset voltage (~ 0.7 V), the characteristics look like that of a MOSFET, multiplied by a p-n-p bipolar junction transistor gain term. The equivalent circuit in this region is shown in Fig. 10–17b. In this regime, not all the injected carriers recombine in the near-intrinsic n^- region. The current they supply, which is essentially the DMOSFET current I_{MOS}, acts as the base current of the vertical p-n-p BJT formed between the p^+ substrate (anode), the n^- base, and the p^- channel of the DMOS device. Hence, the current is now given by

$$I_A = (1 + \beta_{pnp})I_{MOS} \tag{10–9}$$

Figure 10–17
IGBT equivalent
circuit: (a) below
the offset voltage,
for low V_{AK};
(b) above the
offset voltage,
for high V_{AK}.

The shape of the characteristics looks like that of the DMOS device. This is the preferred mode of operation of the IGBT.

Finally, if the current levels are too high, the IGBT latches into a low impedance state like that of a conventional SCR in the "on" state. This is undesirable, because it means that the gate of the DMOS device has now lost control.

The IGBT clearly incorporates some of the best features of MOSFETs and BJTs. Like a MOSFET, it has high input impedance and low input capacitance. On the other hand, in the "on" state, it has low resistance and high current-handling capability, like a BJT or an SCR. Because of these factors, and because it can turn off more easily than an SCR, the IGBT is gradually becoming the power device of choice, in place of the more traditional SCR.

Nanotechnology is sometimes defined as engineered objects in the length scale of 1–100 nm with novel, useful properties. This nanoscale regime, sometimes also known as the mesoscale, lies between the microscale (~microns) and atomic/molecular scale (~0.1 nm). When objects are shrunk from the macro to microscale and beyond, they don't just become smaller, but they also behave *differently*. One way to appreciate this is if one considers the *fraction* of atoms that lie at the surface of a sphere. For macroscopic or microscopic dimensions, the vast majority of the atoms are found to lie in the bulk of the sphere. As one enters the mesoscale, a substantial *fraction* of the atoms are found to be at the surface, which very often have different properties than bulk atoms. In other words, at some point smaller isn't just smaller but *"smaller is different."* On the other hand, if one considers much smaller objects such as atoms/molecules, their properties belong to the realm of quantum mechanics and chemistry. Now, if one considers clusters of these atoms/molecules, as in a nanoscale object, because of collective effects between these atoms, new properties can emerge that are not manifested by the individual atoms. The physicist, Philip Anderson, eloquently described this as *"more is different!"*

10.7 NANOELECTRONIC DEVICES

There are many nanoelectonic devices that are being investigated in research labs. We will briefly discuss a few interesting examples which show novel, nanoscale properties, according to the dimensionality of the nanodevice: zero-dimensional quantum dots, one-dimensional quantum wires and nanotubes, and two-dimensional layered crystals such as graphene. Many of the novel properties arise from the density of states of these low dimensionality systems discussed in Appendix IV.

10.7.1 Zero-Dimensional Quantum Dots

Zero-dimensional quantum dot systems have singularities in the density of states, where $N(E)$ varies as $1/E$. These are sometimes called "artificial atoms." However, the analogy is not perfect. While atoms have a spherically symmetric Coulomb potential, $V(r) \sim 1/r$, leading to energy levels that vary as $1/n^2$ [Eq. (2–15)], the confinement potential in quantum dots can be approximated as a parabloic potential, reminiscent of simple harmonic oscillators, leading to equispaced eigen-energies in the quantum dot according to the rules of quantum mechanics. Quantum dot confinement also leads to an increase of the effective band gap, since the lowest eigenstates in the conduction and valence band are pushed up in energy, leading to an increasing blueshift, as dot sizes are reduced. This can lead to a dramatic change in the colors of quantum dots made of a certain semiconductor, simply by changing the dot size, with obvious applications in optoelectronics. For instance, one can incorporate such quantum dots in the active regions of lasers, and tune the emission wavelengths toward the blue, and sharpen the linewidths compared to three-dimensional active regions. Quantum dots have also been used in solar cells to engineer the aborption characteristics of the cells, and match it better to the solar spectrum.

Quantum dots can be made by so-called *top down* approaches involving nanoscale lithography, followed by etching. Alternatively, *bottom-up* schemes such self-assembled quantum dots can be formed using heteroepitaxy. As described in Chapter 1, if we grow a dissimilar semiconductor on a substrate, if there is a lattice mismatch, it leads to strain in the epitaxial layer. Generally, the initial layers are smooth, which is known as the layer-by-layer Frank-Van der Merwe growth mode. As the layer becomes thicker, often there is roughening of the epitaxial layer because of increasing strain—this is known as the Volmer–Weber growth mode. If the lattice mismatch in the heteroepitaxial system is large, it can lead to very rough morphology or quantum dots forming on the surface of the substrate in a self-assembled fashion. This is known as the Stranski–Krastanov mode, and is the preferred mode of fabrication in many optoelectronic devices where precise location of the dots is not critical. This avoids time-consuming lithography and etching, and allows, for example, inclusion of quantum dots in the cavity of a laser to sharpen the emission linewidth.

An interesting electronic application of quantum dots is in flash memories that we discussed in Section 9.5.2. Recall that electrons can be stored in a non-volatile fashion in the floating gate of an MOS structure, and the presence or absence of these electrons corresponds to digit bits 1 or 0. As one scales down the sizes of these flash memory cells, it would be desirable to scale down the thicknesses of the tunnel dielectric, in accordance with the scaling laws we discussed in Section 6.5.9. However, one finds that if the tunnel oxide is less than ~8 nm, there are inevitably manufacturing "weakspots" in the oxide which cause the stored electrons to leak away and not be retained for the requisite 10 years or longer. If the continuous floating gate electrode is replaced by an array of discontinuous quantum dots, and electrons are stored in them, we can more aggressively scale down the tunnel oxide, and therefore the memory cell. A weakspot in the tunnel dielectric might discharge electrons in a quantum dot in the vicinity of the weakspot, but the vast majority of the other dots which are electrically discontinuous would still retain the stored electrons. This greatly improves the reliability of the flash memory cells.

10.7.2 One-Dimensional Quantum Wires

One-dimensional semiconductor quantum wires or nanowires are an attractive platform for making ultra-scaled MOSFETs. These can be viewed as a natural evolution of the FinFETs or MuGFETs that we discussed in Section. 6.6.3. Recall that having a gate wrapped around three sides of a channel in a three-dimensional structure gives the gate better electrostatic control of the channel potential compared to a bulk MOSFET, and leads to better channel length scalability. In a nanowire MOSFET, the gate can be wrapped all around the channel, leading to even better gate control than in a FinFET. However, the drive current of an individual nanowire FET is generally low. Hence, one needs to make parallel arrays of these devices.

Just as with quantum dots, such quantum wires can be formed by top down lithography and etching techniques, or by novel bottom up schemes. One such bottom up scheme is known as the Vapor-Liquid-Solid (VLS) approach, first developed by Wagner in the 1960s. In this scheme, one patterns metal catalysts such as Au to form quantum dots on a substrate. The structure is then loaded into a chemical vapor deposition system, and appropriate precursor gases are introduced, with the substrate at a high enough temperature that the Au metal catalysts melt. For example, to grow Si nanowires, silane (SiH_4) is flowed in such that it dissolves in the molten Au catalyst dots. There is a supersaturation of Si in the Au, leading to an extrusion of Si atoms as single crystal Si nanowires growing vertically on top of the Si substrate, with the Au catalyst floating on top of the nanowire. At the end of the VLS growth, the Au catalysts can be etched off. Fortunately, due to the low solid solubility of Au in Si, there is negligible Au contamination of the nanowires or the substrate. Vertical FETs can be made in the forest of nanowires, or these nanowires can be harvested and subsequently laid down flat on another substrate for subsequent device processing. Other precursors such as germane for Ge nanowire growth, or III–V nanowires, can be grown by VLS.

Another type of 1D system is the carbon-based nanotube. As we saw in Chapter 1, carbon can be tetrahedrally bonded to four other nearest neighbor carbon atoms via sp^3 bonding, leading to diamond. But C can also undergo sp^2 bonding which leads to a planar structure, such as the sheets of carbon atoms in graphite. This two-dimensional planar bonding arrangement of carbon led to the first nanostructures in C, based on so-called buckyballs or fullerenes.[7] These are spherical shells of carbon atoms reminiscent of the quantum dots we described in the previous section. Fullerenes can be elongated into a tubular structure, leading to carbon nanotubes [Fig. 10–18], and FETs can be made in them. These have somewhat similar properties as nanowire FETs, but there are interesting differences in the density of states

---

[7]The name buckyball or fullerene is based on the American architect Buckminster Fuller who developed the iconic geodesic dome, which looks similar to these carbon zero-dimensional nanostructures.

Figure 10–18
Nanostructures
of carbon:
(a) 2-D graphene;
(b) 1-D nanotube;
(c) 0-D buckyball
(fullerene);
(d) linear
band structure
of graphene
showing Dirac
cones.

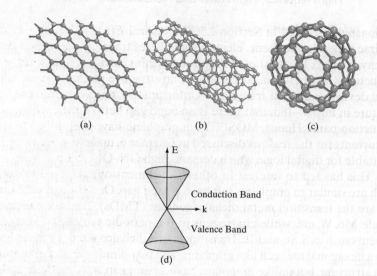

of these carbon-based materials. For instance, depending on precise angular orientation of the carbon atoms in the cylindrical tube, which is known as the helicity or chirality of the nanotube, they behave as semiconductors (which are good for FETs), or metals (suitable for interconnects).

10.7.3 Two-Dimensional Layered Crystals

We have already met two-dimensional systems such as two-dimensional electron gases (2-DEG) in the inversion layer of a MOSFET made in a three-dimensional bulk crystal. Such quasi-two-dimensional systems are formed through electrostatic confinement. Recently, there have been breakthroughs in two-dimensional atomic crystals or layered materials.

Staying with the theme of carbon, it was shown by Geim and Novoselov in 2004 that one can peel off individual sheets of sp^2-bonded carbon atoms from graphite, leading to two-dimensional atomic crystals called graphene. One can also view graphene as carbon nanotubes which are sliced along the axis of the cylinder, and flattened out into monoatomic sheets of carbon. The unit cell of graphene consists of a hexagonal array of carbon atoms with a unique *linear* bandstructure, $E(k)$, shown in Fig. 10–18. This is obviously different from the parabolic $E(k)$ relationship seen in most semiconductors. We saw in Section 3.2.2 that the curvature of these parabolic bands determines effective mass of the electrons and holes. By contrast, the linear bandstructure in graphene is more reminiscent of the linear dispersion relationship of photons, which are known to have zero rest mass, and thus travel at the speed of light, c. The carriers in graphene, in analogy with photons, also have zero effective mass, and are known as massless Dirac fermions, traveling at a group velocity determined by the slope of the $E(k)$ dispersion relationship discussed in Section 1.5. The conical $E(k)$ surfaces are known as Dirac cones. In graphene, electrons and holes travel at a so-called Fermi velocity, which is $10\times$ that of the saturation drift velocity in Si or most semiconductors. Clearly, this makes graphene an attractive platform for very high speed devices such as rf transistors. Unfortunately, one sees from the band structure in Fig. 10–18d, that there is no band gap between the valence and conduction band. Hence, MOSFETs in graphene have high off-state leakage currents for the reasons discussed in Chapter 6, making graphene FETs unsuitable for digital logic which demand high ON–OFF ratio.

This has led to interest in other two-dimensional layered materials which are similar to graphene, but have a band gap. One class of such materials are the transition metal dichalcogenides (TMDs). Transition elements include Mo, W, etc. while chalcogens in the periodic table are Column VI elements such as S, Se, and Te. Transition metal dichalcogenides such as MoS_2 have a hexagonal unit cell like graphene, and two-dimensional mono-atomic sheet structure, but unlike graphene, have a band gap, making these materials attractive for short channel MOSFETs. One could think of them as SOI scaled to the ultimate limit of atomic layer thicknesses.

Yet another set of two-dimensional layered materials which have garnered interested recently are the topological insulators (TI) such as the bismuth-selenide/telluride. This class of solids are insulating in the bulk, but have Dirac cone metallic surface states, similar to graphene, but with a novel twist. Remember that electrons have a quantum number called spin, which can have values of $\pm\frac{1}{2}$, corresponding to spin "up" or "down." Normally, in most semiconductor devices we have equal populations of both spins. The spin simply adds a factor of 2 in the density of states, but otherwise can be ignored. When electrons orbit around the nucleus, they see an effective magnetic field due to the orbital motion, and spin up/down electrons can have slightly different energies in this magnetic field. (The split-off bands shown in Fig. 3–10 are the result of such interactions.) On TI surfaces such as Bi_2Se_3, due to strong spin-orbit interactions in heavy nuclei such as Bi, the spin of the electron is locked orthogonally to the wavevector $\mathbf{k}$, which determines its orbital motion. In other words, if electrons moving to the left on the TI surface have spin up, electrons moving to the right will have spin down. Such intriguing physics may lead to novel nanoelectronic devices in the future which will not only exploit the charge of the electron, but also its spin, a nascent field dubbed *spintronics*, in analogy with electronics.

10.7.4 Spintronic Memory

Although spintronics based on semiconductors is a burgeoning field, spin-based ferromagnetic devices have been used for a long time in hard disks, and more recently in *spin transfer torque random access memory (STTRAM)*. A brief discussion of ferromagnetism in solids is warranted to explain these devices. Spinning electrons can be thought of as tiny, atomic magnets which point up or down. Ferromagnetism is a magnetic state where a majority of the electron spins point one way or the other, even without an applied external magnetic field (which would tend to orient the electron spins.)

As we have mentioned in Section 10.7.3, normally in solids spin up/down electrons are equally likely to be found, and the density of states has a factor of 2 spin degeneracy. We also saw in Chapter 3 that electrons, being fermions, must have an overall wavefunction $\psi(r, s)$, depending on position, r, and spin, s, that is *anti-symmetric*. So, as shown in Fig. 3–2, if the spatial part of the wavefunction is symmetric, the spins are anti-parallel, and vice versa. So, in this case, since the symmetric (bonding) orbital is the lower energy state, it is energetically favorable for spins to be anti-parallel, and the solid is not ferromagnetic. Such solids are paramagnetic, with no permanent magnetism. On the other hand, if free electrons are considered, which are not subjected to a strong ion core potential as in Fig. 3–2, the anti-symmetric orbital (with parallel spins) is energetically favorable because the electrons are further apart on average and, therefore, there is less Coulomb repulsion. Since the spins are parallel, it leads to ferromagnetism. So, what aligns the spinning electrons in a ferromagnet is *electrostatic* Coulomb interactions, rather than the much weaker magnetostatic interactions between the magnetic dipoles. This larger *effective* field is known as the Weiss *exchange* field (because it is driven by the anti-symmetry of electron wavefunctions when two electrons are interchanged). As a result, in a ferromagnet, there is a higher of density of states of the *majority* spins near the Fermi level (Fig. 10–19a).

Figure 10–19
(a) Spin-based memory. Depending on whether the "free" magnet on the right is parallel (anti-parallel) to the "fixed" magnet on the left, we have a low (high) tunneling resistance corresponding to the two memory states. (b) Phase change memory whose resistance changes depending on the crystallinity of the chalcogenide.

This is the basis of a host of ferromagnetic spin-based memories. For example, one can have a permanent *fixed* ferromagnet that always points up, separated by a tunnel dielectric from a *free* magnet which can point up or down. If the two magnets are aligned, there is a high density of initial states and final states for majority spin electron tunneling near the Fermi level. This corresponds to a *low* tunnel resistance, and could correspond to bit 1. (Spins do not flip during the tunneling process.) On the other hand, if the free magnet is anti-parallel to the fixed magnet, there is a mismatch between the initial and final density of states for both types of spin, and the tunnel resistance will be higher, corresponding to bit 0. This is known as *tunnel magnetoresistance* (TMR). This, and similar effects such as giant magnetoresistance (GMR), are used in hard disk memories that are ubiquitous in computers.

These effects are also the basis of STTRAMs which offer a new type of "universal" memory that might one day supplant all the other types of memory that we discussed in Chapter 9 (SRAM, DRAM, flash). In STTRAMs, to write a bit 1, a current flows through the fixed magnet, which spin polarizes the electrons along the majority spin direction. When an electron tunnels into the free magnet, it transfers spin angular momentum to the free magnet, applies a torque, and flips it to make it parallel to the fixed magnet. This sets the STTRAM in the low resistance state (bit 1) during read operation. If the polarity of the write current is reversed, the sign of the angular momentum transfer to the free magnet is flipped, and it becomes anti-parallel to the fixed magnet, setting it into the high resistance state (bit 0).

10.7.5 Nanoelectronic Resistive Memory

As we saw for STTRAMs, memory devices can be based on two resistance states, corresponding to digital bits 1 and 0. In some sense, such memory devices are simpler to make than logic transistors, where requirements, such as ON–OFF ratios, etc., are much more stringent. In recent years, novel nonvolatile memories have been developed based on resistance changes. In resistive RAMs (ReRAMs), a dielectric such as high-k dielectric is sandwiched between two metal electrodes. Flowing a high write tunneling current through the dielectric can create defect trap states or charges in the dielectric, which can modify its resistance. The phenomena are akin to what we discussed in Section 6.4.7 in the context of I–V characteristics of SiO_2. The precise details of programming (called setting) and erase (re-setting) depend on the dielectric used in ReRAMs, and the physics is still somewhat controversial. In titanium oxide-based dielectrics, it is believed that the mechanism involves creation and annihilation of a string of oxygen vacancies, which results in a resistance change. Some dielectrics can be set and reset with unipolar pulses of different amplitude, whereas others require bipolar pulses of opposite polarity. Resistive RAMs are also known by a colorful name, *Memory Resistor* or memristor. Typical changes in resistance in ReRAM are several hundred percent. The challenge in these devices is demonstrating reliability in terms of repeated cycling between the two resistance states, without suffering from TDDB.

Another type of resistive memory, where the resistance difference between states 0 and 1 is much higher than in ReRAM (factors of $\sim 10^5$ are typical), is the phase change memory (PCM) (Fig. 10–19b). Here the memory storage element is a glassy material, perhaps a chalcogenide such as $Ge_2Sb_2Te_5$ (GST). The passage of an electric current through a heating element such as TiN is used to quickly heat and quench the GST, making it amorphous, which is a high resistance phase. Alternatively, it can be held in its crystallization temperature range for some time, thereby switching it to a low resistance crystalline state. Interestingly, phase change materials are not a new idea. They have been used extensively in rewriteable RW compact discs (CDs) as the storage medium. A laser makes the layer amorphous (low reflectivity) or polycrystalline (high reflectivity) for optical storage of the digital bits.

The field of nanoelectronics is still in its infancy. As the great Richard Feynman said, "There is plenty of room at the bottom!"

SUMMARY   **10.1** High frequencies in the microwave regime can be obtained by negative differential resistance achievable by tunneling (Esaki diodes), transferred-electron effects (Gunn diodes), or transit-time effects (IMPATT diodes).

10.2 High power switching is possible with p-n-p-n diodes, thyristors, or SCRs. These devices can be understood in terms of two coupled BJTs. Similar effects in CMOS cause latchup.

10.3 Modern power devices are based on the IGBT, which is a combination of an SCR and a MOSFET.

10.4 Nanoelectronics is based on the mesoscale between the larger (microscale) and smaller (atomic) dimensions where novel phenomena can be beneficially exploited.

PROBLEMS   **10.1** Sketch the band diagram for an abrupt junction in which the doping on the p side is degenerate and the Fermi level on the n side is aligned with the bottom of the conduction band. Draw the forward- and reverse-bias band diagrams and sketch the I–V characteristic. This diode is often called a *backward diode*. Can you explain why?

10.2 What determines the peak tunneling voltage V_p of a tunnel diode? Explain.

If a large density of trapping centers is present in a tunnel diode (Fig. P10–2), tunneling can occur from the n-side conduction band to the trapping level (A–B). Then the electrons may drop to the valence band on the p side (B–C), thereby completing a two-step process of charge transport across the junction. In fact, if the density of trapping centers is large, it is possible to observe an increase in current as the states below E_{Fn} pass by the trapping level with increased bias. In Fig. P10–2, the trapping level E_t is located 0.3 eV above the valence band. Assume that $E_g = 1$ eV, $E_{Fn} - E_c$ on the n side equals $E_v - E_{Fp}$ on the p side, and both $E_{Fn} - E_c$ and $E_v - E_{Fp}$ equal 0.1 eV.

(a) Calculate the minimum forward bias at which tunneling through E_t occurs.

(b) Calculate the maximum forward bias for tunneling via $E_{t'}$.

(c) Sketch the I–V curve for this tunnel diode. Assume that the maximum tunneling current via E_t is about one-third of the peak band-to-band tunneling current.

10.3 (a) Write down the complete continuity equation and solve it. Find the excess minority hole concentration as a function of time (t) for $t \geq 0$. Assume that there is no applied field but recombination is present. Consider an n-type Si sample with donor concentration as $10^{16}/cm^3$ at $T = 300$ K. Due to uniform illumination of light at $t = 0$, EHPs are generated at a rate of $10^{20}/cm^3$. If minority carrier lifetime is 10 nsec, find the excess hole concentration at $t = 5$ msec.

(b) When the steady state excess hole concentration is $2 \times 10^{14}/cm^3$ as $t \longrightarrow \infty$, estimate the minority carrier lifetime

(c) Determine the time at which the excess minority carrier concentration becomes one third of the steady state value obtained in part (b).

10.4 Assuming that n_Γ electrons/cm^3 are in the lower (central) valley of the GaAs conduction band at time t and n_L are in the satellite (L) valleys, show that the criterion for negative differential conductivity ($dJ/dE < 0$) is

$$\frac{\mathscr{E}(\mu_\Gamma - \mu_L)\dfrac{dn_\Gamma}{dE} + \mathscr{E}\left(n_\Gamma\dfrac{d\mu_\Gamma}{d\mathscr{E}} + n_L\dfrac{d\mu_L}{d\mathscr{E}}\right)}{n_\Gamma\mu_\Gamma + n_L\mu_L} < -1$$

where μ_Γ and μ_L are the electron mobilities in the Γ and L valleys, respectively. (*Note:* $n_0 = n_\Gamma + n_L$.) Discuss the conditions for negative differential conductivity, assuming that the mobilities are approximately proportional to $\mathscr{E}^{-1}$.

10.5 We wish to estimate the d-c power dissipated in a GaAs Gunn diode. Assume that the diode is 5 μm long and operates in the stable domain mode.

(a) What is the minimum electron concentration n_0? What is the time between current pulses?

(b) Using data from Fig. 10–9a, calculate the power dissipated in the sample per unit volume when it is biased just below threshold if n_0 is chosen from the calculation of part (a). In general, does operation at a higher frequency result in greater power dissipation?

10.6 (a) Calculate the ratio N_L/N_Γ of the effective density of states in the upper (L) valleys to the effective density of states in the lower (Γ) valley of the GaAs conduction band (Fig. 10–6).

(b) Assuming a Boltzmann distribution $n_L/n_\Gamma = (N_L/N_\Gamma) \exp(-\Delta E/kT)$, calculate the ratio of the concentration of conduction-band electrons in the upper valley to the concentration in the central valley in equilibrium at 300 K.

(c) As a rough calculation, assume that an electron at the bottom of the central valley has kinetic energy kT. After it is promoted to the satellite (L) valley, what is its approximate equivalent temperature?

10.7 Explain why two separate transistors cannot be connected as in Fig. 10–11 to achieve the p-n-p-n switching action of Fig. 10–10.

10.8 In the p-n-p-n diode (Fig. 10–12a), the junction j_3 is forward biased during the forward-blocking state. Why, then, does the forward bias provided by the gate-to-cathode voltage in Fig. 10–13 cause switching?

10.9 (a) Sketch the energy-band diagrams for the p-n-p-n diode in equilibrium, in the forward-blocking state, and in the forward-conducting state.

(b) Sketch the excess minority carrier distributions in regions n_1 and p_2 when the p-n-p-n diode is in the forward-conducting state.

10.10 Use schematic techniques such as those illustrated in Fig. 7–3 to describe the hole flow and electron flow in a p-n-p-n diode for the forward-blocking state and for the forward-conducting state. Explain the diagrams and be careful to define any new symbols (e.g., those representing EHP generation and recombination).

10.11 In a coupled transistor model in presence of avalanche multiplication, the multiplication factor for the electrons is two times larger than that for the holes. The emitter to collector current transfer ratio and the collector saturation current for the n-p-n transistor is four times than that for the p-n-p transistor. Find the expression for the total current flowing through the device.

READING LIST   Baliga, B. J. *Power Semiconductor Devices.* Boston: PWS, 1996.

Esaki, L. "Discovery of the Tunnel Diode." *IEEE Trans. Elec. Dev.,* ED-23 (1976).

Feynman, R. P. "There's Plenty of Room at the Bottom," lecture available online.

Gentry, F. E., F. W. Gutzwiller, N. Holonyak, Jr., and E. E. Von Zastrow. *Semiconductor Controlled Rectifiers: Principles and Application of p-n-p-n Devices.* Englewood Cliffs, NJ: Prentice-Hall, 1964.

Gunn, J. B. "Microwave Oscillations of Current in III-V Semiconductors," *Solid State Comm.,* 1 (1963).

Moll, J. L., M. Tanenbaum, J. M. Goldey, and N. Holonyak. "P-N-P-N Transistor Switches." *Proc. IRE*, 44 (1956).

Read, W. T. "A Proposed High Frequency, Negative Resistance Diode," *Bell Syst. Tech. J.*, 37 (1958).

Ridley, B. K., and T. B. Watkins. "The Possibility of Negative Resistance Effects in Semiconductors," *Proc. Phys. Soc. Lond.*, 78 (1961).

Shockley, W. "Negative Resistance Arising from Transit Time in Semiconductor Diodes." *Bell Syst. Tech. J.*, 33 (1954).

Question 1

SELF QUIZ

Study the ITRS roadmap chapter on Emerging Research Devices available at http://public.itrs.net/. This has projections about next-generation CMOS devices as well as novel devices using nanotechnology.

- Write a report on which of these devices you think will be used in products in the next 5 years, 10 years, and 20 years.

Question 2

In a silicon control rectifier collector currents in one transistor is 0.1 mA and the other transistor is 0.2 mA. The gains combined together is 0.98. Calculate the current flowing through the SCR.

Question 3

In a tunnel diode the peak current is 2 mA at a 50 mV voltage. The vally current is 0.2 mA at a voltage of 300 mV. Calculate the resistance in the −ve resistance region.

Question 4

In a break down diode the current is 1 mA when the voltage across the diode is 10 V which is the regulating voltage. If the voltage is less than regulating voltage the current is 20 uA and voltage is when 1 V. Calculate the resistance in both the cases.

Appendix I

Definitions of Commonly Used Symbols[1]

a	Chapter 1: unit cell dimension (Å); Chapter 6: metallurgical channel half-width for an FET (cm)
$\mathbf{a}, \mathbf{b}, \mathbf{c}$	basis vectors
A	area (cm^2)
$\mathscr{B}$	magnetic flux density (Wb/cm^2)
B	base transport factor for a BJT
B, E, C	base, emitter, collector of a BJT
c	speed of light (cm/s)
C	capacitance/area in MOS (F/cm^2)
C_i, C_d, C_{it}	insulator, depletion, interface-state MOS capacitance/area (F/cm^2)
C_j	junction capacitance (F)
C_s	charge storage capacitance (F)
D, D_n, D_p	diffusion coefficient for dopants, electrons, holes (cm^2/s)
D, G, S	drain, gate, source of an FET
e	Napierian base
e^-	electron
$\mathscr{E}$	electric field strength (V/cm)
E	energy[2] (J, eV); battery voltage (V)
E_a, E_d	acceptor, donor energy level (J, eV)
E_c, E_v	conduction band, valence band edge (J, eV)
E_F	equilibrium Fermi level (J, eV)
E_g	band gap energy (J, eV)
E_i	intrinsic level (J, eV)
E_r, E_t	recombination, trapping energy level (J, eV)
$f(E)$	Fermi—Dirac distribution function
F_n, F_p	quasi-Fermi level for electrons, holes (J, eV)
g, g_{op}	EHP generation rate, optical generation rate (cm^{-3}-s^{-1})

[1]This list does not include some symbols that are used only in the section where they are defined. Units are given in common semiconductor usage, involving cm where appropriate; it is important to note, however, that calculations should be made in the MKS system in some formulas.

[2]In the Boltzmann factor $\exp(-\Delta E/kT)$, ΔE can be expressed in J or eV if k is expressed in J/K or eV/K, respectively.

g_m	mutual transconductance (Ω^{-1}, S)
h	Planck's constant (J-s, eV-s); Chapter 6: FET channel half-width (cm)
$\hbar$	Planck's constant divided by 2π(J-s, eV-s)
$h\nu$	photon energy (J, eV)
h, k, l	Miller indices
h^+	hole
i, I	current[3] (A)
I (subscript)	inverted mode of a BJT
i_B, i_C, i_E	base, collector, emitter current in a BJT (A)
I_{CO}, I_{EO}	magnitude of the collector, emitter saturation current with the emitter, collector open (A)
I_{CS}, I_{ES}	magnitude of the collector, emitter saturation current with the emitter, collector shorted (A)
I_D	channel current in an FET, directed from drain to source (A)
I_0	reverse saturation current in a p-n junction (A)
j	$\sqrt{-1}$
J	current density (A/cm^2)
k	Boltzmann's constant (J/K, eV/K)
k_N, k_P	transconductance of NMOSFET, PMOSFET divided by V_D (A/V^2)
$\mathbf{k}$	wave vector (cm^{-1})
k_d	distribution coefficient
K	scaling factor
K	$4\pi\epsilon_0$ (F/cm)
l, L	length (cm)
L_D	Debye length (cm)
$\bar{l}$	mean free path for carriers in random motion (cm)
m, m^*	mass, effective mass (kg)
m_n^*, m_p^*	effective mass for electrons, holes (kg)
m_l, m_t	longitudinal, transverse electron effective mass (kg)
m_{lh}, m_{hh}	light, heavy hole effective mass (kg)
m_0	rest mass of the electron (kg)
M	avalanche multiplication factor
$\mathbf{m, n}$	integers; exponents
n	concentration of electrons in the conduction band (cm^{-3})
n	n-type semiconductor material
n^+	heavily doped n-type material
n_i	intrinsic concentration of electrons (cm^{-3})
n_n, n_p	equilibrium concentration of electrons in n-type, p-type material (cm^{-3})
n_0	equilibrium concentration of electrons (cm^{-3})
N (subscript)	normal mode of a BJT
N_a, N_d	concentration of acceptors, donors (cm^{-3})
N_a^-, N_d^+	concentration of ionized acceptors, donors (cm^{-3})
N_c, N_v	effective density of states at the edge of the conduction band, valence band (cm^{-3})
p	concentration of holes in the valence band (cm^{-3})
p	p-type semiconductor material

[3]See note at the end of this list.

p^+	heavily doped p-type material
p	momentum (kg-m/s)
p_i	intrinsic hole concentration (cm^{-3}) $= n_i$
p_n, p_p	equilibrium concentration of holes in n-type, p-type material (cm^{-3})
p_0	equilibrium hole concentration (cm^{-3})
q	magnitude of the electronic charge (C)
Q_+, Q_-	total positive, negative charge (C)
Q_d	depletion region charge/area (C/cm^2)
Q_f	oxide fixed charge/area (C/cm^2)
Q_i	effective MOS interface charge/area (C/cm^2)
Q_{it}	interface trap charge/area (C/cm^2)
Q_m	mobile ionic charge/area (C/cm^2)
Q_n, Q_p	charge stored in an electron, hole distribution (C)
Q_n	mobile charge/area in an FET channel (C/cm^2)
Q_{ot}	oxide trapped charge/area (C/cm^2)
$R_p, \Delta R_p$	projected range, straggle (cm)
r, R	resistance (Ω)
R_H	Hall coefficient (cm^3/C)
S	subthreshold slope (mV/decade)
t	time (s)
t	sample thickness (cm)
$\bar{t}$	mean free time between scattering collisions (s)
t_{sd}	storage delay time (s)
T	temperature (K)
v, V	voltage[4] (V)
V	potential energy (J)
$\mathcal{V}$	electrostatic potential (V)
V_{CB}, V_{EB}	voltage from collector to base, emitter to base in a BJT (V)
V_D, V_G	voltage from drain to source, gate to source in an FET (V)
$\mathcal{V}_n, \mathcal{V}_p$	electrostatic potential in the neutral n, p material (V)
V_0	contact potential (V)
V_P	Chapter 6: pinch-off voltage for an FET; Chapter 10: forward breakover voltage for an SCR (V)
V_T, V_{FB}	MOS threshold voltage, flat-band voltage (V)
v, v_d	velocity, drift velocity (cm/s)
w	sample width (cm)
W	depletion region width (cm)
W_b	base width in a BJT, measured between the edges of the emitter and collector junction depletion regions (cm)
x	distance (cm), alloy composition
x_n, x_p	distance in the neutral n region, p region of a junction, measured from the edge of the transition region (cm)
x_{n0}, x_{p0}	penetration of the transition region into the n region, p region, measured from the metallurgical junction (cm)
Z	atomic number; dimension in z-direction (cm)
α	emitter-to-collector current transfer ratio in a BJT

[4]See note at the end of this list.

α	optical absorption coefficient (cm^{-1})
α_r	recombination coefficient (cm^3/s)
β	base-to-collector current amplification factor in a BJT
γ	emitter injection efficiency; in a p-n-p, the fraction of i_E due to the hole current i_{Ep}
δ, Δ	incremental change
$\delta n, \delta p$	excess electron, hole concentration (cm^{-3})
$\Delta n_p, \Delta p_n$	excess electron, hole concentration at the edge of the transition region on the p side, n side (cm^{-3})
$\Delta p_C, \Delta p_E$	excess hole concentration in the base of a BJT, evaluated at the edge of the transition region of the collector, emitter junction (cm^{-3})
$\epsilon, \epsilon_r, \epsilon_0$	permittivity, relative dielectric constant, permittivity of free space (F/cm); $\epsilon = \epsilon_r \epsilon_0$
λ	wavelength of light (μm, Å)
μ	mobility (cm^2/V$-$s)
ν	frequency of light (S^{-1})
ρ	resistivity(Ω-cm); charge density (C/cm^3)
σ	conductivity (Ω-cm)$^{-1}$
τ_d	dielectric relaxation time (s); in a BJT, delay time (s)
τ_n, τ_p	recombination lifetime for electrons, holes (s)
τ_t	transit time (s)
ϕ	flux density(cm$^2-$s)$^{-1}$; potential (V), dose (cm^{-2})
ϕ_F	$(E_i - E_F)/q$(V)
ϕ_s	surface potential (V)
Φ	work function potential (V)
Φ_B	metal–semiconductor barrier height (V)
Φ_{ms}	metal–semiconductor work function potential difference (V)
ψ, Ψ	time-independent, time-dependent wave function
ω	angular frequency (s^{-1})
$\langle \ \rangle$	average of the enclosed quantity

Note: For d-c voltage and current, capital symbols with capital subscripts are used; lowercase symbols with lowercase subscripts represent a-c quantities; lowercase symbols with capital subscripts represent total (a-c + d-c) quantities. For voltage symbols with double subscripts, V is positive when the potential at the point referred to by the first subscript is higher than that of the second point. For example, V_{GD} is the potential difference $V_G - V_D$.

Appendix II

Physical Constants and Conversion Factors[1]

Avogadro's number	$N_A = 6.02 \times 10^{23}$ molecules/mole
Boltzmann's constant	$k = 1.38 \times 10^{-23}$ J/K
	$= 8.62 \times 10^{-5}$ eV/K
Electronic charge (magnitude)	$q = 1.60 \times 10^{-19}$ C
Electronic rest mass	$m_0 = 9.11 \times 10^{-31}$ kg
Permittivity of free space	$\epsilon_0 = 8.85 \times 10^{-14}$ F/cm
	$= 8.85 \times 10^{-12}$ F/m
Planck's constant	$h = 6.63 \times 10^{-34}$ J-s
	$= 4.14 \times 10^{-15}$ eV-s
Room temperature value of kT	$kT = 0.0259$ eV
Speed of light	$c = 2.998 \times 10^{10}$ cm/s

Prefixes:

1 Å (angstrom) $= 10^{-8}$ cm	milli-, m-	$= 10^{-3}$
1 μm (micron) $= 10^{-4}$ cm	micro-, μ-	$= 10^{-6}$
1 nm $= 10$ Å $= 10^{-7}$ cm	nano-, n-	$= 10^{-9}$
2.54 cm $= 1$ in.	pico-, p-	$= 10^{-12}$
1 eV $= 1.6 \times 10^{-19}$ J	kilo-, k-	$= 10^{3}$
	mega-, M-	$= 10^{6}$
	giga-, G-	$= 10^{9}$

A wavelength λ of 1 μm corresponds to a photon energy of 1.24 eV.

[1]Since cm is used as the unit of length for many semiconductor quantities, caution must be exercised to avoid unit errors in calculations. When using quantities involving length in formulas which contain quantities measured in MKS units, it is usually best to use all MKS quantities. Conversion to standard semiconductor usage involving cm can be accomplished as a last step. Similar caution is recommended in using J and eV as energy units.

Appendix III

Properties of Semiconductor Materials

		E_g (eV)	μ_n (cm^2/V-s)	μ_p (cm^2/V-s)	m_n^*/m_o (m$_l$,m$_t$)	m_p^*/m_o (m$_{lh}$,m$_{hh}$)	a (Å)	ϵ_r	Density (g/cm^3)	Melting point (°C)
Si	(i/D)	1.11	1350	480	0.98, 0.19	0.16, 0.49	5.43	11.8	2.33	1415
Ge	(i/D)	0.67	3900	1900	1.64, 0.082	0.04, 0.28	5.65	16	5.32	936
SiC (α)	(i/W)	2.86	500	—	0.6	1.0	3.08	10.2	3.21	2830
AlP	(i/Z)	2.45	80	—	—	0.2, 0.63	5.46	9.8	2.40	2000
AlAs	(i/Z)	2.16	1200	420	2.0	0.15, 0.76	5.66	10.9	3.60	1740
AlSb	(i/Z)	1.6	200	300	0.12	0.98	6.14	11.0	4.26	1080
GaP	(i/Z)	2.26	300	150	1.12, 0.22	0.14, 0.79	5.45	11.1	4.13	1467
GaAs	(d/Z)	1.43	8500	400	0.067	0.074, 0.50	5.65	13.2	5.31	1238
GaN	(d/Z, W)	3.4	380	—	0.19	0.60	4.5	12.2	6.1	2530
GaSb	(d/Z)	0.7	5000	1000	0.042	0.06, 0.23	6.09	15.7	5.61	712
InP	(d/Z)	1.35	4000	100	0.077	0.089, 0.85	5.87	12.4	4.79	1070
InAs	(d/Z)	0.36	22600	200	0.023	0.025, 0.41	6.06	14.6	5.67	943
InSb	(d/Z)	0.18	10^5	1700	0.014	0.015, 0.40	6.48	17.7	5.78	525
ZnS	(d/Z, W)	3.6	180	10	0.28	—	5.409	8.9	4.09	1650*
ZnSe	(d/Z)	2.7	600	28	0.14	0.60	5.671	9.2	5.65	1100*
ZnTe	(d/Z)	2.25	530	100	0.18	0.65	6.101	10.4	5.51	1238*
CdS	(d/W, Z)	2.42	250	15	0.21	0.80	4.137	8.9	4.82	1475
CdSe	(d/W)	1.73	800	—	0.13	0.45	4.30	10.2	5.81	1258
CdTe	(d/Z)	1.58	1050	100	0.10	0.37	6.482	10.2	6.20	1098
PbS	(i/H)	0.37	575	200	0.22	0.29	5.936	17.0	7.6	1119
PbSe	(i/H)	0.27	1500	1500	—	—	6.147	23.6	8.73	1081
PbTe	(i/H)	0.29	6000	4000	0.17	0.20	6.452	30	8.16	925

All values at 300 K.   *Vaporizes

The first column lists the semiconductor, the second indicates band structure type and crystal structure. Definitions of symbols: *i* is indirect; *d* is direct; *D* is diamond; *Z* is zinc blende; *W* is wurtzite; *H* is halite (NaCl). Values of mobility are for material of high purity.

Crystals in the wurtzite structure are not described completely by the single lattice constant given here, since the unit cell is not cubic. Several II–VI compounds can be grown in either the zinc blende or wurtzite structures.

Many values quoted here are approximate or uncertain, particularly for the II–VI and IV–VI compounds. The gaps indicate that the values are unknown.

For electrons, the first set of band curvature effective masses is the longitudinal mass, the second set the transverse. For holes, the first set is for light holes, the second for heavy holes.

Appendix IV

Derivation of the Density of States in the Conduction Band

In this derivation we shall consider the conduction band electrons to be essentially free. Constraints of the particular lattice can be included in the effective mass of the electron at the end of the derivation. For a free electron, the three-dimensional Schrödinger wave equation becomes

$$-\frac{\hbar^2}{2m}\nabla^2\psi = E\psi \tag{IV-1}$$

where ψ is the wave function of the electron and E is its energy. The form of the solution to Eq. (IV–1) is

$$\psi = (\text{const.})e^{j\mathbf{k}\cdot\mathbf{r}} \tag{IV-2}$$

We must describe the electron in terms of a set of boundary conditions within the lattice. A common approach is to use periodic boundary conditions, in which we quantize the electron energies in a cube of material of side L. This can be accomplished by requiring that

$$\psi(x + L, y, z) = \psi(x, y, z) \tag{IV-3}$$

and similarly for the y- and z-directions. Thus our wave function can be written as

$$\psi_n = A \exp\left[j\frac{2\pi}{L}(\mathbf{n}_x x + \mathbf{n}_y y + \mathbf{n}_z z)\right] \tag{IV-4}$$

where the $2\pi\mathbf{n}/L$ factor in each direction guarantees the condition described by Eq. (IV–3), and A is a normalizing factor. Substituting ψ_n into the Schrödinger equation (IV–1), we obtain

$$-\frac{\hbar^2}{2m}A\nabla^2 \exp\left[j\frac{2\pi}{L}(\mathbf{n}_x x + \mathbf{n}_y y + \mathbf{n}_z z)\right]$$

$$= EA \exp\left[j\frac{2\pi}{L}(\mathbf{n}_x x + \mathbf{n}_y y + \mathbf{n}_z z)\right] \tag{IV-5}$$

Let us determine the number of allowed states per unit volume as a function of energy [the density of states, $N(E)$] in various cases such as one, two, or three dimensions. We first count states in **k**-space, then we can use the band structure, $E(\mathbf{k})$, to convert to $N(E)$.

For the 3-D case in Eq. (IV–5), the components of the **k**-vector are $\mathbf{k}_x = 2\pi\, \mathbf{n}_x/L$, $\mathbf{k}_y = 2\pi\, \mathbf{n}_y/L$, and $\mathbf{k}_z = 2\pi\, \mathbf{n}_z/L$. Since there is one **k**-state for every distinct choice of integer quantum numbers, $(\mathbf{n}_x, \mathbf{n}_y, \mathbf{n}_z)$, the volume per **k**-state is $(2\pi)^3/L^3 = (2\pi)^3/V$, where $V = L^3$ is the three-dimensional volume. Hence, the number of states for 3-D in a **k**-space of $\Delta\mathbf{k}$, taking into account the factor of 2 spin degeneracy, is

$$\left\{ \frac{L^3}{(2\pi)^3}\Delta\mathbf{k} \right\} \times (2)\ spin \qquad \text{(IV–6a)}$$

The number of states per unit volume for 3-D is

$$\frac{2}{(2\pi)^3}\,(\Delta\mathbf{k}) \qquad \text{(IV–6b)}$$

In general, for p-dimensions we can generalize this expression as

$$\text{Number of states per unit volume} = \frac{2}{(2\pi)^p}\,(\Delta\mathbf{k}) \qquad \text{(IV–7a)}$$

We can then transform from **k**-space to E-space using the $E(\mathbf{k})$ bandstructure relationship by setting

$$N(E)\Delta E = \frac{2}{(2\pi)^p}\,(\Delta\mathbf{k}) \qquad \text{(IV–7b)}$$

As described in Section 3.2.2, the simplest band structure is parabolic:

$$E(\mathbf{k}) = \frac{\hbar^2 k^2}{2m^*} \qquad \text{(IV–8a)}$$

This is often a good approximation, particularly near the bottom of the conduction band or top of the valence band. Using this, we get the relation between **k** and E as follows:

$$k = \sqrt{\frac{2m^* E}{\hbar^2}} \qquad \text{(IV–8b)}$$

$$dk = \left\{ \sqrt{\frac{m^*}{2}}\frac{1}{\hbar} \right\}\frac{1}{\sqrt{E}}\,dE \qquad \text{(IV–8c)}$$

For $p = 3$ we have the 3-D case, which is typical of bulk semiconductors. The volume in **k**-space between two constant-k spherical surfaces at k and $k + dk$ is (Fig. IV–1a):

$$\Delta\mathbf{k} = 4\pi k^2 dk \qquad \text{(IV–9a)}$$

neglecting terms with dk multiplied by itself.

Figure IV–1
Volume in
k-space:
(a) 3-D systems;
(b) 2-D systems;
(c) 1-D systems.

(a)   3-D

$\Delta k = 4\pi k^2 dk$

(b)   2-D

$\Delta k = 2\pi k dk$

(c)   1-D

$\Delta k = 2dk$

The density-of-states then becomes:

$$N(E)dE = \frac{2}{(2\pi)^3} 4\pi k^2 dk = \frac{\sqrt{2}}{\pi^2}\left(\frac{m^*}{\hbar^2}\right)^{3/2} E^{1/2} dE \qquad \text{(IV–9b)}$$

We see that if we plot $N(E)$ versus E, we get a parabolic density-of-states function in 3-D for a parabolic band structure relationship (Fig. IV–2a).

For $p = 2$, we get a so-called 2-D electron gas (2-DEG) or hole gas. This can arise, for example, in a quantum well (Section 3.2.5) or in the inversion layer of a MOSFET.

In this case, the "volume" in **k**-space is the annular region between two circles, k and $k + dk$, as shown in Fig. IV–1b, where

$$\Delta \mathbf{k} = (2\pi k)dk \qquad \text{(IV–10a)}$$

again neglecting dk^2.

Using Eq. (IV–7a), this leads to a density of states (per unit area)

$$N(E)dE = \frac{2}{(2\pi)^2}(2\pi k)dk = \frac{m^*}{\pi\hbar^2} dE \qquad \text{(IV–10b)}$$

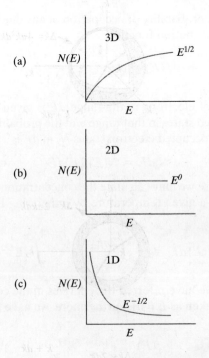

Figure IV–2
Density of states:
(a) in 3-D or bulk;
(b) in 2-D electron
or hole gases;
(c) in 1-D quantum
"wires."

We see that for 2-D, the density-of-states is a constant in energy, unlike the parabolic density of states for 3-D (Fig. IV–2b). Actually, for the 2-DEG in a quantum well or inversion layer (see Chapter 6) we must add the various constant 2-D densities-of-states for the different "particle-in-a-box" levels that were discussed in Sections 2.4.3 and 3.2.5, leading to a so-called "staircase" density of states.

For $p = 1$, we get 1-D quantum "wires." These more esoteric structures can be grown, for example, by MBE or MOCVD. In this case, the "volume" in **k**-space in the region between k and $k + dk$ in 1-D is (Fig. IV–1c):

$$\Delta \mathbf{k} = 2(dk) \qquad\qquad (IV–11a)$$

Using Eq. (IV–7a), this leads to a density of states

$$N(E)dE = \frac{2}{(2\pi)^1}(2dk) = \frac{\sqrt{2m^*}}{\pi\hbar\sqrt{E}}dE \qquad\qquad (IV–11b)$$

By examining the density of states in 3-, 2-, and 1-D [Eqs. (IV–9b), (IV–10b), and (IV–11b), respectively] we notice a very interesting trend. Every time we go to a lower dimensionality system, the dependence of density of states on energy changes by $1/\sqrt{E}$. In fact, one finds that for 0-D quantum "dots" the density of states is indeed proportional to $1/E$. In the 1- and 0-D cases, we see that the density of states has singularities in energy, which has very important implications for semiconductor devices. Such low-dimensional structures are discussed in Section 10.7.

To include the probability of occupation of any energy level E, we use the Fermi–Dirac distribution function:

$$f(E) = \frac{1}{e^{(E-E_F)/kT} + 1} \tag{IV–12}$$

The concentration of electrons in the range dE is given by the product of the density of allowed states in that range and the probability of occupation. Thus the density of occupied electron states N_e in dE is

$$N_e dE = N(E)f(E)dE \tag{IV–13}$$

For the 3-D case we may calculate the concentration of electrons in the conduction band at a given temperature by integrating Eq. (IV–13) across the band:

$$n = \int_0^{\infty} N(E)f(E)dE = \frac{1}{2\pi^2}\left(\frac{2m}{\hbar^2}\right)^{3/2} e^{E_F/kT} \int_0^{\infty} E^{1/2} e^{-E/kT} dE \tag{IV–14}$$

In this integration we have referred the energies in the conduction band to the band edge (E_c taken as $E = 0$). Furthermore, we have taken the function $f(E)$ to be

$$f(E) = e^{(E_F - E)/kT} \tag{IV–15}$$

for energies such that $(E - E_F) \gg kT$.

The integral in Eq. (IV–14) is of the standard form:

$$\int_0^{\infty} x^{1/2} e^{-ax} dx = \frac{\sqrt{\pi}}{2a\sqrt{a}} \tag{IV–16}$$

Thus Eq. (IV–14) gives

$$n = 2\left(\frac{2\pi mkT}{h^2}\right)^{3/2} e^{E_F/kT} \tag{IV–17}$$

If we refer to the bottom of the conduction band as E_c instead of $E = 0$, the expression for the electron concentration is

$$n = 2\left(\frac{2\pi m_n^* kT}{h^2}\right)^{3/2} e^{(E_F - E_C)/kT} \tag{IV–18}$$

which corresponds to Eq. (3–15). We have included constraints of the lattice through the effective mass of the electron in the crystal, m_n^*.

Appendix V

Derivation of Fermi–Dirac Statistics

In this section, we will give a simplified derivation of Fermi–Dirac statistics. We will not go through all the details, but will instead point out the physical assumptions involved. The distribution function is determined by calculating the number of distinct ways (W_k) we can put n_k indistinguishable electrons in g_k states at an energy level E_k, subject to the Pauli exclusion principle.

The assumptions are:

1. Each allowed state has a maximum of one electron (Pauli principle).
2. The probability of occupancy of each allowed (degenerate) quantum state is the same.
3. All electrons are indistinguishable.

The number of distinct ways we can put the electrons in a particular level is

$$W_k = \frac{(g_k)(g_k - 1)(g_k - \overline{n_k - 1})}{n_k!} = \frac{g_k!}{(g_k - n_k)!n_k!} \tag{V–1}$$

For N levels in a band, the number of distinct ways we can put in the various electrons gives us the so-called "multiplicity function,"

$$W_b = \prod_k W_k = \prod_k \frac{g_k!}{(g_k - n_k)!n_k!} \tag{V–2}$$

If we ask, "What is the most probable distribution of the n_k electrons in the various E_k levels (degeneracy of g_k in level E_k)?" the statistical mechanical answer is:

> In thermal equilibrium, the distribution which is most disordered (i.e., has the maximum entropy, or which can occur in the largest number of ways) is the most probable.

We therefore have to maximize W_b with respect to n_k.

We assume here that the total number of electrons in the band is fixed.

$$\sum_k n_k = n = \text{constant} \Rightarrow \sum_k dn_k = 0 \tag{V–3}$$

We also assume that the total energy in the band is constant.

$$E_{tot} = \sum_k E_k n_k = \text{constant, implying } \sum_k E_k dn_k = 0 \qquad \text{(V–4)}$$

To maximize or minimize some function $f(x_i)$ of q variables $x_i(i = 1, \ldots, q)$ subject to the constraints that $g(x_i)$ and $h(x_i)$ are constant, we use the method of Lagrange undetermined multipliers.

We have

$$df = 0 \text{ (for extremal value of } f) \qquad \text{(V–5)}$$

$$dg = 0, dh = 0 \text{ (because } g \text{ and } h \text{ are constant)} \qquad \text{(V–6)}$$

Introducing two Lagrange undetermined multipliers α and β, we get

$$\sum_i \frac{\partial}{\partial x_i}[f(x_i) + \alpha g(x_i) + \beta h(x_i)]dx_i = 0$$

$$\frac{\partial}{\partial x_i}[f(x_i) + \alpha g(x_i) + \beta h(x_i)] = 0 \qquad \text{(V–7)}$$

for $i = 1, \ldots q$

$$g(x_i) = \text{const.} \quad h(x_i) = \text{const.} \qquad \text{(V–8)}$$

We thus get $(q + 2)$ equations in $(q + 2)$ unknowns of (x_i, α, β).

We apply this technique to our problem at hand. Instead of maximizing W_b, we maximize $\ln W_b$, because it makes the mathematics simpler. Since the log function increases monotonically with the argument, maximizing one is the same as maximizing the other.

$$\ln W_b = \sum_k [\ln(g_k)! - \ln(g_k - n_k)! - \ln(n_k)!] \qquad \text{(V–9)}$$

To simplify these terms, we use Stirling's approximation for factorials of large numbers. $\ln x! = x \ln x - x$ for large x.

$$\ln W_b = \sum_k [g_k \ln (g_k) - g_k - (g_k - n_k) \ln (g_k - n_k) + (g_k - n_k) - n_k \ln (n_k) + n_k]$$

$$= \sum_k [g_k \ln (g_k) - (g_k - n_k) \ln (g_k - n_k) - n_k \ln (n_k)] \qquad \text{(V–10)}$$

Now $dg_k = 0$ because these are system constraints. We then get

$$d(\ln W_b) = \sum_k \frac{\partial[\ln W_b]}{\partial n_k} dn_k = \sum_k \ln\left(\frac{g_k}{n_k} - 1\right) dn_k = 0 \qquad \text{(V–11)}$$

Also, from the two constraints we get

$$\sum_k dn_k = 0 \text{ and } \sum_k E_k dn_k = 0 \qquad \text{(V–12)}$$

Then,

$$\sum_k \left[\ln\left(\frac{g_k}{n_k} - 1 \right) - \alpha - \beta E_k \right] dn_k = 0 \qquad (V\text{–}13)$$

$$\ln\left(\frac{g_k}{n_k} - 1 \right) - \alpha - \beta E_k = 0 \qquad (V\text{–}14)$$

From this,

$$\frac{n_k}{g_k} = f(E_k) = \frac{1}{1 + e^{\alpha + \beta E_k}} \qquad (V\text{–}15)$$

From basic thermodynamics, it can be shown that

$$\alpha = -\frac{E_F}{kT}, \quad \beta = \frac{1}{kT} \qquad (V\text{–}16)$$

to get the Fermi–Dirac distribution function,

$$f(E_k) = \frac{1}{\exp\left[\dfrac{E_k - E_F}{kT} \right] + 1} \qquad (V\text{–}17)$$

For the limit of high energies,

$$E \gg E_F, \quad f(E) \cong \exp\frac{E_F - E}{kT}. \qquad (V\text{–}18)$$

This is the classical Maxwell–Boltzmann limit of the Fermi–Dirac distribution function. Once we have the probabilities of electron occupancy, the probability of hole occupancy becomes

$$1 - f(E) = \frac{1}{\exp\dfrac{E_F - E}{kT} + 1} \qquad (V\text{–}19)$$

$g_3 = 6 \qquad n_3 = 3\,e^-$

$g_2 = 5 \qquad n_2 = 2\,e^-$

$g_1 = 3 \qquad n_1 = 3\,e^-$

Figure V–1
Example showing three energy levels in a band, having different degeneracies, g, and electron occupancies, n, as shown.

Appendix VI

Dry and Wet Thermal Oxide Thickness Grown on Si (100) as a Function of Time and Temperature[1]

[1]From **B. Deal.** "The Oxidation of Silicon in Dry Oxygen, Wet Oxygen and Steam." *J. Electrochem. Soc.* 110 (1963): 527.

Solid Solubilities of Impurities in Si[1]

[1]From **F. A. Trumbore.** "Solid Solubilities of Impurity Elements in Si and Ge." *Bell System Technical Journal* 39 (1), 205–233 (January 1960) copyright 1960, The American Telephone and Telegraph Co., reprinted by permission. Alterations have been made to include later data.

Appendix VIII
Diffusivities of Dopants in Si and SiO₂[1]

[1]Silicon diffusivity data from **C. S. Fuller and J. A. Ditzenberger.** "Diffusion of Donor and Acceptor Elements in Silicon." *J. Appl. Physics*, 27 (1956), 544.

SiO₂ diffusivity data from **M. Ghezzo and D. M. Brown.** "Diffusivity Summary of B, Ga, P, As and Sb in SiO₂," *J. Electrochem. Soc.* 120 (1973), 146.

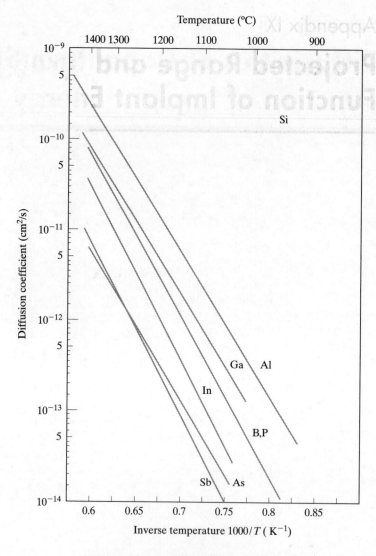

Diffusivity of various impurities in SiO$_2$		
Element	D_o (cm^2/sec)	E_A (eV)
Boron	3×10^{-4}	3.53
Phosphorus	0.19	4.03
Arsenic	250	4.90
Antimony	1.31×10^{16}	8.75

Appendix IX

Projected Range and Straggle as Function of Implant Energy in Si[1]

[1]From **J. F. Gibbons, W. S. Johnson, and S. W. Mylroie.** *Projected Range Statistics: Semiconductors and Related Materials.* Stroudsburg: Dowden, Hutchison and Ross, 1975.

The projected ranges in SiO_2 are very close to those in Si.

Answers to Selected Self Quiz Questions

CHAPTER 1

1. (a) (111); (100); (110)
2. (a) 1 and 2
   (b) {110}
   (c) B
3. (a) C
   (b) (1) zinc blende; (2) diamond
4. 0-D: vacancies, interstitials; 1-D: dislocations; 2-D: grain boundaries, surfaces
6. InP

CHAPTER 2

1. (a) not allowed
   (b) not allowed
   (c) allowed
2. (a) No
   (b) Yes
3. (a) No
   (b) Yes
   (c) Yes
4. Not enough information
5. p_0; unknown; unknown
6. (a) Energy increased; unchanged
   (b) Energy unchanged; decreased

CHAPTER 3

1. (a) Semiconductor, Metal, Insulator
   (b) Material 3
2. (a) X valley
   (b) μ valley
3. (a) GaAs
   (b) GaAs
   (c) 1.4 eV; 0.87 μm; infrared
   (d) 6, 1
4. (a) GaAs
   (b) equal
5. (a) p-type
   (b) equal
   (c) very high acceptor doping
6. (a) 1.08 eV
   (b) $n_0 = 10^{16}$ cm^{-3}; $p_0 = 10^4$ cm^{-3}
   (c) $p_0 = 10^{16}$ cm^{-3}; $n_0 = 10^4$ cm^{-3}
   (d) 0.36 eV

CHAPTER 4

1. (a) 10^{17}/cm^3-s
   (b) 2×10^{17} eV/cm^3-s
   (c) 10^{17} eV/cm^3-s
2. (a) Deep more harmful; Au
   (b) Si; indirect
   (c) increase
3. (a) E_F flat
   (b) Constant electric field points to right
4. (a) left, right, right, left
   (b) left, right, left, right
5. (b) 4
6. (a) right, right, left, right
   (b) right, right, right, left

CHAPTER 5

3. Short
4. 1.5 V
7. (b) ohmic

CHAPTER 6

1. (a) depletion
   (b) weak inversion
   (c) accumulation
   (d) strong inversion
   (e) flat band
   (f) threshold
2. (a) power gain
   (b) d-c power supply
3. (b) $1.2 \ \mu F/cm^2$
   (c) same curve
4. (a) n-channel
   (b) long
   (c) -0.5 V
   (d) depletion mode
5. (a) decrease
   (b) decrease
6. (a) increase
   (b) increase
7. (a) unchanged
   (b) decrease
   (c) decrease
8 (a) 1 mmhos
   (b) -0.2 V
   (c) short channel
   (d) p-channel
   (e) enhancement mode
9 (a) normally ON
   (b) long channel
   (c) 25 mV/decade
   (d) S cannot be less than 60 mV/decade

CHAPTER 7

1. (a) 50
   (c) 6 V
   (d) 21 V

3. (a) increase
   (b) increase
   (c) increase
   (d) decrease
5. (a) increase
   (b) increase
   (c) decrease

CHAPTER 8

1. (a) C
   (b) 0.7 eV
   (c) 7 mW
   (d) 0.4 eV
   (e) 14 mW
   (f) 50%
2. 28 mW
3. 0.5 μm; No; Yes
4. Renewable and green; cost

CHAPTER 9

1. Yes; No
4. Lowest Q_{ox}

Index